EXPERIMENTAL
NUCLEAR PHYSICS

CONTRIBUTORS

VOLUME I

Julius Ashkin

Hans A. Bethe

Kenneth T. Bainbridge

Norman F. Ramsey

Hans H. Staub

VOLUME II

Bernard T. Feld

Philip Morrison

VOLUME III

Martin Deutsch

Otto Kofoed-Hansen

Geoffrey C. Hanna

Edwin M. McMillan

Emilio Segre

EXPERIMENTAL
NUCLEAR PHYSICS

VOLUME II

E. SEGRÈ, Editor

P. Morrison and B. T. Feld

JOHN WILEY & SONS, INC., NEW YORK

LONDON

PREFACE

At the end of World War II many physicists who had been mobilized for the war effort returned to university work and to pure research; a great number of them had worked on nuclear problems and were anxious to resume investigations in this field. Moreover there was a large influx of students eager to start nuclear investigations.

The need was keenly felt for a book which would bring the experimentalist up to date in experimental techniques, point out to him the significant facts and data, and indicate the broad lines of theoretical interpretation.

It was immediately apparent that the field of nuclear physics had grown so much and the various branches had become so specialized that no one person could hope to write a book like the famous treatises of Rutherford (which, however, because of the evolution mentioned above, had by 1930 already become Rutherford, Chadwick, and Ellis), Curie, and Kohlrausch. A cooperative effort like the Geiger-Scheel *Handbuch der Physik* seemed the only solution. Individual authors could undertake to prepare reasonably complete treatises on a restricted field in which they are quite authoritative. By keeping the discussions relatively short, it became possible for a group of authors to cooperate without curtailing their research activity. An incentive for several of the authors, indeed, was the desire to read the contributions of the others.

This work is the outcome of that effort. We hope that it will be useful to the serious student and to the research worker in the field. Each part, with its bibliography, should be sufficient to inform the reader about the main results obtained in nuclear physics up to the end of 1952 and enable him to go directly to the original literature or to the several excellent collections of periodical reviews which are currently appearing (*Annual Reviews of Nuclear Science, Reviews of Modern Physics, Ergebnisse der exakten Naturwissenschaften, Progress in Nuclear Physics,* and others) for further details.

E. SEGRÈ

Berkeley, California
June, 1953

CONTENTS

vii

Contents

PART VI

A Survey of Nuclear Reactions

P. MORRISON

Cornell University

The study of nuclear reactions parallels the familiar study of chemical reactions. Most of the root ideas of chemistry are fundamental for the nuclear physicist. The equation of the reaction, the heat of reaction, the rate of reaction, the "balancing" of the equation—all these have their nuclear counterparts. The fact that the characteristic energy release is the millions of electron volts associated with the binding of nuclear particles, rather than the few volts which result from molecular binding, is the most striking inherent difference between the two fields. The nuclear physicist can detect the reaction not of moles or micromoles of his reactants, but of *individual particles*. This has meant that from the beginning the nuclear physicist has studied not equilibria and the laws of mass action, but the properties of single collisions. Just as the chemist has recently come to regard the individual collision as the center of attention for really fundamental understanding of reactions, so the physicist has now come to study large-scale reactions and even thermal equilibria in the nuclear domain in the light of his newer interest in astrophysical and chain reaction problems. Although the two points of view have tended to merge, it is our task to survey nuclear reactions primarily from the point of view of understanding individual collisions. Clearly this is the key to any genuine insight.

SECTION 1. THE CONSERVATION LAWS

Nuclear reactions, like chemical ones, can be more or less complex. The typical reaction—with which we shall be most concerned—involves a stationary or "target" nucleus bombarded by a relatively light incident nuclear projectile. The products of the reaction may be one, two, or even more nuclei. In the nuclear reactions of most interest before the development of the very high-energy accelerators in 1947, one to three products were by far most common. The target nucleus changes into a nuclear species differing by only a few units in A, the mass number or

1

number of nucleons (protons and neutrons) in the nucleus, and in Z, the number of nuclear protons and, hence, the number of electrons in the neutral atom. Such reactions are designated either in the somewhat redundant notation taken from the chemists, an example of which might be $_{11}Na^{23} + {}_1H^1 \rightarrow {}_{12}Mg^{23} + {}_0n^1$ [$_0n^1$ = neutron], or in an abbreviated scheme, due to Bothe. In the latter, one writes first the target nucleus, indicating its mass number and chemical character (often giving the nuclear charge Z as well), then in parentheses the symbols for the bombarding and emitted particles in order, and finally the residual nucleus. The above reaction would be written $Na^{23}(p,n)Mg^{23}$. If there are more than two products of reaction, one might write, for example, $C^{12}(p,pn)C^{11}$ for the reaction $_6C^{12} + {}_1H^1 \rightarrow {}_6C^{11} + {}_1H^1 + {}_0n^1$.

What physical properties of the system remain unchanged throughout the reaction? These conserved properties provide very valuable information for every reaction. We list conserved properties:

1. In no observed process does the total electric charge change. A proton can change into a neutron, but a positron or positive meson must appear, or an electron disappear, in the process. The familiar creation of electron-positron pairs is a dramatic confirmation of this principle.

2. To this date (1952) no process has been observed in which the total number of nucleons, i.e., the total value of A, is different on the two sides of the reaction. Presumably this is not a fundamental property of nucleons; the creation of positive and negative "proton" pairs is expected when sufficient energy is available. No such process has yet been observed. Nucleon number is conserved in all known reactions.

3. The constants of motion of classical mechanics are conserved, at least to an order of accuracy beyond experimental interest. These are total energy, momentum, and angular momentum. The energies of chemical binding, and the accompanying forces and torques, are negligible compared to the energy transfers in typical reactions; so the colliding particles can be regarded as a mechanically isolated system. (For some special reactions involving very slow neutrons, the chemical binding and the thermal motion of the target nuclei must be considered. Even the whole of a macroscopic crystal may be taken as the target in some situations. Compare Part VII, Section 5.) The conservation of total energy must of course include the energy equivalent of mass changes of the reactants, for this will generally be a large fraction of the available kinetic energy. The conservation of momentum guarantees that the incident and product nuclei move in a plane if only two product nuclei result. The total angular momentum includes of course the intrinsic or spin angular momentum of the reactants combined with the orbital

angular momentum of their relative motion. It is this total which must be conserved, though the breakdown of the total into intrinsic and orbital angular momenta may not be predicted in general. The experimental determination of the angular momentum of individual particles is nearly out of the question, but the statistical angular distribution of reaction products depends on the angular momentum relations. Measurements of such distributions are important aids to analysis of nuclear reactions.

4. The "constants of motion" peculiar to quantum mechanics are also conserved. These are two in number: the parity and the statistics (S3).[1] The parity refers of course to the behavior of the wave function of the system upon inversion of all coordinates in the origin, i.e., upon the changing of right- to left-handed axis systems. No physical property of an isolated system can depend upon the kind of axes used, but the wave function can change sign under such a transformation without affecting any expectation values. Whether the wave function changes sign or remains the same under such an axis inversion is indicated by the parity: *even* for wave functions remaining unchanged, *odd* for those changing sign. The parity of the initial wave function of the whole system must be conserved.

The *statistics* of the system is related to these constants. The interchange of all coordinates of identical particles in any system can lead only to change of sign or to an unchanged wave function. All particles must belong either to the class whose wave functions change sign when identical particles are interchanged (these are called Fermi-Dirac particles) or to the class whose wave functions must remain unchanged (these are called Bose-Einstein particles). From the relativistic theory of wave fields, it can be shown that particles with half-integer intrinsic angular momentum are Fermi particles; those with integer spin, Bose particles. In ordinary reactions, where the nucleons are simply rearranged, this conservation law leads to no new conclusions; but in processes where new types of particles—mesons, neutrinos—are created or destroyed, this condition sharply limits the processes which can take place.

A. Application of Energy-Momentum Conservation

1. **Elastic Collisions.** The simplest application of these principles is to the elastic collision of two free particles. The slowing down of neutrons by elastic collision is the best-known example (see Part VII, Section 4), but, because the treatment is the basis for more complicated processes, we shall give the theory here, using the less familiar, but

[1] References for the text of Part VI will be found on pages 189 to 192.

increasingly useful, relativistic form (B7). The non-relativistic formulas are of course contained in the low-energy limit.

We begin with the target particle at rest in the laboratory coordinate system C. It is a simplification to make a transformation to a moving system C' in which the laboratory and target particle are of course moving, but the total momentum of the colliding particles is zero. Lorentz transformation from this system to C will give us the results we want; we know that the energy-momentum conservation is automatically satisfied in any Lorentz frame if it holds in C'.

Let the target particle of rest mass m_2 be stationary in C, and the other particle of mass m_1 be incident with velocity v along the x axis. In the system C' the particles approach each other with velocities u_1' and u_2' respectively. We require the particles to have the equal and oppositely directed momenta p' before collision. Then

$$p' = \frac{m_1 u_1'}{(1 - \beta_1'^2)^{1/2}} = \frac{m_2 u_2'}{(1 - \beta_2'^2)^{1/2}} \tag{1a}$$

where $\beta' = u'/c$. Using the notation $\gamma' = 1/(1 - \beta'^2)^{1/2}$, we have

$$m_1 \beta_1' \gamma_1' = m_2 \beta_2' \gamma_2' = \frac{p'}{c} \tag{1b}$$

Squaring,

$$m_1^2(\gamma_1'^2 - 1) = m_2^2(\gamma_2'^2 - 1) \tag{2}$$

Since the total momentum remains zero after the collision, the final momenta are easily seen to be equal and opposite, but the particles now are receding instead of approaching. Compare Fig. 1. If particle 1

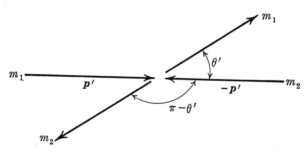

Fig. 1. Momentum relations for collision in center-of-mass system.

is scattered through the angle θ' in C', particle 2 will come off at an angle $\pi - \theta'$ with respect to the initial direction of particle 1. The velocities are not changed because the kinetic energies are conserved in an elastic collision.

We now make a simple Lorentz transformation to the laboratory rest system C. If particle 2 is initially at rest in C, C' must be moving relative to C with velocity u_2' in the direction of the incident motion. Now we know that a four-vector is formed by the momentum components and the total energy E/c^2, transforming under Lorentz transformation like the coordinates x, y, z, t. Therefore the Lorentz transformation gives for the initial momentum of the first particle in the system C' (omitting a factor of $m_1 c$ throughout):

$$(\gamma_1'^2 - 1)^{\frac{1}{2}} = \gamma_2'[(\gamma^2 - 1)^{\frac{1}{2}} - \beta_2'\gamma] = \gamma_2'(\gamma^2 - 1)^{\frac{1}{2}} - (\gamma_2'^2 - 1)^{\frac{1}{2}}\gamma \tag{3}$$

where $m_1 c (\gamma^2 - 1)^{\frac{1}{2}}$ is the momentum, and $m_1 c^2 \gamma$ the total energy of particle 1 in the laboratory system C. The kinetic energy is $m_1 c^2 (\gamma - 1)$. Using (2) and (3), we find

$$\gamma_1' = \frac{\left(\gamma + \dfrac{m_1}{m_2}\right)}{\left[1 + 2\dfrac{m_1}{m_2}\gamma + \left(\dfrac{m_1}{m_2}\right)^2\right]^{\frac{1}{2}}} \tag{4a}$$

$$\gamma_2' = \frac{\left(\gamma + \dfrac{m_2}{m_1}\right)}{\left[1 + 2\dfrac{m_2}{m_1}\gamma + \left(\dfrac{m_2}{m_1}\right)^2\right]^{\frac{1}{2}}} \tag{4b}$$

To obtain relations between the scattering angles, we again use the fact that the momentum and energy E, divided by c^2, form a four-vector. The total energy E_2 of particle 2 after the collision and its momentum components, in the laboratory system, are given by

$$E_2 = \gamma_2'(E_2' - c\beta_2'p'\cos\theta') \tag{5a}$$

$$p_{x_2} = \gamma_2'\left(-p'\cos\theta' + \frac{1}{c}\beta_2'E_2'\right) \tag{5b}$$

$$p_{y_2} = -p'\sin\theta' \tag{5c}$$

where the incident direction is the x axis, and all the momenta lie in a plane. The energy of particle 2 in C' is $E_2' = m_2 c^2 \gamma_2'$, and its momentum $p' = m_2 \gamma_2' c\beta_2'$. Dividing (5b) by (5c), we find the angle of scattering θ_2 of particle 2 in the laboratory system C:

$$\tan\theta_2 = -\frac{1}{\gamma_2'}\cot\frac{1}{2}\theta' \tag{6}$$

The minus sign means that, if particle 1 is scattered above the x axis into the region of positive y, particle 2 recoils below the axis. If θ' is 180° in the center-of-mass system C', $\theta_2 = 0$ and particle 2 recoils forward with maximum energy. As θ' decreases toward zero, particle 2 recoils with decreasing kinetic energy at angles approaching 90°. The case $\theta' = 0$ corresponds to grazing collision, in which particle 1 loses no energy and particle 2 recoils with zero velocity at 90°.

The recoil kinetic energy of particle 2 in the laboratory system is $T_2 = E_2 - m_2 c^2$. From (5a)

$$T_2 = m_2 c^2 (\gamma_2'^2 - 1)(1 - \cos \theta') \tag{7a}$$

Using (6) and (4b), we can write this in terms of the angle θ_2. Finally we may introduce the total energy $E = m_1 c^2 \gamma$ and momentum $p = m_1 c (\gamma^2 - 1)^{1/2}$ of the incident particle, getting

$$T_2 = 2m_2 c^2 \frac{p^2 \cos^2 \theta_2}{(E/c + m_2 c)^2 - p^2 \cos^2 \theta_2} \tag{7b}$$

Evidently $T_2^{(\max)} = T_2(\theta_2 = 0)$.

It is of interest to compute the maximum fraction of the kinetic energy of the incident particle which can be transferred. $T = E - m_1 c^2 = m_1 c^2 (\gamma - 1)$, and

$$\frac{T_2^{(\max)}}{T} = \frac{2(\gamma + 1)m_1 m_2}{m_1^2 + 2\gamma m_1 m_2 + m_2^2} = \frac{2(\gamma + 1)m_1 m_2}{2(\gamma + 1)m_1 m_2 + (m_1 - m_2)^2} \tag{8}$$

This fraction increases monotonically with incident energy from the value familiar in the non-relativistic limit, $4m_1 m_2/(m_1 + m_2)^2$, to unity for very high energies, with $\gamma \gg 1$. If the particles have equal mass, the maximum recoil energy is of course always equal to the incident energy.

If the particle incident is light (e.g., electron or photon), particle 2 can acquire relativistic energies only if $p \cong m_2 c^2$ or $\gamma \cong m_2/m_1$. This is also the condition for transfer of a large fraction of energy from particle 1 to particle 2, if a heavy particle is incident on a light target particle.

We now discuss the relation between the scattering angle θ_1 of particle 1 and its energy loss. The total energy of particle 1 in the laboratory system C corresponding to a scattering through θ' in C' is

$$E_1 = m_1 c^2 [\gamma_1' \gamma_2' + (\gamma_1'^2 - 1)^{1/2}(\gamma_2'^2 - 1)^{1/2} \cos \theta'] \tag{9}$$

where the γ''s are as given by (4a) and (4b). Now we need $\cos \theta'$ in terms of the angle measured in the laboratory system. For this we apply the Lorentz transformation to the energy and momentum of particle 1 in the manner of (3). This shows

$$\tan \theta_1 = \frac{1}{\gamma_2'} \cdot \frac{\sin \theta'}{(\cos \theta' + m_1 \gamma_1'/m_2 \gamma_2')} \tag{10}$$

Solving for $\cos \theta'$ in terms of $\tan \theta_1$, we get a quadratic equation with two roots, indicated by the $\pm$ sign:

$$\cos \theta' = \frac{1}{(1 + \gamma_2'^2 \tan^2 \theta_1)} \left[-\frac{m_1}{m_2} \gamma_1' \gamma_2' \tan^2 \theta_1 \right.$$
$$\left. \pm \left(1 - \frac{m_1^2 - m_2^2}{m_2^2} \tan^2 \theta_1 \right)^{\frac{1}{2}} \right] \tag{11}$$

Since the energy for a definite scattering angle in the laboratory system is given by (9) in terms of $\cos \theta'$, it appears that there are two possible values for the energy of a particle elastically scattered through a definite angle. It is instructive to examine the situation graphically.

For non-relativistic velocities ($\gamma = 1$), Eq. (11) gives the tangent of the scattering angle in C in terms of functions of the angle θ' in C'. For higher velocities, we can define an auxiliary angle ψ by the relation $\tan \psi = \gamma_2' \tan \theta_1$. This angle ψ can be obtained geometrically by adding a vector of length $m_1 \gamma_1'/m_2 \gamma_2'$ along the x axis to a unit vector whose components are $\cos \theta'$ and $\sin \theta'$. The center of a unit circle represents C', and the scattered particle may go off in any direction, along a unit radius vector. The auxiliary angle ψ is then just the angle between the x axis and the resultant of the radius vector in C' added to the vector $m_1 \gamma_1'/m_2 \gamma_2'$. The construction for the three cases we must consider is shown in Fig. 2.

In case (a), with $m_1 > m_2$, there are two possible directions of scattering in C' (i.e., two distinct orientations of the unit vector) for one scattering angle θ_1 in C. There are thus two values for the energy of particle 1, in agreement with (11).

For the case $m_1 < m_2$, Fig. 2b is appropriate. Here the x-axis vector is less than unity, and the construction gives only a single angle θ' to be associated with a definite ψ. The analogue to the second orientation of the unit vector in case (a) corresponds to the angle $(\pi - \psi)$ and gives no additional solution. One of the roots of (11) is to be rejected if $m_1 < m_2$. From the diagram we can see that, if θ_1 is less than 90°, we should take the more positive value of $\cos \theta'$ in (11); for θ_1 greater than 90°, the more negative one.

We shall treat case (c), $m_1 = m_2$, as a limit of either (a) or (b). From the figure we can see that there is an upper limit to ψ and thus to the angle θ_1, corresponding to the case where the line defining ψ is tangent

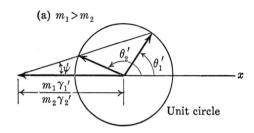

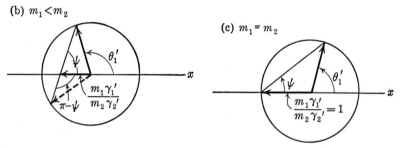

Fig. 2. Scattering angle relations for elastic collisions. Incident particle is m_1; target particle, m_2. The angle ψ determines the laboratory scattering angle. See text for construction.

to the unit circle, and angles $\theta'_{(1)}$, $\theta'_{(2)}$ have coalesced to a single value. The radical in (11) must vanish at this maximum value:

$$\tan^2 \theta_1{}^{(max)} = \frac{m_2{}^2}{m_1{}^2 - m_2{}^2}$$

$$\theta_1{}^{(max)} = \arcsin \frac{m_2}{m_1} \tag{12}$$

In case (b), with $m_1 < m_2$, scattering can clearly occur for all angles between 0 and π. In the limiting case (c), $m_1 = m_2$, the condition of tangency is reached for $\pi/2$.

In the special case (c), all the formulas above are much simplified. From (4a) and (4b) we get

$$\gamma_1' = \gamma_2' = \left(\frac{\gamma + 1}{2}\right)^{\frac{1}{2}} \tag{13}$$

If T^* is the kinetic energy of the particle scattered through angle θ in C, either (5a) or (7b) gives

$$T^* = mc^2 \cdot \frac{2(\gamma - 1)\cos^2\theta}{(\gamma + 1) - (\gamma - 1)\cos^2\theta} \tag{13a}$$

and, with $T = mc^2(\gamma - 1)$,

$$T^* = \frac{T\cos^2\theta}{1 + \frac{1}{2}(T/mc^2)\sin^2\theta} \qquad m_1 = m_2 = m \tag{13b}$$

Although there are still two roots of (11), one of them always corresponds to $\theta' = 180°$. This means of course that one of the colliding particles is projected in the forward direction with the full incident energy, while the other remains at rest. The second root of (11) gives (13a).

The familiar non-relativistic form of (11) is easy to obtain. If $m_1 = m_2$, the scattered particles always come off at right angles to each other, with energies proportional to the squares of the cosines of the angles of deflection. For higher velocities, however, the angle included between the directions of the outgoing particles is always less than a right angle. Changing the sign of θ_2 in (6) and using (10) and (13a) and (13b), we find

$$\tan\theta_1 \tan\theta_2 = \frac{2}{1 + \gamma} \tag{14}$$

Since γ is always greater than unity, $\theta_1 + \theta_2$ is less than 90° except for the grazing collisions in which particle 2 may be thought of as scattered at 90° with zero velocity. A sufficiently accurate measurement of angles θ_1 and θ_2 would serve to determine the incident energy. This method is more sensitive for large values of γ.

Finally we set out the familiar relations for the non-relativistic case. If T_2 is the kinetic energy of recoil of particle 2 and T is the incident kinetic energy of particle 1,

$$T_2 = \frac{4m_1 m_2}{(m_1 + m_2)^2}\cos^2\theta_2 T \tag{15}$$

For the final kinetic energy of particle 1, from the proper limit in (9), we obtain

$$T_1 = T\left(\frac{m_1}{m_1 + m_2}\right)^2\left[1 + \left(\frac{m_2}{m_1}\right)^2 - 2\sin^2\theta_1\right.$$
$$\left. \pm 2\cos\theta_1\left(\frac{m_2^2}{m_1^2} - \sin^2\theta_1\right)^{\frac{1}{2}}\right] \tag{16}$$

The treatment of the two roots is the same as in Fig. 2.

2. Collisions with Creation of New Particles. For sufficiently high-energy collisions of nuclear particles, not only are rearrangements of nucleons possible, in which kinetic energy is transformed into binding energy (or the reverse), but also new particles may be produced whose rest energy comes from the kinetic energy of collision. In a collision in which additional particles are produced whose rest energy totals Mc^2, it is clear that energy conservation requires that at least the incident kinetic energy exceed Mc^2. In addition, because the conservation of momentum requires that the center of mass of the whole system move with unchanged momentum, we must usually provide additional energy to fulfill this condition.

Let us consider the threshold value of the kinetic energy of the incident particle, m_1, on a stationary target particle m_2 (F8). The threshold is the minimum energy below which the production cannot take place. How probable the production becomes just above threshold is of course impossible to tell in general; it will depend upon the particular interactions being considered. It is easy to see that at the energy of threshold the total energy of all particles is a minimum after collision. In the frame C' we know that the final momentum must be zero. These two conditions can be satisfied if all particles after collision are individually at rest in the center-of-mass system C'. Then the initial kinetic energy must have been just equal to the increment in rest mass energy, Mc^2. The total energy in the C' system before collision is

$$E_1' + E_2' = m_1 c^2 \gamma_1' + m_2 c^2 \gamma_2'$$

and from (4) we can write this

$$E_1' + E_2' = c^2 (m_1{}^2 + 2\gamma m_1 m_2 + m_2{}^2)^{1/2} \qquad (17)$$

Equating it to the energy after collision,

$$E_1' + E_2' = c^2 (m_1 + m_2 + M)$$

Solving (17) for γ, we obtain the threshold kinetic energy T of m_1 in the laboratory system from the relation $T = m_1 c^2 (\gamma - 1)$. This gives

$$T = \frac{Mc^2 (m_1 + m_2 + \frac{1}{2}M)}{m_2} \qquad (18)$$

To create a nucleon pair from a proton-proton collision, for example, would require T at least $2 \cdot m_p c^2 (3m_p/m_p) = 6m_p c^2$. If the pair were made by a gamma-ray or electron incident ($m_1 \cong 0$), the threshold would be $T = 4m_p c^2$.

In such collisions the target particle need not be at rest. Here we may think of a target nucleon as one of the nucleons bound in a nucleus, and thus moving with the velocity characteristic of its zero point vibrations. If the collision occurs when the target nucleon is moving with a velocity component directed toward the incident particle, less incident beam energy will be needed. If the target particle m_2 has the initial velocity v_2 in the x direction, Lorentz transformation shows that the threshold energy of (18) becomes reduced to the value

$$T_{\min} = \gamma_2(T - v_2p) + m_1c^2(\gamma_2 - 1) \qquad (19a)$$

where p is the initial momentum of particle m_1, and $\gamma_2 = (1 - v_2^2/c^2)^{-\frac{1}{2}}$. A further reduction comes about if the collision occurs with capture of the incident particle so that binding energy can be released.

It is of some interest to discuss the possible angular and energy distribution of the produced particles. If we restrict ourselves to the case in which the target particle is at rest, and in which only one new particle of mass M is made, we can draw some simple conclusions. It is clear that at the threshold energy there is only one final condition: all the particles move forward with the same velocity, since they are all at rest in the center-of-mass system. As the energy exceeds the threshold, the created particle will in general be able to travel in a distribution of angles around the forward direction. The details will of course depend on the nature of the interaction. But some limits can be given in general. It is clear that the maximum momentum of the new particle will correspond to a case in which M is traveling forward and the two original particles move opposite to M in the center-of-mass system, with the same speed for each. This leads to a value for the maximum kinetic energy of M in the laboratory system:

$$Mc^2 + T_{\max} =$$

$$\tfrac{1}{2}c^2[(\gamma m_1 + m_2)A + m_1(\gamma^2 - 1)^{\frac{1}{2}}B]/(m_1^2 + 2\gamma m_1 m_2 + m_2^2) \qquad (19b)$$

with $A = M^2 + 2(\gamma - 1)m_1m_2$ and $B = \{[2(\gamma - 1)m_1m_2 - M^2]^2 - 4M^2(m_1 + m_2)^2\}^{\frac{1}{2}}$. This has a very simple form at the threshold:

$$T_{\max} = \frac{Mc^2}{m_2} \cdot \frac{M(m_1 + M/2)}{m_1 + m_2 + M} \qquad (20)$$

The angular distributions will be controlled by the relation between the maximum velocity with which M can move off in the center-of-mass system and the velocity of C with respect to C'. Arguments similar to those accompanying Fig. 2 show that here too there are two possibilities: the new particle will be emitted only in part of the forward hemisphere if its maximum center-of-mass velocity $v_M' = c^2p_M'/E_M'$ is less than the velocity of the center-of-mass system, $c\beta_2'$. Then the situation is like Fig. 2a, and a minimum energy for M in the laboratory exists; it is given by (19) with a minus sign instead of a plus sign before the radical. If $v_M' > c\beta_2'$, however, the case is like that of Fig. 2b, and all angles of emission are allowed in the laboratory frame. The minimum energy for M is then zero in the laboratory system.

3. Reaction Energies. The most studied nuclear reactions up to the present time involve neither elastic collisions nor the production of new particles. They consist of the rearrangement of nucleons, with the ejection of different nuclei having correspondingly changed binding energies and rest masses. Just as in chemistry, the heat of reaction Q is a significant quantity. The energy Q is the energy released as kinetic energy (or the energy of photons, etc., set free) at the expense of the internal energy of the colliding systems. We may define Q by either of the relations:

$$Q = c^2\left(\sum_{\text{initial}} m_i - \sum_{\text{final}} m_f\right) = -\sum_{\text{initial}} T_i + \sum_{\text{final}} T_f \qquad (21)$$

where the notation is that of Section 1A2, and the equivalence of the definitions follows from the conservation of total energy; T_i is defined as kinetic energy. We consider first the case of a typical reaction of the two-product type: $\mathrm{T}(i,p)\mathrm{R}$.

It is very easy to treat this case with the target nucleus at rest. Then conservation of momentum in the laboratory system yields the vector relation $\mathbf{p}_i = \mathbf{p}_p + \mathbf{p}_R$. We have only to square this, employ the relativistic connection between momentum and kinetic energy T, $p^2 = T^2/c^2 + 2mT$, and substitute in the definition for Q, eliminating, say, T_R. We have

$$Q = T_p - T_i + m_R c^2 \left\{\left[1 + \left(\frac{m_p}{m_R}\right)^2 \frac{T_p}{m_p c^2}\left(2 + \frac{T_p}{m_p c^2}\right)\right.\right.$$

$$+ \left(\frac{m_i}{m_R}\right)^2 \frac{T_i}{m_i c^2}\left(\frac{T_i}{m_i c^2} + 2\right) - \frac{2 m_p m_i}{m_R^2}$$

$$\times \left[\frac{T_p T_i}{m_p c^2 \cdot m_i c^2}\left(2 + \frac{T_p}{m_p c^2}\right)\left(2 + \frac{T_i}{m_i c^2}\right)\right]^{\frac12} \cos\theta_p\left.\right]^{\frac12} - 1\right\} \qquad (22a)$$

This may be written in the low-energy limit by expanding the radical, neglecting T/mc^2 compared to unity for all particles. The familiar result follows:

$$Q = T_p\left(1 + \frac{m_p}{m_R}\right) - T_i\left(1 - \frac{m_i}{m_R}\right) - 2\frac{(m_p T_p m_i T_i)^{\frac12}}{m_R}\cos\theta_p \qquad (22b)$$

In reactions of this type, with only two product particles, there is evidently a unique value of T_p for a given recoil direction and a given incident energy. When the reaction produces three or more particles, no such simple connection exists. The case is then parallel to the discussion in Section 1A2. A distribution of energies results. If the reaction takes place in two independent stages, first the emission of two particles, then the break-up of one of the pair, somewhat simpler relations can be obtained. Thus, study of the energy distribution can give some insight into the mechanism of the reaction.

The rigid correlation between energy of outgoing particle and angle of emission has been much exploited as a laboratory means for obtaining particles of a well-defined energy. For neutrons especially such monoenergetic beams can hardly be obtained in any other way. Simply as an example, it is interesting to note that the very exothermic reaction $T^3(d,n)He^4$ used with a well-controlled 1-Mev beam of deuterons produces neutrons ranging from almost 16 Mev to under 13 Mev in the backwards direction. A study of a set of such reactions has been made which makes possible the production of monoenergetic neutron beams of energies from a few kilovolts up to about 20 Mev; a source of charged particles of well-defined but rather modest energies of a couple of Mev was used. A valuable review by Hanson et al. (H2) fully discusses the several reactions used most frequently and gives a graphical treatment of the fundamental relations. Graphical treatments of the relativistic case, very useful when it is desired to reduce experimental data, have been given in (B16) and especially in (M1).

It is worth while to make the remark in closing that, in all the relativistic formulas above, the case in which some particle (i) is a photon can be obtained by replacing the total energy $E_i = m_1 c^2 \gamma$ by the quantum energy $h\nu$, and neglecting m_i wherever it occurs *without* a factor γ.

B. Conservation of Angular Momenta

The complementary relation in quantum mechanics between energy momentum and space-time leads to straightforward experimental use of the ideas of energy and momentum, as we have seen. The important canonical variable, angular momentum, is conjugate to angle. We measure the angular momenta of quantum systems mainly by obtaining statistical distributions in angle. The typical nuclear reaction is carried out with a beam of particles; the very term *beam* implies a more or less sharp definition of the direction of motion, and hence a necessarily rough limitation on angular momentum. An infinite plane wave, indeed, contains all angular momenta of orbital motion, with definite amplitudes, and in addition requires supplementing by the wave function factor representing the intrinsic angular momentum of the particles in the beam. Only when there is some reason to limit the states of angular momentum which are of interest—either simply formally in some systematic counting of all angular momentum states (as in the method of partial waves) or physically because for some reason only a limited number of angular momenta contribute to a given reaction—can the angular momentum conservation law be of much value. For example, in the familiar case of thermal neutron reactions, where the incident wavelength is large compared to the region of possible interaction, only the spherically symmetric component—angular momentum equal to zero—of the incident wave can possibly contribute. Other parts of the wave are of vanishingly small amplitude; the "centrifugal barrier" keeps them from the region of interaction. If any specification can be made of the angular momentum (hence of the variation with direction) of the incoming wave, general rules may often become helpful.

The total angular momentum is certain to be conserved; the forces between nucleons are, however, non-central, so that there is a tendency to interconvert intrinsic or spin angular momentum with that associated with orbital motion. Only in special cases can the relative apportioning and hence the complete angular distribution be obtained (Y2). The spin angular momentum affects, of course, not the direction of motion in space but the orientation of the spin axis of the particle concerned. If an unknown spin change can occur, this will clearly affect predictions of angular distribution in a way calculable only under further specification of the interactions involved. There are three general results, interesting to present, which apply quite generally to all nuclear reactions between unpolarized target and unpolarized incident particles:

1. As is clear on physical grounds, there will be axial symmetry about the direction of the incident beam.

2. If, among the incoming partial waves, only those of angular momentum L or below contribute appreciably to a reaction, the angular distribution of any single product particle cannot be more complicated than that of the incoming contributing partial wave. Indeed, the angular distribution of the outgoing particle will be a polynomial in $\cos \theta$, where θ is the polar angle of emission relative to the beam direction, of degree no higher than $2L$. This holds independently of the spin of any particles or of the number which take part. It is restricted to non-relativistic velocities for the incoming particle. In relativistic cases, one higher power of L may occur, but in general it will be reduced by a factor of the order of (v/c). If several partial waves of different L contribute, the polynomial will generally contain all powers of $\cos \theta$ from

the maximum down; if only one wave contributes, only even powers of $\cos \theta$ can occur. These results refer, of course, to the center-of-mass frame of reference.

3. If the distribution of product particles contains any odd powers in $\cos \theta$, i.e., if it is not symmetrical with respect to the plane normal to the beam, two (or more) intermediate states are involved with opposite parities. Thus an even polynomial in $\cos \theta$ is a typical consequence of reactions involving a marked resonance; this will be discussed more fully later.

Most frequently such considerations yield useful information only when there is additional information, for example data permitting the original specification of what partial waves can contribute. This implies some statements about the mechanism of the reaction, some definite nuclear model, and some assumption about the character of nuclear states and of interactions. Then the selection rules which result are often powerful discriminants between possible alternatives. Such cases occur most frequently in nuclei lighter than neon, in which region some progress has been made in constructing detailed models for nuclear systems. Examples will be given in the proper places later.

SECTION 2. THE DATA OF NUCLEAR REACTIONS

The conservation laws are satisfied in every single nuclear collision. But, besides data on the constants of motion, nuclear physics also is concerned with knowing *how many* nuclear processes of a definite kind take place under given conditions. It is evidently beyond us to say whether or not the next proton, say, will initiate a transmutation in a given fluorine nucleus, but we can obtain from both experiment and theory the probability of the process. We can expect to predict with calculable accuracy the fraction of the beam of incident protons which enters the target nuclei.

A. Yields and Cross Sections

The simplest expression for the probability of a nuclear reaction is the *yield*. This is frequently but a semi-empirical expression, stipulating, for a particular experimental arrangement, how many processes occur per incident particle. The statement that a yield of 1/2000 was obtained for the reaction $Li^7(p,\alpha)\alpha$ with a thick target at 3 Mev means only that one lithium nucleus divides for every 2000 protons stopped in the target material. The specification is obviously incomplete. For data about the probability of the reaction itself one would need to know how many encounters occurred and at what energies, whereas here the protons lose energy as they penetrate the target, which is often not even a single nuclear species but a mixture of isotopes or even a compound. Improvement could be obtained by using a target so thin that the energy loss of the beam protons in traversing it was negligible; here at least the energy would be sharply defined. Thin-target or thick-target yield data are common in the literature; each requires special interpretation before any absolute number can be obtained (C6, R1, R2). Such a form of presenting data implies that only some relative feature of the reaction is under study.

The familiar cross section is a complete specification of the probability of nuclear reaction. A cross section σ_{AB} for a reaction in which the particle A is incident with specified properties and the specified set of particles B emerges can be defined by the expression $n_B = I_A \sigma_{AB} N$. Here N is the number of target particles presented to the beam (for example, for thin targets the product of beam area, target thickness, and number of target atoms per cubic centimeter gives N), n_B is the number of the specified particles B emitted per second, and I_A is the incident flux of particles A, the number per unit area and time.[1]

A cross section may be specified for any process or partial process: for example, we can assign a cross section for the emission of gamma-rays of energy E in the direction specified by the polar angles (θ, φ) when protons of energy W are incident on Li^7. Then the number of such gamma-rays emitted in that direction per unit solid angle and per unit energy for unit proton flux is just $\sigma_{p\gamma}(E, \theta, \varphi)$ for each lithium nucleus in the beam. The quantity $\sigma_{p\gamma}$ is called a differential cross section (per unit energy and unit solid angle), since it is defined for an infinitesimal range of the continuous variables E, φ, and θ. The total number of gamma-rays emitted in all directions is of course obtained by summing over all energies and directions. Then the number of gamma-quanta for unit flux and a single target atom is

$$\Sigma_{p\gamma} = \int_0^\infty dE \int_0^{2\pi} d\varphi \int_{+1}^{-1} d(\cos\theta) \sigma_{p\gamma}(E, \varphi, \theta)$$

Here $\Sigma_{p\gamma}$ would be called the *total* cross section for proton capture by lithium for protons of energy W. In this way the frequency of any process or partial process can be described fully by giving the appropriate cross section, which may depend on any set of discrete and continuous

---

[1] Note that for the collisions of identical particles, as in the scattering of protons on protons, incident and recoil particles are not physically distinguishable, and the number of observed events may then be a sum of both.

variables. The cross section for any process is just the area of the incident beam from which particles are removed by the given process, when the beam is thought of as directed at a single target nucleus. Of course, the cross section may be defined not only per nucleus, as we have here done, but also per unit volume, per gram, or in terms of any convenient measure of target atoms. If there were no non-classical wave effects, the cross section for a definite target, summed over all the possible processes which could occur, would be just the geometrical area of the target. We shall see almost this result for the removal of fast neutrons from a beam (B14, L2, M3, W5).

The probability of a nuclear reaction, expressed either as a cross section or only roughly as a relative yield, is most frequently measured for a specific nuclear reaction as a function of the energy of the incident beam. Such a number is called the excitation function of the reaction concerned. (If a change in chemical identity is involved, it is sometimes called a transmutation function.) The chief data of nuclear experiments besides the energy relations and the nature of the reaction are the angular distributions and the excitation functions, which can be reduced to a knowledge of the cross section for the specified reaction as a function of energy of incidence and direction of emission.

B. The Measurement of Yields and Cross Sections

The experimental procedures for the measurement of cross section amount to a good fraction of the subject matter of experimental nuclear physics. It would be presumptuous to try to discuss them in a small space. It seems worth while, however, to give a kind of summarized functional enumeration, not so much of the experimental methods, but of the general procedures and precautions which must be included in any program for the measurement of cross sections. Evidently the type of measurements made will depend on the detail and the accuracy of cross-section knowledge wanted; it is obviously more exacting in general to seek a knowledge of the differential cross section than of the total cross section, and of an accurate absolute value than of a rough relative one.

1. The Beam. If the cross section $\sigma_{i, T}(E, \theta, \varphi)$ is sought as a function of energy, of angle, of type of projectile, it is obvious that the beam must be well defined with respect to these quantities. Usually this definition is imposed on the entire incoming beam of projectiles; sometimes it is possible to study the reaction products and by some condition of the reaction eliminate all events which did not begin with the correct value of one of the variables. These methods frequently involve time-coincidence counting. Generally the entire beam accepted into the region of reaction is known to have the wanted values of its parameters.

The type of projectile is the most general variable which needs control. The emerging beam from a cyclotron is likely to be quite free of all types of ions other than the resonant species, but an electrostatic generator, for example, will equally well accelerate the deuterons and the protons which may leave its hydrogen-ion source. Molecular ions contribute to the current like atomic ions, but not to the yield, and must often be specifically excluded. For such purposes magnetic resolution of the raw particle beam is often used. When unstable particles form the beam, as in the case of pi-mesons, any stretch of beam travel will allow decay particles to enter the beam. Such beams cannot be wholly pure, and corrections for the mixture of particles are needed. Usually charged particle beams are rather easily controlled for beam purity because of the power of ion-optical analysis. Gamma-ray beams, or beams of charged particles energetic enough to yield neutron-emitting reactions in any intervening windows, air, etc., in the path, may require special care. Crude magnetic analysis will generally remove electrons; neutrons are much harder to eliminate and may cause trouble. Deflection of the wanted charged beam will in principle solve the neutron problem, if scattering from the magnets, etc., is not too severe. The problem is one of increasing importance as beam energy, and with it the number of secondary reactions, increases.

The energy is often very well defined by the source used. Control of d-c ripple in electrostatic generators has reached precisions of a few parts in 10^5. Magnetic analysis can be pushed nearly as far even for roughly defined beams like the cyclotron output. Synchrotrons give excellent control over beam energy as well. Any matter which the beam traverses in its path to the target produces energy losses by ionization and excitation of atoms, and also by nuclear events, which smear out the beam energy. This is in principle avoidable by keeping the beam in vacuum, but eventually the beam must strike some target material. The same processes, of course, occur in the target, which must be kept thin (measured in atoms per square centimeter) if the cross section is wanted at a well-defined energy. Thick targets can yield only cross sections integrated over energy, and may cause straggling in direction and even particle type as well. Yield as a function of energy sometimes can roughly replace beam homogeneity by allowing a differentiation of the integral yield.

Homogeneity in energy usually is easier to secure than absolute knowledge of the energy of the beam employed. The energy scale in the region of Mev depends on comparison with a few nuclear resonance energies which have been calibrated absolutely by measuring the trajectory of a proton beam in a known electric field.[1] This gives an accuracy of about one part in a thousand. Magnetic trajectories using the proton magnetic moment resonance frequency for field measurements work about as well, and extend into the 100-Mev region, especially for electrons from gamma-ray beams. Range measurements using the theory for energy loss by ionization are very valuable secondary standards over all energies above, say, a few kev. They have been computed and calibrated over this whole range for nearly all the usual projectiles. The angle of emission of the Cerenkov electromagnetic shock wave in a material of known index of refraction is an elegant method for particles with a velocity such that $\beta n > 1$, where n is the refractive index of the material; velocity measurements by direct time-of-flight determination have also been made. The kinematics of elastic collisions is also capable of giving beam energies expressed as a ratio to the rest energy of the particle, in the relativistic region.

Angle definition for the beam, often called collimation, is of importance for any measurements of $d\sigma/d\Omega$. Here defining slits of some sort are the usual key parts of the apparatus. Sometimes the direction of the track of the product particles themselves, made visible by cloud chamber or nuclear emulsion techniques, replaces slits followed by direction-insensitive counters. The effects of Coulomb scattering from nuclei and electrons of the target itself or any material in the beam path are the main enemy of good collimation. Divergence of the original beam forms in itself no source of error which collimating slits or simple distance of beam travel and choice of detector acceptance angle cannot remove. But good collimation implies loss of total beam intensity, and practical limits of time and background here often are decisive.

Perhaps the most important of all parameters of the beam is the number of particles striking the target in a specified experiment. Often the current is measured and then time-integrated. Monitoring, or control of relative intensities, is frequently used for a series of experiments in which absolute values are either ignored (e.g., all cross sections may be measured relative to a given known cross section) or calibrated against one single measurement. Integrated charge may be measured

---

[1] Typical reference energies in absolute volts are

$F^{19}(p,\alpha\gamma)O^{16}$	0.3404 Mev	Resonance
$Li^7(p,\gamma)Be^8$	0.442	Resonance
$F^{19}(p,\alpha\gamma)O^{16}$	0.8735	Resonance
$Al^{27}(p,\gamma)Si^{28}$	0.9933	Resonance
$Li^7(p,n)Be^7$	1.882	Threshold

See, for example, W. Hornyak, T. Lauritsen, P. Morrison, and W. A. Fowler, Revs. Modern Phys., **22**, 291 (1950).

by measuring the potential change or integrated current flow to a Faraday cup, an insulated conductor so arranged that no secondary charges can leave it and all beam charge is stopped within it. In one high-energy proton experiment the Faraday cup was a forty-pound chunk of brass under magnetic field in a vacuum. More usually it is a small cylinder with a beam window in one end. Ionization is often used to measure intensity by taking advantage of the known space rate of energy loss and the mean energy used per ion pair. Direct counting of ionizing tracks in photoplates can be used. Relative values can be obtained by actually measuring the beam-induced yield of some known reaction, using radioactivity, particle emission, or even collecting the neutral atoms of a stable reaction product, as has been done for such reactions as $Li^6(n,H^3)\alpha$. Even calorimetry of a target which stops a totally absorbed beam has been used for beam intensity.

With particles of non-zero spin (protons or even gammas) there is another possible parameter to control: the spin component. This corresponds to use of a polarized light beam in optical experiments. Apart from magnetic polarization of neutrons, only the slight polarization effects resulting from double scattering have been examined for charged beams. This may become a more important field in the future.

2. The Target. To specify a cross section precisely, the nuclear composition of the target must be well known. This implies pure and homogeneous targets. The isotopic concentration of the target must, of course, be known; this is usually easy if natural targets are used, but special analysis is required with targets prepared from isotope-separated material.

The target nucleus may undergo the looked-for reaction, but in general this is improbable. Most of the target nuclei are not changed by the beam. Their presence is needed because the probability of reaction is proportional to the number of nuclei independently exposed. But their very presence modifies the beam by producing straggling in energy and direction by Coulomb scattering from electron and nucleus, or by occasional nuclear collisions of kinds other than that under study. They may produce a "straggle" in beam particle type by yielding secondaries which go on in the target to induce unwanted reactions of nuclei later in the beam path. They clearly modify the beam intensity. Obviously the use of targets sufficiently thin that the changes in any of these properties is small compared to the resolution desired in each parameter is always a solution. But it may be impossible to employ such a target because the total number of reactions then becomes too small, or because the physical form of the target elements prevents preparation of a thin sample. Then a careful study of the beam behavior in the target material must be made, and corrections made for all the straggling effects. A frequently employed scheme of finding cross-section variation with beam energy is to use a target made of a stack of thin foils, the yield in each of which is measured. The energy variation of the beam with target thickness tells the mean energy in each foil, and thus the excitation function is measured. The scheme demands that the range of the product particles in the target material be less than the range intervals used in choosing the foil thickness; otherwise the yield function is partly displaced in a distance and energy scale, and detail is lost.

Experimental problems of great importance sometimes arise from the heat dissipation and other physical effects of strong ionizing beams. Constancy of the target mass and composition is assumed in nearly all measurements; evaporation, diffusion, coatings from soot of decomposed pump oils, mechanical displacements of target material by melting or otherwise, and radioactive recoil must all be avoided or corrected for.

3. The Measurement of Cross Sections. The most direct method of measurement is an initial absolute measurement of some differential cross section which defines experimentally the angular acceptance, particle type, energy, etc., of the reaction product. Then a count of the number of such events from a fixed target thickness (with corrections pointed out above) and with known beam population yields the cross section directly. The means employed are diverse.

(a) *Measuring the Residual Nucleus by Detecting Radioactivity.* This may be connected with a radiochemical separation of that nucleus from the target matrix. Such a scheme does not define the energy, angle, spin, or any other property of the product nucleus except its chemical, or indirectly its nuclear, identity. It may be combined with the thin-layer target scheme to get excitation functions for a specified reaction.

(b) *Collecting the Product Particle.* If this is done, as usual, while the product particle is in flight, the angle, energy, and type of product may all be defined. Very often ion-optical means are used. Such schemes separate product particles by their differing trajectories in a vacuum chamber with a controlled electromagnetic field and make possible detection of individual levels of the residual nucleus by careful measurement of the energy released. The charge-mass ratios usually fix the product uniquely. Detectors are used to count the product particles, which may be linearly responding ionization chambers or solids giving scintillation response, gas-amplifying counters like the proportional and Geiger counters, photoemulsions, cloud chambers, simple charge collection by Faraday cup, or specific induced nuclear reactions themselves

(W10). The angular resolution is evidently mainly a problem of the disposition of the apparatus. Energy resolution may be secured by such ion-optical means as we have mentioned, or by using absorbers to fix the total energy needed before particle counting. Counter telescopes which require energy loss rates to be within a fixed range, determined by signal levels and the coincident or anti-coincident response of a fixed set of counters and absorbers, are very much used at the high-energy end, where ion optics is more difficult. Cerenkov counters and time-of-flight measurements are among the newest techniques coming into use in this field.

It is possible to measure total cross section, $\sigma = \int d\Omega \, d\sigma/d\Omega$, more easily. Here what counts is removal from the beam. All that is needed then is a comparison of detector response with and without the intervening target. For thin targets having N atoms/cm^2 and "good geometry," then, $I/I_0 = e^{-N\sigma}$. "Good geometry" means such collimation that all particles scattered through any small angle miss the detectors (B14). Since the detectors have finite acceptance in every case, correction is needed for scattering-in (P3). When this correction is sizable, the case is said to be one of bad geometry. Thick targets, where multiple collisions are not negligible, require additional care. The inescapable relation in Eq. (45) between an absorption cross section and elastic scattering means that special care must be taken to correct for the very low-angle forward coherent scattering if the geometry is very good, since scattering-in cannot be estimated from the angular distribution of the main absorptive process. Apart from such questions, it is in general possible to make the only absolute cross-section measurement one of total cross section, done by beam attenuation, and then only relative measurements for all the differential cross sections are needed.

4. Special Problems with Gamma-Rays. The use of gamma-rays as beam projectile, or their measurement as product, has special problems arising from the small interaction with matter. Gamma-rays can be detected only after they have given their energy at least in part to matter, especially to electrons. For this purpose most gamma-ray-detecting schemes make use of a layer of matter of appropriate thickness placed ahead of the detector proper. In this converter layer the gamma-rays produce electrons (or positrons) whose ionization, range, energy, and momentum may be measured by the means described above. At energies in the range of a few Mev it is possible to get absolute measurements of gamma-ray flux by using the known ionization of the electrons secondary to gammas, which of course have a spread of energies as long as Compton scattering is important. At energies above 10 Mev or so, a thin foil in which electron-positron pairs are the principal products may be used. Then a knowledge of the pair production cross section from theory or from total attenuation measurements may be used to compute the incident flux. Calorimetry is possible for strong beams of not too high energy, and special photonuclear processes may also play some part, particularly as secondary standards. Radioactive sources of gamma-rays, or gamma-ray sources which use a nuclear radiative transition like the decay of the familiar state of Be^8 at 17.6 Mev excitation, may be calibrated by using other particles emitted in coincidence, if the details of the disintegration scheme are known. The strong sources are usually gamma-rays produced by the stopping of electron beams by Coulomb scattering, or bremsstrahlung radiation. This radiation is of course continuous, rather than discrete, like that of the nuclear radiative decays. Its energy limit is in general well-known, because the original electron energy can be well-defined and measured. Individual quanta may be selected by using coincidence methods with the electron after the radiative act. In general, though, the whole spectrum is used, or at least that above some threshold for a given reaction, or above a broad limit set by absorbers placed in the beam to remove the softest quanta. In this case cross sections are hard to give for a definite energy. Again differential measurements may be made. Very often the cross sections for bremsstrahlen-induced reactions are given not per quantum of a definite energy, but per effective quantum in the beam. The number of effective quanta Q is defined (B16a) as the ratio $Q = \left[\int_0^{E_{max}} n(E)E\, dE \right]/E_{max}$, where $n(E)\, dE$ is the number of quanta in the beam exposure having energy between E and $E + dE$ and E_{max} is the maximum energy in the beam. The rough form of the spectrum for bremsstrahlen is $n(E)\, dE = N_0\, dE/E$; therefore in this approximation the value of Q for a bremsstrahlung beam is just the number N_0. This is usually satisfactory if the region of interest is well above the low-energy deviations from the $1/E$ distribution for the beam. For quantitative work the exact form of the bremsstrahlung spectrum must be taken into account and the experimental data analyzed by a numerical process indicated, for example, in (K4).

Neutrons present many related problems; their detailed treatment is to be found in Part VII.

5. A Table of Yields. As orientation to the size of yields to be expected in typical practical situations, Table 1 shows a number of thick-target yield values for various nuclear projectiles of widely available energies. In all cases the target is taken to be thick enough to stop the entire beam, and to be the pure element of normal isotope composition.

For gamma-rays and neutrons such a target is not usually practical, but computed values are given for comparison. Only a few values are given for reactions due to other particles than the heavy charged particles of central interest in this chapter. Table 7 contains additional data

TABLE 1

Yields of Some Typical Nuclear Reactions (Thick-Target)

Projectile	Reaction	Product Nuclei/10^6 Projectiles (beam energy in Mev)
Gamma-rays	$Al^{27}(\gamma,p)$	8×10^3 (17 Mev)
	$Al^{27}(\gamma,n)$	3×10^3 (17 Mev)
	$Cu(\gamma,n)$	11×10^3 (17 Mev)
	$W(\gamma,n)$	18×10^3 (17 Mev)
Electrons	$Cu^{65}(e,e'n)$	2 (17 Mev)
Neutrons	n-capture on any but He^4	10^6
	$S^{32}(n,p)$	$\sim 2 \times 10^5$ (5.8 Mev)
Protons	$Cu(p,n)Zn^{63}$	18 (6.3 Mev)
Deuterons	$Be(d,H^3)Be^8$	230 H^3 (14 Mev)
	$Li(d,2n)Be^7$	22 (19 Mev)
	$B(d,n)C^{11}$	1.5 (8 Mev)
	$C(d,n)N^{13}$	1.4 (8 Mev)
	$Na(d,p)Na^{24}$	190 (19 Mev)
	$P(d,p)P^{32}$	88 (8 Mev); 350 (14 Mev)
	$K(d,p)K^{42}$	11 (19 Mev)
	$Ca(d,\alpha)K^{42}$	0.3 (19 Mev)
	$Cu(d,p)Cu^{64}$	330 (14 Mev)
	$Y(d,2n)Zr^{89}$	4.9 (14 Mev); 52 (19 Mev)
	$Mo(d,\alpha)Cb^{90}$	0.4 (14 Mev)
	$Te(d,n)I^{131}$	1.6(8 Mev); 32 (14 Mev)
	$Bi(d,n)Po^{210}$	56 (14 Mev)
Alpha-particles	$A(\alpha,pn)K^{42}$	17 (44 Mev)
	$Pb(\alpha,2n)Po^{210}$	48 (44 Mev)
	$Bi(\alpha,2n)At^{211}$	0.13 (38 Mev); 130 (44 Mev)

on deuteron reactions. Reference (G0) contains still more data on charged particle beams and a very useful survey of chemical methods for preparation of carrier-free radio isotopes.

C. Types of Reactions: A Guide to the Literature

It is not the function of this section to present a complete survey of the thousand-odd nuclear reactions which have been studied. Even a list of reactions by types cannot be exhaustive, since reactions have been observed at high energy in which dozens of products occur. It would be possible to systematize such highly multiple reactions only by giving the relative yields of the various products. Putting aside such processes for the present, most nuclear reactions involve the emission of two particles after the reaction, following the type of reaction $T(i,p)R$. A sizable number of reactions are known in which three or four definite products are emitted; then there is a continuous sequence of more complex reactions which typically occur at high energy. There is also the familiar fission reaction, in which, instead of a rather heavy nucleus emitting several light nuclear particles, the heavy target divides and two heavy fragments come off, accompanied by several neutrons and, infrequently, an alpha-particle. A systematic list of nuclear projectiles, with the products they induce, and references to original literature which describes reactions of the type so defined are presented in Appendix II. The references make no attempt at completeness, nor have they been chosen for the purpose of giving the first papers on the reactions. They are meant to indicate a few recent and rather complete papers, especially those which contain theoretical treatment and good bibliographies. It is hoped that entries in Appendix II will assist the reader both in finding a rather general introduction to the reaction type of his interest and in getting a good start toward an exhaustive search of the literature.

SECTION 3. THE NUCLEAR MODEL

A. Qualitative Account of the Model

We can now begin to construct a nuclear model which will have some connection with the complex reality of nuclear process and structure. In the study of nuclear reactions the comparison of the detailed implications of successive models with experiment has led to a graphic but still by no means adequate model. It is this model we here seek to describe.

It is instructive to compare our knowledge of the atom with that of the nucleus at its heart. We know at last that the atom is fully described as an assembly of rather well-defined electrons, held together by their electrostatic attraction to the dense central nucleus, influencing each other by their mutual electromagnetic interaction, and moving in accord with the principles of quantum mechanics (especially the exclusion principle). The nature and properties of electrons are well-known, all interactions being given in detail by Maxwell's and Lorentz' equations. Only for very few details—the hyperfine structure and isotope shift, the line shift due to electromagnetic radiation field coupling—is further investigation needed. Moreover, the well-marked periodicities and shell structure are themselves evidence that the complex mechanics of a many-body problem are susceptible in the atomic case to far-reaching simplifications in which the many-body problem is soluble by methods which begin with the idea of the independent motion of a single electron.

Contrast the nucleus. Even the forces which act between pairs of nucleons are still without any general expression. In Part IV of Volume I, the two-body problem is discussed at length in an effort to find empirical clues to the force laws. The nuclear forces are short-range forces; no large-scale counterpart exists for laboratory investigation. All our knowledge of nuclear forces is based on nuclear experiment itself. The nucleus is a system of many bodies, whose general mechanics is evidently more complicated than that of the equivalent atom for, although regularities exist in nuclei, they are not so striking as those evident in the periodic table of the atoms. The major regularities, important though they are (see Part IV, Volume I), cannot yet lead to confidence in a simple building-up process like that of the atomic domain. Only in the lightest nuclei, below neon, or even below helium, is more or less easy progress to be hoped for in obtaining a definite and detailed picture of nuclear matter. We shall see how the short-range and exchange character of the forces, the strong component of non-central force, the whole tightly bound character of the nuclear state of matter make difficult its detailed description. The point of view so far most successful in the discussion of reactions, though clearly itself incomplete and often misleading, involves a kind of abstraction from the detailed structure of any particular nuclear species, and an effort to see what types of behavior, what experimentally determined properties, can be used to give an account of nuclear reactions.

1. The Interaction of Nucleons. In the atom, each electron moves in a rather slowly changing force field, the sum of the nuclear attraction and the averaged repulsion of the other atomic electrons. The forces are of long-range nature, and it does not matter much if we neglect the very occasional close collisions between the other electrons and the one whose motion we are considering. We can hope to study the motion of each electron separately, taking account of the others present only in a general and smoothed-over way. The presence even of scores of electrons does not impossibly complicate the problem: we fix on the detailed motion of each in turn, correcting only slightly for the specific behavior of its neighbors. This approximation, known as the Hartree approximation, is excellent for the loose, smooth, open structure of the atom, governed by long-range forces. But in nuclei the scheme seems entirely inappropriate. Here the forces are of a range smaller than the dimensions of the system. The force on each particle depends strongly on the detailed configuration of its neighbors; a small difference in the position of another nucleon can change its interaction from a decisive one to a negligible one. The miniature solar system has disappeared; we think instead of a miniature drop of water, a small drop of quantum-mechanical liquid. Instead of a slowly and smoothly varying mutual interaction, superimposed as a perturbation upon a stronger central force, all of which we can without much error replace by a smoothed-over time average, the interaction energy of a single nuclear particle with the rest of the nucleus is a jagged and highly fluctuating function of time. To average in space over such a function is to conceal its essential features. The continual transfer of energy from particle to particle is the rule; no well-marked center of force exists. It is misleading to try to "peel off the motion of each particle" in turn and try to correct for the average effect of its neighbors.

In this picture the shell structure of loosely coupled particles has no obvious counterpart in nuclei. Yet the lightest nuclei show such properties that for a long while they have been studied by the use of the Hartree approximation and related methods. Moreover, the nuclei all the way up the table exhibit regularities, in their lowest states of excitation at least, which imply a well-defined shell structure. Such properties as (1) special stability of particular values of A and Z (of which the familiar increased stability of even-even nuclei is the prototype), (2) the angular momentum and parity of the ground state and, for many nuclei, of the lowest-lying excited states (isomeric states), and (3) rough values of the magnetic moments of ground states can be rationalized and even predicted by semi-empirical results of what is called the shell model.

In the most recent and remarkably successful of the shell models (M5), the individual nucleons are pictured as moving in Hartree-like shells of well-defined orbital angular momentum and radial quantum number. The order and the total angular momentum of these states can be fixed by arguments based on the picture of strong spin-orbit forces, which couple the spin and orbit of each individual nucleon strongly together, so that the total angular momentum and parity can be established by the analogue of spectroscopic j-j coupling, taken with certain semi-empirical rules for deciding the order of the terms. There results the order of shells, in the familiar spectroscopic notation, shown in Table 2. There is a rapidly growing literature of applications of the shell model to the prediction of the properties of low-lying nuclear levels; it cannot be doubted that no previous effort to describe such states has been so successful, and indeed it seems demonstrated that strong spin-orbit forces must be present.

How the single-particle orbit model, with its marked shells, can be reconciled with our general arguments on the unsuitability of the

TABLE 2

Nuclear Shell Order in the j-j Coupling Model

The suffix indicating the j value has been suppressed, except when the same orbital angular momentum appears in two adjoining shells; then the state of highest j is indicated as lying lower in energy. The symbol $2p$, for example, means both the states $2p_{3/2}$ and $2p_{1/2}$.

Shell Configurations	j Values	Number of Nucleons in Shell	Total Number (Neutron and proton shells are independent)
$1s$	$\frac{1}{2}$	2	2
$1p$	$\frac{3}{2}, \frac{1}{2}$	6	8
$1d, 2s$	$\frac{5}{2}, \frac{3}{2}, \frac{1}{2}$	12	20
$1f, 2p, 1g_{9/2}$	$\frac{7}{2}, \frac{5}{2}, \frac{3}{2}, \frac{1}{2}, \frac{9}{2}$	30	50
$1g_{7/2}, 2d, 3s, 1h_{11/2}$	$\frac{7}{2}, \frac{5}{2}, \frac{3}{2}, \frac{1}{2}, 1\frac{1}{2}$	32	82
$1h_{9/2}, 2f, 3p, 1i_{13/2}$	$\frac{9}{2}, \frac{7}{2}, \frac{5}{2}, \frac{3}{2}, \frac{1}{2}, 1\frac{3}{2}$	44	126

Hartree picture for the strong, short-range, and fluctuating nuclear forces is still by no means clear. But an interesting analogy due to Weisskopf seems to point out the nature of the eventual solution. He recalls the behavior of the Fermi gas of electrons, regarded as non-interacting, and moving in the periodic potential of a metal lattice. Here shells—the Brillouin zones—are very marked, and the neglect of the electron Coulomb interaction, certainly reasonably strong, seems to have very little effect. Qualitatively this must be ascribed to the circumstance that electron-electron collisions can make no physical difference if all states in the momentum space are filled, as required by the exclusion principle for the Fermi gas. Such scatterings represent no change in the total system. If, however, a higher-energy electron enters the metal from without, it carries momentum adequate to excite the electrons of the Fermi gas beyond the Fermi limit; its collisions are rapid, and it loses energy very quickly to the electrons of the metal. In the same way, the low-lying states of the nuclear system may be represented well enough by the non-interacting particle picture; the expected collisions are mostly excluded. Yet for high excitations the regions of momentum space which are not filled can be reached, and the collisions become decisive. This picture fits the real nuclear situation very well.

Although the stationary states of nuclei, and especially of the lighter nuclei, lie beyond the scope of this treatment, it is appropriate to mention here the most powerful of the methods deriving from the Hartree picture, which has found great use in the discussion of just those problems. The method is the Wigner theory of nuclear supermultiplets. Using an extension of the same essentially group-theoretic methods which permit the classification of the spin and orbital quantum states of the atomic system, Wigner considers a nuclear system a collection of particles interacting by forces which depend only on spatial configuration, not on spins or on the charge of the nucleon. Exchange forces may occur, if they are space-exchange forces only. For such interactions, certain quantum numbers can be defined, in extension of the J and S numbers, familiar in atomic multiplets, which characterize the spatial symmetry of the nuclear wave functions for any collection of nucleons. Then, by regarding the Coulomb and the spin-dependent forces as perturbations capable of splitting the highly degenerate levels of the ideal system, a more realistic picture can be obtained which has considerable success in the ordering of the lower-lying states of not too complex nuclei. For specific information the extensive literature may be consulted.

However, it is fundamental to the picture of the nucleus which we shall chiefly employ, the picture appropriate for excited states: that energy exchange with ease between the closely packed nucleons; that the nucleus be regarded as a highly condensed state of matter, a tightly packed quantum liquid, where the relatively small number of degrees of freedom (compared to those of a drop of water), and the diffraction and exchange effects to be expected from quantum considerations at such small distances be thought of as modifying the behavior of a system otherwise very like the thermodynamic system of a familiar liquid drop. We know that the radius of the sphere of nuclear matter is rather well represented by the formula

$$R = r_0 A^{\frac{1}{3}} \tag{23}$$

with A the number of nucleons, and $r_0 = 1.4 \times 10^{-13}$ cm (C10). This is just the assertion of constant density which defines our model as a liquid or a solid, not a gas.

From the simplest Fermi gas model, or what is almost the same, by taking the mean velocity of a nucleon in the nucleus to be that corresponding to a de Broglie wavelength equal to the mean spacing of nucleons, we find that the kinetic energy of a nucleon ought to be some tens of millions of volts. This gives a mean collision time of some 10^{-13} cm per $5 \cdot 10^9$ cm/sec, or about 10^{-22} sec. For any interacting particle which takes a time longer than this to complete its collision with a bound nucleon, we have to regard the nucleus as a closed system, without a sharp separation possible between collisions with a single nucleon and collisions with the whole of the nuclear matter. Only if collisions are made by particles moving so fast, and transferring so much momentum to the struck nucleon, that the collision is complete within the characteristic nuclear time can we think of the nucleus as a collection of free particles. Even then the nuclear "gas" is highly degenerate; quantum levels are filled up to a rather high energy, and low momentum transfers thus are discouraged. It is then clear that, for incident particles with an energy per nuclear mass unit up to 20 or 30 Mev, the nuclear drop must be considered as a whole. Only in the higher-energy domain are we more nearly justified in thinking of a collection of instantaneously free nucleons; and even here there are important effects of the nuclear binding.

Let us continue this qualitative discussion of the collision between a nucleon and the struck nucleus. If the incident nucleon is of high enough energy so that it may be localized (i.e., represented by a wave packet whose main components have wavelengths smaller than nuclear dimensions), we may try to follow the collision classically. The short-range nuclear forces extend about as far as the mean spacing of nucleons within the structure. A colliding particle then has very little chance to travel through the nucleus without striking the nucleons within. At very high energies (say 100 Mev or more) the mean free path for collision with the nucleons of the nucleus has dropped to some 4×10^{-13} cm, but, using the same rough idea of collisions with nearly free neutrons, the free path has dropped to a tenth of that value for ten-million-volt incident particles, and to only 10^{-14} cm at 1 Mev (S7). The last distance is so small that the picture evidently fails, but the conclusion seems confirmed. As soon as the particle crosses the surface of the nuclear sphere, it will interact strongly with the nuclear matter. It may lose only part of its energy to the first particles it encounters, and continue on, transferring energy to the nuclear matter as it goes. Eventually its entire kinetic energy is spread in some way over the many particles of the nucleus, and a new state of quantized collective motion for all the nuclear particles exists, a nearly stationary state of what is called the compound nucleus. We shall say more of this in Section 3A2.

The nuclear drop has of course an energy content, given in an understandable form by the semi-empirical formula discussed in Section 3B4. The electromagnetic properties of the nuclear drop may be computed and measured; indeed, all the properties of the ground state can be ascribed to the model. But the details of nuclear structure cannot be obtained from such simple assumptions as underlie the semi-empirical energy formula, especially the constant density of nuclear matter.

Still less is to be expected from the use of this statistical model in nuclear reactions. In general, it may be said that what we here visualize is not the particular quantum level of a particular nucleus with a well-defined energy, but the average to be expected in a given region of mass number, including many similar but not identical neighboring nuclei. More formally, we shall deal with all the characteristic properties of nuclear states not one by one, but averaged over an interval of excitation energy. Only if the fluctuations in these properties are not too great from level to level, so that the *average* behavior represents the *individual* behavior of states, or if the experimental situation produces averages as the quantities directly observed, can we hope for satisfaction from such a statistical point of view. It is in this charitable sense that the results of the theory are to be taken.

We can summarize the above statements by setting out the two leading assumptions under which the results of the present theory of nuclear reactions are obtained:

I. Nuclear matter is composed of closely packed particles, strongly interacting and capable of rapid interchange of energy, like the particles of a drop of some quantum-mechanical liquid. We may call this assumption close packing.

II. The results obtained from such a consideration are meant to apply not to the particular and specific properties of one well-defined state of motion, but to an average over many states of neighboring energies. Only if the property studied does not fluctuate too widely in such an interval will the conclusions be trustworthy. This we may call the statistical assumption.

2. The Compound Nucleus. In Section 3A1 we discussed the dissipation of the kinetic energy of some incoming particle as it passed into and merged with the closely packed particles of the nucleus. The resulting configuration we called the "compound nucleus." Let us go on with the story of such an event. After the incident particle has merged completely with the nucleus, its energy, no longer concentrated in one particle, is shared by the collective motion of all particles of the new system: the compound nucleus formed by projectile and target. Each of the nucleons will have some additional energy, but none will be likely to have all the incident energy at any one time, or even any very large fraction of it. The energy will be spread among the very many degrees of freedom exactly as the heat energy of a drop of water is kinetic energy spread among many degrees of freedom. But the compound nucleus will eventually lose its energy of excitation. Either radiation, which, as we shall see, is a relatively slow process, will finally remove the energy and thus "cool" the nucleus, or after a long time (time enough for many collisions of nucleons within the nucleus, some ten million in typical cases) the configuration will have the rather unusual property that a sizable amount of energy is concentrated on a single particle, and a particle may escape, cooling the nucleus by "evaporation." It is evident that the escaping particle will not in general be the particle that entered, and that it will have neither the energy nor the direction of the incident particle. Even if by chance a neutron, say, goes out when a neutron enters, this need not be an elastic collision. On the contrary, excitation energy will in general be left behind, to be dissipated in another way; the collision will be inelastic. Elastic collisions do not take place with formation of a compound nucleus except by the re-emission described under the special and rare circumstance that the residual nucleus is left in the single ground state only. The elastic scattering observed includes other effects by which the incident wave function is scattered coherently without the actual formation of a compound nucleus, through purely wave-mechanical processes.

The formation of a compound nucleus may, it is true, take place under rather special circumstances. A gamma-quantum, with wavelength long compared to the nuclear size, may excite proton vibrations with a definite phase relationship. Or, considering the same process from a quite different point of view, the quantum may act upon a single surface proton which receives enough energy to escape without striking other nucleons on its way out. Or the proton coming out may lose energy to a single spot on the nuclear surface, "heating" the nucleus not as a whole but locally. The final reaction might occur by evaporation before the "conduction" of heat away from the hot spot to the rest of the nucleus has taken place. In all these cases—we believe them infrequent but possible—a detailed consideration of the particular process (B17, K1) would be required. However, we shall discuss mainly the fundamental notion of Bohr, which is that the compound nucleus is capable of disintegration in a manner independent of its method of formation. This is perhaps the third assumption of our theory, and we have seen under what circumstances it would require modification. We shall state it explicitly:

III. Nuclear reactions in the domain of statistical theory take place in two separable steps: (1) the formation of a compound nucleus by combination of the incident particle and the target nucleus, and (2) the subsequent disintegration of the compound nucleus, in a manner independent of its method of formation, into the products of the reaction, the emitted particle and the residual nucleus in some one of its quantized energy states. A reaction that leads to more than two products proceeds by a continuation of this scheme: the first product comes off, and the residual nucleus then acts as an excited compound nucleus, emitting another particle, and subsequently even another, and so on. Thus as many as a dozen neutrons may be "boiled off" successively from a highly excited nucleus (T4).

3. Nuclear Energy Levels and Level Widths. So far we have discussed the ideas of the statistical theory from the point of view of the close-packed nucleons, an almost geometrical and quite classical argument. The same conclusions can be expressed in terms of energy levels rather than in geometric terms. We have already shown that the compound nucleus exists for a time long compared to the mean free time for a nucleon collision in the nucleus. This means that, although the description of the individual nucleon as free with a definite energy was very rough, the compound state can be thought of as existing with a wave function which is the approximate eigenfunction of the Hamiltonian of all the nucleons. We restrict ourselves to states which genuinely represent the compound nucleus or its disintegration products: that is, to wave functions which contain no parts corresponding to one particle at a distance from all the others, except where the distant particle is represented by an outgoing spherical wave. This serves to exclude states in which a free particle exists which could not have been emitted by the compound state. Under these conditions we can write

$$\Psi_n = \psi_n \cdot e^{[E_n - (i\Gamma_n/2)]t/\hbar} \tag{24}$$

where the energy is no longer a real eigenvalue but contains an imaginary part. This is the familiar procedure for a damped oscillator (H6). The fraction of systems in the state n will vary with time like the factor $e^{-\Gamma_n t/\hbar}$. Thus $\Gamma_n/\hbar$ is the reciprocal mean lifetime of the state; Γ_n is called its *width*. The usual expression of the uncertainty principle $\Delta E \cdot \Delta t \simeq \hbar$ is exemplified here.

What does the spectrum of a nucleus look like? Simply by considering the distribution of energy among the many particles of a tightly bound system we can form some idea. We begin with the fact that the binding energy of a particle in the nucleus is only a few times smaller than the rough estimate we can make of its kinetic energy. If the particles did not interact strongly—a bad assumption—we could think of forming the excited levels of the nucleus by giving all the excitation energy to one nucleon, or dividing it among two, three, $\cdots$, and so on. Now, since the well in which we could imagine the particles to be moving (see Fig. 3) is far from fully occupied with particles, we can find levels for each nucleon which lie quite close to its ground level. Thus the distribution of a few Mev of excitation energy could be accomplished in a very great number of different ways. Most of these would correspond to the general spreading out of the excitation energy among the many nucleons; very few indeed would be the states in which all the energy was used to promote one or even a few nucleons. The coupling of the particles of course means that the levels are of mixed character. A level cannot be ascribed to a specific distribution of energy, spread among a definite set of particles. In any state, part of the energy is sometimes concentrated on one, sometimes on two, etc. Each eigenfunction could be expanded into a series of terms corresponding to the various partitions of energy. But, with so many possibilities available, the contribution

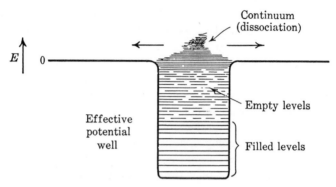

Fig. 3. Schematic nuclear potential well and nucleon energy levels.

of a partition which corresponds to assigning all the energy to one or even two nucleons will be very small indeed. The total number of levels will evidently be extremely large.

These levels, as we have said, are not completely sharp. Only the ground level is quite sharp (even *it* is widened imperceptibly by the possibility of beta- or alpha-decay or of spontaneous fission). As we add excitation energy, the levels become wider because of possible radiative transitions to the lower states through emission of quanta. For some sufficiently high excitation energy, the nucleus will be capable of emitting one particular particle, say a neutron. This will, of course, represent a widening of the levels. But, since so little of the wave function represents a configuration with all the available energy concentrated in one neutron, the effect will be by no means large. The level width will not change markedly as a new decay process appears. The levels will simply widen progressively as more and more possibilities of decay become energetically allowable. The character of the levels will not change abruptly with their energy. Only the appearance of a small probability of emission of a particular particle will indicate the crossing of the energy threshold. As the energy of excitation increases, the total width of levels rises. Moreover, the increase with energy of the number of ways the energy can be partitioned is marked. Finally, the spacing is so small and the width so large that the levels overlap and the familiar continuum has been reached. Even here fluctuations in level density and special selection rules may maintain the features of a discrete spectrum. Only when the excitation is comparable to the total binding energy—say 6 to 8 Mev per particle—does the character of the levels change qualitatively. In such a region the concentration of sufficient

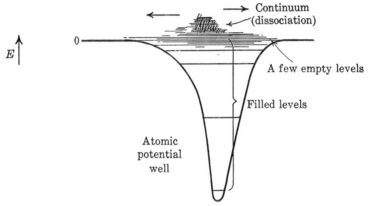

Fig. 4. Schematic atomic potential well and electron energy levels.

energy in one nucleon to allow its escape is the rule and not the exception. Under these circumstances a genuine continuum of levels exists.

In Fig. 4 is shown the parallel situation in the case of an atom with many particles. From the geometrical point of view, the atom is a loose open structure. Its long-range forces mean that elastic collisions are the rule; even if an incident particle excites the atom, the energy of excitation is given to one or perhaps a few of the valence electrons. The K shell electrons have in a heavy atom about a hundred thousand volts of binding; the valence electrons, only a few. Even the L electrons are bound only by some tens of kilovolts. The possible energy levels thus are as shown in the figure: very narrow bands of close levels with great empty spaces separating the bands. Thus in general there is little chance that the energy of an incoming electron lies in a region where levels of the compound system exist. For atomic collisions these nearly stationary states are of little importance. Almost any system which has energy enough to release an electron will rapidly do so. It is interesting, however, that, even in a system so simple as the beryllium atom, terms have been found which give rise to broadened lines. These terms correspond to states in which the total excitation of the atom is greater than the ionization potential but is divided between two electrons. These states often have large widths and short lifetimes, because they can decay by radiationless transitions, emitting electrons. The analogy to the nuclear case is close. In molecules, of course, predissociation is a prominent effect.

Although the concepts of level spacing and level width are entirely quantum-mechanical, Weisskopf has suggested a very pretty semi-classical picture of their significance. Consider a complicated many-particle system like a nucleus, but for simplicity with a large number of *equally spaced* levels, with energy of the nth level, $E_n = E_0 + n\delta$. We can make up a wave packet by combining a great number of energy eigenfunctions $\varphi_n(\mathbf{r})$ corresponding to the stationary states E_n. The total wave function is then

$$\psi = \sum_{n=1}^{N} a_n \varphi_n e^{-iE_n t/\hbar} = \left(\sum_{n=1}^{N} a_n \varphi_n e^{-in\delta t/\hbar} \right) e^{-iE_0 t/\hbar}$$

Now it is evident that

$$\left| \psi \left(t + \frac{2\pi\hbar}{\delta} \right) \right|^2 = |\psi(t)|^2$$

Thus we have constructed a wave function which is by no means a stationary state; in it the configuration of the system repeats itself after the lapse of a time τ, which we can call the recurrence time. If the level spacing is δ, the recurrence time is given by the relation $\tau = 2\pi\hbar/\delta$. Of course, a real nucleus has levels which are not equally spaced, but a similar physical interpretation may be given to the quantity D, the mean level spacing at a given excitation energy. Closely spaced levels imply long times of recurrence, and conversely. It is also instructive to consider the distance traveled by an identifiable nucleon of the wave packet during the duration of one period of the motion. If the mean velocity of the nucleon is given by something like a Fermi gas model, chiefly the zero-point motion arising from the confinement within the nuclear volume, we get for the velocity $v = \hbar/Mp_F$. Then the path length l traveled by a nucleon which had, say, just penetrated the nuclear surface from without before it found itself back in the original configuration again would be $l = 2\pi\hbar^2/MDp_F$. Taking a level spacing of 10 ev, appropriate for the region of slow-neutron capture in heavy nuclei, the value of $l \sim 10^{-6}$ cm, which is about a million times the nuclear diameter. This makes picturesque the complex motion in a compound state, and adds some confidence to our ideas about the statistical theory. On the other hand, if $D = 1$ Mev for the low-lying states of light nuclei, the recurrence path is only a dozen diameters or so, and the picture of an orbital motion for a single particle becomes plausible once more.

The level width can be given a similar interpretation. If a state has energy enough to emit a nucleon, we can imagine the packet so built as to describe the configuration existing when a given nucleon has just entered the nuclear surface. Now, after the recurrence time τ, the nucleon would be back at the surface again, with the same energy, ready to leave in just the manner in which it entered. If it were actually to leave at this first recurrence, the implication would be that the lifetime of the state, $\hbar/\Gamma$, was just equal to the recurrence time. Then the spacing and width would be of the same order, and the idea of well-defined compound state hard to justify. This is plainly one limiting case. But we must recall that at the nuclear surface there is a sharp change of potential. Within the surface, the strong nuclear forces act; outside (a distance only a couple of times 10^{-13} cm outside), there are no nuclear forces at all. At this potential jump, the particle de Broglie wave suffers reflection. Suppose that the probability for penetration of the barrier is P. Then the width can be given in terms of the recurrence time: $\Gamma \sim \hbar/(\tau/P)$; and hence, in terms of the level spacing, $\Gamma \sim P \cdot D/2\pi$.

For the case in which the barrier is entirely nuclear (no Coulomb or centrifugal forces, realized by an s wave neutron), the penetrability is simply given by the familiar quantum formula $P = 4k/K$, where the quantities K and k are, respectively, the wave numbers for the nucleon de Broglie wave within and without the nuclear surface, and we have gone to the limit $k \ll K$. This is a very important result of our detailed theory, to be discussed later at length. Of course, in the present account we have disregarded the fact that there are alternative modes of decay, and the fact that there are constants of the motion besides energy, like angular momentum and parity, which must be conserved but which may vary from level to level. In the calculation of the appropriate D, such classes of states are to be regarded as contributing independently. In general, the statistical theory we discuss here is limited to the treatment of levels *en bloc*, without much hope of identifying states of a specific kind or of predicting energy levels. Since it is clear that the many well-defined observed levels in thermal neutron absorption in the heavy elements (spaced as they empirically are some 10 ev, and lying 8 Mev above ground) must be not far from millionth members of some series of terms, it is not unexpected that we would make more progress, in heavy nuclei at least, by some general statistical treatment than by a method based on classifying and identifying individual terms.

Individual levels can be observed at low energies in all nuclei, e.g., wherever gamma-ray spectra can be studied. In the lighter nuclei, such levels are visible up to tens of millions of volts of excitation; in heavier nuclei, not more than a million volts beyond the neutron binding energy. The most general features of observed level distribution is the steady increase of level density with excitation energy by a function which becomes the steeper as we go to heavier nuclei. A few examples of

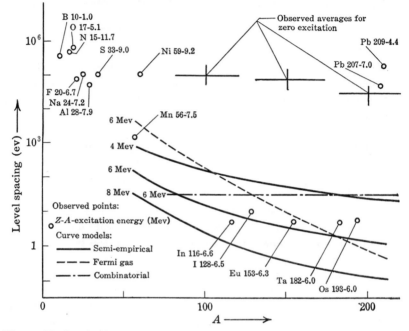

Fig. 5. Nuclear level spacing. This figure presents the nuclear level spacing as a function of the mass number A for various nuclear excitation energies. The marked curves are plots of the results of various models discussed in the text. The circles mark individual observed levels; the nucleus and its excitation are marked beside each experimental point. The three horizontal lines show the spacing observed at zero excitation, averaged over a fair number of nuclei in each region of A. The roughly satisfactory nature of the theoretical curves is shown, as well as their inadequacy for both light nuclei and heavy nuclei, like Ni and Pb in which the influence of shell structure is marked, especially at modest excitation energy.

estimated average spacing, taken from the few known levels in the various regions of interest, are given in Fig. 5. It is noteworthy that the average spacing near zero excitation decreases from the lightest to the heaviest nuclei by a small factor, perhaps by about a factor of 10, while the spacing at some 8 Mev excitation changes by five orders of magnitude. It will, of course, not escape the reader that the application of the statistical notion of level density to the few levels of the lightest nuclei is a dubious business.

The width of the levels increases as their spacing decreases. We expect levels that overlap one another in particle excitation of reasonably heavy nuclei some 10 Mev above the ground state. Unfortunately the difficulty of producing closely monoenergetic beams with high kinetic energy has limited the possibilities of experimental check. The use of endothermic neutron-yielding reactions has been about the only direct test of this point. The work of Barschall with total neutron cross sections at energies around $\frac{1}{2}$ Mev on many elements indeed serves notice that this picture is too simple (B3). The levels vary greatly in spacing and strength; for certain nuclei the whole level structure is far too coarse-grained for the validity of our picture. This is primarily a result of the fact that the shell structure strongly modifies the binding energy of the added neutron. Excitation by neutron capture with low kinetic energy may excite some nuclei (those with closed shells) by only a fraction of the usual 8 Mev. At the lower excitations, the level density is much reduced. Other reasons may also be involved.

B. Calculation of Level Densities

Again disregarding certain details of structure, we may proceed to calculate mean level densities for some statistical models of the nucleus. We shall present two of the most instructive in some detail, giving only a sketchy account of some other schemes which have been proposed.

1. Combinatorial Model. We have already discussed qualitatively the simple model for which we here calculate the mean level density. It is based upon the idea of a set of independent particles among which we divide the energy of excitation. Suppose that each of the N particles has an identical energy spectrum, which we shall take to be of the simplest possible form: a set of equidistant levels of uniform spacing δ. Then the excitation energy W can be written as

$$W = \sum_{1}^{N} n_i \delta$$

where the n_i are integers showing which level of its own spectrum each particle occupies. A given energy W can then be realized in as many different ways as there are ways to sum integers to a given integer total. The states thus formed would be highly degenerate, the degree of degeneracy being equal to the number of ways in which the fixed sum can be realized. If we now take into account the interaction of the particles, the degeneracy will be split, and each level will be split into as many levels of the whole system as the value of its degree of degeneracy. In this way the level density can be calculated. The result is based upon the asymptotic formula of Hardy and Ramanujan (H4) for the number of different ways, $p(n)$, to form a given number n by any of the possible sums of smaller integers:

$$p(n) = \frac{1}{4(3)^{\frac{1}{2}}n} e^{\pi(\frac{2}{3}n)^{\frac{1}{2}}}$$

If we take as a value for the unit level spacing δ the average observed separation between the lowest levels of heavy nuclei, $2 \cdot 10^5$ ev, we get, for the degree of degeneracy expected for a total excitation energy W of 8 Mev,

$$p\left(\frac{W}{\delta}\right) = p(40) = 4 \cdot 10^4$$

which gives an average level separation for the whole excited nucleus of about 5 ev, which very roughly corresponds to the density of level separation estimated from slow-neutron collisions. The level separation,

$$\frac{\delta}{p(W/\delta)^{\frac{1}{2}}} = 4(3)^{\frac{1}{2}}We^{-\pi(\frac{2}{3} \cdot W/\delta)^{\frac{1}{2}}}$$

depends exponentially on the excitation energy; this is characteristic of all nuclear models and is displayed even by this very simple one.

2. Gas-Like Models. In this model the nucleus is visualized, in the first approximation, as consisting of gas—a set of non-interacting particles—held in a spherical box of nuclear size. The two Fermi gases present (neutrons and protons) occupy all the lowest levels in the box. As the nucleus is excited—"heated"—some of the higher levels are occupied with increasing excitation. Bethe has given a careful statistical calculation for this model, following the usual methods of statistical mechanics (B13). He has used a statistical ensemble with energy, particle number, and angular momentum taken as given constants. The calculation is of course quite parallel to the calculation of the entropy of the system, since entropy is proportional to the logarithm of the number of states of the system. Somewhat greater care is required for the computation of the number of states than for its logarithm. If W is the energy of excitation and A the number of nucleons, he obtains, for the mean spacing D (in ev) of nuclear levels of some definite angular momentum J,

$$D = 5 \cdot 10^4 \cdot \left(\frac{AW}{2.1}\right)^2 e^{-(AW/2.1)^{\frac{1}{2}}} \tag{25}$$

In this formula we have assumed the usual $r_0 = 1.5 \cdot 10^{-13}$ cm, and W is in Mev.

A similar but more sophisticated model was proposed by Bardeen (B2). He solved essentially the same problem, but he made use of the properties of the exchange forces in nuclei. It has been shown that the two-body problem in a square well with exchange forces could be reduced to the one-body problem except that the potential acting on one particle now depends on the wave number of the interacting particle. It turns out that the total energy of the equivalent particle motion increases more strongly with the wave number than the kinetic energy alone. This effectively increases the phase volume available for levels, reduces the number of individual particle states, and therefore much more strongly reduces the density of levels of the whole system. The effect is quite analogous to the effect of the correlations of electrons which obey the exclusion principle in changing the interaction energy of electrons in a metallic lattice. The model of Bardeen is often referred to as the free-particle model with correlations. The energy dependence of the result is given by Eq. (25) with $(AW/2.1)$ replaced by $(AW/4)$.

3. The Liquid Drop. The idea of regarding the nucleus as a classical drop, with volume energy and surface tension, is by now a familiar one. On this basis the normal modes of vibration of a liquid drop may be computed: there are surface vibrations and transverse and longitudinal volume waves. The surface energy and the compressibility of the nuclear matter may be estimated from the semi-empirical energy content given in Section 10. Then the vibrations of each normal mode are thought of as quantized, and energy distributed among them according to Planck's distribution law. The nuclear matter is so "cool" that equipartition is far from achieved; the excitation energy is not very large compared to the zero-point energy. From the treatment of Bethe, numerical results can be obtained (B13). Here again the energy dependence is given roughly by the formula

$$D \sim \exp\ (-cW^{\frac{4}{5}}),\quad W \text{ small} \qquad D \sim \exp\ (-c'W^{\frac{3}{4}}),\quad W \text{ large} \qquad (26)$$

It is interesting that in this treatment one can show that only a few normal modes of surface vibration are present for heavy nuclei in the region of 1-Mev excitation or lower. The possibility of rotation of the drop, associated of course with its angular momentum and the multipole moments of its low-lying states, has been considered. Though the idea is a satisfying one, it can be said that the drop model does not account quantitatively for the low-lying levels of high angular momentum which seem to be responsible for nuclear isomerism. On the contrary, direct calculation of the spacing of rotational levels gives for their energy, for a lead nucleus say, only a few kilovolts. Such fine structure has not yet been observed. It has been pointed out that particles whose wave functions must satisfy symmetry properties may, unless very rigidly bound, be unable to rotate as a rigid body rotates because some rotational states of motion are not allowed. Indeed, it has been shown (T3) that only for high angular momenta, of the order of 50 units, will nuclear rotational levels have the order normal for a rigid body or a classical drop rotating as a whole. At such angular momenta, the excitation energy is some Mev, and vibrational motion is of course important. The suggestion that a drop or a solid be used to represent the lowest states of nuclei has not proved very satisfactory; as a matter of fact, the magnetic moments of ground states are much better represented by the idea of an odd particle rotating about a non-rotating core containing all but the odd nucleon (S4). Again, we may expect better results for the drop model in highly excited states than near ground. A formulation of the structure of nuclei, where individual level properties are decisive, is still beyond the scope of the present models, although for the lowest states the individual-particle shell model in j-j coupling form has had remarkable success.

4. Thermodynamic and Semi-Empirical Results. The general behavior of the level density as a function of energy is similar in all the models discussed. The details are not correct, and the constants deduced compare indifferently with experiment. It seems reasonable then to compute a general form of the level density as a function of energy from the most general statistical or "thermodynamical" point of view, and to adjust the constants until we get reasonable agreement with the not very well-known level spacings observed.

Let us begin with the fundamental statistical-mechanical relation for the sum over states (B13)

$$Z = \sum_i e^{-E_i/\tau}$$

where the values E_i are the energies of the states of the whole system, and τ is the parameter which we can identify with the usual kT, the temperature measured in units of energy. Since we are dealing with dense levels, we can rewrite the sum as an integral:

$$Z = \int \rho(E) e^{-E/\tau} \, dE \tag{27}$$

But let us introduce the function A, the Helmholtz free energy of thermodynamics, by the relation: $Z = e^{-A/\tau}$. Now, if the system has a large number of degrees of freedom and the distribution is one of equilibrium, we expect that the contributions to the integral in (27) come mainly from the region near the maximum, which we call W, the mean excitation energy of the nuclear system. We then rewrite the expression as

$$Z = \int e^{\ln \rho - E/\tau} \, dE$$
$$= e^{\ln \rho(W) - W/\tau} \cdot \int e^{\frac{\partial(\ln \rho)}{\partial E}(E - W) + \frac{\partial^2 \ln \rho}{\partial E^2} \cdot \frac{(E - W)^2}{2} + \cdots \frac{-(E - W)}{\tau}} \, dE$$

Expanding the integrand about its maximum by the familiar saddle-point method, we obtain

$$Z = \rho(W) e^{-W/\tau} \cdot \left[-2\pi \Big/ \frac{\partial^2 (\ln \rho - E/\tau)}{\partial E^2} \Big|_W \right]^{\frac{1}{2}} = e^{-A/\tau} \qquad (28)$$

Now let us introduce the familiar thermodynamic function, the entropy S, by the relation

$$A = W - \tau S \qquad (29a)$$

We expect this function to be proportional to the logarithm of the density of states. From (29a) we get the elementary definition of entropy:

$$\frac{dS}{dW} = \frac{1}{\tau} \qquad (29b)$$

and we can use this in (28) with $d(\ln \rho)/dE \,|\, W = 1/\tau$, to get

$$\rho(W) = \frac{e^{S(W)}}{\tau (2\pi \, dW/d\tau)^{\frac{1}{2}}}$$

We then have, for the general connection between density of states $\rho = 1/D$ and the thermal properties of the system,

$$\rho(W) = \frac{e^{\int_0^W dW'/\tau}}{\tau (2\pi \, dW/d\tau)^{\frac{1}{2}}} \qquad (30)$$

To determine the level density for any system, then, we need to find the entropy of the system, which we can always do by integrating (29b), if we know only the expression for the heat content as a function of temperature, that is, the relation between excitation energy and the temperature parameter $\tau(W)$.

Next, the procedure is either to adopt a model, and so work out the heat content as we have indicated in the previous sections, or to make some general assumptions for the temperature dependence of the heat content, and then fit the constants to the data.

We can proceed in a general way by using thermodynamic arguments. We expect the heat capacity for nearly any system to be a steadily increasing function of the temperature. If the temperature of a system is so high that for all the degrees of freedom the energy τ is large compared to the quantum energy $\hbar\omega_0$, the classical limit of equipartition is reached, and the heat capacity is constant. But the nucleus, as we have said before, is generally rather "cold." The simple model of the Fermi gas of A nucleons in volume $\frac{4}{3}\pi R^3$ yields the result (M4) that the "gas" is degenerate if the excitation energy is small compared to $A\hbar^2/2MR^2$ $\sim 8A^{1/3}$ Mev. Then heavy nuclei are highly degenerate below excitation energies of some 50 Mev. The interaction of nucleons does not affect this conclusion, just as the electron gas in metals is degenerate in spite of the electron-electron forces.

Now we can write the heat content as a function of temperature in the power series:

$$W = c_0 + c_1\tau + c_2\tau^2 + \cdots$$

From the general quantum ideas of the third law of thermodynamics, we expect the specific heat to vanish as $T \to 0$. Thus the expansion of W near zero temperature, i.e., in the strongly degenerate region, ought to begin with at least a quadratic term, with all higher powers negligible. The familiar Debye specific heat for metals [1] actually vanishes at low temperatures with an even higher power of the temperature, since the heat content goes to zero like T^4. If we assume then any simple power law dependence, $W = c\tau^n$, we can integrate

$$\frac{dS}{dW} = \frac{dS}{d\tau}\frac{d\tau}{dW} = \frac{1}{\tau}$$

letting

$$S = \frac{n}{(n-1)} \cdot c\tau^{n-1}$$

With this expression, we obtain for $\rho(W)$ the value

$$\rho(W) = \frac{1}{(2\pi n)^{1/2}}\left(\frac{c}{W^{n+1}}\right)^{n/2} \exp\left(\frac{n}{(n-1)} \cdot c^{1/n}W^{1-1/n}\right)$$

For the Fermi gas, the exponent contains $1 - \frac{1}{2}$, for the liquid drop the power $W^{3/5}$ to $W^{3/4}$ at low and high temperatures respectively.

It seems appropriate to use the very simple form

$$\rho = C \exp (aW)^{1/2} \tag{31a}$$

If we do this, and try to make a rough fit to the data, we obtain (following Weisskopf) (W5) for nuclei heavier than $A = 60$ a result which is approx-

[1] See (M4), p. 253, for formula; p. 248 for derivation.

imated by the simple form, for nuclei of odd or even Z and $N = A - Z$,

$$\frac{1}{2}C_{\text{odd-odd}} = C_{\text{even-odd}} = C_{\text{odd-even}} = 2C_{\text{even-even}} = \frac{12}{(A-40)} \text{ (Mev)}^{-1}$$

$$a = 3.4(A - 40)^{\frac{1}{2}}(\text{Mev})^{-1} \tag{31b}$$

We present in Fig. 5 a few selected data on observed level spacing, together with the values calculated from the three nuclear models described. There is some inconsistency in what the figures represent, for the experimental data from slow-neutron capture, as well as the free-particle model calculation, refer to levels of a definite angular momentum (or within $\pm\frac{1}{2}\hbar$ from the ground state). The thermodynamic calculation certainly includes all levels. Here there is a chance to add some more definite assertion to the general statistical notions; all we can do at present is regard all levels as more or less uniformly distributed in regard to most not very large values of angular momenta. This vague statement is typical of our statistical theory, and it may account for discrepancies observed in individual cases where specific angular momentum properties may be involved. The least we can do to recognize the great importance of nuclear energy shells is to use differing constants for odd- or even-Z nuclei.

SECTION 4. NUCLEAR LEVEL WIDTHS

We have already mentioned the concept of level width, which is defined as Γ_n in the expression for the approximately time-independent (because long-lived) quasi-stationary state wave function for the compound nucleus,

$$\Psi_n = \psi_n e^{-(E_n - i\Gamma_n/2)t/\hbar}$$

From this form for the decaying amplitude of the wave function the width can be related to the mean lifetime in the usual way: $\Gamma_n = \hbar/\tau_n$. This expression naturally refers to the change in amplitude with time of the compound state regardless of the products of its decay; it is the total width, and τ_n is the total lifetime. Naturally, the compound state may in general decay in more than one way; a single set of reactants may have many alternative sets of products. We may generalize the notion of width to include the idea of partial width by writing $\Gamma_n = \sum_{i\alpha} \Gamma_{i\alpha}(n)$, where the $\Gamma_{i\alpha}$ are the partial widths, which we index here, somewhat redundantly, with two indices: i, which designates the kind of particle emitted, as neutron, gamma, proton, etc.; and the index α, which gives the state of the residual nucleus. It is evident that the same particle can be emitted with different properties, as different energy or angular momentum, leaving behind generally, though not necessarily, a different state of the residual nucleus. The argument of the function $\Gamma_{i\alpha}(n)$ refers to the state n of the compound nucleus whose width is here written. Clearly the partial width for the emission of, say, a neutron to any possible state of the residual nucleus might be the experimentally useful quantity, and it would involve the sum $\sum\limits_{\alpha,\text{neut}} \Gamma_{\text{neut},\alpha}(n)$ over all accessible states which can be left behind after a neutron is emitted.

To speak somewhat academically, Γ_n is strictly zero for almost no states of nuclei. Even the ground state is not wholly stable; in radioactive nuclei it may decay by beta- or alpha-emission, and in nuclei not observed to be radioactive we know that in general a state of less energy content can be reached either by a process like spontaneous fission or, if the nucleus is a rather light one, by combination with a neighboring nucleus of the matter present. Such lifetimes are long, perhaps enormously long, compared to actual nuclear reaction times, under terrestrial conditions at least. It is conventional therefore to disregard such forms of radioactive decay, and especially beta-decay, and to regard the levels as widened only by the possibility of radiation or by the emission of a heavy particle. This implies that, while Γ_β may be different from zero, its study belongs properly to radioactivity theory, and not to the dynamics of nuclear reactions. The levels of a typical nucleus then can decay only by gamma-emission, which slowly widens the states as their excitation increases until the excitation energy reaches a value which makes heavy-particle emission energetically possible. For nuclei whose ground states are empirically alpha-radioactive, of course, this condition is fulfilled for every level, but for most nuclei from the middle to the top of the periodic table such a value is reached only at the binding energy of a proton or neutron. The binding energy lies near 8 Mev for the entire middle of the table; for the lightest nuclei, up to neon, say, it is widely varying; for the nuclei from gold or lead and up, it has fallen to 5 or 6 Mev (W3). Up to a level of the compound nucleus, then, which has an energy content at least 5 to 8 Mev above the ground state, only gamma-radiation will introduce a finite width; beyond it, first the emission of one particle, then of another, and finally of even more kinds and a greater number of particles will widen each level. Moreover, not only do the values of $\Gamma(n)$ increase because there are more possible Γ_i, but in addition more states are available in the residual nucleus, so that α takes on more possible values. The widths themselves increase slowly, as we shall see, with the kinetic energy of the emitted particles and the energy of the gamma-rays.

A. Level Widths and Reaction Cross Sections: Statistical Relations

We have already indicated that the fundamental idea underlying the present statistical treatment of nuclear reactions is the separation of the process into two independent steps: the formation of the compound nucleus, and its subsequent independent decay. Upon the basis of this assumption there can be derived a useful relation between level widths and cross sections. The method of the derivation is the familiar statistical-mechanical one of detailed balancing (W5).

Let us consider an equilibrium mixture of three kinds of systems: the compound nucleus we are studying, and its two decay products, the "emitted particle" and the residual nucleus. The equilibrium reactions are the decay of the compound, and its formation by recombination of the two decay products. We may write

$$C^* \rightleftarrows p + R_\alpha$$

We do not consider every possible state of the residual nucleus R and the particle p which might combine to form the given state of the compound nucleus, but only particles of such energy, angular momentum, etc., that they can combine with a residual nucleus R_α in a definite state α to produce a particular state of the compound nucleus C^*. It is clear that we must be sure of a random statistical ensemble: we must be certain that special phase relations do not exist between the wave functions of the decay products and the compound nucleus which emits them or is formed from their combination. To insure this, and to free ourselves from the possible special character of individual states of the compound nucleus, we have to regard the levels of the entire system as very closely spaced, and be sure that the energy interval is large enough to include many levels of the system. Our widths and cross sections are then averages over this small interval of energy, small compared to the scale of variation we are interested in, but large enough to include many levels. All phase relations are then lost in the averaging. This is the usual procedure required to define a quantum-statistical ensemble.

Now we apply the almost revered formula of the time-dependent perturbation theory, which gives the transition probability per unit time for the transition from the almost stationary state (A) of a system to a continuum of states B at the same energy. This is

$$w_{A \to B} = \frac{2\pi}{\hbar} \mid M_{AB} \mid^2 \rho_B \Omega$$

where $\mid M_{AB} \mid^2$ is the square of the matrix element of the perturbing operator between the initial and final states involved (the final state is chosen as any one of the continuum having the correct energy), and ρ_B is the density of states of the final system, per unit energy in the volume Ω within which the wave functions are normalized. Now the inverse process is given by the same formula written for $w_{B \to A}$. But, since the operator is certainly Hermitean, $|M_{AB}|^2 = |M_{BA}|^2$. We then obtain the expression for detailed balancing in its general form

$$w_{A \to B} \cdot \rho_A = w_{B \to A} \cdot \rho_B \qquad (32)$$

The use of perturbation theory conceals the generality of the result; any order of the perturbation will give the same dependence on the absolute square of a Hermitian matrix element, so that the result is quite general. Applying it to the situation described above, with a compound nucleus of excitation energy W decaying to two reaction products, we may write

$$\frac{\Gamma_{pa}(W)}{\hbar} \cdot \rho_C(W) = v\sigma_{pa} \cdot g_R \frac{4\pi p^2}{(2\pi\hbar)^3} \cdot \frac{dp}{dW}$$

Here we have used the relation between width and lifetime, $w = 1/\tau = \Gamma/\hbar$, and found ρ_B by using the density of states for a free particle with mass m_p, momentum p, velocity v, and kinetic energy E_p, $4\pi p^2/(2\pi\hbar)^3$, and converting the density in momentum space to the density in energy by the factor dp/dW. Note also the important relation $w = v\sigma$ for any collision between two particles of relative velocity v, in normalizing volume. The factor g_R is the statistical weight (degree of degeneracy) of the residual nuclear state. We may finally write

$$\Gamma_{pa}(W)\rho_C(W) = \frac{g_R}{2\pi} \cdot \frac{\sigma_{pa}}{\pi\lambdabar^2} \qquad \text{with } \lambdabar = \frac{\hbar}{m_p v} \qquad (33)$$

This formula tells us that the mean level width, measured in units of the level spacing, is just equal to the cross section for the inverse reaction, σ_{pa}, measured in units of the maximum cross section for absorption of particles of the given kinetic energy, apart from small statistical weight factors. It is interesting to recall that the maximum absorption cross section for s waves is just $4\pi\lambdabar^2$, and thus the width for s wave emission is at most $2g_R/\pi$ times the level spacing.

The use of the detailed balancing formula for connecting lifetimes to cross sections as demonstrated here is only one of its applications. By considering an over-all reaction $i + T \to p + R$, two cross sections may be similarly connected. In general,

$$\sigma_{iT}p_i^2 = \sigma_{pR}p_p^2$$

where p_i and p_p are respectively the initial and final relative momenta.

In (33) we could have defined $\Gamma_{p\alpha}$ and ρ_C somewhat freely. They might contain averages over all levels in a narrow band of energy, or they might be restricted to levels of a single class, e.g., only those for which the angular momentum involved could in fact be given to the particle p. Since the level densities are not accurately known, such distinctions are ordinarily not carefully made.

B. Calculation of Level Widths

The assumption of the independent decay of the compound nucleus can be exploited in detail for the calculation of level widths. With this idea we combine the evident fact that the forces on nuclear particles which operate at *large* distances from the nucleus—distances large compared to the range of nuclear forces—are, we believe, completely known. These forces are, of course, (1) the very important Coulomb force on all charged particles, and (2) the effect of angular momentum, the centrifugal force associated with non-vanishing angular momentum. Most of the success of the statistical theory really comes from the fact that nuclear reactions are greatly affected by these essentially non-nuclear forces, and separation and calculation of their consequences is itself a considerable step toward explanation of the most evident phenomena of the reactions.

We shall show that under suitable conditions the partial width for emission of a definite particle with given orbital angular momentum l and energy E_p, leaving behind a particular state of the residual nucleus, can be written as the product of three factors:

$$\Gamma_{pl\alpha}(W_n) = k\gamma(n)P_{pl}(E_p) \tag{34a}$$

where k is $mv/\hbar$ for particle p, $\gamma(n)$ is a factor which depends only upon the state of the compound nucleus, particularly its excitation energy W_n, and P_{pl} is the usual coefficient of penetrability of whatever barrier the particle encounters from electrostatic or centrifugal forces.

Let us begin by writing the total width of a given state of the compound nucleus, which we shall index by $\Gamma(n)$, as a sum over the partial widths, one for emission of each kind of particle indexed by i, with angular momentum l, leaving the residual nucleus in state α. [Compare (33) and (34a, b).] This implies that the wave equation $H\Psi_n = W_n\Psi_n$ for the whole system has been solved by the wave function $\Psi_n = \Sigma\varphi_\alpha\psi_i$, where by i we index all possible emitted particles, for which ψ_i is the wave function outside the nucleus, and φ_α is the wave function of the corresponding residual nucleus in state α. We obtain a set of discrete but widened levels by imposing this condition on the solution, with the specification that the function ψ_i contain only outgoing and no incoming spherical waves. Below the energy for which some particle can be emitted, the function ψ_i will correspond to a bound state for that particle; above the threshold, to an outgoing spherical wave. It may be noted that, just as the presence of non-zero $\Gamma(n)$ means that the states of the compound nucleus are broadened, and that their amplitude decays, so the complex $W_n = E_n - i\Gamma_n/2$ results in a complex wave number k_p for the outgoing particle. The amplitude of the outgoing particle wave function is greater at large distances, since the particles represented as farthest from the nucleus were emitted earliest, when the compound nucleus had its largest amplitude. The asymptotic expression for the radial part of an outgoing wave e^{ikr}/r will be damped by the presence of an imaginary term in k. Below the threshold for emission, this is the only term. Above the threshold, we can neglect this imaginary part so long as the width Γ_n is small compared to the kinetic energy of the emitted particle. With this in mind, we write

$$\psi_p = \sum_{l,m} \frac{Y_l^m(\theta,\varphi)R_{pl}(r_p)}{r_p}$$

where R_{pl}/r_p is the radial part of the wave function of particle p, and Y_e^m is the normalized spherical harmonic.

1. Barrier Penetration. The value of a partial width $\Gamma_{pl}(n)$ is just $\hbar/\tau_{pl}$, and hence just $\hbar$ times the number of particles emitted per second from one compound nucleus. We normalize R_{pl} by the condition that $\int_{\text{nucl}} |\psi_{p\alpha}|^2 \, dV = 1$, where the integral is extended over the spatial region "within the nucleus," say out to a fixed distance R. This implies that Γ_{pl} is small, so that we can neglect the more remote part of the wave function of the compound state. This is closely related to our general assumptions. Then the width is just $\hbar$ times the outgoing flux of particles integrated over a distant sphere of radius r_∞. We obtain

$$\Gamma_{pl}(W_n) = \hbar r_\infty^2 \cdot \int v_\infty |\psi_{pl}(r_\infty)|^2 \, d\Omega = \frac{\hbar^2}{m_p} \cdot k |R_{pl}|^2 \tag{34b}$$

We have required that very far away, beyond a radius r_∞, the radial dependence of R_{pl} be simply $e^{i(kr+\delta)}$. This means that we have chosen r_∞ so large that in that region the kinetic energy $\hbar^2 k^2/2m$ is very large compared to the electrostatic or centrifugal barriers. From this point on, the flux of outgoing particles falls off only geometrically, with $1/r^2$. Hence the width becomes independent of r. But, in the region between the radius R which marks the boundary of the compound nucleus, and r_∞, which is the force-free region, the behavior of the wave function is fully known. It is attenuated by the requirement of penetration through a potential barrier, which may be zero for neutrons of zero orbital angular momentum, but would be very considerable for alpha-particles of any orbital angular momentum if the kinetic energy were not high compared to the Coulomb energy, and would be appreciable even for neutral particles of non-zero angular momentum. We shall write $R_{pl}(r_\infty)$ in terms of the value of $R_{pl}(R)$ at the nuclear surface R. The quantity P_{pl}, which we call the penetrability of the barrier, we define as the fraction of the initial intensity of particles, of the type indexed by p and angular momentum l, with kinetic energy E, which penetrates to a field-free region. We can write the Schrödinger equation in the field-containing region for the radial variation only:

$$\left[\frac{d^2}{dr^2} - \frac{2m_p}{\hbar^2}(E - V_{\text{ext}}) - \frac{l(l+1)}{r^2}\right] F_{pl}(r) = 0$$

If the solution F_{pl} is that which corresponds to a unit outgoing wave, with asymptotic value $e^{+i(kr+\delta)}$, then evidently

$$P_{pl} = \frac{\text{external intensity}}{\text{intensity at nuclear surface}} = \frac{1}{\left| F_{pl}(R) \right|^2} \tag{35}$$

For uncharged particles the solutions F_{pl} are well known to be the half-integer-order Bessel functions. The boundary conditions are satisfied by the so-called Hankel function of the first kind,

$$F_{pl} = \left(\frac{\pi kr}{2}\right)^{1/2} \cdot H_{l+1/2}^{(1)}(kr)$$

A few penetrabilities for uncharged particles of various angular momenta can be given:

$$P_{n,0} = 1 \qquad P_{n,1} = \frac{x^2}{1 + x^2} \qquad P_{n,2} = \frac{x^4}{x^4 + 3x^2 + 9}$$

$$P_{n,3} = \frac{x^6}{x^6 + 6x^4 + 45x^2 + 225} \tag{36a}$$

with $x = kR$. And, for general l values, if the wavelength is long or l large, i.e., if $x = kR \ll l$,

$$P_{n,l} = \frac{x^{2l}}{(2l - 1)^2(2l - 3)^2(2l - 5)^2 \cdots 1^2} \tag{36b}$$

A table of such functions has been published (U1).

The calculation of Coulomb barriers is much more difficult, because of the well-known slow convergence of the asymptotic expressions for

Coulomb wave functions. There are two approaches: an exact calculation can be made by using the published tables of Coulomb wave functions (Y5). Such a calculation has been made and graphs published for exact penetrabilities for protons for various angular momenta emitted from the lightest nuclei, from Li to F (C5). The other method is the familiar approximate solution for the wave equation in the classical limit. This is the W.K.B. method, useful under conditions in which *the distance traversed by the particle while its wavelength changes appreciably is many wavelengths.* If the usual graph of the energy barrier is recalled, it will be seen that the approximation is good only when the energy of the particle does not come near the top of the barrier. This means that the W.K.B. method is useful either in the trivial case far above the barrier when the penetrability is evidently unity, or in the very useful case of low penetrability. In the transition region, for P of the order of unity, the W.K.B. approximation is not reliable. The relevant formulas will be given here, though they are common in the literature.

The Coulomb penetrability from the W.K.B. approximation can be written

$$P_{pl}(E) = \left(\frac{B_l}{E} - 1\right)^{1/2} \exp\left(-2C_l\right) \tag{37a}$$

Here B_l is the barrier height for a particle of charge ze, reduced mass $m = m_p M/m_p + M$, and angular momentum l; Ze is the nuclear charge and R the nuclear radius. The quantity C_l is the familiar phase integral

$$C_l = \left(\frac{2m}{\hbar}\right)^{1/2} \int_R^{r_e} (V - E)^{1/2}\, dr \tag{37b}$$

where the potential energy, including Coulomb and centrifugal terms, is

$$V(r) = \frac{zZe^2}{r} + \frac{l(l+1)\hbar^2}{2mr^2} \quad \text{and} \quad V(r_e) - E = 0; \quad B_l = V(R) \text{ for any } l$$

The value for C_l is complicated:

$$\frac{C_l}{\left(\frac{2zZe^2 Rm}{\hbar^2}\right)^{1/2}} = \frac{1}{2(x)^{1/2}} \left(\frac{\pi}{2} + \arcsin\frac{1 - 2x}{(1 + 4xy)^{1/2}}\right) - (1 + y - x)^{1/2}$$

$$+ (y)^{1/2} \log \frac{(1 + 2(y)^{1/2}[y^{1/2} + (1 + y - x)^{1/2}])}{(1 + 4xy)^{1/2}} \tag{37c}$$

with $y = l(l+1)/(2zZe^2 Rm/\hbar^2)$, and $x = E/B_l$. A plot of C_l has been published for a sizable range of x and y; when used with the other graphs in Appendix I, it makes the necessarily long computations as convenient as can be expected.

It is plain from formulas (37) that the orbital angular momentum of the partial wave concerned plays a large part in determining the amplitude at the nuclear surface. High orbital momenta mean higher centrifugal barriers, and the penetrability through the centrifugal barrier may be small for high l, even when the simple Coulomb barrier has been surmounted. It is useful to plot a few barrier heights to show where this approximation may be expected to be satisfactory. We assume the usual formula $R = r_0 A^{1/3}$ with $r_0 = 1.5 \times 10^{-13}$ cm.

TABLE 3

BARRIER HEIGHTS (IN MEV) FOR VARIOUS PARTICLES AND ANGULAR MOMENTA †

Nucleus Particle Emitted	Angular Momenta	Ne_{10}^{20}	Ca_{20}^{40}	Zn_{30}^{66}	Sn_{50}^{112}	Yb_{70}^{174}	Th_{90}^{232}
p	0	3.5	5.6	7.1	10.0	12.1	14.1
	1	6.1	7.2	8.3	10.8	12.7	14.5
	2	11.1	10.4	10.6	12.4	13.8	15.5
	3	18.7	15.2	14.0	14.8	15.6	17.0
d	0	3.5	5.6	7.1	10.0	12.1	14.1
	1	4.8	6.4	7.7	10.4	12.4	14.3
	2	7.3	8.0	8.8	11.1	13.0	14.8
	3	11.1	10.4	10.6	12.3	13.9	15.5
α	0	7.1	11.2	14.3	20.0	24.1	28.1
	1	7.7	11.6	14.6	20.1	24.3	28.2
	2	9.0	12.4	15.2	20.5	24.5	28.5
	3	10.9	13.6	16.0	21.1	25.0	28.8

† These barrier heights were computed by using $R = 1.5 \times 10^{-13} A^{1/3}$ cm.

Now we can collect the results of the last paragraphs. Using (34b) and (35), we can write

$$\Gamma_{pl}(W) = \frac{\hbar^2}{m_p} \cdot k \cdot | R_{pl}(R) |^2 \cdot P_{pl}(E) \tag{38}$$

We identify this expression with our formula (34a), if we set for the factor G

$$\gamma = \frac{\hbar^2}{m_p} \cdot | R_{pl}(R) |^2 \tag{39}$$

It is evident that the effect of the external barrier is contained wholly in P_{pl}; we can call the product $k\gamma_{pl}$ the "width without barrier." The argument of the function R_{pl} contains explicitly the nuclear radius, and the function represents the motion of the emitted particle within the reach of the specific nuclear forces. It is clearly a function of the internal state of the compound nucleus, as we had expected for γ. Strictly speaking, it will also depend on the wave function and its derivatives outside the nucleus, on the kind of particle, and so on, for the function R_{pl} must be a continuous solution of the wave equation. It is the point of the statistical treatment to ignore the dependence of γ on the external part of the wave function. Especially if we remember that the nuclear forces are strong, that the radius R is rather well-defined though not sharply so, and that we should try to apply the theory to the average behavior of levels and not to specific ones, will we accept this assertion. A more formal argument has been given, but it cannot be made airtight because of the very nature of the theory. It seems more satisfactory to accept this simplification in the spirit of the main Bohr assumption: that the compound nucleus decays in ways independent of its mode of formation and of the details of single levels.

SECTION 5.   THE COURSE OF NUCLEAR REACTIONS

A. The Steps of the Reaction

We can now proceed to the discussion of the nuclear reaction as a whole. The process of formation of a compound nucleus and its subsequent disintegration can be described by a reaction cross section written this way:

$$\sigma_{ip} = S_i(E) \cdot \xi \cdot D_p \tag{40}$$

Here S_i is a cross section for reaching the nuclear matter, a process supposed to depend only on extra-nuclear forces; ξ is a number of the order of unity which is called the sticking probability. It is roughly the probability that the incident particle will enter to form the compound nucleus once it has reached the nuclear radius. The factor ξ will carry our uncertainty about the validity of the statistical assumptions; it is in this factor that we can throw all the features about the phase relationship of the possible decay products which form part of the wave function of the compound state. If the nucleus is excited only at a "hot spot," where the lifetime of the whole compound nucleus is long compared to the time of possible emission of particles from the locally excited region of only a few nucleons, we expect the sticking probability to decrease. In general, the more nearly independent of energy and exact reaction ξ is, the more satisfactory is the statistical model.

We have written as a separate factor, again in the spirit of our ruling assumptions, the probability D_p of disintegration of the compound nucleus, once formed, into the particle p. This can, of course, be written in terms of the various partial widths:

$$D_p = \frac{\Gamma_p}{\sum_i \Gamma_i} \tag{41}$$

where the denominator contains a term for all the possible products of the disintegration of the compound state. The possibility of alternative reactions, and their relationships as the incident particle type and energy vary, is evidently expressed by the changing magnitudes of the various Γ's.

B. The Contact Cross Section

1. Elastic Scattering and Diffraction Effects. The value of σ_{pl} will, of course, not really be a smooth function of energy. It will reflect, through a variation in D_p, the presence of resonances where they are well defined. For energies high enough so that the classical idea of the collision can be applied, but not so high that the collision times for bound nucleons are long compared to the time of interaction of the incoming particle, the simplest picture of the compound nucleus would lead us to think of ξ as approaching unity: every particle that comes to the surface of the nucleus—as well as that can be defined—will stick to form the compound state. We should like to compute the factor S_i by referring as completely as possible to the region outside the nuclear volume. This is of course not rigorously possible. The incoming wave which represents the incident particle will be modified by the presence of the nucleus in many ways. Those scattered components which are not coherent with the incoming wave, but which represent inelastic scattering or the occurrence of a genuine nuclear reaction, can all be referred to events within the compound nucleus. There are scattered coherent waves which represent the actual formation of a compound nucleus, with the subsequent chance emission of a particle of the original energy and type. Much more important coherent scattered components, however, come from the effects of the extranuclear forces, from the diffraction by the geometrical surface of the nucleus, and from the "reflection" by the nuclear potential. These cannot be distinguished physically in any way from the elastic scattering following compound nucleus formation. The inverse process alone provides a means for evaluating the probability of such elastic scattering by compound nucleus formation, and thus a precise definition for S_i.

Let us write the usual expression [1] for the wave function of an incident plane wave of particles of wave number $k = mv/\hbar$, where m is the mass and v the velocity of the incoming beam in the center-of-mass rest system. This expression is a sum of partial waves written in spherical coordinates, each corresponding to a given value of the orbital angular momentum. We normalize to an incoming flux of unity by writing

$$\psi = \frac{1}{(v)^{\frac{1}{2}}} e^{i\mathbf{k}\cdot\mathbf{r}} = \frac{2\pi}{(2krv)^{\frac{1}{2}}} \sum_{l=0}^{\infty} (2l+1)^{\frac{1}{2}} \cdot i^l \cdot J_{l+\frac{1}{2}}(kr) Y_l^0(\theta) \quad (42a)$$

Here $J_{l+\frac{1}{2}}$ is the Bessel function, and Y_l^0 the normalized spherical harmonic. At great distances from the scattering center we obtain

$$\psi \rightarrow \left(\frac{\pi}{v}\right)^{\frac{1}{2}} \cdot \frac{1}{kr} \sum_0^\infty (2l+1)^{\frac{1}{2}} \cdot i^l \cdot (e^{-i(kr+l\pi/2)} - e^{+i(kr+l\pi/2)}) Y_l^0 \quad (42b)$$

This is in the absence of any effect of the scatterer. But the scatterer may change in general the phase and amplitude of the outgoing part of the wave at large distances. Suppose that the relative phase and amplitude of the outgoing wave after scattering is given by the complex number η. Clearly $|\eta|$ is at most 1. Then the wave function in the presence of the scatterer is no longer given by (42b) but by a sum of incoming and outgoing waves proportional to e^{-ikr} and e^{+ikr} respectively. The incoming portion is

$$\psi_{\text{in}} = \Sigma\psi_{\text{in}}^{(l)}, \quad \psi_{\text{in}}^{(l)} \rightarrow \left(\frac{\pi}{v}\right)^{\frac{1}{2}} \frac{i^l}{kr} (2l+1)^{\frac{1}{2}} e^{-i(kr+l\pi/2)} Y_l^{(0)} \quad (43a)$$

and the outgoing

$$\psi_{\text{out}} = \Sigma\psi_{\text{out}}^{(l)}, \quad \psi_{\text{out}}^{(l)} = \left(\frac{\pi}{v}\right)^{\frac{1}{2}} \frac{i^l}{kr} (2l+1)^{\frac{1}{2}} (+\eta) e^{+i(kr+l\pi/2)} Y_l^{(0)}$$

$$(43b)$$

For a particular value of l the number of particles absorbed per second is just the difference between incoming and outgoing flux evaluated over a large sphere:

$$r^2 \int [v|\psi_{\text{in}}^{(l)}|^2 - v|\psi_{\text{out}}^{(l)}|^2] \, d\Omega = \frac{\pi}{k^2}(2l+1)(1-|\eta|^2) \quad (44a)$$

Since we normalized the incoming wave to unit flux in the beam, the cross section for absorption is given by

$$\sigma_{\text{abs}} = \Sigma\sigma_{\text{abs}}^{(l)} \quad \sigma_{\text{abs}}^{(l)} = \frac{\pi}{k^2}(2l+1)(1-|\eta|^2) \quad (44b)$$

[1] This whole treatment follows closely that of (F7).

The elastically scattered wave has to be added to a plane wave in order to get the actual perturbed wave $\psi_{in} + \psi_{out}$. This is simply $\psi_{in} + \psi_{out} - e^{i\mathbf{k}\cdot\mathbf{r}}/(v)^{1/2}$. Again the flux in this wave integrated over a large sphere gives the elastic scattering cross section:

$$\sigma_{el} = \Sigma\sigma_{el}^{(l)} \qquad \sigma_{el}^{(l)} = \frac{\pi}{k^2}(2l+1)|(1+\eta)|^2 \qquad (44c)$$

It is valuable to consider the relations between these waves. The total cross section $\sigma_{tot} = \Sigma\sigma_{tot}^{(l)}$ can be written:

$$\sigma_{tot}^{(l)} = \sigma_{el}^{(l)} + \sigma_{abs}^{(l)} = \frac{2\pi}{k^2}(2l+1)[1 + Re(\eta)] \qquad (45)$$

There is a well-known and interesting result which follows from this formula. Consider the cross section of an obstacle in the classical limit, with the radius (R) of the scatterer very large compared to $\lambda = 1/k$. We expect the classical absorption cross section, summed of course over all values of l to obtain the total cross section, to be πR^2 if the object is "black" i.e., if it absorbs every particle whose trajectory strikes it. But in this case $\eta = 0$, and the total cross section $\sigma_{tot} = 2\pi R^2$. Where does the additional πR^2 of elastic cross section arise? This is the familiar "shadow scattering," now observed repeatedly for neutrons of 90 Mev and less on heavy nuclei (C10). The black sphere clearly casts a shadow in the beam. This shadow must, on the wave picture, as in the familiar Kirchhoff treatment of physical optics, be produced as the result of interference between the incident wave and a scattered wave. The total intensity of scattering, to produce a shadow the size of the object, evidently corresponds to a cross section just equal to the geometrical one, πR^2. Thus there must be an elastic cross section of πR^2. This can be observed because, especially in the nuclear case, the shadow does not extend to infinity even in a parallel incident beam. On the contrary, diffraction by the sphere means that the direction of the scattered wave is changed by an angle of the order of λ/R. This has the consequence that the shadow is dissolved by the diffracted beam in a distance of R^2/λ from the scattering center, and the elastic scattering can there be observed.

The angular distribution of the shadow scattering is easy to compute for a black sphere, in the limit $\lambda/R \ll 1$. The result is that

$$\frac{d\sigma(\theta, \varphi)}{d\Omega} = \frac{R^2 J_1^2(kR\sin\theta)}{\sin^2\theta} \qquad (46)$$

where $k = 1/\lambda = \hbar/M_v$, R is the nuclear radius, θ and φ the scattering angles, and $J_1(z)$ the Bessel function of the order of unity. Actually the contributions of partial waves with $l \sim R/\lambda$ are small but complicated. If $\lambda/R \sim 1$, the effect of important values of l will not be given correctly by (46), and the distribution and magnitude of the elastic shadow scattering will be more complicated. The success of this result has suggested a nuclear model of optical type in which the nuclear volume is regarded as a sphere of "gray," not black, material which both absorbs the incident wave in part and disperses it, as a result of the phase shift due to the mean potential which the incident nucleon feels in passage. This model has given interesting results in the high-energy region, which is discussed in more detail in Section 11.

It is worth pointing out that the maximum value of $\sigma_{\text{abs}}^{(l)}$ is $(2l+1)\pi\lambda^2$, and that this maximum can be reached only if $\eta = 0$. The maximum value of $\sigma_{\text{el}}^{(l)}$ is $(2l+1)4\pi\lambda^2$ and can be attained only when $\eta = +1$. There is in general a range of values of $\sigma_{\text{el}}^{(l)}$ possible for each value of $\sigma_{\text{abs}}^{(l)}$. That the maximum scattering cross section is four times the maximum capture cross section reflects the fact that maximum scattering comes from just reversing the phase of the incoming wave to form the scattered outgoing wave. This has the effect of adding to the plane wave just twice its outgoing part, while complete absorption simply removes the outgoing portion of the plane wave. Thus the cross section for scattering depends on the square of twice the amplitude corresponding to complete absorption, which gives four times the cross section.

2. Influence of Extranuclear Forces. We have so far considered only maximum and minimum values for scattering and absorption, obtained by assuming values for the quantity η. It is clear that a real calculation of η would require the solution of the many-body nuclear problem,[1] and this is precisely what we are unable to do. But we can try to bring explicitly into view the effect of extranuclear forces, reserving ξ to describe the effect of the specific nuclear interaction and the formation of the compound state.

The nucleus, in absorbing the incident beam, changes the intensity of the outgoing portion of the wave. If there is no absorption, $|\eta| = 1$ and we can write $\eta_l = e^{2i\delta_l}$ and $|\psi_{\text{in}}|^2 = |\psi_{\text{out}}|^2$. With absorption, some of this wave is removed, and we can write $|\psi_{\text{out}}|^2 = |\psi_{\text{in}}|^2 - |\psi_{\text{removed}}|^2$. But we will regard the wave removed as altered by the nucleus proper only at the nuclear surface, writing then:

$$|\psi_{\text{out}}|^2 = |\psi_{\text{in}}|^2 - f^2|\psi_{\text{surf}}|^2 = |\psi_{\text{in}}|^2 - f^2|\psi_{\text{in}}|^2 \cdot \frac{|\psi_{\text{surf}}|^2}{|\psi_{\text{in}}|^2} \quad (47)$$

[1] An important paper (W7) is based on an effort to throw the whole burden of describing the reaction onto the quantity η. We shall discuss this in Section 6.

with the quantity f representing that fraction of ψ_{surf} which is removed by the effect of the specific nuclear forces. But we have already shown, in (35), that we could write $|\psi_{\text{surf}}|^2/|\psi_{\text{in}}|^2 = P$. With Eqs. (44) in mind, we get

$$|\psi_{\text{out}}|^2 = |\psi_{\text{in}}|^2(1 - f^2P) \qquad \sigma_{\text{abs}} \sim |\psi_{\text{in}}|^2 - |\psi_{\text{out}}|^2 \sim f^2P|\psi_{\text{in}}|^2 \tag{48}$$

where we can regard f^2 as an expression of the sticking probability ξ, discussed above. This would allow us to extend the notion of the sticking probability, as some authors have done, even to reactions where the statistical notions were not strictly applicable, in order to give a kind of transition between statistical and other views. We then can take as a fundamental relation for the cross section for compound nucleus formation:

$$\sigma_{il} = (2l + 1)\pi\lambdabar_i^2 \cdot P_{il}(E_i) \cdot \xi_{il} \tag{49}$$

with the barrier penetrability and sticking probability explicitly indicated.

C. The Disintegration of Compound States

1. Competition. The next step in the nuclear reaction, the disintegration of the compound state, takes place with a probability $D_p = \Gamma_p/\Sigma\Gamma_j$ (41), as we have already said. We ought to recall here the nature of the assumption behind this way of writing the reaction: we assume that particular features of any single compound level are not important. Many states are involved, with random phase relations, either because of the poor definition of the particle energy in the incident beam, or because the states are so widened as to overlap. Otherwise, the results we give will be valid only for averages over many states or even over many similar but not identical nuclear species.

The most striking consequence of the expression (41), for D_p is the phenomenon of competition. Evidently once the compound state is formed it can decay in many ways, for each of which there is a value of the appropriate Γ_j. The energy of the compound state will determine the value of the Γ_j's in our approximation at least. As the energy varies, given reactants may produce different products. As each new energy threshold for particle emission is passed, the corresponding Γ_j rises from zero, and the compound state has then another possible decay mode. Since the total cross section is limited, the rise of one Γ_j must reduce the yield for the others. This is called competition. For a definite example, consider the reactions induced by neutrons incident on Br^{81}. The reactions which have been observed are four (S5):

(i) $\qquad\qquad\qquad\qquad Br^{81}(n,\gamma)Br^{82}$

(ii) $\qquad\qquad\qquad\qquad Br^{81}(n,p)Se^{81}$

(iii) $\qquad\qquad\qquad\qquad Br^{81}(n,\alpha)As^{78}$

(iv) $\qquad\qquad\qquad\qquad Br^{81}(n,2n)Br^{80}$

At very low incident energy (thermal neutrons) only Γ_γ is different from zero, and the first reaction takes place exclusively. As the energy increases, the threshold for the second reaction is reached at a couple of Mev, and it begins to appear. At still higher energies the latter two reactions are possible, and their competition is noticeable in the cross section of the (n,p) reaction. It is clear that the computation of σ_n for the formation of the compound nucleus will apply to all these reactions (though the resonance neutron capture will need special treatment) and that the values of the individual cross sections can be obtained if only the relative Γ's are known.

2. Specific Level Widths for Particle Emission. We have already described, in Eq. (33), how the widths are related to cross sections, and we have given formulas for the computation of individual widths. In practice, of course, we want not so much the width for emission, say, of the proton in reaction (i) above, leaving the Se^{81} nucleus in a given state, but rather the total width for the entire range of proton energies and residual nuclear states which are available. Of course, we have but to build this up out of the various individual widths, and we shall obtain at the same time the often interesting energy distribution of the outgoing protons.

From (33) we have the value of $\Gamma_{p\alpha}$ for the emission of a given particle with definite energy (averaged over many levels). If now the residual nucleus can be left in many possible states α, so close that they too can be represented by the statistical expression for the level density, we obtain, for the total width for particle p, $\bar{\Gamma}_p = \sum_{l,\alpha} \Gamma_{pl\alpha}$, which we can write in favorable cases as an integral:

$$\bar{\Gamma}_p = \frac{1}{\pi^2 \rho_c(W)} \cdot \int_0^{E_p{}^{\max}} \frac{mE}{\hbar^2} \sigma_p(E)\rho_R(E_p{}^{\max} - E_p)\, dE_p \qquad (50a)$$

Here all factors are known: σ_p is obtained from suitable use of (49), the level densities are given by some model, taken say from Eqs. (31), and only the factor ξ which occurs in σ_p expresses the model's lack of preciseness. (We suppress the weight g_R, including it in the value of ρ_R, the level density.) We hope to find the ξ variation small, and the value of ξ near unity except in special cases. Thus $\bar{\Gamma}_p$ can be computed for charged nuclear products or for neutrons. We shall have to reserve the gamma-ray width calculation for a later section; it is almost always small compared to heavy-particle widths as soon as the emission of heavy particles is energetically allowed. For the computation of D_p clearly the factor $1/\rho_c(W)$ is contained in all terms Γ_j, and the result is a function of E_p^{max} only. The dimensionless integral of (50a), without the factor $1/\pi^2\rho_c$, is referred to in the literature (W6) as the $f_p(E_p^{max})$ for a given state (S5). Under specific headings we shall discuss the calculation of these f's in more detail:

$$f_p(E_p^{max}) = \pi^2\rho_c(W)\bar{\Gamma}_p \tag{50b}$$

3. The Thermal Analogy: Temperature, Cooling, Evaporation. From the definition of the function f_p it is seen that f_p is just the width for emission of particle p from the excited compound nucleus, measured in terms of the mean spacing of levels at that excitation of the compound nucleus. There is in addition the numerical factor π^2. For this reason we shall refer to the dimensionless f function as the *specific width* for emission of particle p.

It is interesting to view the process of emission of particles from the compound state as a kind of thermal evaporation. Just as a water molecule may evaporate from a drop of water, so does one of these nucleons leave the excited nucleus, in which the excitation energy plays the role of thermal agitation. Equation (50a) leads to an expression for the energy distribution of the emitted particles, which is of course just the integrand in the expression for $\bar{\Gamma}_p$. We have for $I(E_p)\,dE_p$ the relative number of particles p emitted with energy E_p in the interval dE_p:

$$I(E_p)\,dE_p = I_0 E_p \sigma_p \rho_R(E_p^{max} - E_p)\,dE_p \tag{51}$$

where the constants have been lumped into I_0. Now from Eq. (30) we can write the level density ρ_R in terms of the entropy of the nucleus, S. We get

$$I = \frac{I_0 E_p \sigma_p \exp\left[S_R(E_p^{max} - E_p)\right]}{\tau(2\pi dW_R/d\tau)^{1/2}}$$

Now we shall make an approximation which is justifiable only for sufficiently high values of the excitation energy of the residual nucleus $(E_p^{max} - E_p)$. We shall expand the entropy about the maximum value of excitation energy which can be left behind in the residual nucleus, namely about $E_p{}^{\max}$. We obtain then

$$S(W_R) = S(E_p{}^{\max} - E) = S(E_p{}^{\max}) - E_p \left.\frac{\partial S}{\partial E_p}\right|_{E_p{}^{\max}}$$

Now, remembering that the exponential varies much more rapidly than the factor $1/(dW_R/d\tau)^{1/2}$, we use the familiar thermodynamic relation $\partial S/\partial E_p = 1/\tau$. Inserting this, we get

$$(IE_p) = \text{const} \times E_p\sigma_p \exp\left(-\frac{E_p}{\tau}\right) \tag{52}$$

Here τ is the temperature (in energy units) at which the excitation energy of the residual nucleus is on the average $W_R = E_p{}^{\max}$. If the function

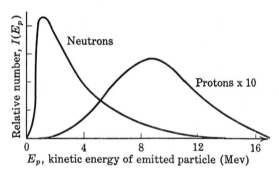

Fig. 6.   Energy spectra of evaporated nucleons. Note reduction of proton evaporation due to Coulomb barrier.

$E_p\sigma_p$ is not too rapidly varying, as it is not for neutrons of some Mev energy, for example, the emitted particles have exactly the Maxwell distribution in energy, just as do the molecules evaporating from a drop. The temperature T corresponds to the temperature of the drop after emission of the particles—the temperature of the *residual* nucleus—which is not the same as that of the compound state, for of course the single emitted particle has a non-negligible fraction of the excitation energy. This makes the evaporation analogue somewhat less exact; we must think of a drop with only a hundred water molecules. If the particles p are charged, the cross section will be quite energy-sensitive; low values of E_p will mean that the penetrability of the barrier is low, and will distort the Maxwell distribution, shifting the maximum to high energies (see Fig. 6).

If the variation of σ_p with E_p is neglected, the maximum energy of emitted neutrons will lie at $E_p = \tau$. Table 4 gives temperature as a function of excitation energy for several nuclei; these temperatures were obtained by using the level density expression of (31). That they are clearly rather small compared to the excitation energy helps justify the approximations made. This means also that the outgoing particles

TABLE 4

NUCLEAR TEMPERATURE IN MEV, ATOMIC NUMBER AND EXCITATION ENERGY

A =	80	120	160	200	240
Excitation Energy (Mev)					
2	0.61	0.51	0.46	0.43	0.41
5	0.96	0.81	0.73	0.68	0.65
10	1.36	1.15	1.04	0.96	0.91
20	1.93	1.62	1.47	1.36	1.29

will in general take away only a small part of the excitation energy, leaving behind an excited residual nucleus, which may in turn boil off still another particle, and so on. It is this process of gradual "cooling" by "evaporation" which is often the origin of the complicated multiple processes listed in Appendix II.[1]

It is not easy to justify the two assumptions: (a) the statistical treatment of the level density, and (b) the neglect of E_p compared to E_p^{max}. The level density formulas certainly overestimate the density of the lowest levels, or at least the lowest ones accessible from a compound state experimentally defined. Certainly the formula will not be very reliable below E_p^{max} of 5 Mev, and for $E_p^{max} - E_p$ of less than a couple of Mev. Above that it should be fairly reliable, until the excitation energy reaches values of 10 Mev or more per particle. The lightest nuclei will of course make difficulties for the statistical treatment.

The release of neutrons from the moving fission fragments by evaporation is to be expected and should account for the prompt fission neutrons, and a spectacular example of "boiling off" is found in the high-energy fission of bismuth, where apparently the most probable fission fragments indicate that the compound nucleus which divides by fission is 12 mass units lighter than the state initially formed. This implies the loss of many neutrons by something very like the evaporation we have described. The nuclear "stars" of cosmic rays often represent such processes. We shall discuss them at greater length in Section 11D1.

[1] See, for example, (T5).

SECTION 6. THE DISPERSION THEORY:
RESONANCE REACTIONS

The statistical theory which we have described has been based on an avoidance of reactions in which the properties of a single compound state are prominent. But some of the best-known and most interesting nuclear reactions are exactly those in which spectacular resonances indicate the importance of the properties of the individual states. Starting from the idea that such levels must be considered in detail as individuals, several authors (B13, B21, K2, S9) have tried to find a general quantum-mechanical solution of the many-body problem presented. They based their treatment on the same two-step notion of the reaction as does the statistical treatment of Bohr. The compound nucleus is the system of incident particle plus target, a system whose eigenvalues are not real and whose eigenstates are not stationary but widened and quasi-stationary, as we have described them. The forces of interaction between incoming particle and target cause transitions between the initial state of the incident particle and an intermediate state which is one of the widened states of the whole system. Then this state, by virtue of the internucleon and nucleon-radiation perturbing couplings, itself decays to the state which contains outgoing particle and residual nucleus. This description was called the "dispersion theory" because of its formal near-identity to the calculation of the optical dispersion of atoms, in which the incident quanta are first absorbed by the atom, and then another quantum, perhaps the same in energy as the first, is re-emitted by the excited atom. The initial and final states of the nuclear system, then, are combined only by the mixing through the compound state, and not with any considerable probability directly. This is the consequence and of course the motivation of the idea of the compound nucleus. The "mixing" is strongest when the energy of the initial system coincides with some more or less well-defined energy level of the compound state. It is of course the intention of this form of theory to give a complete account of nuclear reactions, and the results of statistical theory are expected to follow from dispersion theory calculations when suitable averages are taken, and suitable assumptions made about the relative phases of the wave functions involved and about the character of the levels of the compound state. Whenever really sharply defined incident energies are experimentally available, and whenever the states of the compound nucleus are reasonably well-defined, the dispersion theory ought to yield more information than the statistical model, however improved.

The program of the dispersion theory is too ambitious for full success. The method of perturbation theory which works well for the weak radiation coupling of the electrons in an atom cannot be expected to give, even in theory, an adequate scheme for the calculation of the result of the strong interactions among nucleons.

Wigner and co-workers have given a beautiful general theory (see Appendix II), if a rather complicated one, which does not employ the ideas of perturbation theory but insists only that the nuclear forces act within a well-defined and not too large region of space. Using the ideas of the ordinary Schrödinger wave equation, we shall indicate the physical connection between a simple one-body model of nuclear reactions and the most useful results of the complete dispersion theory, but for full discussion of Wigner's S-matrix treatment the literature should be consulted.

A. The One-Body Model and Its Difficulties

The principal notions of nuclear reactions before the early 1930's were based on a model much simpler than the one we have been discussing. It was built up largely from a study of the decay of alpha-radioactive nuclei and the light nuclear resonance reactions with alpha-particles. The picture was that of the Hartree model of the nucleus, i.e., that the many nucleons produced a net potential well, a combined force field in which the particle to be studied moved. In alpha-decay the alpha-particle shuttled back and forth in this well, until, once in a while, by chance it leaked out of the barrier by the familiar "tunnel effect" of quantum mechanics. For scattering, the nuclear forces supplied a potential well in the same way. To account for the resonances observed, the charged particle was thought of as penetrating the external barrier and moving into the potential well; when the particle wavelength was just such that the particle could produce a standing wave in the well by virtue of in-phase multiple reflections, the particle energy was in resonance with one of its possible stationary states in the potential well. Constructive interference built up the wave function strongly, and absorption grew very rapidly at several well-defined energy levels. This worked quite well for such reactions as $Mg^{24}(\alpha,p)Al^{27}$. It seemed indeed to be a reasonable model. The first slow-neutron resonance work showed up its major weaknesses. It became evident that in this theory scattering and absorption cross sections should increase together. Barring unusual selection rules, the increased particle amplitude inside the well should lead to increased re-emission—scattering—no less than to increased absorption. Even if capture were somehow prevented for some scattering resonances by peculiar effects, which might limit the dropping down of the particle through radiation to a lower level in the potential well, it seemed hard to understand why every level which permitted capture would not yield an even stronger resonance scattering. The simple analogue of the absorption of sound of the resonant frequency by a Helmholtz resonator is complete. The constructive interference of the wave reflected within the resonant cavity builds up its amplitude; sound energy is not only absorbed, but also strongly re-radiated. Yet experiment showed that strong absorption is not accompanied in general by strong scattering.

We have already formulated the general problem of scattering and absorption by a nuclear center of force. Let us inquire into the results of a one-body model, using this formalism (Eqs. 41 et seq.). Consider the case appropriate for thermal neutrons, with wavelengths very large compared to nuclear dimensions. Then we can write for the radial part of the wave function in the region outside the nuclear radius R

$$\psi = \frac{1}{(v)^{1/2}} \frac{u(r)}{r} \qquad u(r) = \eta e^{ikr} + e^{-ikr} \qquad (53)$$

Only the $l = 0$ partial wave is important, and outside the radius R there are no forces. From Fig. 7 we can see that this external wave function

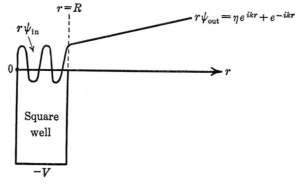

Fig. 7. Wave function for scattering of thermal neutrons from nuclear potential.

must be joined to the internal solution. For definiteness let us consider that the internal potential acting within the radius R is represented by a rectangular well. This is in no way essential for the result, but it simplifies calculation greatly—at the expense of realism. Within the nucleus, then, the neutron has the wave function

$$\psi_{\text{int}} = \frac{u(r)}{r} \qquad u(r) = A \cos (Kr + \epsilon) \qquad (54)$$

with K some wave number, much larger of course than the wave number k of the slow neutron outside the nucleus, and ϵ some phase constant. The boundary condition at the origin will demand that $\epsilon = n\pi/2$, with n odd. The wave equation now requires that the constants be so adjusted that both ψ and $d\psi/dr$ remain continuous across the nuclear boundary. Let us define the quantity f, the logarithmic derivative of the wave function at the nuclear edge made dimensionless by a multiplicative constant:

$$f = R \, (du/dr)/u \, |_{r=R} \tag{55}$$

Then the continuity conditions are both satisfied if we require $f_{\text{in}} = f_{\text{out}}$, or

$$-KR \tan (KR + \epsilon) = ikR \frac{(\eta e^{ikR} - e^{-ikR})}{(\eta e^{ikR} + e^{-ikR})} \tag{56}$$

Solving for η, we obtain

$$\eta = -e^{-2ikR} \frac{(if_{\text{in}} - kR)}{(if_{\text{in}} + kR)} \tag{57}$$

Recall expressions (44). They give

$$\sigma_{\text{abs}}{}^{(0)} = \frac{\pi}{k^2} \left(1 - |\eta|^2\right) \quad \text{and} \quad \sigma_{\text{sc}}{}^{(0)} = \frac{\pi}{k^2} \left(|1 + \eta|^2\right)$$

If we find η, both cross sections are determined. Clearly we have not yet allowed for the possibility of absorption—we have used only one level within the well—and our $|\eta|^2 = 1$. This follows from the form of (57) and the fact that f_{in} is purely real. Now we make use of the small value of $kR \ll 1$ for slow neutrons. We can write (57) as

$$\eta \cong -\frac{(-if + kR)(if - kR)}{f^2 + k^2R^2} \quad \text{and} \quad [1 + \text{Re}(\eta)] = \frac{k^2R^2}{f^2 + k^2R^2}$$

by expanding. Then the cross section becomes

$$\sigma_{\text{sc}}{}^{(0)} = \frac{\pi}{k^2} [1 + |\eta|^2 + 2\text{Re}(\eta)] = \frac{4\pi}{k^2} \cdot \frac{k^2R^2}{f^2 + k^2R^2}$$

$$= \frac{4\pi}{K^2} \cdot \frac{1}{\tan^2 (KR + n\pi/2) + k^2/K^2} \tag{58}$$

This cross section shows a maximum at zero energy regardless of the nuclear size. But, for nuclear sizes and internal motions such that $KR + n\pi/2 = 0, \pi, \cdots$, the small cross section at low energy becomes instead an infinite peak. If we fix a definite value of slow-neutron energy and imagine that the nuclear radius, say, varies smoothly, strong scattering resonances will appear for special values of the nuclear radius. Somewhat more familiar-looking resonances, appearing for definite values of incoming neutron energy, would have resulted had we considered partial waves of higher angular momentum, but the general features would not have been very different.

Now, moreover, we can calculate the amplitude of the wave inside the well, taking an incident wave of unit flux. Using (54) and (56), we get

$$A^2 \cong \frac{1}{K^2} \sin^2 \left(KR + \frac{n\pi}{2} \right)$$

Thus the amplitude of the neutron wave inside will become large at resonance, and in fact we can write the cross section for scattering in terms of that amplitude, at least near resonance:

$$\sigma_{sc}{}^{(0)} \cong 4\pi A^2 \quad \text{near resonance}$$

But, clearly, the radiative transitions to a lower state will have a matrix element proportional to the amplitude A, and the probability of such transitions, and thus the cross section for absorption, will vary like A^2, as we should physically expect from the fact that A^2 measures the time the particle spends inside the nucleus. The ratio σ_{abs}/σ_{sc} will therefore show no marked change at resonance; strong scattering and absorption resonances will be found at the same energy. This is contrary to all experience. Furthermore, it is easily seen that the resonance levels are spaced in energy much too little to correspond to adding another half-wave to the inside wave function, and that the variation of cross section with nuclear radius (i.e., with the mass number A) is far too erratic to be accounted for on such a picture. The one-body model gives much better results when the *external* wave function determines the broad course of events, as in alpha-particle radioactivity. Where the interior state of the nucleus is decisive, the model is inadequate. The strong physical plausibility of the compound nucleus picture, added to the difficulties of the one-body description of neutron capture, gives it its present importance. The modifications which the strong effects of shell structure will certainly require, especially at moderate excitation, have still not been completely worked out.

B. The Dispersion Theory for an Isolated Resonance

The difficulties which surround the derivation of the theory of nuclear reactions by perturbation methods have led to reconsideration of the basis of the whole matter. It turns out that the most important features of the theory arise from the fundamental nature of scattering and absorption processes themselves, which are displayed fully only in the rather complex nuclear domain. The general theory has been developed by Wigner and several of his co-workers. We shall discuss mainly a quite satisfactory but much simpler and less general approach developed by Weisskopf and others. In it the features of the one-body model which make scattering and absorption so pictorial are generalized to fit the physical picture of a compound nucleus. In the one-body model we have shown that, for a case when only two alternatives, elastic scattering and absorption, are possible, the logarithmic derivative function f determines the amplitude η, and hence both cross sections. But in the one-body model the complex number f (which must be complex to allow absorption) is fixed by the nuclear potential well. Both modulus and phase are given. Weisskopf regards this same quantity f, now in general a complex number, as determined by the whole structure of the nucleus. It will be different from level to level, varying in a manner much more complicated than does the one-body f, and in particular having modulus and phase independently varying. We define the resonance energies and level widths by giving the properties of f. Thus we have a kind of phenomenological compound nucleus picture into which the properties of many levels enter, but through a single function whose determination from the actual make-up of the compound nucleus we leave perforce to the physics of the future. We shall require that (1) f is a function only of the energy (and other constants of the motion) of the compound nucleus, and not explicitly dependent on the incoming particle, and (2) f is a well-defined function, defined by (55), in spite of the uncertainty of the value of R, the nuclear radius, at which internal and external waves are to be fitted. Both of these conditions can be met by the requirement that the wave function just outside the nucleus vary only slowly over a distance which corresponds to the mean spacing of the nucleons within the nuclear matter. We can regard the value of R as a parameter to be chosen to give the most reasonable average behavior of f. Some values of R, and the related internal wave number κ, will not work. No value will allow us to assign the behavior of f uniquely, but the best values will yield reasonable statistical agreement with the observed properties of many levels.

1. Derivation of the One-Level Formula. (a) *Without External Forces.* Guided by physical considerations, we shall now try a generalization of the one-body model. The function f is defined by the expression

$$f = R \, (du/dr)/u \, \big|_{r=R} \tag{55}$$

We expect zeros of f when the slope of the wave function vanishes at the nuclear edge, and infinite values if the wave function itself vanishes there. Without loss of generality we can take over the special form of f from the one-body theory:

$$f = -\kappa R \tan z(W) \qquad (59)$$

The tangent function no longer has as argument the simple and well-defined phase of the internal wave function in the one-body potential well, $\kappa R + \epsilon$. It now has instead a function $z(W)$, which increases monotonically as the excitation energy $W = E_{bind} + E_{kin}$ increases, and takes the value $n\pi$ at each of the successive resonance energies $W_r = E_b + E_r$, but may vary as it will in between. The results of the theory now depend only on the assumption that the variation of $z(W)$ with energy is as smooth and simple as possible. We shall see how all the properties of the successive resonances can be described by a suitable trend for z near each resonance. The prediction of the behavior of z in detail is given up for the present theory; it could be determined only if the actual motion of the entire compound nucleus in every eigenstate were known.

But the one-body picture did not explicitly include absorption. We allow for that here in the familiar way: we introduce a damping factor to reduce the amplitude of the now only approximately stationary state. The damping arises of course out of the possibility that the system can change its state not simply by decomposing to re-emit the incident particle, but in some other way. Such a damping will as always be expected to widen and depress the resonance peaks. We write the energy as a complex quantity: $\overline{W} = W - i\Gamma_a/2$ so that the energy eigenfunction becomes

$$\psi(t) = \phi(\mathbf{r})e^{-iWt/\hbar} \cdot e^{+i(i\Gamma_a)t/2\hbar}$$

Now the probability of occupation of the given state decays in time with the factor $e^{-\Gamma_a t/\hbar} \mid \psi(0) \mid^2$, and the mean lifetime of the state is given by $\tau = \hbar/\Gamma_a$ while as usual the uncertainty principle will imply that the state is defined only up to a width $\Gamma_a \sim \hbar/\tau$. This will indeed follow from the calculated resonance shape.

Evidently the concept of resonance level is useful only if the energy $\overline{W}$ has but a small imaginary part, i.e., if $\Gamma_a/W \ll 1$. Although we could write the function quite generally, we shall use the approximation of expanding f in the neighborhood of the resonance energy, leaning heavily upon the smooth behavior of $z(W)$ and the expected smallness of Γ. We write then

$$f(\overline{W}) = f(W) - \frac{i\Gamma_a}{2} \frac{df}{d\overline{W}} \bigg|_{\overline{W} = W} + \cdots$$

Taking our cue from the one-body model, let us define the resonance energy, E_r, by the relation

$$f(W_r) = f(E_b + E_r) = 0$$

and continue to expand f near the value E_r. We get

$$f(\overline{W}) = (E - E_r)\left.\frac{df}{dE}\right|_{E_r} - \frac{i\Gamma_a}{2}\left.\frac{df}{dE}\right|_{E_r} + \cdots \tag{60}$$

where we use the kinetic energy of the incoming particle, E, as measure of the excitation energy W.

This linearization greatly simplifies our theory. It is certainly no serious source of error provided that we look in the near neighborhood of a resonance level. How far that neighborhood extends depends of course on the variation of the argument $z(W)$ with energy. Now we can use the relation between the function f and the phase shift η, just as we did in the earlier model, from Eq. (57). We take the value of f near resonance from (60). If we introduce explicitly the functions $f_0(E)$ and $g(E)$, the real and negative imaginary parts of the function f, we obtain

$$f(E) = f_0(E) - ig(E) = (E - E_r)\delta + \frac{i\Gamma_a}{2}\delta \tag{61}$$

where we have written δ for the quantity $(df/dE)|_{E_r}$, and $\Gamma_a = -2g/\delta$. Using (57), there follows from (44)

$$\sigma_{\text{abs}}{}^{(0)} = \frac{\pi}{k^2}(1 - |\eta|^2) = 4\pi\lambda^2 \cdot \frac{kRg}{(g + kR)^2 + f_0{}^2} \tag{62a}$$

We can write $\sigma_{\text{sc}}{}^{(0)}$ similarly. The fact that resonance is marked by $f_0 = 0$ is now plain, and the whole expression gives just the familiar one-level Breit-Wigner formula of dispersion theory; compare (62b).

Now, writing the cross sections out in full, but replacing the functions f_0 and g by the more physical widths from (61), and defining a width Γ_n by the relation $\Gamma_n = -2kR/\delta$, analogously to (61), we have

$$\sigma_{\text{abs}}{}^{(0)} = \pi\lambda^2 \cdot \frac{\Gamma_n\Gamma_a}{\left(\dfrac{\Gamma_n + \Gamma_a}{2}\right)^2 + (E - E_r)^2} \tag{62b}$$

$$\sigma_{\text{sc}}{}^{(0)} = 4\pi\lambda^2 \left| \frac{kR}{i(kR + g) - f_0} + e^{ikR}\sin kR \right|^2$$

$$= 4\pi\lambda^2 \cdot \left| \frac{\frac{1}{2}\Gamma_n}{E - E_r + \dfrac{i}{2}(\Gamma_n + \Gamma_a)} + e^{ikR}\sin k\,R \right|^2$$

From the results of (62) we can go much further in the interpretation of the argument function $z(E)$ of (59). Plainly it goes through multiples of π, giving zeros for the logarithmic derivative function f at each resonance. It is also clear that the contribution to absorption, say, of any level will fall off on each side of the resonance energy, with a characteristic width given by $\Gamma_n + \Gamma_a = \Gamma$. But this width is inversely

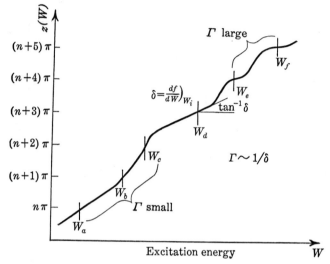

Fig. 8. The argument function $z(W)$ as a function of the excitation energy W in a region containing several resonances, W_a, W_b, $\cdots$, with differing widths (F7).

proportional to the slope of the f function near the resonances. From (57) it is easy to show that

$$|\eta|^2 = \frac{1 + a^2 \text{Im} \ (f)}{1 - a^2 \text{Im} \ (f)}$$

where a^2 is positive definite; and, since we require from the absorption cross-section formula (44) that $|\eta|^2 \leq 1$, it follows that $\text{Im} \ (f) \leq 0$, and in our expansion therefore δ must be non-positive. This justifies our use of the minus sign in the definition of Γ_n and Γ_a and confirms the choice of the tangent function in (59). We can now see graphically the meaning of Fig. 8, in which the function $z(E)$ is plotted schematically in a region of several resonances. The width is given in our approximation by $\Gamma = - \text{const}/\delta = - \text{const} \cdot dz/dE$. Since δ is necessarily non-positive, z does increase monotonically, as we expected. Where z changes rapidly with E near a resonance, δ is small and the widths large. We have drawn narrow levels at resonance energies a, b, c, wider ones at d and e, and a very wide one at f. We cannot predict the level positions or the slope near those values.   But we have thrown the whole burden of the determination of reaction and scattering cross sections into the behavior of a single function z, which is a kind of equivalent internal phase.   If z varies smoothly, we can expect that dz/dE will be small, and the widths small when the levels are closely spaced; and reverse will also hold.   By such simplifying assumptions on the smoothness and statistical regularity we can produce various results concerning the average behavior of nuclear resonance lines.   Individual levels must be examined empirically, but can be fully described by this theory.   The choice of the matching radius R can be fixed by the pragmatic test of how simple and statistically unbiased is the behavior of the many levels, for R must divide the region outside the nucleus from the one within, and this division will be physically most clear cut for a particular R. Improper choice of R will allow the behavior of z to be affected by the external region and will distort the expected intelligibility of the properties of z.

(b) *With Barrier.*   So far we have considered only the case appropriate to slow-neutron reactions, where the orbital angular momentum $l = 0$, and neither centrifugal nor Coulomb forces are present.   Outside the nuclear radius R the potential is strictly zero.   In this case, and in this case only, the external wave function is given not just asymptotically but everywhere outside the nucleus by the partial plane waves of (53). It is not very hard to extend the calculation to the more general case. We write the radial part of the wave function in the external potential as before, for a definite value l of the orbital angular momentum.   But, as we approach the nucleus, the wave function is no longer a simple plane wave.   We introduce the independent solutions of the wave equation with the given external potentials which go over asymptotically into incoming and outgoing partial plane waves.   These solutions we call u_i and u_o for incoming and outgoing parts, respectively.   (The Coulomb potential can be thought of as screened very far away to avoid the logarithmic term in the asymptotic phase shifts.)   We write, for unit flux,

$$\psi_l(r) = \frac{1}{(v)^{\frac{1}{2}}} \frac{u_i(r) + \eta u_o(r)}{r} \xrightarrow[r \to \infty]{} \frac{1}{(v)^{\frac{1}{2}}} \frac{e^{-i(kr - l\pi/2)} + \eta e^{+i(kr - l\pi/2)}}{r} \quad (63)$$

Now, as we come in to the matching radius R, the behavior of the solutions u_i and u_o is completely known for any given external potential. Since they are adjusted asymptotically to the same amplitude, and one solution could be obtained from the other by simply reversing the direction of time, one is the complex conjugate of the other, $u_i = u_o{}^*$.   We shall also need the penetrability of the external barrier, which we can define, as in (35), by the relations

$$P^{(l)} = \frac{|u_i(\infty)|^2}{|u_i(R)|^2} = \frac{1}{|u_i(R)|^2} = \frac{1}{u_i(R)u_o(R)} \tag{64}$$

Here we affix the l value corresponding to the orbital angular momentum partial wave involved. We shall also make use of the Wronskian relation, obtained in the usual manner by writing the wave equation for each solution, cross-multiplying, and subtracting, to get

$$\frac{d}{dr}\left(u_i \frac{du_o}{dr} - u_o \frac{du_i}{dr}\right) = 0 \qquad u_i u_o' - u_o u_i' = \text{const}$$

Since this is true for all values of r, we evaluate for $r \to \infty$ to obtain

$$u_i u_o' - u_o u_i' = 2ik \qquad \frac{u_o'}{u_o} - \frac{u_i'}{u_i} = 2ikP^{(l)} \tag{65}$$

Now let us define the quantities $F_{i,o} = Ru_{i,o}'/u_{i,o}|_{r=R}$ by analogy to the function f. With all this not very complicated machinery, we have the solution at hand. Again we write down the matching condition at the nuclear edge, just as in (56):

$$f_{\text{in}} = kR(u_i' + \eta u_o')/(u_i + \eta u_o)|_{r=R}$$

Solving for the amplitude η, we get

$$\eta = -\frac{u_i(R)}{u_o(R)} \frac{F_i - f_{\text{in}}}{F_o - f_{\text{in}}} = -\frac{u_i(R)}{u_o(R)} \cdot \frac{(if_{\text{in}} - i\Delta + \gamma)}{(if_{\text{in}} - i\Delta - \gamma)} \tag{66}$$

where we have written the expression in the form closest to (57) and have introduced the notation $F_{i,o} = \Delta \pm i\gamma$ for the complex numbers $F_{i,o}$. Writing $f_{\text{in}} = f_o - ig$ as before, and evaluating γ from relation (65),

$$F_i - F_o = 2i\gamma = -2ikRP^{(l)} \qquad \gamma = -kR \cdot P^{(l)} \tag{67}$$

we get from the fundamental relation (44) between σ_{abs} and η, the result:

$$\sigma_{\text{abs}}^{(l)} = (2l + 1) \frac{4\pi\lambda^2 \cdot kRP^{(l)}g}{(g + kRP^{(l)})^2 + (f_{\text{out}} - \Delta)^2} \tag{68a}$$

This is very like the result for the s wave obtained in (62a), and, indeed, for $l = 0$ and no external forces, $u_{i,o} = e^{\pm ikR}$, $P^{(0)} = 1$, and $\Delta = 0$, which gives exactly (62a).

If we write for the unimodular number $u_i(R)/u_o(R) = e^{-2i\alpha}$, which was just e^{-2ikR} for the no-force case, we can write the scattering cross section as well, and, if we introduce the same linear approximation as the expansion of (61), we have

$$\sigma_{abs}^{(l)} = \pi\lambda^2 \cdot (2l + 1) \frac{\Gamma_n \Gamma_a}{(E - E_r)^2 + (\Gamma_n + \Gamma_a)^2/2} \qquad (68b)$$

$$\sigma_{sc}^{(l)} = 4\pi\lambda^2 \cdot (2l + 1) \left| \frac{\frac{1}{2}\Gamma_n}{(E - E_r) + (i/2)(\Gamma_n + \Gamma_a)} + \sin \alpha e^{i\alpha} \right|^2$$

in which we have set

$$\Gamma_n = -2kRP^{(l)} / \frac{df}{dE}\bigg|_{E_r^{(0)}} \qquad \Gamma_a = -2g / \frac{df}{dE}\bigg|_{E_r^{(0)}} \qquad (68c)$$

and defined the resonance energy E_r by the relation

$$(E_r - E_r^{(0)})\delta - \Delta = 0 \qquad (68d)$$

$$E_r = E_r^{(0)} + \frac{\Delta}{\delta} \qquad \text{with } f_0(E_r^{(0)}) = 0 \qquad \delta = \frac{df}{dE}\bigg|_{E_r^{(0)}}$$

Equations (68) are the principal results of the one-level theory, and they exhibit a number of interesting properties which we shall discuss briefly.

2. Features of the One-Level Theory. (a) *Level Shift*. It will be observed that the resonance energy is increased by an amount $\Delta_r = \Delta/\delta$ from the value of the energy $E_r^{(0)}$ at which the value of z was set equal to $n\pi$. Since this value of the energy is in any case not observable directly, nor calculable in the present theory, the shift might be regarded as meaningless. It has been pointed out, however, that in the comparison of the successive levels of mirror nuclei, whose energy levels might be expected to differ by an easily calculated Coulomb energy, and in no other way, the effect of Δ_r could be seen, for the excited states of two mirror nuclei will in general be capable of different modes of decay, since thresholds for charged particle emission will differ. Thus Δ_r will differ for the two nuclei, and the observed resonances will not show energy displacement exactly equal to the Coulomb energy differences. Qualitative agreement with the observations has indeed been found in at least one case (E1), that of the pair N^{13}, C^{13}. Physically the level shift can be ascribed to the fact that in a compound level the particle which ultimately leaves the nucleus spends considerable time outside the nuclear radius and within the external force field before its departure; its wave function extends with sizable amplitude beyond the distance R. A more formal but somehow familiar description is to observe that such a shift represents the reactive part of that coupled impedance whose resistive part gives the familiar level broadening and damping.

(b) *Reduced Widths.* The particle width Γ_n is given by (68c) as just

$$\Gamma_n = 2kRP^{(l)} \left(-\frac{df}{dE}\bigg|_{E_r} \right)^{-1}$$

It is easy to compare this with the result of the compound nucleus approach in Eq. (38). We see that here too we can define a "width without barrier," or reduced width, by writing $\Gamma_n = 2kRP^{(l)}\gamma_r$. The magnitude γ_r is just the reduced width, which is dependent only upon the internal state of the nucleus, as described by the function f. Comparison with (38) shows that the reduced width is a measure of the probability of the particle being at the nuclear surface. The absorption width also can be written in this form, introducing a wave number κ to represent some characteristic wave number for internal nuclear motion. We write the hitherto unspecified imaginary part of f near resonance in the form $+g = \kappa Rh_a$, and then we obtain Γ_a also in terms of the reduced width and of a dimensionless expression giving the imaginary part of f:

$$\Gamma_a = 2\kappa Rh_a\gamma_r$$

The *observed* width of a level is not always given by these formulas, since the variation of Δ in (68a) as the incident particle energy is varied is not always negligible; this effect can be computed by expanding Δ_r itself about the resonance energy in (68a), and retaining only the linear variation. For s-wave neutrons, of course, $\Delta = 0$, and there is no such effect; but cases have been exhibited in which the observed width differed from the value of $\Gamma = \Gamma_n + \Gamma_a$ by as great a factor as 2 or 3.

(c) *Negative Peaks.* Formula (68b) for the scattering cross section exhibits some very odd properties, which arise from the possibility of interference between the resonance term and the second term, called the potential scattering term. This scattering term arises from the effect of the well-defined volume in which the nuclear forces act, and also from the summed influence of all the other levels of the compound system. There is no rigorous distinction between these two ideas; in our more formal picture we can think of the potential scattering as coming from the fact that between resonances the value of f is such that the surface wave must be of very small amplitude, much as though the nuclear surface were the surface of an impenetrable sphere. Taking the presence of a potential scattering term as our model gives it, then, let us examine its possible consequences, at least reasonably near a single resonance level.

It is convenient to observe that the resonance term, with its varying denominator which gives rise to the familiar witch-shaped peaks, can be written in terms of a phase angle θ. With the notation

$$\frac{\frac{1}{2}\Gamma_n}{(E - E_r) + (i/2)(\Gamma_n + \Gamma_a)} = \frac{r}{\Delta + i}$$

$$r = \frac{\Gamma_n}{(\Gamma_a + \Gamma_n)} \qquad \Delta = \frac{2(E - E_r)}{(\Gamma_n + \Gamma_a)}$$

we write

$$\frac{r}{\Delta + i} = \frac{r}{\cotan \theta + i} = r \sin \theta e^{-i\theta}$$

which yields the very symmetrical form:

$$\sigma_{sc}{}^{(l)} = \pi \lambda^2 \cdot (2l + 1) \left| r \sin \theta e^{-i\theta} + \sin \alpha e^{i\alpha} \right|^2$$

If we consider the resonance term alone, the familiar peak is produced by the variation with energy of the phase angle θ, going from a value of zero far below the resonance energy, taking a value of $\pi/2$ at exact resonance, and going to π far above the resonance energy. When the interfering term is considered as well, we may write the cross section in the following way to exhibit the interference:

$$\bar{\sigma} = \frac{\sigma_{sc}{}^{(l)}}{\pi \lambda^2 (2l + 1)} = \sin^2 \alpha + r^2 \sin^2 \theta + 2r \sin \theta \sin \alpha \cos (\theta + \alpha)$$

Here it is clear that, if $r = 0$, we have pure potential scattering, which is constant with energy (for not too great changes in energy, we stay in the neighborhood of one single level); if $\alpha = 0$, we have the pure resonant peak. The interference is described by the cross term, linear in r. A somewhat more understandable form of the expression can be obtained by a not very obvious transformation, using the trigonometric expressions for sums and differences freely, and employing the identity $\sin x + a \sin (x + y) = (1 + a^2 + 2a \cos y)^{1/2} \sin (x + \epsilon)$, $\tan \epsilon = a \sin y/(1 + a \cos y)$, which is best derived directly from the indicated geometrical construction. The transformed expression becomes

$$\bar{\sigma} = \frac{r^2}{2} + (1 - r) \sin^2 \alpha - \frac{r}{2} [r^2 + 4(1 - r) \sin^2 \alpha]^{1/2}$$

$$+ r[r^2 + 4(1 - r) \sin^2 \alpha]^{1/2} \sin^2 (\theta + \phi)$$

where

$$\tan 2\phi = \frac{2 \sin \alpha \cos \alpha}{r - 2 \sin^2 \alpha} \qquad (69)$$

Here it is explicitly seen that the entire energy variation is contained in a $\sin^2$ term, which recalls the general results of the method of partial waves. The phase θ of the resonant contribution always increases by π as the energy rises through the resonance. But the value of the potential scattering phase angle ϕ will determine the shape of the observed "peak," which will be a normal-appearing peak only if $\phi = 0$, π, and a negative peak when $\phi = \pi/2$, with a dip-and-peak combination for intermediate values. Such "negative resonances" have been observed, and the dip preceding a peak has been found in a number of cases. The scattering maximum will be displaced from the energy value E_r of the absorption maximum because of the potential scattering interference. Such displacements are typically rather small, and no clear example can be cited. Use of (69) and related generalized forms to examine the properties of particular levels, especially statistical weights and hence spins, is frequent.

3. Spins and Statistical Weights. Up to this point we have ignored the existence of intrinsic spin for the fundamental particles involved in reaction, and of total angular momenta for the complex systems. We fix our attention on a single level of the compound nucleus. We shall assume that such a level has no degeneracies—all accidental ones being removed by coupling forces of some finite size, even if very small, within the nucleus—except the necessary degeneracy in spatial orientation of the total angular momentum vector **J**. This implies, in the absence of external forces, a $(2J + 1)$-fold degeneracy of the compound state. But the compound nucleus can be formed in many ways. If the incoming particle has intrinsic angular momentum s, if we consider only the single orbital angular momentum partial wave l, and if the target nucleus has initial total angular momentum I, then the total number of different ways to form a compound nucleus is $(2s + 1)(2l + 1)(2I + 1)$. Of these only $2J + 1$ will correspond to the given compound level of angular momentum in question. Thus, for unpolarized beams incident on unpolarized target nuclei, and with no measurement of the spin of the resultant particle, we must multiply the cross-section formulas (68) by the statistical weight factor:

$$g_J = \frac{2J + 1}{(2s + 1)(2l + 1)(2I + 1)} \tag{70}$$

The absorption cross section for the familiar one-level case with $l = 0$ becomes, for example,

$$\sigma_{\text{abs}} = \frac{2J + 1}{(2s + 1)(2I + 1)} \pi \lambda^2 \frac{\Gamma_n \Gamma_a}{(E - E_r)^2 + [(\Gamma_n + \Gamma_a)/2]^2}$$

In general, of course, J is not known, and several possibilities exist. Even for the specially simple case of thermal neutrons, where only

$l = 0$ can contribute, and $s = \frac{1}{2}$, we get the alternatives $I + s = J_+$, $I - s = J_-$, and the $g_{J_\pm}$ factor is ambivalently $\frac{1}{2}[1 \pm 1/(2I + 1)]$. Sometimes J values can be assigned by study of the cross-section magnitudes.

C. The Generalized Theory of Dispersion: Many Levels and Many Decay Modes

We have treated the theory of reactions only in the simplest case. We have considered only two alternatives: the incoming wave is coherently scattered, or it is absorbed. In general the theory must take account of many possible consequences of the formation of the compound state. It may be that the energy is not near a single resonance, but lies between two resonant values; or the widths may be comparable to the spacing, so that the effect of two resonances may overlap; or simply that compound states of different J can contribute to the emission of a single outgoing wave of fixed l, if spins are present. In all these cases, as in the case where several product particles are energetically allowed, we have to take into account the various possible courses for the reaction.

In a series of papers (see Appendix II), Wigner and co-workers have presented a beautiful generalization of the process here applied in the one-level, two-alternative case. The phase shift η which described the reaction by the relation $\sigma_{sc}^{(0)} = (\pi/k^2)(|1 + \eta|^2)$ is generalized by introducing a unitary matrix U, such that

$$\sigma_{if} = \frac{\pi}{k_i^2} \cdot |(U - 1)_{if}|^2$$

where i, f index initial and final particles, not only as to type, but also as to internal state (excitation), spin orientation, and relative orbital angular momentum. The theory now produces values for the matrix elements of $(U - 1)$, often called the collision or S matrix, between all the states representing the various alternatives. Unlike the $f(E)$ of our phenomenological theory, the matrices are given explicitly in terms of the Hamiltonian describing the interaction of all the nucleons in the total system. Progress is made, however, only by the demonstration that much of the behavior of the cross-section formulas can be studied by knowing precisely only the interactions outside the nuclear radius, and then replacing a detailed knowledge of the interior by certain boundary conditions on the nuclear surface. This is in strict parallel with the progress of the derivation we have given. Indeed, the more general method differs mainly by the complete generality into which it has been cast, and by the somewhat more complete dynamical specification of the quantities which give the important results. The theory places the assumptions of our point of view in full sight, and demonstrates that the chief features of a theory of reactions come from the ability to specify with more or less definiteness a surface which can divide a region in which the Hamiltonian is fully known from one where it is not. We shall not further discuss the more general theory here, but refer instead to the literature.

Here it is appropriate, however, to indicate one entirely formal scheme of generalizing our formulas, like (68), to include explicitly the properties of more than one level. It will be seen that there is full equivalence between representing the behavior of the cross sections between resonances (i.e., where more than one state must be taken into account) (1) as we have done it, following Weisskopf, by the use of a function $f(E)$ whose properties, however, cannot be simply given except in the neighborhood of one level; or (2) by considering the summed contribution of a large, or strictly an infinite, number of levels, whose phase relationships and individual widths and locations can be known only in principle. In the absence of a detailed solution of the eigenvalue problem of the whole compound nucleus, no dispersion theory approach which is not statistical in nature can give useful results except in the neighborhood of a single level, or at most of a small number near-by, whose properties can be approximated.

The formal equivalence of the two points of view comes out clearly by examining (66). We can write the denominator factor in this way:

$$g(E) = \frac{1}{f_{\text{in}}(E) - (\Delta - i\gamma)} = \sum_j \frac{c_j}{s_j - E}$$

This is an identity where the sum is to be carried out over all the poles s_j of the function g, i.e., the zeros of its denominator. Placing the sum into (62a) and remembering the linear expansion approximation, we can write the simpler formula of (62b) as

$$\sigma_{\text{abs}} = \pi\lambda^2 \left| \sum_j (\Gamma_n{}^j \Gamma_a{}^j)^{1/2} \middle/ \left[E - E_j + \frac{i}{2}(\Gamma_n{}^j + \Gamma_a{}^j) \right] \right|^2 \tag{71}$$

The virtue of this way of writing the formula is that it exhibits the possible interference of the contributions of many levels. It is this interference which must be taken into account to explain angular distribution of reaction products, especially in light nuclei, where broad levels are the rule. Here phase relations are evidently decisive. But the existence of constants of the motion, such as angular momentum and parity, will imply selection rules. The mode of formation of the compound nucleus can influence the phase of the matrix elements which occur in the $(\Gamma_n{}^j)^{1/2}$ of the many-level formulas. In those cases the basic simplifying assumption of the independent decay of the compound nucleus will not be valid.

When, as above, the total cross section, integrated over all angles of product emission, is calculated, any interference terms arising between compound levels which have *different* values of the constants of motion, total angular momentum, or parity drop out. However, for differential cross sections experimentally given by angular distribution or correlation measurements, these interferences are decisive. Indeed, every case in which the angular distribution of some product exhibits asymmetry with respect to a plane normal to the beam axis must arise out of such an interference between compound levels of differing parity. The best-studied example is that of the gamma-rays from proton capture in Li^7 near a strong 440-kev resonance. No general form of the complicated formulas involved is available,[1] though special applications occur quite completely worked out in the literature. The Γ_r's are best represented as matrix elements between the states involved, and close attention must be paid to the coherent l states in the incident beam, and to the various combinations of l, s, s_z which can give rise to each compound level of fixed J_r and parity.

D. Statistical Estimates

It is interesting to look at the value of $\sigma_{\text{abs}}{}^{(0)}$ in the case contemplated by the statistical theory. We think of many levels contributing in a region of energy ΔE at E, with $\Delta E/E \ll 1$; and we examine the average absorption cross section $\bar{\sigma}_{\text{abs}}$ giving only average values for the properties of the individual levels. Formula (62) gives the contribution of each level. Replacing the quantity $(E - E_r)$ by a variable of integration, and using the fact that the width Γ is small compared to the region ΔE so that we can treat λ as constant over the level, we get, for each level,

$$\bar{\sigma}_{\text{abs}}{}^{(0)} \, \Delta E = \frac{2\pi^2 \lambda^2 \Gamma_n \Gamma_a}{(\Gamma_n + \Gamma_a)}$$

and, for the entire set of N levels in the interval ΔE,

$$\bar{\sigma}_{\text{abs}} \, \Delta E = \sum_r^N \frac{2\pi^2 \lambda^2 \Gamma_n{}^r \Gamma_a{}^r}{\Gamma_n{}^r + \Gamma_a{}^r} \doteq \frac{2\pi^2 \lambda^2 N \Gamma_n \Gamma_a}{\bar{\Gamma}_n + \bar{\Gamma}_a}$$

[1] For an interesting account of the general properties of angular distributions see (Y3).

We then write for the number of levels its mean value, $N = \Delta E/D$, where D is the mean level spacing, and we obtain

$$\bar{\sigma}_{\text{abs}}{}^{(0)} = \frac{2\pi^2 \lambdabar^2 \bar{\Gamma}_n \bar{\Gamma}_a}{D\bar{\Gamma}} \qquad \bar{\Gamma} = \bar{\Gamma}_a + \bar{\Gamma}_n \tag{72}$$

It is clear that this expression is the same as the appropriate form of Eq. (40), with (49):

$$\sigma_{\text{abs}}{}^{(\text{statistical})} = \pi\lambdabar^2 \cdot D_{\text{abs}} \cdot P_0 \xi = \pi\lambdabar^2 \cdot \frac{\bar{\Gamma}_a}{\bar{\Gamma}} \cdot 1 \cdot \frac{2\pi\bar{\Gamma}_n}{D}$$

where the sticking probability is now $2\pi\bar{\Gamma}_n/D$, which is proportional to $k \sim v$ at low energies. We have shown how the resonance contributions of the one-level dispersion theory sum to the statistical form if $D \gg \bar{\Gamma}$, as we expect.

Before we leave the dispersion theory, we shall cite one useful result which follows more directly from the generalized theory, or from the perturbation theory than from our phenomenological approach. The (reduced width)$^{1/2}$, $\gamma_r{}^{1/2}$, is shown in the generalized theory of Wigner (J1) to be expressible as an integral over the nuclear surface of the product of two wave functions, one corresponding to the interior state of the nucleus, the other referring to the external motion of the product particle. The reduced width depends explicitly not only on the state of excitation of the compound nucleus, indexed by r, but also on the nature of the state of the residual nucleus, and therefore on the quantum state of the emitted particle. We have neglected the latter dependence, saying that only the external motion of the emitted particle was important. If, however, we sum over all the possible states f of the residual nucleus, we obtain a limit for γ_r which cannot be exceeded. This limit may be approximately evaluated by using the familiar sum rule for the product of the two matrices, $\gamma_{rf}{}^{1/2}$, and regarding the internal wave function as expressing the fact that the nucleus has a roughly constant density. The upper limit thus approximated for γ_r is

$$\gamma_r = \frac{\Gamma_{r,n}}{2kRP_n{}^{(l)}} \leq \sim \frac{3}{2} \frac{\hbar^2}{M_n R^2} \sim \frac{3}{A^{2/3}} \text{ Mev, \quad for nucleon width} \tag{73}$$

This upper limit sometimes permits the exclusion of certain partial waves, when the low penetrabilities associated with high l would imply a γ_r violating the sum rule limit. The similarity between this limit and Eq. (39) is evident; from the general scheme it follows that we would expect widths near the limit for a one-body model, which would diminish as more and more levels contribute, or more and more particles take part in the nuclear motion. In general, our phenomenological theory would lead to the result that for a smooth enough variation of the function f the value γ_r/D would be roughly constant (D is the level spacing). The departure from this result will measure the significance of deviations from the statistical theory.

SECTION 7. SOME TYPICAL NUCLEAR REACTIONS

In this part we shall apply the theory of the earlier sections to some typical nuclear reaction types which it has helped to explain. In each case a much more detailed account can be obtained in the original literature; it is the purpose of this section to indicate the method of using the theory in sufficient detail, and to point out as well its difficulties and pitfalls, so that the reader may extend the few examples given, necessarily briefly, here to the whole range of experimental material.

A. Resonance: The Region of Dispersion Theory

Clearly marked nuclear levels, and incident particle beams with well-defined energy, are known in only two types of reactions. The most important of these (discussed also in Part VII) is the interaction of slow neutrons with nuclei, leading usually to capture, but often to scattering or even particle emission.[1] The second type is the class of reactions using charged particle beams up to a few Mev of energy on target nuclei from the very lightest up to the region of, say, aluminum. In these reactions well-marked levels can often be found (see Figs. 10 and 11), the wavelengths involved are not small compared to nuclear dimensions, and the whole approach must be based on using the maximum information about individual levels.

1. Thermal Neutron Reactions. This large class of reactions is discussed in Part VII, Section 2B2. We shall here discuss it in sufficient detail to illustrate the use of the theory presented in Part VII.

In the thermal region, the neutron wavelength is very large compared to nuclear dimensions. The neutron de Broglie wavelength $\lambda = \hbar/mv$ is just $\lambda = 0.045 \ A/(E)^{1/2}$, where E is the kinetic energy in electron volts. For energies from a few millivolts up to, say, a thousand volts, which broadly defines the region of interest in these experiments, λ ranges from 2 A to 10^{-3} A. Throughout this range, the partial wave corresponding to $l = 0$, the so-called S wave, alone will be effective in reaching the nuclear surface. The penetrability of all other partial waves is so greatly reduced by the centrifugal barrier that they can be

---

[1] See, for example, the collection of results and references in (G6).

neglected. From this follows the isotropic distribution of scattered thermal neutrons and of capture gamma-rays in the center-of-mass system.

(a) *Effects of Target Motion and Binding.* It is well to introduce here a note of caution. The usual neglect of the chemical forces acting on the target nucleus, of the thermal or zero-point motion of the target nucleus, and of the possible coherent scattering from the neighboring nuclei of the target material cannot be justified in the thermal neutron reactions. The coherent scattering of neighboring nuclei (discussed in Section 5 of Part VII) will show up strongly in cross-section measurements as long as the neutron wavelength is near the values which fulfill the Bragg condition $n\lambda = d \sin \theta$ for the lattice spacing d of the crystal or microcrystals involved. This means that, in the range above 0.1 ev, the effect is not important for most target materials. The molecular binding effect is very important in determining the energy loss upon elastic collision, but again does not affect cross sections much in the region where the energy of the neutron is greater than the smallest vibrational level difference in the target molecule or crystal; and in addition this effect is of small importance for reasonably heavy nuclei. We shall treat here briefly the effect of the thermal motion of the target nucleus—the so-called Doppler effect.

Let the velocity of the neutron be v in the laboratory system, and the component of the nuclear velocity toward the neutron beam be V. Then the relative velocity of neutron and nucleus is $(v + V)$, and the relative kinetic energy

$$E_{\text{rel}} = \frac{m}{2} (v + V)^2 = E_n + (2mE_n)^{\frac{1}{2}}V \qquad (74)$$

to the first order in V/v. Here m is the neutron mass, E_n the neutron kinetic energy. If the target atoms were those of a gas, they would move with the Maxwell distribution, giving for the fraction f of atoms having the velocity component V, with atomic mass A,

$$f(V) \, dV = \left(\frac{A}{2\pi kT}\right)^{\frac{1}{2}} e^{-AV^2/2kT} \, dV \qquad (75)$$

Inserting expression (74), we find, for the probability of a given E_{rel},

$$f(E_{\text{rel}}) \, dE_{\text{rel}} = \frac{1}{(\pi)^{\frac{1}{2}}} \cdot e^{-(E_{\text{rel}} - E_n)^2/D^2} \frac{dE_{\text{rel}}}{D} \qquad D = 2\left(\frac{mE_n kT}{A}\right)^{\frac{1}{2}} \qquad (76)$$

where D is the "Doppler width." The cross section is given by the one-level formula written in the form appropriate for neutron capture (or scattering), near the resonance energy, E_r:

$$\sigma(E_n) = \frac{\sigma_0}{1 + [(E_n - E_r)/(\Gamma/2)]^2} \tag{77}$$

and E_n here is of course to be replaced by the relative energy $E_{\rm rel}$. The term $(2mE_n)^{1/2}V$ is the correction for the motion of the center of mass. With this we obtain, for the effective cross section $\bar\sigma(E_n)$,

$$\bar\sigma(E_n) = \int \sigma(E_{\rm rel})f(E_{\rm rel})\, dE_{\rm rel} = \sigma_0 F\left(\frac{\Gamma}{D}, x\right)$$

with $x = (E_n - E_r)/(\Gamma/2)$, the deviation from resonance in units of the total width, and the integral

$$F\left(\frac{\Gamma}{D}, x\right) = \frac{1}{2(\pi)^{1/2}} \frac{\Gamma}{D} \int_{-\infty}^{\infty} e^{-\Gamma^2(x-x')^2/4D^2}\, \frac{dx'}{1 + x'^2}$$

This function simplifies for large natural width to the form of (77) exactly as without temperature motion. But, for small natural width compared to Doppler width, the cross section at resonance is changed and the shape of the curve altered. In this case, with $\Gamma/D \ll 1$, we obtain simple expressions for both:

(1) E very near the resonance energy, $(E_n - E_r)/D \ll D/\Gamma$, when

$$F \to \frac{(\pi)^{1/2}}{2} \cdot \frac{\Gamma}{D} \cdot e^{-(E_n - E_r)^2/D^2}$$

(2) E very far from resonance, $(E_n - E_r)/D \gg D/\Gamma$, and

$$F \to \frac{1}{1 + [(E_n - E_r)/(\Gamma/2)]^2}$$

the value without Doppler motion.

For $E_n = E_r$, exact resonance, we can easily obtain

$$F\left(\frac{\Gamma}{D}, 0\right) = \frac{(\pi)^{1/2}}{2} \cdot \frac{\Gamma}{D} \cdot e^{\Gamma^2/4D^2} \left(1 - \frac{2}{(\pi)^{1/2}} \int_0^{\Gamma/2D} e^{-y^2}\, dy\right)$$

If $\Gamma/D \gg 1$, this reduces to $F = 1$, and the cross section at resonance for large natural width is just $\bar\sigma(E_r) = \sigma_0$. For exact resonance, and small natural width $\Gamma/D \ll 1$, $F(\Gamma/D, 0) = (\pi)^{1/2}/2 \cdot \Gamma/D$, and the measured cross section at resonance becomes

$$\bar\sigma(E_r) = \frac{(\pi)^{1/2}}{2} \cdot \frac{\Gamma}{D} \cdot \sigma_0$$

much reduced by the Doppler broadenings. Lamb (L1) has shown that these same formulas hold even if the target—as is usually the case—is not a perfect gas but a Debye solid (other models will give similar results). In fact, if we replace D in (76) by a new value $D = 2(E_n \cdot kT_{eq})^{\frac{1}{2}}$, where T_{eq} is the equivalent temperature corresponding to the mean energy per vibrational degree of freedom (i.e., kT_{eq} = mean vib. energy/vib. degree of freedom), then the formulas are unchanged. This holds as long as either the natural or the Doppler width is large compared to the Debye temperature. For a not too sophisticated application of the Debye theory, the equivalent temperature is simply related to the Debye temperature. A few values are shown in Table 5. For other

TABLE 5

EQUIVALENT TEMPERATURES OF CRYSTAL VIBRATIONS

T_{eq}/T	T/θ_{Debye}
1	2
1.06	1
1.15	0.75
1.35	0.5
1.8	0.25

cases, consult Lamb and the other references. It will be observed that all this discussion applies only in the case where the wavelength is such that neither crystalline nor molecular diffraction effects are appreciable.

(b) *Level Widths and Positions.* With such conditions in mind, we can look into the Breit-Wigner one-level formula for neutron resonance absorption or scattering. From (62) or (70) we obtain

$$\sigma_{abs,sc} = \frac{\pi \lambda^2}{2} \cdot \left(1 \pm \frac{1}{2I + 1}\right) \frac{a(E)^{\frac{1}{2}}}{(E - E_r)^2 + (\Gamma/2)^2} \times \begin{cases} \Gamma_a & \text{for abs} \\ a(E)^{\frac{1}{2}} & \text{for sc} \end{cases}$$

(78)

Here we have written for the neutron width, Γ_n, the value $\Gamma_n = a(E)^{\frac{1}{2}}$, and we assume that the radiation width Γ_a is constant. These two simplifications follow from the most marked feature of slow-neutron work: the fact that we are here studying, with resolution of a fraction of an electron volt, a very small portion of the level spectrum of the compound nucleus, some 5 to 8 Mev excited. We can safely regard all factors in the widths which depend on the compound nucleus as constant over the whole resonance, and from the formula we have the results employed.

A few thermal neutron reactions are exothermic for heavy particle emission, as for example those with neutrons on H^3, Li^6, B^{10}, N^{14}. Here the widths are very large on the scale of thermal energies, many kilovolts at least, and the cross sections become simply $\sigma_{\text{abs}} \sim \lambda^2 (E)^{1/2} \sim 1/(E)^{1/2}$. This is the famous $1/v$ law. Even in heavier nuclei where gamma-emission dominates, the $1/v$ behavior appears for a range in neutron energy small compared to the energy of the lowest-lying resonance. Only where the resonance lies very near zero energy (either above it as in Gd^{157} or below it as in, say, Hg) does the $1/v$ law fail at low energies (apart from crystal and chemical binding effects, of course).

A great body of experimental information has been obtained (and compiled in useful form by Adair (A1)) on the shape of the transmission curve and from it the cross sections for very many isotopes. These yield on analysis (for the narrow isolated levels for middle to high A) fairly reliable values for the three most characteristic parameters: the resonance energy E_r; the total width Γ and the neutron width evaluated at 1 ev energy; a, taken from the measured cross section at exact resonance, $\sigma(E_r)$. We tabulate a few typical values in Table 6.

TABLE 6

SOME SLOW-NEUTRON RESONANCES AND THEIR PROPERTIES

Nucleus	E_r (ev)	Γ (ev)	$a \times 10^3$ (ev)$^{1/2}$	σ_0 (barns)	Remarks	References
Na^{23}	3,000	$\sim$170	$\Gamma_\alpha < \Gamma_n/100$	550	sc	1
Mn^{55}	300	$\sim$10	...	$\sim$4,000	sc	2
Co^{59}	115	2–5	...	$\sim$12,000	sc	2, 3
Rh^{103}	1.21 $\pm$ 0.02	0.21	0.5	2,700	abs	4
Cd^{113}	0.176 $\pm$ 0.001	0.115	2.2	58,000	abs	5
In^{115}	1.44 $\pm$ 0.03	0.085	2.2	27,600	abs	6
Sm^{149}	0.096	0.074	2.0	110,000	abs	7
Eu^{153}	0.54	0.15	1.7	20,000	abs	8
Gd^{157}	0.028	0.12	4.5	290.000	abs	9
Au^{197}	4.8	<1	...	>3,000	abs (unresolved)	10

1. C. T. Hibdon et al., Phys. Rev., **77**, 730 (L), (1950).
2. F. Seidl, Phys. Rev., **75**, 1508 (1949).
3. C. Hibdon and C. Muehlhause, Phys. Rev., **76**, 100 (1949).
4. R. Meijer, Phys. Rev., **75**, 773 (1949).
5. L. Rainwater et al., Phys. Rev., **71**, 65 (1947).
6. B. McDaniel, Phys. Rev., **70**, 832 (1946).
7. W. J. Sturm, Phys. Rev., **71**, 757 (1947).
8. L. B. Borst et al., Phys. Rev., **70**, 557 (1946).
9. T. Brill and H. Lichtenberger, Phys. Rev., **72**, 585 (1947).
10. W. Havens et al., Phys. Rev., **75**, 165 (1947).

It is seen that for all good absorbers the width Γ is indeed much greater than the neutron width, $a(E)^{1/2}$. It is moreover reasonably constant among nuclei. This reflects the fact that it is made up of a sum of partial transition widths for the emission of gamma to all the possible lower states of the compound nucleus, which tends to average out fluctuations. But recent measurements on capture gamma-rays do appear to demonstrate a greater individuality among capture gamma-ray spectra than this point of view would lead one to expect; if those results are correct, we are seeing again a reflection of the special features of nuclear level spectra, perhaps arising from the importance of shell structure.

A few examples of resonance scattering have been observed in some detail, both for slow neutrons, with $l = 0$, and for faster ones. The interference between potential and resonance scattering is plainly seen, along with the expected dip in the cross-section curves. Most thermal scattering, however, is simply scattering far from resonance—that contributed by the potential scattering term. The cross sections observed fluctuate more or less widely about the value $4\pi R^2$, where R is the nuclear radius. The nuclear boundary cannot of course be very sharply defined for this process. Near-by levels will cause deviations which arise from the interference of other resonance terms. For the lighter elements, below A about 100, the level spacing is large, and the possible neutron widths therefore also larger (see Fig. 8); we may expect some sizable resonance scattering effects to show up, even rather far from resonance and without sign of much capture. The actual resonance scattering observed in Co and Mn is then complemented by some rather large deviations from the expected value, without evidence of actual resonance, in Cu, Ni, Fe, and a few other nuclei. Mn itself shows an abnormally low value of σ_{sc} at thermal energy (H9, S6).[1]

The magnitude of the scattering cross section σ_{sc} is measured of course by transmission. Recently experiments which make ingenious use of molecular and crystal coherent scattering effects have been applied to observe the phase change on scattering. These results demonstrated that most heavy nuclei showed a change in phase of π between incident and scattered wave (F4). This would be expected from the model we have used, for, wherever the "potential scattering" term was the most important, the phase change ought to be just that produced by an impenetrable sphere. The extension of the ideas of the one-body model made by the method of Weisskopf *et al.* still leaves unchanged many of the simple conclusions from that picture!

[1] This whole treatment follows closely that of (F7).

The high distribution of high capture cross sections through the periodic table reflects the notion that the presence of a resonance level just at the excitation energy of the compound nucleus is a matter of sheer chance, since we have magnified a single half-volt region out of many millions. This consideration allows us to ascribe the fluctuations—which are indeed wild—to simple chance positioning of levels, and of the general trend to the gradual increase of level density. The cross sections for capture slowly rise, with fluctuations of course, until in the rare earths and beyond high cross sections are common. The sharp decline in the cross section of lead and bismuth is attributed to a decrease in neutron binding energy, also implied by the general kink in the mass-defect curve which is responsible for the natural radioactive elements. The level density, which ought to increase as the particle number increases for a given excitation energy, actually declines, partly because of the smaller excitation energy yielded by neutron capture, and partly because of the influence of closed shells. This is another reflection of the presence of structural detail superimposed on the statistical behavior of the nuclear drop; compare Fig. 17.

2. Charged Particle Reactions on Light Nuclei, at Moderate Energy. The special ease of defining zero kinetic energy, which makes slow neutrons so nearly monoenergetic, cannot apply to charged particle reactions. Slow protons are not very hard to make—hot atomic hydrogen—but they obviously will penetrate the Coulomb barrier so little as to make them useless for study of nuclear reactions until the temperature reaches that of stellar interiors, $\sim 10^7$ °K, where indeed thermal protons are of the utmost importance in inducing nuclear reactions, and are the agents of the release of stellar energy. But beams of charged particles up to a few Mev energy can be produced which are well-defined in energy and direction. Indeed the latest techniques [1] allow an over-all resolution, including the effects of the slowing of the protons in the material of the target, of the order of 100 ev out of a couple of Mev. For nuclei and excitation energies in a range where charged particles of this energy will penetrate the barrier, and where the level spacings are large compared to such a figure, we may expect to apply the dispersion formalism to the computation of excitation functions.

It will be clear that the general trend of all such reactions, which are primarily those with protons and alphas (or any charged projectile) on nuclei up to $A \sim 50$, will be governed by the effects of the Coulomb barrier. This will determine the width for entry Γ_p and for re-emission of any charged particle. But, superimposed upon this easily understood

---

[1] See the work of the Wisconsin group as described in (H7), for example.

extranuclear factor will be the effects of strong resonances, which give the complex results seen in Figs. 10 and 11. We want to discuss here the method of treating such reactions; it is already obvious that only detailed attention to the properties of individual levels will be adequate.

(a) *The Reaction* $Li^7 + p$. Figures 9 and 10 show the simplified experimental results for the two sets of products 2α and $(\gamma + p')$— inelastic scattering—from the same reactants $Li^7 + p$.[1] The smooth rise in Fig. 9 is indeed just a penetrability curve, following the formula

$$\sigma \sim \lambda_p{}^2 \frac{\Gamma_\alpha \Gamma_p}{(\Gamma)^2} \qquad \Gamma_p = P^{(1)}(E)G$$

with a width without barrier, G, large compared to the energy variation for the protons, and an alpha-particle width which is independent of energy, since the reaction is exothermic by some 17 Mev and the alphas are far above the barrier. But the rise is *not* that appropriate for a pure Coulomb barrier, *s*-wave particles alone coming in without angular momentum; it is necessary to assume that the incoming particles pass as well through a centrifugal barrier, with $l = 1$. The *S*-wave penetrability would lead to a curve whose rise was nearly complete after about 500 kev; even more striking, the cross section observed is about fifty times smaller than such similar reactions as $Li^6(p,\alpha)He^3$. This points again to the absence of *s*-wave particles, which experience a much smaller barrier. We must assume that such particles cannot induce the reaction from the compound state of Be^8 involved. The reaction is governed by a strong selection rule: the conservation of parity. The two identical alphas emitted obey Bose statistics; they must have a wave function invariant under their exchange. But to exchange two alphas is equivalent to reflecting their wave function in the origin, since they have no spin. The alpha wave function must then have even parity. Their relative orbital motion will have a parity of $(-1)^l$, where l is the orbital angular momentum. We have then shown that the parity of the system is *even* in the final state. Since parity is conserved, it must also have been even in the initial state. But all simple nuclear models agree in giving the ground state of Li^7 odd parity. The incoming proton must therefore have had odd parity if the two alpha-particles are to be formed. This requires that the wave function for orbital motion of the incoming proton have an l such that $\psi \sim Y_l{}^m$ gives odd parity. The values $l = 1, 3, \cdots$ will do this; of these, the most easily penetrating partial wave is that with $l = 1$, the *p*-wave protons we observe. Thus we can account for the excitation

[1] See (H11) and (H12).

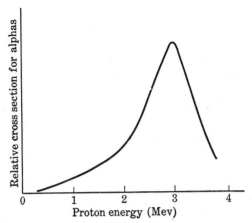

Fig. 9. Relative cross section as a function of incident proton energy for the reaction $Li^7(p,\alpha)\alpha$.

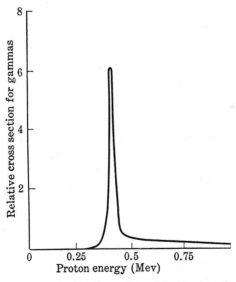

Fig. 10. Relative cross section as a function of incident proton energy, for the production of gamma-rays by the reaction $Li^7(p,p')Li^{7*}$ in the region of the major sharp resonance at 0.44 Mev.

curve and the low yield by assuming even parity for the compound state involved.

The angular momentum of the compound state must be the resultant of the incoming proton spin, $S = \frac{1}{2}$, and the target nuclear $J = \frac{3}{2}$, combined with the orbital angular momentum $l = 1$. This means that the total angular momentum of the compound nucleus J_C must be $J_C = 0, 1, 2,$ or 3. But, if the state is to emit alphas, which have no spin, the angular momentum must be even (from the Bose statistics) and the state is then described by the quantum numbers $J = 0$ or 2, even parity. The angular distribution of the alphas with respect to the fixed direction of the incoming beam can be no more complicated than the partial wave of the incoming beam, and in fact the wave function will be of the form $\psi_\alpha \sim a + b Y_1{}^0$. Since Bose statistics requires that the wave function of the outgoing alphas be even in $\cos\theta$, the most general form possible is $a + b(E) \cos^2\theta$. This fits the experiment reasonably well up to some hundreds of kilovolts. Lately the higher-energy angular distribution has shown (H8) terms of the kind $\cos^4\theta$, which imply that incoming f-wave particles must be considered. The general features of the discussion are unchanged.

But what of Fig. 10? The very sharp resonances for the emission of a 17-Mev gamma-ray must be explained. The cross section for this reaction at resonance energy, with I the spin of the target nucleus, is

$$\sigma_\gamma(E_r) \sim \frac{\pi \lambda^2 \Gamma_p \Gamma_\gamma}{(\Gamma_p + \Gamma_\gamma)^2} \cdot \frac{2I + 1}{2}$$

and, since the measured value of $\sigma_\gamma(E_r)$ is 7.2 millibarns, with a resonant energy of 440 kev and a measured total width of 12 kev (F9, F10), we can write the value of Γ_γ as

$$\Gamma_\gamma \sim \frac{\sigma_\gamma \Gamma_{\text{abs}}}{(2I + 1)\pi\lambda^2 \cdot \frac{1}{2}}$$

assuming only that $\Gamma_\gamma / \Gamma_p \ll 1$. This yields a gamma-ray width for the excited state of the compound nucleus Be^8 of about 30 ev. Obviously a strong selection rule must be in play to prevent the decay of the compound state by alpha-emission, which would be expected to have a width of hundreds of kev. The possibilities are two: (1) Only s-wave protons are captured to form this level, giving it angular momentum $J_C = 1$ or 2, odd parity, or (2) the same p-wave protons which give the previous reaction are captured, giving states with even parity, but with spins $J_C = 1$ or 3. In either case, whether the compound state in question has odd parity or odd J_c, it cannot emit two alphas. To distinguish between the alternative, as to fix the J_c in the two alpha-emitting states, requires further information.

This has been provided by a beautiful experiment (D3) in which accurate measurements were made of the angular distribution of the gamma-rays. The experiments fully confirmed the dispersion formula in the interference form, Eq. (71), by the observed variation of the angular distribution as the proton energy was varied through resonance. Forward-to-backward asymmetry proves that two levels are involved in the gamma-emission, with opposite parities. It is natural to identify the wide interfering state with some state of the (p,α) reaction, necessarily even, and then the narrow resonant state must be odd, formed by s-wave capture. This is consistent with the observed isotropy of the gamma-rays near the sharp resonance. Two lower states take part in the gamma-emission: the ground state, transitions to which yield the famous 17.6-Mev gamma-ray; and a state at about 3 Mev excitation, nearly 2 Mev wide. Both these lowest states decay by alpha-emission. The general rule about the zero spin of even-even ground states would lead to the conclusion that the ground state here has $J = 0$. Some experimental evidence for a lifetime of this state near 10^{-14} sec does not seem strong enough to upset the rule, and evidence from the beta-decay of Li^8 (that the two lowest Be^8 states differ in J) supports the rule. The near-equality of the gamma-ray transition rates from the resonant state to the two low states suggests that they do not differ by many units in J. It seems likely that the 3-Mev state has $J = 2$, parity even. Then the choice between the two possibilities $J_c = 1$ and $J_c = 2$ for the sharp state seems direct; we assign the resonant state the quantum numbers $J_c = 1$, odd, and all the effects are described; both gamma-rays are electric dipole, thus fitting with the sizable width.

This neat account seems disproved by observations (C9) of the elastic scattering of protons at the 440-kev energy. The presence of a scattering resonance whose interference with the Coulomb scattering has been studied shows that at least most of the compound nuclei are formed by p-wave, and not by s-wave, capture. Then the isotropy of the resonant gamma-rays is in the nature of an accident, (C4) implying not that the protons brought in no evidence of direction, but that the compound state with $J = 1$ was formed with equal probability in the three sub-states $J_z = \pm 1, 0$. This would give isotropy; it will take place, according to the rules for combination of angular momentum matrices, if the triplet proton wave (spin parallel to orbital angular momentum) is captured about one-fifth as frequently as the quintet wave (D4). Then the interfering state is some non-resonant odd state, and the sharp resonant state must be assigned the description $J_c = 1$, even. The gamma-rays are magnetic dipole and electric quadripole in a particular mixture. This is a less simple and less satisfying story, but it seems required by experiment.

This account is a rather sketchy summary of one reaction, given as an example of the many-sidedness of the problem of nuclear reaction spectroscopy in the region where individual levels are of importance. The example at hand is not the simplest known case, but it is very far from the most complicated. The discussion of each reaction in great detail will be the content of a final nuclear spectroscopy.

(b) *Some Other Examples.* Proton capture by C^{12} and C^{13} has been much studied. Here the fit to the one-level dispersion formula is excellent, though one must take into account the variations in Γ_p coming from the appreciable change in penetrability over the 40-kev width of the resonance, which is some 2 Mev below the top of the barrier. It is worth while to note that the shape of the 440 kev resonance in the $Li^7(p,\gamma)$ reaction does not fit the Breit-Wigner formula especially well. There is a superimposed asymmetry, with a rising gamma-ray yield on the high-energy side of the resonance. But in order to ascribe this to a variation in penetrability—arising from the capture of a proton partial wave with high l—a very high centrifugal barrier would have to be invoked (B19), and this would make the cross section absurdly small. Some more complex level scheme must be employed.

The complicated and beautiful studies of the reactions arising from $F^{19} + p$ have led to repeated analysis from the point of view of the one-level formula (Fig. 11). Here the problem is to see if all the fifteen or more levels observed can be fitted into a scheme which gives reduced widths γ_r for the various reactions, each roughly independent of the level involved, and tries to account for the great experimental variation in width and strength of levels on the basis of penetrability changes due to energy and angular momentum values alone. The situation is still not entirely unraveled, but the scheme is probably workable without too much arbitrariness (S2).

There is increasing evidence of the value of another approximate constant of the motion, the so-called "isotopic spin" (W8). This quantity describes the spatial symmetry of the nuclear wave function under the interchange of any two nucleons. It can only be approximately conserved, of course, since in fact the neutron and proton differ at least by Coulomb effects. Isotopic spin would be an accurate quantum number, and the nuclear wave function would consist of functions with one well-defined isotopic spin value, only if all nucleon-nucleon interactions were identical, independent of the type of nucleons involved. How strong this partial conservation law really is has not yet been established. A similar situation exists for the spin, which can be interconverted with orbital angular momentum only in the presence of noncentral forces. Strong forces of this type exist, and hence spin is in general not even approximately conserved; only total angular momentum, a strict quantum number, remains as a good basis for angular momentum selection rules.

Whether the spectroscopy of nuclear levels based on the dispersion theory can be carried beyond these light nuclei is dubious. Even here

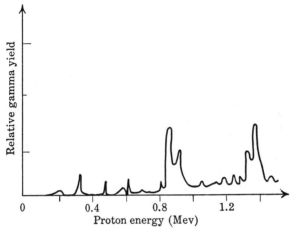

Fig. 11. Relative gamma-ray yield (schematized) as a function of incident proton energy for the reactions coming from $F^{19} + p$ in the region below 1 Mev incident energy. Note the many and varied resonance peaks.

the level schemes which have been proposed are highly complex. Without an *a priori* guide to the position and character of nuclear levels, the job of spectrum analysis is difficult. It will be noticed that the problem of the light nuclear reactions is quite parallel to the problem of the low-lying states revealed in the gamma-decay schemes of radioactive nuclei. In the present example, however, the natural widths of levels is directly measured, while the number of possible reaction products adds the complicating factor of competition. But there seems little reason to doubt that the general scheme proposed is adequate.

B. Reactions without Marked Resonance

We have seen in Section 5 how the statistical theory of reactions proceeds by looking apart from the details of individual levels, and in Section 7A we have discussed in detail some reaction types which are clearly suited to the description of dispersion theory, in which the properties of single levels are made the basis for understanding. Here we shall apply the ideas of the statistical theory to the large class of reactions in which no marked properties of levels are observed; the theory is intrinsically suited to such reactions. We remark first that these reactions are generally characterized by high excitation of the compound nucleus. Wherever this occurs, the level spacing decreases and widths increase, as we have seen, so that either for all circumstances or for the conditions of nearly all practical experiments the importance of individual resonances is negligible.

Excitation of nuclei by neutrons means the formation of a compound nucleus with energy of excitation equal to the neutron binding energy at least. As shown in Section 7A, this region (say 8 Mev in nuclei from $A \sim 100$ to about 200, and perhaps 6 Mev or less thereafter) is marked by discrete levels, spaced from a few hundred to a few electron volts, when the incoming neutron has negligible kinetic energy. As the kinetic energy of the neutron beam increases through the region of marked resonances, the level density increases rapidly. At a few kilovolts at most, the present technique does not permit resolution of individual levels. We have already shown [e.g., in (72)] that the average over many levels of the dispersion formula leads to a result agreeing with the statistical theory. It is of interest to apply this idea to the actual case of the absorption of neutrons with energy in the range from a few to a few thousand electron volts, with the middle and heavy nuclei as targets.

If we stick to s-wave neutrons only, we can write for the average absorption cross section, averaged over many levels, with level density ρ

$$\bar{\sigma}_a{}^{(0)} = 2\pi\rho \cdot \pi\lambda^2 \frac{\bar{\Gamma}_n \bar{\Gamma}_a}{\bar{\Gamma}_n + \bar{\Gamma}_a} \qquad \text{(bars indicate average value} \quad (79) \\ \text{over many levels)}$$

[Compare (71).] From the expansion for $f(E)$ given in (60) we can write $\bar{\Gamma}_n = -2k\bar{R}/\bar{\delta}$, with $\bar{\delta}$ and $\bar{R}$ constants which can be given a rough interpretation as determining properties of the function $z(E)$ [see (62)ff.] or can be regarded as empirically determined. We find that $\bar{\Gamma}_a \gg \bar{\Gamma}_n$ for energies below a few kilovolts, and then in this region we would expect

$$\bar{\sigma}_a{}^{(0)} \doteq \frac{\bar{R}}{k} \cdot \frac{4\pi^2 \rho}{\bar{\delta}}$$

where $\bar{R}$, ρ, a, $\bar{\delta}$ can be roughly estimated. Note that this applies to averages over many levels, not to thermal cross sections. Although there is no direct check yet on this prediction, it seems consistent with the general knowledge of absorption cross sections. A more detailed extension of this similar theory has given results [1] which are not wholly in accord with the data, at higher energies especially, but which seem to demonstrate the essential correctness of the approach, granting its rather high degree of arbitrariness in fitting the results of single experiments.

The scattering cross section can be treated in the same way. Here of course the potential scattering term $e^{i\delta} \sin \delta$ is important. Even for very simple assumptions about level widths, a rather complicated result is obtained which is not yet wholly confirmed. Both at thermal and at higher energies the importance of the "impenetrable sphere" effects of the potential term are evident in the total cross sections where no strong absorption resonance is present. Variations of radius R as well as special structural features of some nuclei seem to be present in the detailed comparison of theory with experiment.[1] Agreement is much better for some heavy and for some lighter nuclei; a few middle-weight nuclei do not give even the expected energy dependence of $\sigma_n{}^{(0)}$, i.e., $1/E^{1/2}$.

1. The Statistical Approach. For sufficiently high energy of the bombarding particle, no resonances will be observed. This can arise out of the experimental conditions: it is hard to define the beam to a very small energy range as its mean energy grows, and even the temperature motion of the target nuclei will produce a comparatively large uncertainty in relative energy for high bombardment energies, as we can see from relation (74). More significant, however, is the fact that the levels themselves become broader as the energy of excitation increases. This is the obvious consequence of the fact that higher excitation energy quite generally makes available many more modes of decay from a given level. In this region of high energy, then, the dispersion theory will have little value, for many levels, each with its unknown but specific properties, will take part in every reaction.

In the preceding section we showed how the dispersion theory treatment went smoothly over into an entirely statistical form when the level spacing was small compared to the level width, for the particular case of neutron absorption. We replaced the precise values of the level widths by averages over many levels; such averages ought to vary smoothly with energy. In a sense we here calculate not the result of a particular reaction with a definite target nucleus, but a kind of average over many nuclear species very close in A and Z to the actual target. This ought to give then the general course of any reaction, fluctuations about the average behavior which will show up in particular cases being disre-

[1] This whole treatment follows closely that of (F7).

garded. The recent neutron scattering work of the Wisconsin group seems to show such fluctuations (B3).

The fundamentals of the statistical theory were given in Section 4; here we propose to apply them. The main relations are two in number. The first, which is given in Eqs. (40) and (44), is the statement of the main Bohr idea of the nuclear reaction progressing in two independent steps:

$$\sigma_{i,p} = S_i \cdot \xi \cdot \frac{\Gamma_p}{\sum\limits_j \Gamma_j} = \pi \lambda_i^2 \sum_l (2l + 1)P_{il}\xi_{il} \cdot \frac{\Gamma_p}{\Sigma\Gamma_j} = \sigma_i(c) \cdot \frac{\Gamma_p}{\sum\limits_j \Gamma_j} \quad (80)$$

Here we have introduced the cross section $\sigma_i(c)$ for formation of the compound nucleus with incident particle i. The second is the statistical relation between level width for a given disintegration and cross section for the process inverse to the disintegration [see (33) and (34a)]:

$$\Gamma_{i\alpha}(W)\rho_c(W) = \frac{g_R}{2\pi} \cdot \frac{\sigma_{i\alpha}}{\pi\lambda^2} \quad (81a)$$

and

$$\Gamma_{nl} = kGP_{n,l} \quad (81b)$$

From these two we can find either the width or the cross section, using basic ideas, and compute the other from their relations.

(a) *Neutron Reactions.* Here we have only the centrifugal barrier opposing the contact of neutron and target nucleus. Let us consider first the case of high-energy neutrons, with energies so high that the wavelengths corresponding are small compared to nuclear dimensions. In such a case we may follow the classical trajectory of the incoming particles. They will form the compound nucleus with sticking probability whenever they strike the nuclear disk. Moreover, it is evident from our whole nuclear model that for energies above, say, a few Mev the value of ξ_{il} is essentially unity: every particle that touches the nuclear matter sticks. Now we may write the contact cross section for *neutrons* in the partial wave of orbital angular momentum l as we did in Eq. (49):

$$\sigma_{n,l} = (2l + 1)\pi\lambda_n^2 P_{n,l}\xi_{n,l} \quad (82)$$

But for high energies we set $\xi_{nl} \to 1$, and the quantities $P_{n,l}$ [found in (36)] take the values $P_{n,l} \to 1$ for low l's, such that the centrifugal barrier is well below the energy available, say for l below l_c, the critical angular momentum. For $l > l_c$, the values $P_{n,l}$ rapidly approach zero, and, if many l's are involved, we can neglect the transitional cases near l_c.

Then just as in (44b) the cross section $\sigma_n(c)$ for formation of the compound can be written

$$\sigma_n(c) = \Sigma\sigma_{il}$$

$$= \pi\lambda^2 \sum_{l=0} (2l + 1)P_{n,l} \rightarrow \pi\lambda^2 \sum_{0}^{l_c \sim kR} (2l + 1)P_{n,l}$$

$$\cong \pi R^2 \quad \text{(high energy)} \tag{83a}$$

which is of course the classical value.

At low energies, we can give no *a priori* guess about the quantity $\xi_{n,l}$. But relations (81) for level width can be applied. We write

$$\Gamma_{nl} = k\gamma P_{n,l} = \frac{g_R}{2\pi\rho} \cdot \frac{\sigma_{nl}}{\pi\lambda^2} = \frac{g_R}{2\pi\rho} (2l + 1)P_{n,l}\xi_{n,l} \tag{84}$$

It now seems inviting to make the identification:

$$\xi_{n,l} = k \cdot \frac{2\pi\rho\gamma}{g_R} \tag{85}$$

Here the functions ρ and γ depend only on the compound nucleus [while g_R is the statistical factor needed in σ_{nl}, by (69)], and will vary very little for small changes in neutron kinetic energy. We write this:

$$\xi_n = \frac{k}{K}$$

and

$$\sigma_n(c) = \pi\lambda^2\Sigma(2l + 1)P_{n,l} \cdot \frac{k}{K} \quad \text{(low energy)} \tag{83b}$$

with the constant K to include the unspecified functions above. The result is then a sticking probability which is proportional to k for slow neutrons, which can be justified from the side of the dispersion-theoretic discussion in Section 5. As energy increases, the sticking probability goes over to 1 gradually, and we may choose the constant K to give a smooth extrapolation from low- to high-energy values, from (83a) to (83b). The resulting neutron cross section behaves like

$$\sigma_n = \pi\lambda^2 \cdot P_{0,l} \cdot (k/K) \sim 1/v$$

at the lowest energies, where only the s wave, with $l = 0$, contributes and gradually falls with increasing energy until it approaches the geometric cross section.

It is to be remembered that all this refers to the cross section for actual formation of a compound nucleus. The "potential scattering" term $e^{i\delta} \sin \delta$ of (68) is present in addition. Part of the compound nucleus formation cross section may indeed lead to re-emission of a neutron with just the incident energy, a process of elastic scattering after compound nucleus formation.[1] This part can in fact give coherent interfering contributions to the diffraction effects. Such interference terms can complicate the shadow scattering. In principle we would expect angular distributions of elastically scattered neutrons to show a more or less isotropic part, coming from the re-emission of absorbed neutrons from several overlapping levels in the compound nucleus, together with a more complex and usually well-collimated part, which would contain the diffracted shadow waves plus interference terms from both sources. In the statistical theory, however, we expect the part of the cross section of compound formation we discuss to approach the value πR^2 for high energies, though the total cross section, including the elastic diffraction or shadow scattering, will become very nearly twice that.

(b) *Charged Particle Reactions.* Here the Coulomb barrier introduces an added complication. We begin with the last member of (80):

$$\sigma_i(c) = \pi \lambda_i^2 \Sigma (2l + 1) P_{il} \xi_{il} \tag{80}$$

It is now in the spirit of our statistical approach to give the sticking probability the same form for charged particles, once they have reached the nuclear surface, as we found it to have for neutrons, for the nuclear forces are predominant there. If now we write the W.K.B. expression for the penetrability $P_{i,l}$ from Eq. (37), we have, in the region $E/B \ll 1$, where the W.K.B. method is reliable:

$$\sigma_i(c) = \pi \lambda^2 \Sigma (2l + 1) \xi_{il} \cdot \left(\frac{B_l}{E}\right)^{\frac{1}{2}} e^{-2c_l} = \pi \lambda^2 \Sigma (2l + 1) e^{-2c_l} \frac{k}{(E)^{\frac{1}{2}}} \frac{B_l^{\frac{1}{2}}}{K}$$

Now the constant K can be chosen to make the cross section for the low-energy, high-barrier region, where the W.K.B. expression is adequate, go smoothly over to the high-energy limit, which is just

$$\sigma_i(c) = \pi \lambda^2 \Sigma (2l + 1) P_{n,l} \to \pi R^2$$

with the same arguments about the critical angular momentum l_c as in the case of the neutron. We finally obtain then, for incident charged particles, i,

$$\sigma_i(c) = \pi \lambda^2 \sum_{l=0} (2l + 1) e^{-2C_l} \quad \text{for all energies} \tag{86}$$

A long literature exists on the points we have treated here quite heuristically. By and large, the simplest justification for our treatment is found in the related discussion of Section 5, but compare also the papers

[1] Cf. discussion following Eq. (45).

of Konopinski and Bethe (K8) and Bethe (B13), whose results we have essentially set out above, but by rather different methods.

We include here a number of graphs (Figs. 12 to 14) showing the results of computations of the cross section for compound nucleus formation, based on (83) and (86), and using the same value both for the target radius ($R = 1.4 \cdot A^{\frac{1}{3}} \cdot 10^{-13}$ cm) and for the radius of the projectile.

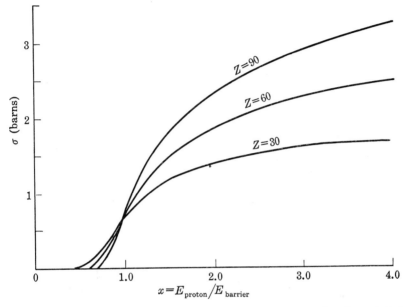

Fig. 12a.   Cross sections for protons, for formation of the compound nucleus, plotted linearly.

The graphs apply to protons, alphas, and neutrons over a wide range of energies, for typical target elements over the upper two-thirds of the periodic table. Following these graphs, we include graphs (Fig. 15) of the specific widths, the functions defined in (50b). These graphs are based on the cross sections given in (83) and (86), and on the assumption concerning the statistical level density of compound nuclei, given in (31). From the specific width graphs we may compute the function $D_p = \Gamma_p/\Sigma\Gamma_j = f_p/\Sigma f_j$ for any definite reaction, and hence the total reaction cross section on the statistical theory. The special problems raised by the deuteron and the gamma-ray will be discussed later. The specific widths are given for typical nuclei as functions of the energy of excitation of the compound nucleus, for the several possible emitted particles.

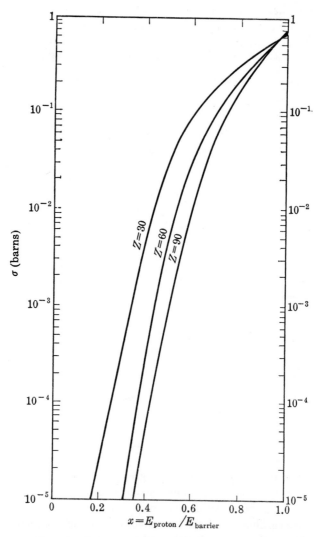

Fig. 12b.   Logarithmic plot of proton cross sections.

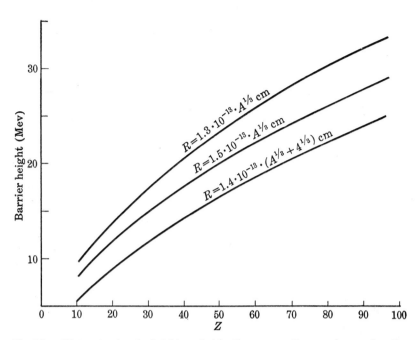

Fig. 12c. The proton barrier height needed for the cross-section graphs, as a function of Z. The parameter x is given in terms of proton kinetic energy measured in the laboratory frame. Several values for R have been assumed. In the cross-section curves we use $R = 1.4(A^{1/3} + 1)10^{-13}$ cm.

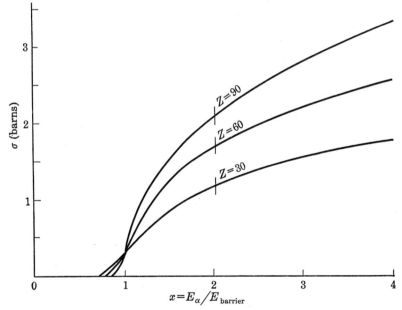

Fig. 13a. Cross sections for alpha-particles, for formation of the compound nucleus, plotted linearly.

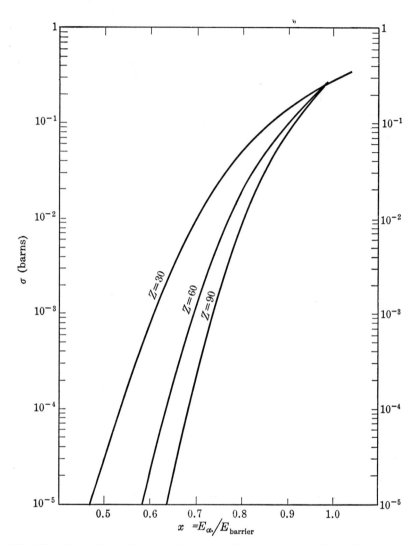

Fig. 13b. Logarithmic plot of alpha cross sections, for energies below the barrier.

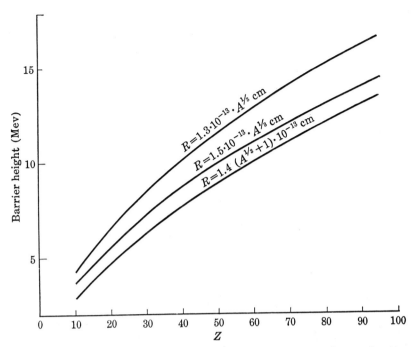

Fig. 13c. The alpha-barrier height needed for the cross-section graphs, as a function of Z. The parameter x is given in terms of alpha-particle kinetic energy measured in the laboratory frame. (Lowest barrier has been used in cross-section graphs.)

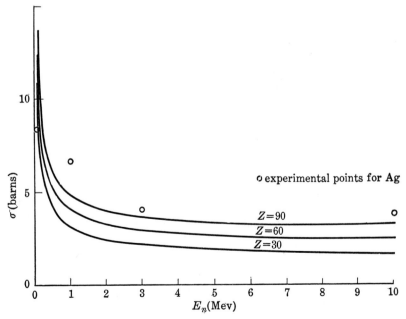

Fig. 14. Cross sections for neutron absorption in three elements.

The same calculations which lead to the specific widths give (before integration) the energy spectrum of emitted particles. We have already shown a typical set of spectra in Fig. 6.

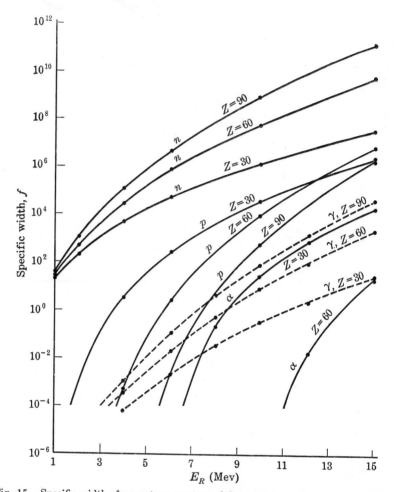

Fig. 15. Specific widths for neutron, proton, alpha-particle, and gamma-ray emission from several compound nuclei, as a function of energy of the emitted particle. The specific widths are computed for residual nuclei of even A and Z. For odd-even or even-odd residual nuclei, multiply the plotted width by 2; for odd-odd residual nuclei, multiply plotted width by 4. Interpolation for other Z can be made directly.

The application of these formulas to all the reaction types listed, in the appropriate energy region, is straightforward. To point out a few of the more general consequences, and to provide a model for calculation, we shall discuss one or two particular reactions which can be compared with experiment.

(c) *Competition.* The reactions (α,n) and $(\alpha,2n)$ on Ag^{109} have been studied by Bradt and Tendam (B20, G1). Figure 16 is a simplified version of their experimental results, and of some later work on similar

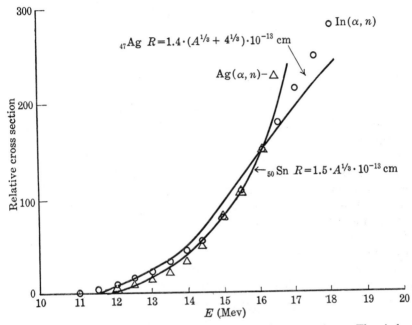

Fig. 16. Comparison of experimental and theoretical cross sections. The circles refer to the measured relative cross section for $In(\alpha,n)$ (see reference G1), and the triangles to the work of (B20) for $Ag(\alpha,n)$. Two theoretical curves are fitted: one with $R = 1.5 \cdot A^{1/3} \cdot 10^{-13}$ cm, and one with $R = 1.4 \cdot (A^{1/3} + 4^{1/3}) \cdot 10^{-13}$ cm. The difference is a fair indication of the limit of reliability of our statistical theory as well as of the assumption $R \sim A^{1/3}$.

reactions. The cross section for formation of the compound nucleus, with sticking probability near unity for these energies, is plotted as well (the graphs of Figs. 12 to 14 were used). The compound nucleus can emit a neutron, two neutrons, charged particles, or gamma-rays. The nucleus is excited by the energy $E_\alpha + B_\alpha$. The binding energy of the alpha, B_α, is not known, but can be written $B_\alpha = -4B_n + 28$ Mev, where B_n is the average binding energy of each of the nucleons brought in, and the mass defect of the alpha is known to be 28 Mev. We cannot give B_n with any accuracy in this region of the table, but it is pretty surely between, say, 4 and 8 Mev. The compound nucleus is then excited to between 15 and 20 Mev in these experiments. Such an excitation energy brings us well into the region of dense levels. The escape of a gamma-ray will be negligible here, for, as we shall see, the gamma widths are always small compared to heavy-particle widths when the excitation is appreciable.

Charged particle widths will also be small compared to neutron widths, even though the excitation energy is a good deal beyond the barrier for protons, because, from expression (52) the release of a proton with the full available energy is not probable. It is probable that the emitted particles take off energy corresponding to the nuclear temperature, here some 2 Mev, and for such protons the barrier is still effective. We expect that neutrons will go off almost all the time: $\Gamma_n \gg \Gamma_p$. The results of experiment agree nicely with this idea from the lowest energies measured up to about 15.5 Mev. Here the rate of increase of the cross section for (α, n) drops sharply. With alpha-particle energy of 4 Mev higher, the value of $\sigma_{\alpha, n}$ has fallen to a third or less of the value of $\sigma_\alpha(c)$. This is the typical effect of competition. The factor D_n has changed from very near unity to something much smaller because the threshold for a new reaction has been reached at 15.5 Mev. The new reaction is the $(\alpha, 2n)$ reaction, which leaves the residual excited nucleus In^{111}. We may estimate the probability of this reaction very roughly as follows: The cross section for formation of the compound nucleus is $\sigma_\alpha(c)$, given in Fig. 13; ξ is about unity; and the fractional number of neutrons emitted with energy E_n is, from (52), just

$$\frac{I_n(E_n)}{I_0} = E_n \sigma_n e^{-E_n/\tau} \tag{87}$$

In order to emit a second neutron, the first neutron must leave the residual nucleus sufficiently excited to emit the second one. This will occur whenever the residual nucleus has even slightly more energy (by a few kev) than the binding energy B_n of the neutron in the residual nucleus, for the gamma-width is then negligible, and charged particle widths are all extremely small because of the Coulomb barrier. We can then write

$$\sigma(\alpha, 2n) = \sigma_\alpha \frac{\displaystyle\int_0^{E_{n,\text{max}} - \Gamma_{2n}} I_n(E_n)\, dE_n}{\displaystyle\int_0^{E_{n,\text{max}}} I_n(E_n)\, dE_n} \tag{88}$$

where the integral in the numerator is carried from zero removed energy to $\Delta E = E_{n\,\text{max}} - \Gamma_{2n}$, with Γ_{2n} the threshold energy for emission of a second neutron. Both integrals can be approximated by using the

Maxwell distribution of (87):

$$\sigma(\alpha,2n) \doteq \sigma_\alpha \frac{1 - (1 + \Delta E/\tau)e^{-\Delta E/\tau}}{1 - \left(1 + \dfrac{E_{\max}}{\tau}\right)e^{-E_{\max}/\tau}} \tag{89}$$

where $\Delta E = E_{\max} - \Gamma_{2n}$ is the excitation energy surplus beyond the threshold of the $2n$ reaction, $E_{\max} = E_\alpha + B_\alpha - B_n$. The threshold for the observed reaction in silver is 15.5 Mev, and $E_{\max} \sim 2$ or $3\Delta E$, so

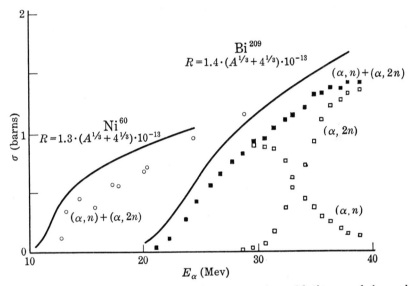

Fig. 17. Comparison of theoretical contact cross sections with the sum of observed (α,n) and $(\alpha,2n)$ cross sections. The solid curves are the theoretical values and are marked with the radii assumed. Ni^{60} data from (G2); Bi^{209} data from (K5).

we can set the denominator equal to 1, and the fit with theory is then excellent up to 18 or 19 Mev, as far as the experiments go. Agreement was obtained by choosing the best value of the temperature τ, which turned out to be the very reasonable value 1.8 Mev. Our simple model (Table 4) gives this value for silver excited about 18 Mev, which is not far from what we would expect for the excitation of the residual nucleus to the limit of the neutron spectrum, with alphas of about 15 Mev. Other multiple reactions, as $(n,2n)$, and even the more highly multiple reactions, may be treated in a similar fashion. The literature contains discussions of the most characteristic features of many other reaction types (see Appendix II). We include more experimental comparisons in Fig. 17; the entry of successive competing reactions is beautifully shown (G2, K5).

SECTION 8. THE DEUTERON AS A PROJECTILE

We have not so far discussed what is the most commonly used nuclear projectile excluding pile neutrons. This is the deuteron, $_1H^2$. It is essentially different from the proton and the alpha-particle, because neither is it a simple nucleon, nor is it so tightly bound, like the alpha, that its state of lowest internal energy alone plays a part in nuclear reactions at ordinary energies. On the contrary, the deuteron is so loosely bound—only $(2.23)/2$ Mev per nucleon—and so large a structure, with its constituent nucleons often 3 or $4 \cdot 10^{-13}$ cm apart, that these properties play the major part in determining the course of deuteron-induced reactions.

The use of deuterons to produce nuclear reactions, especially for the copious production of radio isotopes, is by now traditional. An excellent set of data (C7) has been published which gives the practical yields—often quite large—from deuteron bombardment at moderate energy. We give a few typical numbers in Table 7. Perhaps the most evident

TABLE 7

SOME SELECTED EXPERIMENTAL YIELDS WITH 14-MEV DEUTERONS

(THICK-TARGET)

Reaction	Product Isotope	Yield (nuclei/10^6 deuterons)
$Mg^{24}(d;\alpha)$	$_{11}Na^{22}$	500
$Na^{23}(d;p)$	$_{11}Na^{24}$	1400
$Al^{27}(d;p,\alpha)$	$_{11}Na^{24}$	5.7
$P^{31}(d;p)$	$_{15}P^{32}$	860
$Cr^{52}(d;2n)$	$_{25}Mn^{52}$	140
$Cu^{63}(d;p)$	$_{29}Cu^{64}$	270
$Br^{81}(d;p)$	$_{35}Br^{82}$	220
$Te^{130}(d;2n)$	$_{53}I^{130}$	95
$Te^{130}(d;n)$	$_{53}I^{131}$	180

consequence of deuteron bombardment is the high excitation of the compound nucleus formed by deuteron capture when it takes place. The nucleus is excited by the kinetic energy of the beam plus the full binding energy of a proton and a neutron, reduced only by the weak 2-Mev binding of the free deuteron. This amounts in general to some 14 Mev plus the kinetic energy. Such an excitation implies the validity of the statistical theory. The penetrability may be calculated as in (37) and in Figs. 12 to 14 in a fair approximation to the deuteron contact cross section, for a deuteron of energy E_d on a nucleus of charge Z is that for an alpha-particle with energy $(2^{1/2}E_d)$, but with a target nucleus of charge $Z/2^{3/4}$, i.e., an alpha with $E' = 1.4E_d$, $Z' = 0.6Z$. (This implies the rather rough approximation, A proportional to Z.)

Such deuteron-induced reactions would lead nearly always to neutron emission, and often to multiple-particle emission. The neutron can take off sizable energies because of the high nuclear temperatures. It is nevertheless striking that many reactions have been observed, especially with the heavier nuclei, in which proton emission was of comparable frequency with neutron emission. This is the case not only at higher energies, where the proton barrier might be unimportant for the nuclear temperature involved, but even at moderate energies, and especially in the heaviest nuclei. We should like to discuss this phenomenon in detail; it is the result of break-up of the deuteron, and it is called stripping.

A. The Oppenheimer-Phillips Reaction: Low-Energy Stripping

The deuteron moves toward the nucleus in the presence of the large electrostatic field produced by the nuclear Coulomb charge. The proton in the deuteron is repelled from the nuclear surface, but the neutron feels no such force. For the highest energies, or for light nuclei, when the Coulomb barrier is unimportant, the deuteron is polarized by the Coulomb field, but it may not break up. In cases where the Coulomb barrier is important—say comparable to the binding energy I of the deuteron— the proton will not reach the nuclear surface when the neutron does. The Coulomb forces will repel the proton, and the nuclear forces will seize the neutron. The compound nucleus then will be formed not by the capture of a deuteron, but only by that of a neutron, and the proton, which will never have come within the range of the nuclear forces at all, will fly off with a gain in kinetic energy, both from the recoil of the broken deuteron bond, and from the Coulomb repulsion. The ratio of the barrier height to the deuteron binding energy will be a very rough measure of the importance of the process. This process is sometimes called, after the first authors to recognize it, the Oppenheimer-Phillips process (O1).

The process can be treated by dividing it as usual into several steps. We write the cross section for a reaction initiated by a deuteron of energy E_d resulting in the release of a proton of energy E_p in the interval dE_p as follows:

$$\sigma(E_d, E_p) \, dE_p = \sigma_d(p_0, R)\xi T(E_p) \, dE_p \qquad (90)$$

Here σ_d is the contact cross section for penetration of the proton component of the deuteron, not to the nuclear surface, but to the more or less well-defined distance p_0 to which the proton has the maximum probability to penetrate; $T(E_p)$, called the transfer factor, takes into account the gain in energy of the proton as it moves out, and ξ is the sticking probability of the neutron averaged over all available levels into which it may be captured.

The modified penetrability function for the deuteron, $\sigma_d(p_0R)$, taking into account the polarization produced by the Coulomb field, has been given, with useful graphs (V1). The factor ξ will increase with energy of excitation, perhaps as rapidly as the level density, and will become unity for high excitation energy, which means low proton energy. High proton energy will mean low excitation energy, and may indicate the existence of individual levels. For low deuteron energies, the excitation of the nucleus will be quite low, even less than that following slow neutron capture, since the binding energy of the deuteron will be lost to the compound nucleus. The neutron sticking probability can be quite low at such "negative kinetic energy" but, even then, the easy escape of the proton from its rather distant point of closest approach will result in a large Oppenheimer-Phillips cross section and a small deuteron capture. This cross section will be larger than deuteron capture just for this reason, even when the neutron does not always stick.

For higher deuteron energies, the proton can approach the nuclear surface rather closely, and the most probable distance, p_0, will not be much greater than R. Then the ordinary deuteron capture and neutron emission will have an excitation function much like that of the Oppenheimer-Phillips (d,p) process. But, by reason of the high excitation following capture of a deuteron, the (d,p) process dominates the (d,n) process up to energies well above the barrier, since the (d,pn) process is very likely to occur after deuteron capture.

B. Stripping Reactions at Higher Energy

Even at very high energies, of course, the passing deuteron is distorted by the nuclear Coulomb field, and the Oppenheimer-Phillips process takes place. Here one may think not so much of the purely electrostatic forces as of the passing deuteron in a varying field due to the nucleus. In a frame of reference in which the deuteron is at rest, and the heavy nucleus is moving almost undeflected past it, the electric field experienced by the deuteron is a highly transverse field, owing to the Lorentz contraction of the nuclear force lines. This pulse of electric field can be Fourier-analyzed into a collection of nearly transverse waves of a wide spread of frequencies. These waves behave nearly like quanta, and are often called "virtual quanta" in this method of calculation (D1). The virtual quanta may induce photodisintegration of the deuteron as they pass by. In the laboratory system, where the deuteron is moving, the process becomes an electromagnetically induced stripping. It is in general a minor contributor to deuteron reactions compared to specifically nuclear effects at high energy.

But, much more important in the high-energy limit, where the deuteron may be handled classically, with a well-defined trajectory, is a process we may call collision stripping (S7). Here the deuteron is broken up by actual contact of one of its particles with the nuclear matter, while the other particle flies off with the momentum it had at the instant of collision, the resultant of its share of the deuteron center-of-mass motion and of the internal motion within the deuteron. This process yields neutrons and protons in equal numbers, and in a cone restricted to the forward direction, with a half-angle given by the simple relation $\theta \sim (W_d/E_d)^{\frac{1}{2}}$, and energies given by $E_p \sim E_n \sim \frac{1}{2}(E_d^{\frac{1}{2}} \pm W_d^{\frac{1}{2}})^2$, where W_d is the deuteron binding energy. The process is evidently one which leads to different energy and angle distribution from the low-energy Oppenheimer-Phillips reaction, or from emission after formation of a compound nucleus. Although detailed agreement with this simplified form of the theory is to be expected—and has been verified—only for really high-energy deuterons, at 190 Mev, the process must contribute continuously at lower energy, and finally merge with the standard Oppenheimer-Phillips case, in which the "stripping" occurs with by no means negligible reaction between the captured nucleon and the one that goes free, and in which the trajectory is spread heavily by diffraction (P2).

With deuterons in the region of moderate energy, say from 5 to 20 Mev, the stripping process is still dominant. Forward-peaked and even more complicated angular distributions of neutrons from these projectiles on a variety of targets of nearly any range of A indicate that neither compound nucleus formation nor a statistically treated stripping, in which classical ideas are used and all orbital angular momenta are regarded as contributing, can completely account for the process (B23). With good energy definition of the incident beam, it is possible to fix upon a group of outgoing protons of a definite energy. These protons arise from the capture of the neutron into one specific level of the product nucleus. At these moderate energies the excitation of the nucleus may be less even than that following capture of a free neutron, because the deuteron binding energy must be supplied to free the outgoing proton. This implies that individual levels will separately contribute. Since the incident deuteron momentum in the stripping approximation point of view is just equal to the sum of the momentum of outgoing proton and of the neutron before capture, forward-emitted protons may carry most of the available momentum. The internal deuteron motion does not often permit large values of momentum for both nucleons. Thus the captured neutrons frequently have long wavelengths, and quantum effects become decisive. The loose deuteron structure means, moreover, that large values of the orbital angular momentum of neutron with respect to nucleus can be important, while only a few l values can be captured into a single level. Then penetration effects may show up strongly in the angular distribution of the stripped protons, especially at small angles. Study of the fine structure of these distributions determines the partial waves captured, and becomes a powerful means of level spectroscopy (B22).

The really complicated behavior of the deuteron as a projectile, which arises from its loose structure and internal motion, seems qualitatively explained by the various processes outlined; it is by no means clear in full detail.

SECTION 9. RADIATIVE PROCESSES IN NUCLEAR REACTIONS

The all-important role which radiation plays in the de-excitation of atomic states is diminished in nuclear reactions by the numerous alternative means of decay. In nearly all reactions, nevertheless, gamma-rays are observable products, since particle emission cannot always be expected to leave the nucleus in the ground state, and, once the cooling nucleus has dropped below the energy content representing the threshold for particle emission, only radiation can take away the remaining energy. With the new machine sources of continuous gamma-spectra, moreover, nuclear reactions induced by gamma-rays are of high interest. The fact that the electromagnetic interaction between field and charge-current is completely known makes the study of nuclear structure through radiation, rather than particle collision, seem attractive. The somewhat illusory nature of this argument comes both from the experimental difficulty of accurate measurement for processes of generally low yield under conditions of poor energy resolution and from the complex character of the charge-current vector within nuclei, which turns out to depend on rather fine detail of nucleon motion, as on the presence of exchange forces and other phenomena connected with the intranuclear motion of the meson cloud. But the whole subject is full of interest.

A. The Multipole Classification

Just as the emitted particles are classified by the orbital angular momentum of their partial waves, which determines angular correlations and penetrabilities, so it is useful to classify radiation from any charge-current system contained in a limited volume of radius R in a similar way, according to the successive terms of a general expansion. This expansion is called the multipole representation, and it amounts to a sorting by angular momentum and parity. The electromagnetic field is a vector field, with some special properties due to the zero mass of the particles of the field—photons—and it turns out that there are two independent partial waves (analogous to the familiar two types of polarization) for each value of total angular momentum radiated away. Speaking physically, one would expect three possible angular momentum values for each orbital value, since the photon has unit spin. But the condition of transversality, which is closely related to the zero mass of the photon, excludes one orientation. In Table 8 are presented the

TABLE 8

MULTIPOLE FOR GIVEN TRANSITION

Parity Change	Radiated Angular Momentum, J_γ					
	0	1	2	3	L (even)	L (odd)
Yes	None	Elec. dipole	Mag. quadripole	Elec. octopole	Mag. 2^L-pole	Elec. 2^L-pole
No	None	Mag. dipole	Elec. quadripole	Mag. octopole	Elec. 2^L-pole	Mag. 2^L-pole

selection rules and the type and order of multipole for a given parity change and radiated angular momentum. The radiated angular momentum is of course to be taken in the usual sense of the vector model: if J_i and J_f are initial and final angular momenta, the relation $J_i + J_\gamma \geq J_f \geq |J_i - J_\gamma|$ must be fulfilled.

In general only the lowest order of multipole allowed by the selection rules contributes; e.g., if the transition is $J_i = 2$, odd $\rightarrow J_f = 1$, even, we expect electric dipole only. The magnetic multipole of order L is reduced in intensity with respect to the electric dipole of the same order in the ratio $(\hbar/McR)^2$. For electric and magnetic dipole this is easy to see by simply writing the ratio of the familiar dipole moments:

$$\frac{\text{elec. dipole moment}}{\text{mag. dipole moment}} \sim \frac{eR}{e\hbar/Mc}$$

It holds more generally. The absence of any $J_\gamma = 0$ forbids zero-zero transitions completely, with one quantum emitted. For a transition in which a magnetic multipole fulfills the selection rules with the lowest value of multipole order L, the next higher electric multipole may contribute radiation less by an order of magnitude, since the reduction from order to order in L is estimated to be in the ratio $(R/\lambda)^2 < (p/Mc)^2 \sim (\hbar/McR)^2$. If the lowest contributing multipole is of electric type, the magnetic multipoles are negligible.

1. Reduction of the Nuclear Dipole Moment. Classically, and even in atoms, the electric dipole transition is the most intense for radiation not too small in wavelength compared to the dimensions of the system. From our selection rules we could expect to see forbidden transitions, slow and non-dipole in character whenever large angular momenta have to be radiated. This is of course the origin of the well-known nuclear isomers, and of certain forbidden lines in the nebular atomic spectra. But there is a general argument which indicates that electric dipole transitions will not be so important, at least for nuclear gamma-rays up to some 10 Mev.

The interaction, energy between a system of charges and the electromagnetic field may be written:

$$H_{\text{int}} = \sum_i \mathbf{A} \cdot \mathbf{j}_i = \sum_i \mathbf{A} \cdot (\rho \mathbf{v}_i)$$

In the usual dipole approximation, we replace the operator $\mathbf{v}_i$ by $\mathbf{p}_i/m$, and use the familiar relation between matrix operators, $\mathbf{p} = m \, d\mathbf{r}/dt$. Then the dipole moment operator becomes

$$\mathbf{D} = \Sigma e_i \mathbf{r}_i \propto \frac{\Sigma e_i \mathbf{p}_i}{m_i}$$

But plainly it is only the net displacement of the charges with respect to the center of mass which produces radiation from an isolated system. Then the operator whose matrix element between initial and final states determines the rate of radiation is

$$\mathbf{P} = \sum_{\text{all particles}} \frac{e_i}{m_i} (\mathbf{x}_i - \mathbf{X}) \qquad \text{with} \qquad AM\mathbf{X} = M \sum_p \mathbf{x}_p + M \sum_n \mathbf{x}_n$$

where M is the nucleon mass, for a nucleus with A nucleons, Z protons, and therefore $N = A - Z$ neutrons. Here $\mathbf{x}_p$ is the vector position of the pth proton, $\mathbf{x}_n$ that of the nth neutron, and $\mathbf{X}$ is the coordinate vector of the center of mass, all in an arbitrary reference system. Now we can write

$$\mathbf{P} = \frac{1}{M}\left[e\left(1 - \frac{Z}{A}\right)\sum_p \mathbf{x}_p - e\frac{Z}{A}\sum_n \mathbf{x}_n \right] = \frac{e}{M}\frac{N}{A}\sum_p \mathbf{x}_p - \frac{e}{M}\frac{Z}{A}\sum_n \mathbf{x}_n$$

(91)

This is as though we calculated the dipole moment considering each nucleon with actual charge e_i to have an effective charge only $e_i - Ze/A$. Clearly, if all the particles of the nucleus had $e_i/m_i = e/M$, there would be no electric dipole radiation whatever; the charge center and mass center would coincide, and the mass center clearly could not oscillate. In less extreme cases, where the motion of protons and neutrons is very similar—if they stick, say, more or less tightly together in alpha-particle sub-units—the electric dipole transitions would be at least much diminished. There is no such general restriction upon the other multipoles. Indeed, magnetic multipoles will contain contributions both from the intrinsic magnetic moments of the nucleons and from other magnetizations arising out of the transient currents coming from meson flow within the nucleus. These can be shown to be an inescapable consequence of exchange forces of various kinds (S1). In the deuteron photoeffect these currents are probably observable at low energy, where the major contribution is from a magnetic dipole transition. In general, then, we expect the magnetic multipoles to give somewhat larger contributions than the estimate made earlier would indicate, and we look for the electric dipole term to be much reduced, perhaps so much that the electric quadripole and magnetic dipole will overshadow its effects.

2. The Sum Rules. This reduction of the dipole moment is limited by a very general result, an extension of the Thomas-Reiche-Kuhn sum rule long used in the atomic case. We can write for the integrated dipole absorption cross section

$$\int_0^\infty \sigma_\alpha(E_\gamma)dE_\gamma = \frac{2\pi^2 e^2 \hbar}{Mc}\sum_n f_{on}$$

Now, *independently* of how the so-called oscillator strengths, $f_{on} = |X_{on}/\lambdabar_{on}|^2$, vary with the energy difference between ground and excited state, $E_n - E_o = \hbar^2/2M\lambdabar_{on}^2$, the value of the sum is just

$$\sum_n f_{on} = \frac{M}{\Sigma m_i}\sum_{i,j}\frac{m_i m_j}{2e^2}\left(\frac{e_i}{m_i} - \frac{e_j}{m_j}\right)^2 \qquad \text{with } M \text{ any particle mass } m_i$$

(92)

provided only that the system absorbing the radiation consists of particles of charge e_i, mass m_i, and that the forces between them are ordinary forces. Exchange forces contribute a correction of similar size. Applying (92) to the nuclear case yields the result

$$\int_0^\infty \sigma_d(E_\gamma)\, dE_\gamma = \frac{2\pi^2 e^2 \hbar}{c} \cdot \frac{1}{A M_p} \cdot \left(2 \sum_{n,p} \frac{e^2}{2e^2}\right) = \frac{\pi^2}{137} \left(\frac{\hbar}{M_p c}\right)^2 M_p c^2 \cdot \frac{NZ}{A}$$

$$= 0.058 \frac{NZ}{A} \qquad \text{Mev-barn} \tag{93}$$

From (92) it follows that a nucleus with $N = Z$, consisting of a set of infinitely well-bound alpha-particles, would have a strictly vanishing f sum. This is the result the previous section predicted. But, since actually we take the nucleus to contain not fundamental alpha-particle building blocks, but protons and neutrons, perhaps bound with finite forces into alpha-particle-like units, the integrated cross section will be given by the form of (93). Taking the two results together, we can reconcile them by observing that the cross section will remain low, and we shall have little or no contribution to the f sum, as long as the energy of the gamma-ray is insufficient to break up any strong correlations into alpha-like structures. But the dipole transitions cannot really be prevented by any such internal binding of finite strength; they can merely be deferred. Sooner or later, as energy increases, transitions are made to states lying high enough so that any given sub-unit is broken up, and the f sum begins to grow, reaching finally the total given by (93), which any system of protons and neutrons must eventually show, whatever their internal motion. (We exclude exchange forces for the moment; they change nothing qualitatively.)

From these general considerations we would expect that the gamma-ray transitions from nuclei would be electric dipole, magnetic dipole, or electric quadripole in most cases, with the last two having possibly somewhat higher probability, for transitions involving only a few Mev (W1). But, for higher-energy gamma-absorption or -emission, say from 15 to 20 Mev—energies large enough to excite any transient configuration of nucleons, even the stable alpha-particle—the dipole transitions begin to show their deferred dominance and lead to integrated dipole absorption cross sections of the order of an Mev-barn (D5), for nuclei of middle A. This indeed seems to be a fair picture of what is still a murky experimental domain.

Further extension of the sum rule type of calculation leads to rough information on the values of quantities like $\int \sigma_\gamma(E_\gamma) E_\gamma{}^n\, dE_\gamma$; these, taken with the experimental data (H1, K3), tend to confirm the picture of the last paragraphs at least roughly (L4).

B. Calculation of Radiation Widths

The familiar formula for the rate of radiation of a quantum-mechanical system with dipole moment D radiating light of frequency ν is

$$\text{Energy/second} = \frac{4}{3}\frac{\nu^4}{c^3}\left| D_{if} \right|^2$$

Introducing a self-evident notation for the type of multipole involved, and suppressing numerical factors near unity because of the roughness of our estimates, we may write the resulting width for electric dipole (2^1-pole) radiation:

$$\Gamma_1{}^{\text{elec}} = \frac{\hbar}{\tau} = \hbar \cdot \frac{\nu^4}{c^3}\frac{\left| D_{if} \right|^2}{\hbar\omega} = \frac{\nu^3}{c^3}\left| D_{if} \right|^2$$

But now we can estimate that, for a single particle moving in a region of radius R with charge e, the dipole moment is $D_{if} \cong eR$. For electric multipoles of successively higher order we can similarly estimate that, apart from numerical factors, the radiation intensity is reduced for each successive order in the ratio $(R/\lambda)^2$. Magnetic multipole moments are smaller than the electric moment of a given order by the factor $(\hbar/McR)$, which, using the nuclear radius value $R = 1.5A^{\frac{1}{3}} \cdot 10^{-13}$ cm, leads to

$$\Gamma_l{}^{\text{elec}} \cong \frac{1}{137}\left(\frac{R}{\lambda}\right)^{2l} E_\gamma \cdot \frac{1}{[1\cdot 3\cdot 5\cdots(2l+1)]^2}$$

$$\Gamma_l{}^{\text{mag}} \cong \left(\frac{\hbar}{McR}\right)^2 \Gamma_l{}^{\text{elec}} \cong 0.02A^{-\frac{2}{3}}\Gamma_l{}^{\text{elec}}$$

(94)

These estimates will be reasonable ones for the low-lying states of nuclei if the independent-particle, Hartree-like model is not too misleading. (We have suppressed factors depending on l, which would arise in a more consistent calculation from the complex angular behavior of the higher multipole radiation.) It seems not inappropriate to apply these formulas for the rough computation of those long-lived low-lying states of nuclei which are responsible for isomerism. The detailed comparison with experiment is beyond the scope of the present work; we make no correction for the additional non-radiative transitions due to internal conversion, and so on. But it is useful simply to show that the radiation widths we compute would give the possibility of lifetimes like those observed for reasonable values of radiated angular momentum and energy. Table 9 shows lifetimes like those observed for the very transitions which the shell model predicts for the lowest states.

TABLE 9

LIFETIMES FOR RADIATIVE DECAY OF LOW-LYING STATES

Multipole	$A = 100$ Energy = 200 kev	$A = 200$ Energy = 100 kev
Electric 2^3-pole	0.029 sec	0.9 sec
Magnetic 2^4-pole	1.5 years	21 years

We cannot expect the estimates of (94) to hold in the region where the level density is very high, and the idea of the excitation of a single particle no longer plausible. The sum rules themselves show that the estimate of a constant dipole moment, independent of energy, must fail; the f sum would not even converge. A very rough idea of what to expect, consistent at least with the notion of a compound nucleus, may be gotten in this way. We expect the single-particle estimate to apply not to one single level of a highly excited nucleus, but to a whole group, dividing up the width, so to speak, among a great many levels each of which shares some part of the combining possibilities with the ground state. But, over how big an energy range must we spread the radiative width? A guess is afforded by the spacing of levels near the ground state, where it is not unreasonable to think that only a single particle has been excited. That spacing measures the energy region to be assigned to the excitation of one particle. Purely as a very rough orienting estimate, let us write for the radiative width of an average level in the region where levels are dense:

$$\bar{\Gamma}_l^{\text{elec}} = \frac{1}{137} \left(\frac{R}{\lambda}\right)^{2l} E_\gamma \times \frac{\rho(0)}{\rho(E_\gamma)} \frac{1}{[1 \cdot 3 \cdots (2l + 1)]^2}$$

$$\bar{\Gamma}_l^{\text{mag}} = 0.02 A^{-\frac{2}{3}} \bar{\Gamma}_l^{\text{elec}}$$

(95)

where $\rho(0)$ and $\rho(E_\gamma)$ are of course the number of levels per unit energy (really of levels with certain fixed J values) at excitation energies 0 and E_γ.

The actual radiation from any level formed in a nuclear reaction will of course involve transitions not simply to a fixed state below, but to all combining levels at lower energy. The total radiation width then for a given type of multipole radiation can be written

$$\Gamma_{\text{tot}}^{l,\,\text{elec}} = \sum_{\text{all } f} \bar{\Gamma}_l^{\text{elec}}(E_i - E_f)$$

Replacing the sum by an integral, and using the form of (95), we get

$$
\Gamma_{\text{tot}}^{l,e} = \int_0^{E_{\gamma\,\text{max}}} \frac{\rho(0)}{\rho(E_{\gamma\,\text{max}})} E_\gamma^{2l+1} \, \rho(E_{\gamma\,\text{max}} - E_\gamma) \, dE_\gamma
$$
$$
\times \frac{(R/\hbar c)^{2l}}{137[1\cdot 3\cdots(2l+1)]^2} \quad (96)
$$

The integrand represents the gamma-ray spectrum immediately following decay, without taking into account any of the subsequent cascade gamma-rays. The most common example of such radiation is that following thermal neutron capture. The spectra as measured (K7) show very marked effects of transitions to a few specific low-lying levels, such as the ground state itself, and do not fit our statistical estimates very well. There is not much information about the wide gamma-ray spectra which do seem to underlie these special lines and which presumably correspond to what we have estimated (D2).

We tabulate, for nuclei in various regions of mass number, the computed radiation width following neutron capture, for radiation of various multipole types. The level densities are taken from (31), and the whole calculation is very rough. There seems here, too, to be evidence against

TABLE 10

TOTAL RADIATION WIDTH AFTER NEUTRON CAPTURE: VARIOUS MULTIPOLES

A	Max $E_\gamma \doteq B_N$ (Mev)	Widths in Electron Volts				
		$\bar{\Gamma}_1^{\text{elec}}$	$\bar{\Gamma}_1^{\text{mag}}$	$\bar{\Gamma}_2^{\text{el}}$	$\bar{\Gamma}_2^{\text{mag}}$	$\bar{\Gamma}_{\text{observed}}$
60	8	4	5×10^{-3}	2×10^{-3}	30×10^{-7}	0.2
120	7	0.4	0.3×10^{-3}	0.2×10^{-3}	2×10^{-7}	
200	6	0.1	0.07×10^{-3}	0.05×10^{-5}	0.3×10^{-7}	

the full contribution of electric dipole radiation. Probably there are such transitions; some appear to have been identified in light nuclei, but they do not exceed in probability either magnetic dipole or electric quadripole by as much as an order of magnitude.

C. Photo-Induced Reactions

From the theory so far given, the behavior of gamma-ray-induced nuclear reactions follows in a somewhat sketchy way. The general statistical theory describing the reaction as a two-step process is here applied:

$$\sigma_{\gamma,p} = S_\gamma(E)D_p \tag{97}$$

where the cross section S_γ is the absorption cross section for the gamma-ray, and the factor D_p, as in Eq. (40), describes the break-up, by emission of particle p, of the compound nucleus—here just an excited state of the target nucleus—exactly as in particle reactions. Below the binding energy of a single neutron, no particle reaction can be observed, of course, since D_p is exactly zero. Elastic and inelastic scattering of gamma-rays are possible, and would be governed by an analogue of the usual atomic dispersion theory, with the electric dipole moments perhaps not predominant. As the particle threshold is crossed, D_p rising from zero, the cross section $\sigma_{\gamma p}$ rises as well, probably remaining rather small though increasing with a fairly high power of the energy, as a result of the importance of electric quadripole transitions. Only at energies where the excitation of the alpha sub-units becomes likely will the dipole moment assert itself; there the cross section S_γ rises to high values. As soon as a few Mev of excitation are available beyond the threshold for two-neutron, or even neutron-plus-proton, emission, this process will effectively eliminate the simple initial (γ,n). Thus a peak will be observed in the excitation function, with a width governed largely by competition. This peak, coming wholly from the factor D_p, is superimposed on a fairly rapid rise and subsequent fall of the dipole cross section S_γ. There is still no clear division of the observed peak into the two factors; it is now fairly sure that the simple competition cannot be the entire reason for the width of a few Mev of the so-called "resonance" for the (γ,n) reaction on a variety of targets (K4). The growth in neutron yield for a given gamma-energy, examined as a function of A, does, however, appear to be due mainly to the decreasing neutron binding energy and, hence, increased opportunity for two-neutron emission, as A grows.

That the compound nuclear state formed by gamma-excitation might be of a rather special kind, with a particular internal motion, has been suggested (C11, S10, T2). No clear evidence for this view has been produced which could not be duplicated on the present picture. The over-all $\int \sigma(E)\, dE$, the presence of an apparent resonance due to competition, and the variation of neutron yield with A cannot distinguish the special motion from rather generalized features of any dipole absorption. Good measurements of the peak widths and the relative yields of the various reactions are not yet at hand.

That the assumption (97) is not entirely right seems demonstrated by the rather high yields of charged particles, especially of protons, from gamma-ray-excited nuclei. These yields are far in excess of those calculated from statistical theory whenever, as for medium or heavy nuclei, the statistical emission of protons is much reduced by the Coulomb barrier. The protons tend to be distributed in angle more transversely than isotropically. All of this suggests that a process which contributes only a small part of the total reaction—for medium nuclei, the protons are only a few percent at most—can occur in which protons are as frequent as or more frequent than neutrons. Any process which amounts to the leakage of the protons out of a small region of the nucleus before that region has lost its excitation energy by conduction of the "heat" to the whole nuclear volume will do. A direct photoeffect, in which the single proton is ejected from the smooth nuclear potential well, is an extreme case of this view (B15). Something between this and the statistical equilibrium idea is more likely to be correct. Emission of alphas, deuterons, and other fragments seems to give further signs of the need for a more detailed theory.

Reactions may be induced by the varying electromagnetic field of a charged particle. This problem has been discussed in terms of the method of virtual quanta, mentioned in Section 8, mainly for electrons.

SECTION 10. NUCLEAR FISSION

No nuclear reaction type has been so much discussed, and none has attracted so many workers,[1] as the curious reaction called fission. The fact that this reaction involved so profound a rearrangement of nuclear matter that neutrons were emitted in greater numbers than one per divided nucleus permitted the chain reaction, and thus the large-scale release of nuclear energy, even under terrestrial conditions of pressure and temperature. We shall discuss fission rather sketchily and semi-quantitatively here, with major attention not to detailed experimental results, but to the features of most general interest. All information here presented, without exception, is from the published literature, much of it from the spate of studies of fission in the first two or three years after its discovery (T6). This section does not pretend to be a full guide to the present state of knowledge of fission.

A. The Energetics of Fission

The fission reaction cannot conveniently be written as we have written all others: $T(i,p)R$. The projectile may indeed be a proton or neutron, or the reaction may be observed to occur spontaneously, but the product nucleus is not one of the light nuclear particles, with a heavy residual

[1] See, for example, the semi-annual reports of the U. S. Atomic Energy Commission.

nucleus. On the contrary, the products of fission are nuclei of sizable charge and mass, covering a range of scores of charge and mass numbers. In Fig. 18 we present the yield curve for several typical fission reactions (G3, N1). The target nucleus has divided into two major fragments

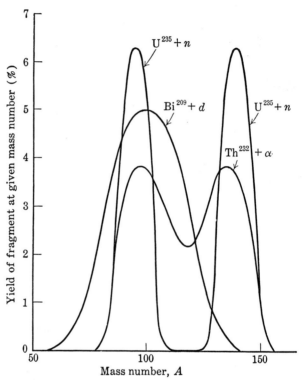

Fig. 18. Percentage of occurrence of product nuclear fragment of mass number A, plotted against mass number, in three different fission reactions. The neutron fission goes with slow neutrons; the alpha-induced, with alphas of 38 Mev; the deuteron fission, with 200-Mev deuterons. Note the trend toward a symmetrical distribution, and the invariably large spread in fragment masses.

(with a few light particles sometimes also in a kind of spray). It is clear that the description of the emission of a particle p from an essentially unaffected residual nucleus R is inappropriate.

But the phenomenon can be pictured in a very simple and convincing way from the most fundamental ideas of the nuclear model, treated in a nearly classical fashion.[1] We have throughout referred to the nuclear matter as a kind of "quantum liquid" of nearly constant density, some

[1] Bohr and Wheeler (B18) gave the first extended treatment of the theory; we follow them rather closely.

1.45×10^{14} g/cm^3. A heavy nucleus is then a small nearly spherical drop of this fluid, with radius $R = r_0 \cdot A^{1/3}$ cm. In such a nucleus, looking apart from the entire complexity of quantum effects, odd-even regularities, etc., we can recognize a static equilibrium for the configuration. The attractive forces which cause the drop to cohere are, just as in a drop of water, short-range forces for any given nucleon saturated by the interaction with its nearest neighbors among the nucleons. In the roughest way, then, the binding energy of a nucleus of mass A, charge Z is just proportional to the number of nucleons present, each forming its full number of bonds with other nucleons. The negative of the binding energy, $-E_B$, we define as usual as the total energy of the neutral atom (nucleus plus its surrounding electrons) minus the total energy of its constituent neutrons and protons when removed to large separations, including the energy of the electron needed to neutralize each proton. Then stability means *positive* E_B. Then $E_B \sim$ volume, and, assuming constant density, the volume energy alone gives $-E_B = -a_V A$. But, like any liquid drop, the nucleus has a surface. Even for the heaviest nuclei, many nucleons lie on the surface of the drop. Their bonds are not all saturated; there is a net deficiency in binding energy, a positive surface energy exactly like the surface energy of a water droplet, but clearly of the greatest importance. We then expect $-E_B \sim -a(\text{volume}) + b(\text{surface})$, under the same constant density assumption. There is yet another classically evident contribution to the nuclear energy. This is the mutual Coulomb repulsion of all the protons in the nucleus. It is not a saturating force, with finite bond numbers and a short range. On the contrary, it is a long-range force to which all the protons contribute. On the most naive assumption of constant charge density, the Coulomb energy of a spherical drop of radius $R = r_0 A^{1/3}$ is simply the integral

$$\left(\frac{Ze}{\text{vol}}\right) \cdot \left(\frac{Ze}{\text{vol}}\right) \iint_{\text{sphere}} \frac{dV \, dV'}{|r - r'|} = \frac{3}{5} \frac{Z^2 e^2}{R} = \frac{3}{5} \frac{Z^2 e^2}{r_0 A^{1/3}} \qquad (98)$$

Purely classically, then, the binding energy of a liquid drop of constant density and uniform charge density [1] is given by the form

$$-E_B = -a_V A + a_S A^{2/3} + a_C \frac{Z^2}{A^{1/3}} \qquad (99)$$

These simple ideas lead to a classical theory of fission. Suppose that now we have such a charged classical drop. If we slowly deform it by

---

[1] For a careful discussion of this whole procedure, and of the limitations of these ideas, see (F2).

elongating it, we clearly increase the surface area: this costs us surface energy. But the two halves of the drop are now found at a larger distance from one another than in the spherical form. This means that their mutual Coulomb repulsion has decreased, and we have gained binding. As we deform the drop more, we increase surface energy and decrease Coulomb repulsion still more. Finally we can divide the drop into two remote spheres, each of half the original charge. In this state the Coulomb energy has been much reduced, and the surface increased. For a sufficiently high charge density, however, the Coulomb reduction must outweigh the surface energy increase, and the fissioned drops will be the stable configuration. The original sphere may then be in fact in a state of unstable equilibrium; any finite distortion from the sphere will cause the droplet to divide. Or it may be that, originally, small distortions into an ellipsoid will cost more surface energy than they gain in Coulomb energy, and the original sphere will be in a state of stable equilibrium. Yet finite displacements—distortion into something nearer a dumbbell shape—may so reduce the Coulomb energy that some intermediate distorted shape is a state of unstable equilibrium, capable of going either back to the original sphere, or on to two divided droplets. In this case the original drop is only relatively stable, and a genuine disturbance might cause fission. We shall see that this is the actual nuclear case at hand.

1. The Semi-Empirical Theory. We can make all these notions more precise. Let us go back to the drop-model energy content appropriate for the constant-density nucleus. We wish to evaluate the constants for volume, surface, and Coulomb energy. In addition, we shall add two terms which represent an effort to make the drop idea conform more closely to nuclear experience. It is fundamental in nuclei of course that the exact numbers of individual nucleons have a real role, unlike the molecules in any large-scale drop, where small fluctuations in mass have an unimportant effect. There are two reasons for the effect, and both of them reflect the essentially quantum character of the nucleus: first, the total number of particles is small, so that quite generally small changes in A could have important effect; and, second, the strong interactions seem to result in something like the atomic shells showing as fine detail on the general course of the liquid-drop energy content. We shall throughout disregard the details of this phenomenon. There is a second consequence of the special nuclear forces: the protons and the neutron seem to tend to group in pairs or even in alpha-particle-like units. There is a binding energy bonus for having the neutrons and protons equal in number. We shall introduce semi-empirically, then, two terms into our binding energy formula:

(1) A term, called the symmetry energy, which depends on the square of the difference between the number of protons Z and the number of neutrons $N = A - Z$. The fact that the term is quadratic represents the fit in first approximation to the trough of the valley in a binding energy surface, plotted against A and Z. The most stable isotopes lie in a crooked valley furrowing this surface; we imagine that the bottom of this valley can be approximated in cross section by a parabola. If we associate with each unpaired particle a definite energy, the whole term can be written

$$E_{\text{sym}} = a_\tau \frac{(N - Z)^2}{(N + Z)} = \frac{a_\tau}{A} (A - 2Z)^2 \tag{100}$$

(2) A term to stand for the last unpaired particle, expressing the fact that nuclei of even N and even Z are the most stable for a given A, and that those with N odd, Z odd are the least stable, while the odd-even or even-odd category is intermediate. This term may be empirically determined from the difference in energy between successive beta-transformations down a chain. With these additions, the semi-empirical formula becomes

$$-E_B = -a_V A + a_S A^{\frac{2}{3}} + a_C \frac{Z^2}{A^{\frac{1}{3}}} + a_\tau \frac{(N - Z)^2}{A} \pm \delta(A) \tag{101a}$$

We can evaluate a_V and a_S by fitting the formula to the known mass-defect curve, which is by no means very accurate in the region above $A = 40$ or so. The procedure is made easier if we first evaluate a_τ in terms of a known a_C. This we can do by fitting the valley of the stable isotopes, i.e., by finding the Z which corresponds to the most stable isobar for each A. The data fix this for odd Z at least to within about $\pm \frac{1}{2}$ for Z, making the valley pass between the two most abundant isobars. From our formula we need find only $\partial M(A, Z)/\partial Z$ and set it equal to zero. This should mark the trough of the valley. [Note that $M(A, Z) = -E_B + AM_n + Z(M_H - M_n)$.] From $\partial M/\partial Z = 0$ we get a relation between Z and A. The function so determined, called Z_A, is given by the expression

$$\frac{Z_A}{A} = \frac{(0.00081 + a_\tau)}{2a_\tau + 0.00125 A^{\frac{2}{3}}}$$

using $a_C = 0.584$ Mev, as given below. If we smooth over the data, neglecting several kinks in the Z_A function, we can find that, with a_C as given, if $a_\tau = 0.083$ mass unit, the fit to the empirical course of the curve is good. We consider throughout only nuclei above $A \sim 20$. A set of good values for all the constants then is

$$-E_B(Z, A) = -14.0A + 13.1A^{\frac{2}{3}} + \frac{77.3}{A}\left(\frac{A}{2} - Z\right)^2$$

$$+ 0.584\frac{Z^2}{A^{\frac{1}{3}}} + \begin{cases} \pm 34/A^{\frac{3}{4}}; & Z \text{ odd, } A \text{ even} \\ & Z \text{ even, } A \text{ even} \\ 0; & A \text{ odd} \end{cases} \quad (101b)$$

where we have expressed E_B in Mev.

A similar semi-empirical formula due to Fermi has been extensively tabulated (M7) for nuclei of all plausible Z and A, going far beyond the known range. The form there used does not display the Coulomb energy directly, but combines it with the symmetry energy, using as a reference the bottom of the actual valley of stability Z_A rather than the artificial situation of equal neutron and proton number. Written for the atomic mass in mass units, the Fermi form is

$$M(A, Z) = 1.01464A + 0.014A^{\frac{2}{3}} - 0.041905Z_A$$

$$+ 0.041905(Z - Z_A)^2/Z_A$$

$$+ \begin{cases} \pm 0.036/A^{\frac{3}{4}}; & Z \text{ odd, } A \text{ even} \\ & Z \text{ even, } A \text{ even} \\ 0; & A \text{ odd} \end{cases} \quad (101c)$$

with $Z_A/A = 1/(1.9807 + 0.01496A^{\frac{2}{3}})$. An earlier version of the formula is cited in a more accessible place (S11). Our (101b) is in reasonably good agreement with the Fermi formula, but the latter (101c) is preferable for actual calculations. (See Section 3B in Part IV of Volume I.)

A more elaborate treatment has been given which includes a measure of the compressibility of nuclear matter, i.e., a departure from the constant density assumption (F2). The effect is quite small. The Coulomb constant a_C is not in fact evaluated from the semi-empirical formula for a large number of nuclei, but is given from the comparison of the so-called "mirror nuclei," isobars with $N - Z = \pm 1$, where direct measurement of beta-decay energy has been made (F1, F3). The radius it corresponds to is somewhat larger than that we have taken from high-energy nuclear reactions; it gives $r_0 = 1.48$ and not 1.4×10^{-13} cm. This difference may reflect in part the tendency for the protons to move to the outside of the nucleus, or it may simply reflect the inadequacy of the rather crude semi-empirical formula.

Let us now consider the energetics of fission with formula (101b). A very simple model of fission may be made by assuming that the drop divides into two drops, each of the same charge density, proportional to Z/A. Let one fragment have charge fZ, the other $(1 - f)Z$, and similarly with the A's. Then the energy released on such a fission, say $\Delta E(f)$, is given by the expression

$$\Delta E(f) = 13.1 A^{2/3}[1 - f^{2/3} - (1 - f)^{2/3}]$$

$$+ 0.584 \frac{Z^2}{A^{1/3}} [1 - f^{5/3} - (1 - f)^{5/3}] \quad \text{in Mev} \quad (102)$$

The volume and symmetry energies do not change; we neglect the small term δ of (101), since we have not required integer values of Z or A. The treatment is entirely classical, and depends only on the assumed surface and Coulomb energies of drops of constant charge density. We plot in Fig. 19 the net energy release $\Delta E(f)$ as a function of f for nuclear drops of several charges. Note that, above a certain value of Z, fission will release energy for a wider and wider range of fragment sizes. For high enough Z, indeed, very small fragments—resembling alpha-particles—may be released with a net gain in stability. This simple theory predicts the occurrence of fission and of alpha-radioactivity for high Z. Below the limiting Z value of course not fission, but *combination* of light nuclei, will represent a gain in stability.

So far we have discussed only the energy difference between initial spherical drop and final spherical fragments. If this energy difference, $\Delta E(f)$, is positive, the process will proceed spontaneously. But the rate of fission, which will determine whether or not the process is observable (rates corresponding to half-lives of more than $T_{1/2} \sim 10^{21\text{-}22}$ years are not now observable), is still entirely open. In Fig. 20 we have represented quite schematically this complicated process. We have plotted the energy difference between initial spherical drop and distorted drop against a single parameter—some measure of the effective distance of charge separation. Of course the distortion can in fact be represented only by many parameters. In our simplified plot, the value ΔE is measured from the initial energy to the final energy, from E_i to E_f. We have plotted four cases: reference to the figure will make them clear. In case (1) fission is not an exothermic process and cannot occur. In cases 2, 3, and 4, it is exothermic and occurs spontaneously. In all of these, the initial sphere is in equilibrium at sp under the mutual action of surface and Coulomb forces. But in case 4 the equilibrium is unstable; any finite disturbance will cause fission. The actual nucleus would last only a time comparable with the characteristic nuclear times, for the zero-point oscillations would cause the needed displacement. Cases 2 and 3 show initially stable nuclei; small displacements will not lead to fission, but will be followed by a return to the initial spherical equilibrium. Only finite displacement, adequate to supply energy greater

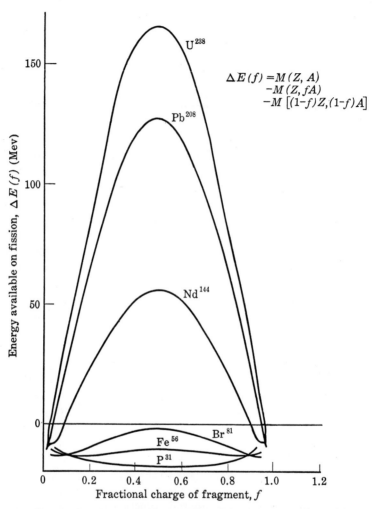

Fig. 19a. Potential energy classically available for fission into two fragments of the original charge density, but charges fZ and $(1-f)Z$, plotted as a function of fragment size, f, for several nuclei. For heavy nuclei, division into fragments of a wide range of sizes is exothermic; for nuclei lighter than, say, bromine, fission is endothermic even with the most favorable fragment size, and symmetric with $f = 0.5$.

than the height of the barrier, at P, will lead to fission. Classically, it will never occur spontaneously; the initial state is a state of relative stable equilibrium. Quantum-mechanically, in the actual nuclear case, spontaneous fission can occur, by the tunneling effect—diffraction beneath the barrier. Whether or not this will occur at an observable rate will depend on both the height and width of the barrier. In case 2, the barrier is high and wide; we may expect that spontaneous fission will not occur observably, and that large energies of excitation comparable with ΔE would need to be added to such a drop before fission could occur. This might be the case of a nucleus well beyond the limiting Z near 35, but not one of the natural radioactive series.

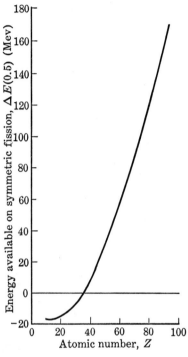

It is evident that the most useful application of these ideas would be the calculation of the barrier heights, or fission threshold energies. The potential energy contour of the drop plotted as a function of some representative parameters determining its distortion from the sphere (of course two parameters are all we can plot) is a surface with a flat portion far away from the center (where the two fragments are far apart), rising to a fairly high elevation as the fragments approach and feel the Coulomb repulsion; in the very center

Fig. 19b. Maximum potential energy classically available on fission into two drops of equal charge and mass, plotted as a function of atomic number Z.

of the contour map, where the drop is almost spherical, there is a crater-like bowl in the center of which lies the original sphere before fission. Small displacements will never cross the lip of the crater, but there are passes in the crater wall, the lowest of which lies above the crater center by just the fission threshold energy. This pass, or saddle point, is what we want to find, in respect to both its height and its position on the map, i.e., to the shape of the drop at the unstable equilibrium position, where it can either go on to fission or return to the original sphere. (See Fig. 21.)

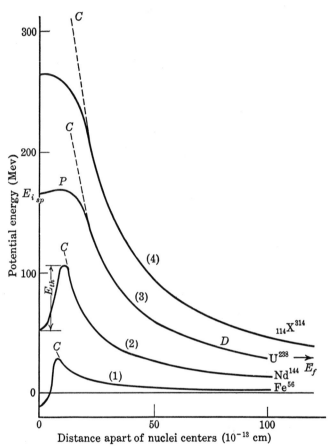

Fig. 20. Potential energy of nuclear drop as a function of distortion. The complicated distortion is here represented by a single parameter, some measure of effective
distance of charge separation. The energy surface is plotted in the plane which
represents the most favorable distortion, through the "pass" in the energy crater.
Note the stable position at sp, the original spherical shape, the increase in potential
energy to reach the pass at P, the energy threshold for fission, E_{th}, and the long
decline down the curve to D and beyond. The distant part of the curves is simply
the $1/R$ behavior of the Coulomb energy of spherical charges. If continued in until
the fragments touched, any distortion being neglected, this would reach the points
marked C, the end of the Coulomb barrier. How the drop distortion allows fission
at much lower thresholds is seen from the bending over before point C.

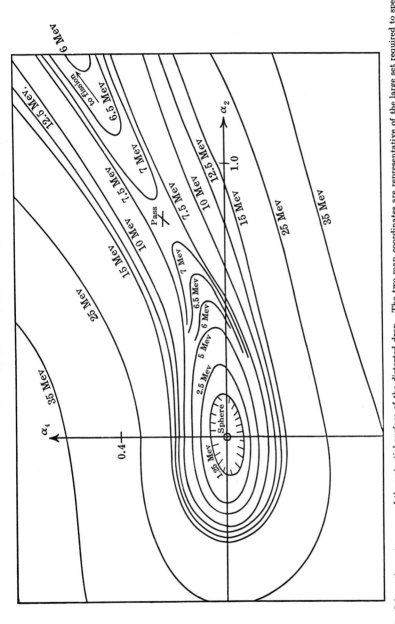

Fig. 21. Schematic contour map of the potential surface of the distorted drop. The two map coordinates are representative of the large set required to specify a general displacement of the drop. The contour lines are marked in Mev difference from the origin of map coordinates, which is the undistorted spherical drop. Note the crater and the pass over the lip of the crater. The height of the pass is about right for a nucleus with $Z = 90$. The shape of the surface is adapted from an actual numerical calculation of the energy of distortion in an imaginary case where the distortion was restricted to a function of only the two parameters plotted for the map (Fll). The radius as a function of co-latitude angle, $\gamma(\theta)$ was taken to be $R[1 + \alpha_2 P_2(\theta) + \alpha_4 P_4(\theta)]$, and the energy plotted as a function of α_2 and α_4 as shown in the map.

The full calculation is of course difficult. The number of degrees of freedom of a classical charged drop under axially symmetric distortions is very great, but some important consequences can be obtained quickly.

(1) Let us consider the limiting case, where the charge density is small and the surface energy far outweighs the Coulomb repulsion. In this case, the drop will try to minimize its surface at all deformations, and the spherical shape will be stable for every distortion up to the very radical one of allowing the drop to be molded into two spheres and mov-

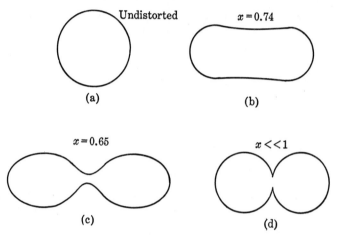

Undistorted $x = 0.74$

(a)   (b)

$x = 0.65$ $x \ll 1$

(c)   (d)

Fig. 22. A series of equilibrium shapes for the nuclear drop. Shape (a) is of course the original sphere; (b) the shape of the drop at the critical distortion for $x = 0.74 = (Z^2/A)/(Z^2/A)_{\lim}$; (c) critical shape for $x = 0.65$; (d) the shape corresponding to $x \ll 1$, division into two nearly tangent spheres, where the Coulomb tidal distortion is neglected (low Z).

ing those spheres just out of the range of the surface forces. The shape of Fig. 22d is the case we shall compute. Here the Coulomb energy is not strictly zero, but only very small. The critical shape will then still allow for a tiny neck connecting the two fragment drops, which can be torn apart by the Coulomb repulsion. If we neglect the energy of the neck, which is very small in our case, we can simply compute the difference between the energies of the two equal spherical fragments and the original sphere. The fission threshold energy, E_{th}, will in this case be

$$E_{\text{th}} = 2 \cdot 4\pi \left[\left(\frac{A}{2} \right)^{\frac{1}{3}} r_0 \right]^2 \sigma - 4\pi [(A)^{\frac{1}{3}} r_0]^2 \sigma + 2 \cdot \frac{3}{5} \frac{(Ze/2)^2}{(A/2)^{\frac{1}{3}} r_0}$$

$$+ \frac{(Ze/2)^2}{2(A/2)^{\frac{1}{3}} r_0} - \frac{3}{5} \frac{(Ze)^2}{A^{\frac{1}{3}} r_0} \quad (103)$$

(with σ = nuclear surface energy/cm^2) from which

$$\frac{E_{th}}{4\pi(A^{1/3}r_0)^2\sigma} = 0.260 - 0.065\,\frac{Z^2}{A} \cdot \frac{e^2/r_0}{4\pi r_0^2\sigma} \qquad (104)$$

where the parameter $\dfrac{e^2/r_0}{4\pi r_0^2\sigma} \cdot \dfrac{Z^2}{A}$ is just $\dfrac{5}{3} \cdot \dfrac{\text{Coulomb energy}}{\text{Surface energy}}$.

(2) Now we consider the other limiting case, with the original droplet so packed with charge that the slightest displacement from the spherical shape will produce fission. Here $E_{th} = 0$. To compute this we consider small constant-volume distortions, axially symmetric, without motion of the center of mass, but otherwise arbitrary. We may represent the radius of the drop surface as a function of the co-latitude angle, θ, by a series in the orthonormal set of Legendre polynomials

$$\frac{\gamma(\theta)}{R} = 1 + 0 \cdot P_1(\cos\theta) + \alpha_2 P_2(\cos\theta) + \alpha_3 P_3(\cos\theta) + \cdots \qquad (105)$$

Here the coefficient of $P_1(\cos\theta)$, α_1, is set equal to zero, since for small displacements (where the higher harmonics may be expected to grow small), it corresponds to displacement of the center of mass. One condition is set on the motion by this requirement. The purely mathematical requirement that the function $\gamma(\theta)$ be single-valued for representation as a Legendre polynomial expansion does restrict the physical motion somewhat. Such a shape as that of the other limiting case—two near-spheres joined by a thin thread—cannot be so represented. This turns out to be an unimportant restriction; our answer is very far from such a shape for the observed fissioning nuclei.

If we make the calculation of the classical area and Coulomb energy with assumption (105), and keep only the leading term, in α_2, we obtain these results for surface and Coulomb energies of an infinitesimally distorted drop (81), neglecting all terms of higher order in the small coefficients α_n:

$$E_C - E_C^{\text{sphere}} = -\frac{3}{5}\frac{(Ze)^2}{A^{1/3}r_0}\left(\frac{\alpha_2^2}{5} + \cdots\right)$$

$$E_{\text{surf}} - E_{\text{surf}}^{\text{sphere}} = 4\pi A^{2/3}r_0^2\sigma\left(\frac{2\alpha_2^2}{5} + \cdots\right) \qquad (106)$$

Then the fission threshold energy, measured in units of the undistorted surface energy, becomes

$$\frac{E_{th}}{4\pi A^{2/3}\gamma_0^2\sigma} = \frac{\alpha_2^2}{5}\left(2 - \frac{E_C^{\text{sphere}}}{E_{\text{surf}}^{\text{sphere}}} + \cdots\right) \qquad (107)$$

We can read off the result: any displacement will lead to fission (i.e., $E_{th} \leq 0$) if $E_C^{\text{sphere}}/E_{\text{surf}}^{\text{sphere}} \geq 2$. Writing this result in terms of the semi-empirical constants, we have

$$E_C/E_{\text{surf}} \big|_{\text{lim}} = Z^2/A \big|_{\text{lim}} \cdot a_C/a_S = 2 \qquad \therefore \ Z^2/A \big|_{\text{lim}} = 45.0 \qquad (108)$$

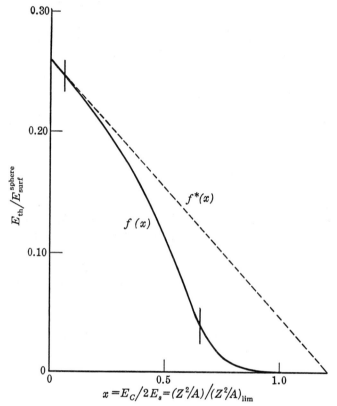

Fig. 23. The fission threshold energy, E_{th}, as a function of the parameter x. The dimensionless function $f(x)$ is just E_{th} measured in units of the nuclear surface energy in its undistorted spherical form, and x is defined by the relations $x = E_C^0/2E_s^0 = Z^2/A/(Z^2/A)_{\text{lim}}$. From fitting the experimental data for U^{239}, we get $(Z^2/A)_{\text{lim}} \sim 48$ (see text). The function $f^*(x)$ is the energy difference between the sphere and the shape of Fig. 22d, two equal nearly tangent fragments, again measured in units of the surface energy. For small x, below the vertical stroke on the curve of $f(x)$, the function $f(x)$ is taken from its limiting value for small Z; above the right-hand vertical mark, $f(x)$ has been calculated numerically. Between the two strokes $f(x)$ has been simply interpolated free-hand.

We can of course continue the series still further, and examine how $E_{th}/E_{\text{surf}}^{\text{sphere}}$, which we will write as $f(x)$, behaves as a function of $x = E_C/2E_S$. This has been done out to quite high powers of the small coefficients—with as many as six or eight harmonic terms. A numerical calculation, done with high-speed calculators (F11), has been carried out with ten harmonic terms, and without making any power-series expansion in the coefficients. The function $f(x)$ is known near $x = 0$ from the calculation in case 1 above, and near the limit $x = 1$ we have plotted the calculated results in Fig. 23. The dashed part of the curve is a reasonable interpolation. We can regard x either from a theoretical point of view, as the ratio $E_C/2E_S$, or in a form more directly comparable with experiment, as $(Z^2/A)/(Z^2/A)_{\lim}$. In the latter form, we see that we can read off the value of the fission threshold E_{th} for any nucleus by computing the surface energy $a_S A^{2/3}$, noting that $E_{\text{th}} = f(x) \cdot a_S A^{2/3}$.

We can now apply these results best not by taking the limiting $(Z^2/A)_{\lim}$ entirely from our semi-empirical constants, but by fitting one observed fission threshold (S8) to the $f(x)$ curve. If we fit $E_{\text{th}}(\text{U}^{239}) = 6.67$, and take, for the surface energy for U^{239}, 502 Mev, we obtain $f[x(\text{U}^{239})] = 0.0132$. This yields $Z^2/A|_{\lim} = 47.8$, which can be compared to 45.0, obtained by taking the constants directly [Eq. (108)].

2. Quantum Effects. We have treated the problem wholly classically. It should be observed that this neglects two quantum-mechanical effects. First, fission may take place for excitation energies below the fission threshold by reason of the tunneling effect; if the representative point comes near the pass over the crater lip, it will often go through the thin barrier remaining. In addition, the vibration of the drop in the distorted mode will have a zero-point energy. Both of these effects can be estimated by computing how the barrier looks as the representative point moves in its path over the energy surface. This can be done under the assumption that the drop distorts through the sequence of shapes near the saddle-points for larger values of x. With this assumption, Frenkel and Metropolis (F11) calculated the barrier as a function of distortion. The Gamow penetration could then be estimated by using this potential barrier, and an effective mass estimated from hydrodynamic arguments. They obtained a penetration probability P for various E_{th} given by $P = 10^{-7.85 E_{\text{th}}}$. The zero-point energy can be calculated from the shape of the crater near zero distortion. This gives a result of some 0.4 Mev for the uranium case and leads to an estimate of the oscillation frequency. Such a zero-point energy, small compared to the excitation involved, implies that the motion can be represented classically as a rather well-defined trajectory by building up wave packets from the actual quantum states. The threshold estimate is then made as follows:

$$E_{\text{th}}(\text{classical}) = E_{\text{zero-point}} + T_{\text{neutron}} + E_{\text{neutron binding}}$$

Using the results that neutron binding in U^{239} is 5.2 Mev (from the semi-empirical formulas) and that the measured neutron kinetic energy is 1.0 Mev, we get the 6.6 Mev used above for E_{th}(classical).

Only qualitative results can be expected from this theory. The actual fission is not into symmetric fragments at these excitations, and the fission thresholds do not in detail vary from nucleus to nucleus in the smooth way here predicted. Moreover, the spontaneous fission rates are in poor agreement. It must be observed that the very large exponents which occur mean that a small error in the barrier will lead to enormous errors in the rate calculations. Perhaps only the *logarithm* of the decay rate should be expected to be of some significance, within a small factor of the truth. Arguing the other way is more sure. It turns out from the $f(x)$ curve (it will be an interesting exercise for the reader) that for $Z > 98$ the typical isotope would be radioactive to such an extent that it would probably disappear from the earth in geologic time, not because of the accidents of alpha-particle disintegration rates (which vary both up and down in just a few Z or A units), but because of the inescapable effects of fission. Thus the fact that the heaviest nucleus occurring in nature is uranium is a consequence only of the kinks in the binding energy curve, coming from the closed shells at $Z = 82$, $N = 126$; this means that the next few elements have short lives against alpha-decay. But the more fundamental reason that no elements of $Z = 100$ or up are found is certainly fission. It will be interesting to see the first nuclear species whose lifetime is controlled by spontaneous fission.

There is one more deduction from this simple theory which is of interest. The calculation of Eq. (104), which we can plot as the function $f^*(x)$ for $0 \leq x \leq 1$ (see Fig. 23), gives the energy difference between the original sphere and the nuclear matter arranged as two equal fragment spheres just touching. Now the energy released on symmetrical fission is a given function of Z and A, independent, of course, of the path followed in dividing. If the released energy is $\Delta E(\frac{1}{2})$, then the energy difference between the critical distorted shape and the separated fragments is just $f(x)a_S A^{2/3}$, while that between separated fragments and two tangent fragment spheres is $f^4(x)a_S A^{2/3}$, which is, from Fig. 23, some 25 or 35 Mev greater in the region of the fissionable nuclei. This means that, when the distorted surface finally tears to release the two fragments, which when far away will eventually come to their stable spherical shape, the difference of about 30 Mev is stored as energy of distortion— energy of excitation—in the two fragments. It is, moreover, plain that the reverse of fission—union—will in general require much more kinetic energy than that released in fission. It will be very unlikely that the special distortion which leads over the low pass in the crater lip will be achieved in the random collisions of nuclei.

B. The Products of Fission

The most obvious consequences of the simple theory given above are in fact not observed. The fission fragments do not appear as equal nuclei with $f = \frac{1}{2}$. On the contrary, the distributions of Fig. 18 are those observed experimentally. No clear explanation of this fact has yet been given. It seems almost sure that there is no complex distortion type which leads to a low-lying pass for some asymmetric distortion of the classical drop. It is much more probable that again we have to do with a reflection of the nuclear shell structure, permitting some motions, some ratios of charge to mass in division, more easily than others. The closed-shell N's at 50 and 82 do seem to mark near-maximum yields. There is some evidence that isotopes of those stable elements with highest $N - Z$ are favored, but the expected predominance of even products is not yet found in the admittedly complex chains of fission fragments. It should be obvious by now that the initial products of fission are not in general stable nuclei, but are very neutron-rich, and begin chains of beta-decays to reach the appropriate ratio of Z/A for their smaller A (B18, W4). It has been shown that, in this beta-decay chain, excitations are in some cases in excess of the neutron binding energies for the product nucleus of a given beta-decay. This leads to the emission of delayed neutrons whose time of emission after fission is determined by the preceding beta-decay processes. Much more numerous are the so-called prompt neutrons, which emerge after a time short compared to any possible beta-decay. It seems very likely that these neutrons are evaporated from the highly excited fragments as they fly apart after the fission act. This would imply that some two or three neutrons are emitted, and that their energy spectrum and angular distribution would be the quasi-Maxwellian one of our statistical theory (compare Fig. 6). The fission fragments, however, continue in motion at their high speeds of near 1 Mev/nucleon for a distance of a few milligrams per square centimeter, or some 10^{-3} cm, in solid matter. The evaporation will occur with neutron widths measured in many kev at least, or in times short compared to the fragment time of flight. So the neutrons will evaporate isotropically from the moving fragment, and in the laboratory system will be emitted preferentially forward, since their kinetic energy will be quite comparable to that of the fragment, expressed as Mev per nucleon. Some evidence has been obtained to confirm this picture as well (W9).

The products of fission, then, are mainly the two large fragments and the prompt neutrons. The fragment decay leads to beta-particle chains, gamma-rays, and the delayed neutrons. But there are other charged particles which emerge at least occasionally upon fission. In about one fission in five hundred an alpha-particle forms the third fragment, with kinetic energy from a few to about 25 Mev (M2). It seems well established that these smaller fragments actually originate from the compound nucleus, and from a tendency to come off at right angles to the direction of the main fragments, and that they arise during the act of fission.

The systematic change in shape of the fission fragment size-distribution curve with energy of the bombarding particle is the most striking feature of Fig. 18. Apparently, as the excitation exceeds the fission threshold more and more, the tendency toward the symmetrical fission expected in the simple theory becomes stronger. Slow-neutron uranium fission is never symmetrical; at energies around 100 Mev, the symmetrical division is the most probable. Direct measurement of the ionization energies of the fragments confirms the observation on the masses of the fragments (J4). Whatever special effects produce the asymmetry are increasingly unimportant as more energy becomes available to the vibrating drop. It does not seem true, however, that the fragments of an asymmetric division have total fission product energies higher than the fragments of nearly symmetric division; there is even some tendency toward the reverse.

C. Fission Cross Sections

Fission, as a mode of decay of a compound nucleus, should be produced by any means that excited the nucleus above the required threshold energy. This has been verified for slow and fast neutrons, for protons, deuterons, and for alpha- and gamma-rays. In general the cross section can be computed by our usual methods—simply writing the cross section for formation of the excited compound nucleus by a particle of energy E_p, and following it by the factor for its competitive disintegration:

$$\sigma_f(E_p) = \sigma(E_p) \frac{\xi(W)\Gamma_f(W)}{\Gamma_f + \Gamma_n + \Gamma_\gamma + \cdots} \tag{109}$$

where Γ_f is the width for fission from a compound nucleus of excitation W. The calculation of the fission width is the calculation of how the excitation of the nuclear drop is distributed among all its possible modes of motion: there is available a large amount of phase space for motions which lead to distortions from which the drop cannot divide; only a small volume in phase is assigned to such motions of the point representing all the parameters of distortion as do lead over the pass in the wall of the energy crater. Below the threshold for fission, the excitation energy can be lost by any other energetically available means, usually gamma-radiation or neutron evaporation, but not by fission. As the excitation $W = E_p + E_B(p)$ increases to near the classical fission threshold, tunnel effect can lead to fission. The fission width will increase, and fission will become a competitive reaction. We can expect the fission width to rise rapidly, perhaps something like exponentially, as the fission threshold is considerably exceeded. What the cross sections will be then will depend largely on how high the fission threshold is relative to the excitation energy of a given mode of excitation. Thus $\sigma_f(E_n)$ for $U^{238} + n^1$ is zero until a threshold of about 1 Mev, from which it rises slowly to a value comparable with πR^2. It stays nearly constant because for some time Γ_f and Γ_n rise about in the same way. We know from the experiments with very fast fission, on elements like bismuth, where the fission threshold is some 12 Mev or more, that the neutron specific width rises more rapidly than that for fission. Very high excitation in Bi^{209} leads mainly to multiple neutron evaporation; some ten or twelve neutrons are boiled off before fission becomes a very important competitor. Only when the fission threshold has come down, because of the gradually increasing value of Z^2/A in this neutron boiling-off, does σ_f begin to grow to a value comparable with unity, actually about 0.1 or 0.2. This is confirmed both by the fission-product distribution (which is that of fission by a nucleus of $A \sim 200$) and by the fact that the fission fragments come apart with energy near that expected from fission near the threshold energy. The distribution of fragment sizes becomes broader with increasing excitation; the mode of division does not need to be so special. Even so, it is plausible that there are many more ways for a highly excited drop to emit neutrons than to divide by fission, so that, while the Γ_f rises rapidly, it does not rise so rapidly as the other terms of total Γ, almost all of which, at these energies, arise from neutron evaporation.

Special processes, like photofission and fission in the region of application of the dispersion formulas, have been discussed in the literature (B18, G3, N1).

SECTION 11. NUCLEAR REACTIONS AT HIGH ENERGY

The processes we have discussed so far are characterized by the fact that the energy of the incoming nucleon, both potential and kinetic, becomes quickly shared among all the particles of the nucleus. After a relatively very long time, during which numerous nucleon collisions occur, this energy may again become concentrated in a particular nucleon, or in some special mode of motion, and the nucleus will de-excite by particle emission, fission, or the slow processes of radiation. As the energy brought in grows, the number of available modes of disintegration naturally increases, and the lifetime of the compound nucleus becomes shorter and shorter. With energies in the range up to some 30 to 50 Mev, the nucleus will emit typically several nucleons before it cools, and the reactions are increasingly complex. Such reactions as $(p,3n)$ and $(p,4n)$ have been studied (K5). But, as the energy increases, there is a gradual transition to a state of affairs which is best described in a conceptual framework quite the opposite from that suited to the compound nucleus. This high-energy point of view works best above some hundreds of Mev of incoming nucleon energy, and the two schemes will merge in the broad transition region between.

Most characteristic of the high-energy region is the fact that the mean free path, in nuclear matter, of the fast nucleon is comparable with the radius of the nucleus itself. The nuclear matter is no longer a black, impenetrable obstacle, which traps the incoming particle, but a kind of sphere of dilute gas, through which the fast-moving nucleon has an appreciable chance to penetrate without any collision whatever. Even a collision or two do not by any means rob the incoming nucleon of most of its energy. The momentum transfer in such a collision, which is typically transverse to the classically pretty well-defined trajectory of the short-wavelength incident nucleon, is of the order $\Delta p \sim \hbar/R$, where R is the range of nuclear forces (S7). This implies an energy transfer of some 30 Mev. In the short time of such a collision ($\sim 10^{-22}$ sec) the struck nucleon will make only very few, if any, collisions with the neighboring nucleons of the nucleus, and, although the momentum transfer is not so large that we are wholly safe in regarding the struck nucleons as free, still that will be a reasonable initial approximation. We shall see that the principal effects of the nucleon environment are consequences of the Fermi degeneracy of the nucleon matter. The collision will be modified by the impossibility of leaving the struck nucleon in a momentum state already occupied by some other nucleon of the nucleus.

The geometry of the approach of the nucleon will determine the sequence of events. If it passes through the nuclear edge, it may make no collision, or perhaps one. A very fast nucleon, having lost only 30 Mev, will emerge. The nucleus left behind may be excited by the full amount of the energy given to the struck nucleon, or by very much less if the initial path of the struck nucleon allowed it as well to leave the nearby nuclear surface without further collisions. A fast particle striking the very center of the nucleus, where the nucleus is thickest, may have to travel a few mean paths in nuclear matter, and will typically make several collisions, leaving in its wake a few nucleons of 20 to 30 Mev energy each, perhaps losing all its energy, being finally captured. The secondary nucleons in turn can escape only if they are close to the nuclear surface and moving outwards. Some may do so; others will collide with many nuclear particles, and gradually spread their energy around among many modes of motion, forming a heated compound nucleus, which will cool off just as in the reactions of lower energy. A typical many-particle nuclear reaction, often called, from its appearance in nuclear emulsion photographs or in the cloud chamber, a "star," can then be thought of as a kind of approach to thermal equilibrium, beginning with a well-defined single-particle trajectory, followed through a cascade of secondary, tertiary, etc., collisions, and ultimately resulting in a diffusion of excitation energy like heat through a conducting sphere.

The initial stages form the high-energy limit; here the reaction is to be described by a step-by-step following out of the nuclear cascade, taking into account collisions with one or with a few correlated nucleons; finally, the energy is shared by the collective motion, in something like transient thermal equilibrium, which is the low-energy, compound nucleus picture. A single star event may exhibit both features; it is the fact that the first stage takes a time $\sim 10^{-22}$ sec, very much less than the 10^{-16} sec of the last stage, which permits a more or less sharp division into the two stages. On this sharp division, which is only approximate, the simplicity of the picture depends. The intermediate time, during which the energy is distributed among too many degrees of freedom to be described in detail, but too few to approach any sort of quasi-equilibrium, is beyond the present theory; such complex cases will be especially important in the lighter nuclei, and for a mass A nucleus at energies 10A Mev, enough to dissociate the whole nucleus. Our treatment will deal wholly with the two well-separated stages: the initial cascade and the final thermal equilibrium.

A. The Nuclear Cascade

The initial cascade has been followed out by the most direct means. The theory has been the semi-empirical one of the so-called Monte Carlo method (G5), in which after the establishment of the model and the appropriate cross sections—which are the decisive features for the accuracy of the results—the calculation is done by considering the successive events in the motion of the incoming nucleon and all its collision partners, with their collisions in turn; choosing the actual steps by a series of random choices; and finally cutting off the whole process when some arbitrary low-energy limit is reached beyond which the energy is assigned as equilibrium excitation of the compound nucleus. This step-by-step process is extremely tedious, and only a few hundred individual "stars" have been followed through on paper. The results are subject then to a fair degree of statistical uncertainty over and beyond shortcomings of the model. But enough has been done to make the general features of the high-energy stage in star formation fairly clear.

1. Fermi Gas Model of the Initial Nucleus. The short collision time and high recoil energy make most plausible the use of the simplest of

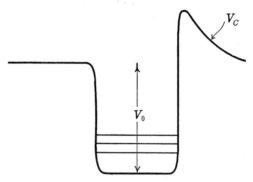

Fig. 24. Diagram of the potential well in which the nucleons are bound in the simple Fermi-gas model. The Coulomb barrier affects only the protons. The well depth is determined by the nuclear density and the assigned binding energy.

nuclear models, that of the Fermi gas of non-interacting nucleons contained in a well of assigned diameter and depth. Naturally the correlations actually arising from the nuclear forces, here ignored, will be important eventually. One clear sign of this is found in the process of the pick-up of a nucleon from the nucleus, to emerge bound to another outgoing nucleon in an emitted deuteron, a process far more important than the Fermi gas model would predict. But, aside from such details, it is appropriate to begin with a Fermi gas.

The procedure is the familiar statistical one for finding the distribution of a completely degenerate Fermi gas, at $T = 0°$. The nucleus is replaced by a spherical potential well in which the particles move without interacting. Each particle has a wave function which is simply a plane wave; the finite depth of the well, and hence the leaking of the plane waves into the classically forbidden region outside the well, is neglected. Then a particle of each spin is placed in every momentum state until all particles are accounted for. The neutrons and the protons are regarded as entirely independent and as moving in separate wells; the additional Coulomb barrier for the protons may be regarded as beginning at the well edge. Figure 24 shows the model schematically. Replacing the sum over the filled states by an integral, and remembering that $(2s + 1)$ particles with different spin orientations may be placed in each cell in phase space, of volume $(2\pi\hbar)^3$, we obtain for the number of particles of a given kind, with spin s, in a sphere of volume V,

$$N_s = V \cdot \int_0^{p_F} (2s + 1)p^2 \, dp \, d\Omega/(2\pi\hbar)^3$$

where p_F is the limiting momentum to which the states are occupied, and the energy corresponding to p_F, the Fermi energy E_F, is given by $E_F = p_F{}^2/2M_s$. If we take the sphere of nuclear matter to be a sphere of constant density independent of the mass number A, as is usual, and write for the radius of the nucleus $R = r_0 \cdot A^{1/3}$, we can easily find an expression for the Fermi energy for the nucleons of one kind: $E_{F_s} = (18\pi)^{2/3}/8 \times \hbar^2/Mr_0{}^2 \cdot (N_s/A)^{2/3}$, where N_s is either the atomic number Z for the protons, or the neutron number $N = A - Z$ for the neutrons. This gives the numerical result: $E_{F_s} = 9.7(N_s/A)^{2/3}(a_0/r_0)^2$ Mev, where we have written a_0/r_0, the ratio of a_0, the classical electron radius, 2.82×10^{-13} cm, to the nuclear radius parameter. For orientation a few values are listed in Table 11. The well depth is now fixed to give the

TABLE 11

PROTON AND NEUTRON FERMI ENERGIES FOR VARIOUS NUCLEI

	Cu^{65}		Cs^{133}		Pb^{208}	
$r_0 =$	1.4	1.6	1.4	1.6	1.4	1.6×10^{-13} cm
E_F(protons)	22.6	17.5	22	16.9	21	16.1 Mev
E_F(neutrons)	26	20	27	20.7	28	21.5

highest-lying neutron state about 8 Mev binding energy, and an additional Coulomb barrier may be assigned for the protons. This implies a nuclear potential well for neutrons in lead about 35 Mev deep, using the smaller value of the radius parameter, and an additional Coulomb barrier V_C for the protons about $0.5(Z/A^{1/3})(a_0/r_0)$ Mev high, or ~14 Mev for lead. In the calculations the two types of nucleons are often represented by a single gas of about average properties.

In the region of high energies, the simple Fermi gas model has two characteristic consequences which are certainly to be expected even from more realistic models of the internal nucleon motion. It is perfectly clear that the complete neglect of nucleon interactions is an extreme procedure which tends to underestimate the range of momenta represented in the statistical motion of the nucleons. One can regard this lack of a high-momentum tail as implying either the neglect of spatial correlations, in which the nuclear density fluctuates toward higher values because of the nucleon interaction and the transient formation of sub-units of two, three, or four nucleons, or as a neglect of occasional transitions, made possible by nucleon interaction, from the lowest states of the Fermi gas to some of the higher unoccupied momentum states. Both ways amount to the same thing; they form the basis for regarding the Fermi gas calculation as a first step in a systematic approximation method. We shall look here, however, into the consequences of the raw Fermi model as they affect high-energy interaction events.

(a) *Influence of the Exclusion Principle.* In this model, the incoming nucleon, once it enters the nuclear volume, fills a hitherto unoccupied momentum state. Now it enters into a collision with some one of the nucleons already present, lying in one of the filled levels below the limiting Fermi momentum p_F. The spirit of the model, representing all nucleons as free, now clearly requires that the momenta of the two collision partners after the collision lie in an unoccupied region of the momentum space. A simple exchange of momenta corresponds to an elastic collision. Any other event must begin by fulfilling the condition of entering fresh momentum space regions. Evidently a small momentum transfer to the struck nucleon is forbidden unless the nucleon initially lies very near the edge of the sphere in momentum space of radius p_F. As long as momentum transfers not very great compared to p_F are of importance in the process, which means that the incident particle may have momentum up to many hundreds of Mev/c (or even considerably higher if forward scattering alone is under consideration), the cross section for collisions with the average nucleon of the Fermi gas will be much reduced by the requirements of the exclusion principle. This will evidently increase the chance of passing through nuclear matter without collisions, and will tend to reduce the relative probability of small-angle scattering, both near zero degrees in the center-of-mass frame and, because the projectile also satisfies the exclusion principle, near 180° as well.

Figure 25 presents the geometrical considerations in momentum space. A calculation (G5) on this purely geometrical basis shows that the exclusion principle reduces an assumed isotropic cross section for scattering in the ratio:

$$\sigma_{av} = \sigma_{free}\left(1 - \frac{7}{5}\frac{p_F{}^2}{p_i{}^2}\right)$$

where σ_{free} is the isotropic scattering cross section per unit solid angle for a free nucleon, and p_i is the incident nucleon momentum. This formula holds only for values of $p_i \geq 2^{\frac{1}{2}}p_F$; below that incident momentum the result is more complicated. The direct analytical evaluation has not yet been performed for a case with the cross section anisotropic. The angular distribution can be approached through the same geometrical scheme, if the scattering cross section is taken as a function of the momentum transfer $|\, p_i - p_f \,| = |\,\delta\,|$ only, which corresponds to the Born approximation without exchange.

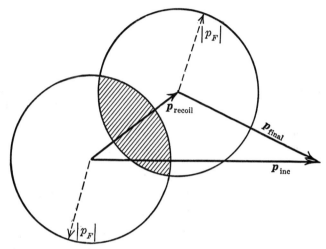

Fig. 25. Kinematics of the collision between an incoming nucleon and the nucleons of the Fermi gas. The incident, recoil, and final momentum vectors are shown, with spheres of radius in momentum space just p_F, the Fermi momentum. The shaded region is excluded; no collision in which the vectors p_{recoil} or p_{final} terminate within this region is permitted by the Pauli principle.

(b) *Influence of the Zero-Point Motion.* The angular distribution of particles scattering from the Fermi gas involves two distinct and important effects: the exclusion of low-momentum transfer collisions, and the smearing out of the otherwise unique correlation between scattering angle and energy of emerging particle, which can be regarded as the effect of the zero-point motion of the struck nucleons of the Fermi gas, which of course spread over a wide range of momenta, and hence of relative velocities, as seen from an incoming nucleon of fixed energy. The geometry of the event is just that of Fig. 25, and one can write rather complicated expressions for the cross section in the laboratory system for scattering a particle into the element of final momentum of the scattered particle, $\mathbf{p}_f$:

$$\frac{d\sigma}{d\mathbf{p}_f} = \sigma(\delta)f(p_F, p_f', \theta) \tag{110}$$

where f is a function of the momenta and scattering angle, and the regions of integration for the total cross sections can be found from the figure. Since the cross section for neutron-proton scattering, for example, is far from simple in the relevant energy regions, only numerical calculations have been made. Figure 26 shows the general results to be expected: the curves correspond to special choices for the cross section.

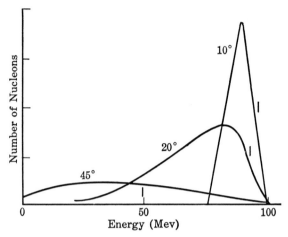

Fig. 26. The energy distribution of nucleons scattered at a fixed laboratory angle by a single collision with a nucleon in the nucleus. The effects of the Fermi motion and of the exclusion principle have been included. The incident energy is 100 Mev; an empirical fit to the neutron-proton scattering cross section was used. The vertical strokes mark the energy expected at the three angles shown if the collision was with a free stationary nucleon, in which case the energy would be a unique function of angle. The spreading effect of the Fermi motion is conspicuous (65).

The smearing of the energy-angle correlation and the shifting of the scattering toward right-angle scattering is at least made qualitatively evident. All this applies of course to an event in which only a single primary collision is made within the nucleus.

2. Following the Cascade: The Monte Carlo Method. The absence of any theoretically based analytical form for the nucleon-nucleon scattering cross sections, and the rather complicated geometry in coordinate and momentum space required to treat the problem, have led to the use of an interesting method which enables not only calculation of the results of a single collision, but also actually follows out step by step the development of what may be called a nuclear cascade.

In this application of a general computational scheme, called for obvious reasons the Monte Carlo method, a single incident nucleon of given energy is allowed to enter the nuclear volume. Its collisions are followed in complete kinematical detail, and the subsequent collisions of all its collision partners are followed as well until either: (1) any of the excited nucleons passes outside of the nuclear volume, after which of course no further interest attaches to it except that it is an emitted nucleon, with its energy, direction, and charge; or (2) any of the nucleons involved, while still within the nuclear sphere, reaches an energy below some previously selected value, after which it is regarded as captured, and its excitation energy passes eventually into the motion of an excited compound nucleus.   Then follows the process of nucleon evaporation, regarded as separate from the initial cascade. The cascade computations are usually made graphically.   The distinguishing feature of the method is that the decision as to which of a set of equally probable events occurs is made by some procedure of random choice, using tables of random numbers, spinners, etc.   Various simplifications of geometry may be made, and the continuous functions of angle, etc., which occur are typically stepwise approximated by dividing the interval into a set of discrete subintervals, giving the function some constant value as an approximation throughout the whole of the subinterval.

Let us follow a neutron of energy E incident on a nucleus of fixed A and radius.   Where does it make its first collision?   Its point of entry is chosen by making a random choice among the rings of equal area normal to the direction of the beam.   Then its distance of travel is found by assuming that it moves with a mean free path given by the assumed total interaction cross section with free nucleons of the given density (the effect of the exclusion principle can come in only *after* the collision has been made).   A distance δ which is small compared to λ, the mean free path in nuclear matter, and which gives a probability of collision δ/λ, can be chosen, and a random decision made as to whether or not it collides in this line segment.   The nucleon continues to progress segment by segment in a straight line, until either it leaves the nuclear volume or it makes a collision.   Typically at these energies a fair fraction of the nucleons traverse the nucleus without collision, especially those which enter near the edge.   When the nucleon has made a collision, a whole set of random choices must be made.   First, the momentum of the struck nucleon drawn from the Fermi gas must be found, by picking at random from intervals of equal probability in momentum space, weighting the flat Fermi momentum distribution by the dependence of the collision cross section on relative momentum.   Then the angle of scattering must be found.   Usually it is best to work in the center-of-mass system, and to approximate the differential cross section for scattering by a dozen or so steps.   Once the angle of the collision has been found by a random choice, the final momentum vector of each of the collision partners is fixed uniquely by the conservation law, since the collision is regarded as free. Now one may see if the collision is allowed by the exclusion principle. If both the final vector momenta do not lie outside the filled sphere, the collision is nullified, and the original particle continues undisturbed until it makes another collision. If the collision is permitted, then each of the collision partners is now a nucleon of definite vector momentum at a specified point in the nuclear sphere. The history of each can now be followed until it in turn escapes or is absorbed. Account is of course kept of all partners in each collision, and the event associated with one incident nucleon is not complete until every struck nucleon has been emitted or absorbed. It is obvious that the computation is tedious; it is equally clear that it is an extremely flexible method, capable of high accuracy. It is hardly a calculation so much as an experiment in thought, using a well-defined model.

Two calculations have been worked out on these lines for incident energies 90 and 400 Mev, and reported in some detail (B10, G5). They are unfortunately not strictly comparable, mainly because different fundamental cross sections for collision were used. In one case the target nucleus was lead, whereas in the other it was $A = 100$, more like the heavy nuclei of photographic emulsion. In Fig. 27 is drawn a typical cascade event just as it was followed. Here the approximation was made of treating the nucleus as a two-dimensional circle, after the first collision; the graph then gives directly the projected angles of emission. In the event shown a 400-Mev nucleon entered, making its first collision about one-third of the way across the nucleus. The two partners of this collision were nucleons initially of 431 and 13 Mev of kinetic energy. It will be noted that a nuclear potential well of 31 Mev is assumed, with an additional barrier of 4 Mev (half the Coulomb barrier, since protons and neutrons are not distinguished). One of the first pair of collision partners leaves the nucleus directly, as a fast cascade fragment of 282 Mev. The other goes on to try to make a collision in a short distance, at the point marked by a circle, but it is forbidden to do so by the exclusion principle. Then it goes on to an allowed collision with a rather fast nucleon of the Fermi gas. In all, this event consisted of six nucleon collisions: one nucleon enters the nucleus with 400 Mev kinetic energy outside; and three leave, taking with them over 300 Mev, mostly in the kinetic energy of the one very fast collision partner of the first collision; while four more are excited but "captured," leaving the residual nucleus excited by 66 Mev, with the mean binding energy per particle taken at about 8 Mev.

The collection of results for both calculations gives some impression of the nature of nucleon cascades. The mean excitation energy of the nucleus changes very slowly with the energy of the incident particle: the 90-Mev neutron on lead left a mean thermal excitation energy of some 44 Mev, the 400-Mev proton on emulsion nuclei only about 50 Mev. This slow rise of excitation with incident energy is partly an artifact of the somewhat forced comparison, but it is actually to be

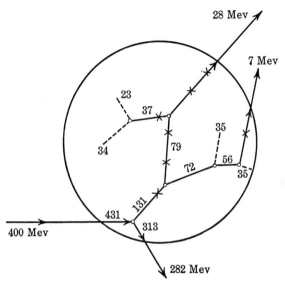

Fig. 27. A projected diagram of a nuclear cascade event, followed by the Monte Carlo method. The entering nucleon has 400 Mev of kinetic energy; the numbers mark the energy of each of the nucleons participating. The path of each nucleon is shown until it leaves the nucleus, or until it reaches an energy below 35 Mev, taken as the threshold for capture. Along the path of each particle an effective collision is marked with an open circle; a cross implies a collision which was forbidden by the exclusion principle. Note that in this event three cascade particles emerged, all in the forward hemisphere, and the nucleus was left excited thermally with about 65 Mev, enough to evaporate several neutrons isotropically before becoming stable. From (B10).

expected as a general result, since the high-energy nucleons make high-energy secondaries, which typically depart from the nucleus with most of their energy, since the mean free path rises with nucleon energy.

In both calculations also there is a rather wide distribution of energies among the cascade products, and a considerable fraction of the energy almost always goes to them, as the low mean excitation indicated. With the lower energy and the bigger nucleus, however, about 5 percent of those incident particles which made any collisions whatever left their whole energy in nuclear excitation, with no cascade particles emitted. In the high-energy, $A = 100$, case, no event of this kind occurred at all (among sixty studied); the minimum energy found in the cascade particles was about half the incident energy, 200 Mev.

The general nature of the cascades can be seen from Table 12 and

TABLE 12

NUCLEAR CASCADES STUDIED BY THE MONTE CARLO METHOD

	90-Mev Neutron on Pb	400-Mev Proton on $A = 100$
Fraction of incident particles traversing nucleus without any collision	0.15	0.33
Fraction of cascades without emerging particles	0.05	0
Mean thermal excitation energy	43 Mev	50 Mev
Mean number of cascade particles emerging per cascade event	1.2	3.2
Maximum number of emerging cascade particles	3	~6–8

Figs. 26 and 27. It should be remembered that the sampling error alone in all these calculations is still quite large. Only a few hundred cascade particles have been "seen to emerge," and information about any special category of them is necessarily only qualitative in character.

It is quite clear from the results that this process does not much resemble the evaporation model. The large number of emitted particles with quite high energy, and the strong departure from anything like isotropic distribution in angle, are distinguishing features of the nuclear cascade. The present experimental material is fully consistent with the model we have outlined here. Of course, the evaporation of low-energy particles, among them often complex nuclei of A from 2 to 10, with isotropic directional distribution, is expected and observed to follow, completing the de-excitation of the struck nucleus (B11, H3).

In both calculations reported, the neutrons and protons were not distinguished, but replaced by a gas of nucleons with about average properties. This reflects the feeling that the cascade particles will roughly be randomly divided into neutrons and protons, without much correlation between particle type and either direction or energy. The fact that in heavy nuclei, especially, there are more neutrons than protons is perhaps the principal difference to be recalled, apart from the collision cross sections. The Coulomb barrier and the binding energy differences, especially the symmetry energy, which tends to keep the nucleus from becoming either proton- or neutron-rich in excess, will be unimportant factors in modifying the cascade, because of the typically high energies of the emitted nucleons, in strong contrast to the evaporation mode of disintegration. Some detailed examination of the Monte Carlo results tended to verify the idea that nucleons emitted would be about half protons and half neutrons, for the nucleus with $A = 100$ and a 400-Mev incident proton. It is important to keep this feature of the cascade in mind when discussing the experimental data, which for the most part give information concerning only the ionizing prongs of the star event. There is ample empirical evidence, however, that the neutrons are in fact emitted (C8).

The actual collision cross sections for free collisions are still of course not entirely certain. The empirical situation is discussed in Part IV, Volume I, but the principal question comes from the very curious observed behavior of $\sigma_{p\text{-}p}$, which is so strikingly independent of both energy and angle above about 100 Mev. Whether this property is one characteristic of the special states allowed by the exclusion principle in a proton-proton collision, or whether it reflects some deeper difference between the behavior of protons and neutrons, is a matter which will much affect the easy treatment of nucleons on an equal footing. It is this flatness of the cross section which is responsible for the increase of the proton energy loss in nuclei of medium size at high energies, and consequent growth in star size as the nucleon energy goes from 100 to 400 Mev, even in medium-A nuclei.

B. Correlations among Nucleons

Of course, the neglect of all nucleon interaction in the Fermi gas model is to be regarded as a zeroth approximation. In fact, the nucleons are not uniformly distributed either in momentum space or in coordinate space. The nuclear matter is lumpy, with constantly forming and dissolving groups of nucleons. When a given nucleon enters into a collision, it is not free. Some momentum may be transferred to a neighbor through the force binding the two; or the recoil may be regarded as shared by a correlated spatial cluster of two or even more nucleons. In the complex process of the cascade, with high momentum transfers and repeated events, these effects show up only as eventual improvements to our present crude theory; but there are already known processes in which these correlation effects are, so to speak, the whole story. In the single elastic scattering of fast protons by light nuclei (where the cascade has no room to develop), in processes of typically low momentum transfer (as reactions induced by gamma-rays and by the absorption of slow mesons), and in the so-called "pick-up" processes (the inverse of deuteron stripping, in which a fast nucleon leaves the nucleus no longer alone but now paired with another nucleon which originated in the target, to form a stable fast-moving deuteron), the influence of the correlations and their consequent momentum distribution is decisive.

The probability for finding two nucleons of the Fermi gas at positions r_1 and r_2 respectively is of course given by the integral

$$P(\mathbf{r}_1, \mathbf{r}_2) = \sum_{sp} \int d\tau_3 \cdots d\tau_N \left| \Psi(\mathbf{r}_1 \cdots \mathbf{r}_N) \right|^2$$

where the wave function Ψ is given by the determinantal expression

$$\Psi = \begin{vmatrix} \varphi_a(\mathbf{r}_1)\varphi_a(\mathbf{r}_2) \cdots \\ \varphi_b(\mathbf{r}_1)\varphi_b(\mathbf{r}_2) \cdots \end{vmatrix}, \quad \varphi_\alpha(\mathbf{n}_j) = \frac{1}{V^{\frac{1}{2}}} e^{i\mathbf{k}_\alpha \cdot \mathbf{r}_j} \chi(\sigma_j)$$

Using the orthogonality of the individual plane waves for different allowed momenta $\hbar k_\alpha$, and replacing the sum over values of $\mathbf{k}_\alpha$ by an integral over momentum space $\sum_{\mathbf{k}_\alpha} \rightarrow \frac{V}{(2\pi\hbar)^3} \int_0^{p_{max}} d\mathbf{p}$, we obtain the result

$$P(\mathbf{r}_1, \mathbf{r}_2) = \sum_{\sigma,\tau} \frac{(1 - \delta_{\sigma_1\sigma_2}\delta_{\tau_1\tau_2}w^2)}{4V^2} \tag{111a}$$

where the $\sigma_{1,2}$ give the spin, and $\tau_{1,2}$ the character, of the nucleon at points $\mathbf{r}_1$ and $\mathbf{r}_2$. The space function w depends only on the distance between the nucleons and is given by

$$w(| \mathbf{r}_1 - \mathbf{r}_2 |) = w(\delta) = \frac{3(\sin \delta - \delta \cos \delta)}{\delta^3} \qquad \hbar\delta = p_{max}| \mathbf{r}_1 - \mathbf{r}_2 | \tag{111b}$$

Thus there is no correlation in position between unlike nucleons, or like nucleons differing in spin; but between nucleons alike in type and spin there is a definite spatial correlation arising from the exclusion principle, *even if all forces between nucleons are neglected.* Presence of interaction forces of course affects the wave function and hence the correlations. Using the Fermi gas as a zeroth approximation, calculations have been made to find what the spatial correlation is like under various assumed forces. Figure 28 shows the general character of the results. The momentum space distribution is given with and without interactions. The details of course depend on the forces assumed to act, but the general effect is to replace the rectangular Fermi gas momentum distribution with one which contains some components of higher momentum— traceable in the usual perturbation theory to transitions to unoccupied states of the Fermi gas spectrum induced by collisions. The actual distribution, with interactions, is somewhat as though the Fermi gas were present but not at zero temperature. A calculation by Watanabe, assuming certain Gaussian potentials, indicated that the ground state of the nucleus of high A might correspond roughly to the momentum distribution in a Fermi gas of nucleons at a temperature of 6 or 8 Mev (W2).

There are many processes, mentioned above, which reflect the momentum distribution of the nucleons in the nucleus. One of the most

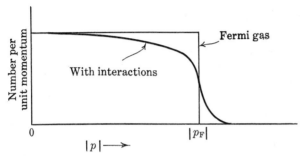

Fig. 28. The momentum distribution of nucleons in a Fermi gas at zero excitation, and the same distribution when interactions are considered. Note that the effect of interactions in momentum space simulates the presence of thermal excitation.

interesting is the rather unexpected process called "pick-up." Table 13 gives a summary of some experimental results which make it plain that the pick-up process is by no means a rare one (Y4).

TABLE 13

PICK-UP CROSS SECTIONS FOR 90-MEV NEUTRONS

	C	Cu	Pb	
$\sigma_{\text{inelastic}}$, all events	0.2	0.8	1.8	barns
Relative cross section for events yielding:				
Cascade protons with $E_p > 20$ Mev	40%	30%	25%	
Pick-up deuterons $(E_d > 27$ Mev$)$	12%	7%	4%	

Evidently the escape of the deuteron intact is relatively more difficult for the larger nuclei. It is to be expected that a deuteron can leak out of a good-sized nucleus at these energies only if it is formed in the far surface region; otherwise one or the other of the nucleons within it will collide in leaving the nucleus. This implies that the formation of such a system is really quite probable when the whole nucleus is taken into account.

The process can be described in rather classical language as the encounter of the incoming nucleon with another nucleon, of the right type and moving with the right direction and speed, so that the two move along together, forming a deuteron when the binding forces become effective. The whole event is by no means localized in a small region of space within the nucleus, since the deuteron is a big structure. Presumably the nuclear edge contributes most of the pick-up processes, when nucleon passages outside the nuclear volume by distances as great as the range of the nuclear forces often contribute. Energy and momentum must be pretty nearly conserved between the two particles, since a strong recoil would imply the break-up of the weak deuteron bond. The whole picture is roughly confirmed by experiment; deuterons do appear in fair number, coming off mostly forward, with about the energy of the incoming particle. At other angles the effect is smaller, and the typical energies lower. The incoming nucleon seeks a partner moving with the same momentum; then the two could move with negligible relative kinetic energy, and deuteron formation would be easy. But such a process would rob the nucleus of a great deal of energy, since essentially it would then emit two particles each with kinetic energy equal to that brought in by only one. The over-all energy and momentum conservation then implies emission of somewhat slower deuterons.

The process is treated by an approximation that is physically very satisfactory. We make two assumptions: (1) The incoming neutron interacts with only a single proton at a time. All multiple events, subsequent collisions, etc., are neglected, to be treated separately. We will find the cross section for a single proton and simply multiply the result by Z. (2) During the collision, the forces between the collision partners are so strong that they overwhelm all the forces which bind the struck nucleon into the nucleus. The whole effect of the binding forces, which are by no means neglected, is thought of as determining the initial momentum distribution of the struck nucleon in the original nuclear ground state. For this second assumption, the approximation has been given the name of the impulse approximation; it has found application in a variety of problems involving collisions with a complex system (C1).

We write the usual form for the cross section per proton from the time-dependent perturbation theory:

$$d\sigma_{df} = \frac{2\pi}{\hbar} \rho_f \left| H_{of} \right|^2 dE$$

Call the final deuteron momentum, measured in the center-of-mass system of the struck nucleus, $\hbar \mathbf{K}$; the initial neutron momentum $\hbar \mathbf{k_0}$. Write the energy of excitation of the residual nucleus $W_f = E_f - E_0$, and the deuteron binding energy B. If we normalize the continuum states of the initial neutron and the final deuteron center-of-mass motion to unit volume, we have for the cross section per proton, for deuteron emission into solid angle $d\Omega$ leaving the nucleus with excitation W_f,

$$\sigma_{df}\, d\Omega = \frac{2\pi}{\hbar} \rho_f \big| H_{of} \big|^2 d\Omega = \frac{2\pi}{\hbar} \cdot \frac{M}{\hbar k_0} \cdot \frac{2M\hbar K}{(2\pi\hbar)^3} \big| V_{of} \big|^2 d\Omega$$

$$= \frac{1}{2\pi^2\hbar^4} \cdot \frac{M^2 K}{k_0}\, d\Omega \big| V_{of} \big|^2 \qquad (112)$$

The matrix element $\big| V_{of} \big|$ is that of the neutron-proton interaction taken between the initial and final states normalized as described. These would be unit-amplitude plane waves for the incident neutron and the outgoing deuteron center-of-mass if we used the Born approximation, but the present calculation is not restricted to that simplification. For present purposes, we will simplify by neglecting the change of deuteron momentum with W_f, which is good in the limit of high neutron momentum, and take merely some average W_f. Now let us take as given the undisturbed wave function for the proton in its initial state, bound to the nucleus. Call this $\psi_i(\mathbf{n}_p)$, writing it as usual as a function of the proton position, $\mathbf{r}_p$. We can find from this by Fourier transformation the momentum-space wave function,

$$\varphi_i(\mathbf{k}_p) = \frac{1}{(2\pi)^{3/2}} \int e^{i\mathbf{k}_p \cdot \mathbf{r}_p} \psi_i\, d\mathbf{r}_p$$

where now $\big| \varphi_i \big|^2$ is the probability for an initial proton momentum $\mathbf{k}_p$. The chief assumption of the impulse approximation now tells us that this initial momentum distribution alone affects the process, which in all other respects behaves as though the proton were initially free. Then over-all conservation requires the two conditions:

(a) $$\mathbf{K} = \mathbf{k_0} + \mathbf{k}$$

$$\tag{113}$$

(b) $$\frac{\hbar^2 K^2}{4M} = B + \frac{\hbar k_0^2}{2M} + W_f$$

We will also write the wave function for the neutron-proton system in the initial and the final states as ψ_D, ψ_0 respectively. Here each is a "deuteron" wave function: in the initial state, the "deuteron" is of course highly excited, with a large positive energy, while in the final state the outgoing deuteron is bound, in its ground state, ψ_0, of internal motion. These functions, like the interaction potential, we take to depend only on the relative coordinates of neutron and proton; the center-of-mass coordinates simply lead to the required momentum conservation. In the initial state the relative internal momentum of the neutron and proton is given by $(\mathbf{k}_p - \mathbf{k}_0)/2 = \mathbf{K}/2 - \mathbf{k}_0$. The factor of one-half arises in the usual way from the introduction of the reduced mass in the equivalent one-body problem expressing the relative motion. Now the squared matrix element of the interaction, which determines the cross section, can be written, for a single proton,

$$| H_{of} |^2 = | \varphi_i(\mathbf{k}_p) |^2 \times \left| \int d\tau \psi_0^*(\mathbf{r}_n - \mathbf{r}_p) V(\mathbf{r}_n - \mathbf{r}_p)\psi_D(\mathbf{r}_n - \mathbf{r}_p) \right|^2$$

(114)

The content of the impulse approximation is just the writing down of this expression, first, to be summed over all the protons, and, second, as a simple product of the two-particle scattering matrix element with the probability for a given proton initial momentum. Now we can write the wave functions and scattering potential $V(\mathbf{r}_n - \mathbf{r}_p)$ in the momentum representation, giving them as a function of the relative momentum, say $\mathbf{q}$, and the matrix element can be written

$$(0| V |D) = \left[\varphi_0(\mathbf{q}), V(\mathbf{q})\psi_D \left(\frac{\mathbf{K}}{2} - \mathbf{k}_0 \right) \right]$$

(115)

Thus the scattering amplitude in this two-body collision determines the whole process, using (114). In principle, this amplitude could be obtained by a complete knowledge of neutron-proton scattering experimental values, though the most important range of $\mathbf{q}$ is not easily studied in this way. The energy conservation (113) can be used to fix $| \mathbf{q} |$. A related calculation has been carried out numerically by Heidmann (H5).

It is instructive to apply the Born approximation to our somewhat more general result. For simplicity let us neglect spin questions, and consider only the triplet states of the original collision, putting a factor of $\frac{3}{4}$ into the cross-section formula (112). Then we will replace the initial neutron-proton wave function ψ_D by a plane wave, giving simply a delta-function in momentum space. We can write for V just $T_{n\text{-}p} - E$, and the matrix element for the scattering, $(0 | V | D)$, becomes

$$(B + \hbar^2(\mathbf{K}/2 - \mathbf{k}_0)^2/M) \times \varphi_0(\mathbf{K}/2 - \mathbf{k}_0)$$

The operator $T - E$ has been transposed, so that it acts on the final state wave function φ_0. With this done, we can write the entire quantity $|H_{of}|^2$, which we need to sum over all the protons, in the form

$$\sum_p |H_{of}|^2 = Z|\varphi_i|^2 \times (B + \hbar^2(\mathbf{K}/2 - \mathbf{k}_0)^2/M)^2 \times |\varphi_0(\mathbf{K}/2 - \mathbf{k}_0)|^2$$

(116)

The first factor $Z|\varphi_i|^2$ is simply the number of protons to be found with initial momentum $\mathbf{K} - \mathbf{k}_0$ in the original nucleus; the second factor is the energy operator; and the third factor just the probability for a definite relative momentum $\mathbf{q} = \mathbf{K}/2 - \mathbf{k}_0$ in the deuteron ground state. With a reasonable choice of ψ_0, say the familiar Hulthén (C2) approximation, $\psi_0(\mathbf{r}) = \text{const.}\ (e^{-\alpha r} - e^{-\beta r})/r$, it turns out that the last two factors roughly compensate, so that the variation of σ_{df} with neutron energy is dominated almost wholly by the proton momentum distribution.

The cross sections given by the impulse approximation certainly account for the rather surprising frequency of pick-up deuterons, and for their distribution in energy and angle. Indeed, the calculations apparently overestimate the frequency of pick-up, presumably because subsequent interactions break up the nascent deuterons. But it is most satisfactory that this process, so unexpected at high energy, can, especially in just that region, be given such a simple explanation in terms of momentum transfer.

The pick-up process is the first of many found to lend themselves to the impulse treatment, and hence found to depend very much upon the momentum distribution within a nucleus: elastic scattering of nucleons, photon absorption, and many meson processes, like production by nucleons and gammas and capture by nuclei, are in this category (C3, F15). The description of the nuclear matter in momentum space, both by statistical and by more detailed methods, is sure to become more important and more familiar, supplementing the present description given most frequently in coordinate space only.

C. The Optical Model for the Scattering of Nucleons

At high energies, as indeed even at lower ones, the simplest of scattering experiments is the measurement of the over-all attenuation of a beam of incident nucleons. If the experiment is done under conditions in which the energy is well-defined, and with so-called "good geometry" (i.e., an arrangement such that particles which have deviated even slightly from the original beam direction are excluded from detection), it is possible to measure also the fraction of the beam which has been elastically scattered. The convenience of such experiments has led to the use of a quite abstract and general nuclear model, which is tailor-made to give elastic and total cross sections without at all worrying about the details of the nuclear collisions. In an earlier section we saw how the assumption that the interaction between neutron or proton and nucleus was strong led to the idea of a sticky nucleus, opaque to the passage of nucleons, and then to a total cross section which for energies sufficiently high became just twice the geometrical cross section of the nucleus. The elastic scattering was represented by the portion of the emergent wave which produced the ordinary shadow behind the nuclear obstacle by interference with the incident wave. For a black obstacle we saw that this gave a coherent elastic, or "shadow scattering," cross section which was just equal to the inelastic cross section πR^2. Its angular distribution was also determined. The optical model here used (F6) is a straightforward generalization of the results obtained earlier, extended to the case where the obstacle is no longer black but "gray," for the free path for nucleon collision in nuclear matter is no longer negligible, as we have seen above, in the hundred-Mev region. The ideas of physical optics, however, in the familiar Kirchhoff-Fraunhofer approximation, become better and better because $\lambda/R \ll 1$.

For this model, we think of the nucleus as a gray refracting sphere. Its opacity, or optical density, and its index of refraction for the Schrödinger waves characterize the model. Then the amplitude of the scattered waves, and the damping due to absorption, can be computed, generally neglecting all interface reflections, and considering only "volume" effects, in analogy with the W.K.B. approximation. In its simplest form, the model regards all nuclei as uniform gray spheres, which differ only in diameter. This geometry is of course too simple, and in no way required by the optical approximation. It may be better to think of the nuclear matter more realistically as thinning out gradually toward the edge from a uniform central core; there is some evidence for such a model in exactly this sort of calculation.

The nuclear matter is assigned a complex refractive index, $N = n + i\tau$. Here n is the ratio of the nucleon wave number k at a given point within the nuclear volume to the wave number $k_0 = (2ME)^{1/2}/\hbar$ of the incident nucleon outside in free space (neglecting Coulomb forces). The quantity τ specifies the amplitude damping within nuclear matter; the wave amplitude changes by a factor $1/e$ in a traversal of a distance within the nuclear matter equal to one wavelength of the incident particle, $\psi(x) = \psi_0 \cdot e^{-xk_0\tau}$, and is related to the mean free path for interaction in nuclear matter $l = \frac{1}{2}k_0\tau$. The inelastic scattering which we will calculate includes all exchange and absorption effects; it depends only upon the imaginary part of N, that is, on τ. The real part of the index of refraction will determine the coherent scattering, in which the scattered wave represents particles of the same type as those of the incident beam and having exactly the same energy in the center-of-mass system. We will consider only the uniform-sphere model; for this, N is constant within the nuclear sphere of radius R, and unity everywhere outside.

In the shadow of the sphere, the transmitted wave which passes at a distance from the central diameter of the sphere (see Fig. 29) emerges with an amplitude $a(\rho)e^{ik_0 R}$, where $e^{ik_0 R}$ is the amplitude of any portion of the incident plane wave which misses the sphere. The region of the shadow must contain a wave of lessened amplitude whose intensity

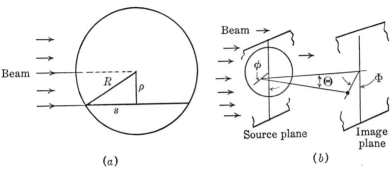

Beam →

R ρ

s

Beam

Beam →

ϕ

Θ

Φ

Source plane   Image plane

(a)   (b)

Fig. 29. The geometry of the optical model for nuclear scattering. In (a) the beam is shown incident on the nuclear sphere of radius R. The path length of a particular ray will clearly be $2s$. In (b) the geometry of the diffraction calculation is shown. The source and image planes are normal to the incident beam direction. For each scattering angle Θ and azimuth Φ in the image plane, the total contribution is found by integrating the contributions of every radius and azimuth angle ϕ in the source plane. This is the familiar Fraunhofer procedure.

decrease gives the total incoherent absorption cross section, simply the total contribution to $1 - |a|^2$ integrated over the whole area of the obstacle. To obtain the coherent, elastic, or diffraction scattering, one has instead to find the net amplitude which, added to the incident plane wave in the shadow region, will yield the transmitted amplitude a. This is plainly $1 - a$, and gives a cross section $|1 - a|^2$.

In the case of a spherical obstacle, the factor $a(\rho)$ is evidently

$$a(\rho) = e^{ik_0(R-2s)} \cdot e^{(n+i\tau)2ik_0 s} = e^{ik_0(n-1) \cdot 2s - 2\tau k_0 s} \tag{117}$$

with $s^2 = R^2 - \rho^2$. Integrating $1 - |a|^2$, we obtain the absorption cross section:

$$\sigma_{\text{abs}} = \int_0^R \rho\, d\rho \int_0^{2\pi} d\varphi (1 - e^{-4\tau s k_0}) = 2\pi \int_0^R s\, ds (1 - e^{-2s/l})$$

$$= \pi R^2 \left[1 - \frac{1 - (1 + 2R/l)e^{-2R/l}}{2R^2/l^2} \right] \tag{118}$$

The elastic scattering is rather more complicated. It is given by the integral (F6):

$$\sigma_{\text{diff}} = \int_0^R \rho \, d\rho \int_0^{2\pi} d\varphi \left| 1 - e^{-s(1/l - 2i(n-1)k_0)} \right|^2 \qquad (119)$$

The angular distribution of the diffraction scattering can be obtained in a similar way. The approximation here is to sum the contributions reaching a given image point, far behind the sphere, from every source point in a plane wave front of amplitude $a - 1$ within the geometrical shadow. Then the Kirchhoff integral (of optics) can be written

$$a_{\text{sc}} = \frac{\text{const}}{R} \cdot \iint d\varphi \, \rho \, d\rho \, e^{ik_0 R \cdot \rho / |R|} \times [1 - a(s)] \qquad (120)$$

where the geometrical relations are those of Fig. 29. Using polar coordinates in the effective source and image planes, we can write

$$\frac{R \cdot p}{|R|} = \rho(\cos \varphi \cos \Phi + \sin \varphi \sin \Phi) \times \sin \Theta$$

and the entire integral becomes

$$\iint \rho \, d\rho \, d\varphi \, e^{ik_0 \sin \Theta \cos (\varphi - \Phi)} [a(s) - 1]$$

Using a familiar representation for the Bessel function, we can write (F6)

$$a_{\text{sc}} \sim \int_0^R \rho \, d\rho \, J_0(k_0 \rho \sin \Theta)[1 - a(s)] \qquad (121a)$$

and the differential scattering cross section $d\sigma/d\Omega$ is just proportional to $|a_{\text{sc}}|^2$. We can evaluate the constant in the limiting case of $R/l \to \infty$. For a totally black sphere, this goes over to the case already given in Eq. (46), namely: $d\sigma/d\Omega = R^2[J_1(k_0 R \sin \Theta)/\sin \Theta]^2$. For the gray spheres here under consideration, the evaluation can be carried out. By replacing the integral over ρ by the sum over l, in which $l + \frac{1}{2} = k\rho$ and the relation $J_0[(l + \frac{1}{2}) \sin \Theta] = P_l(\cos \Theta)$, valid for large l and small Θ, is employed, we find

$$a_{\text{sc}} \sim \sum_0^{l + \frac{1}{2} \leq kR} (2l + 1) P_l(\cos \Theta)[1 - a(s_l)] \qquad \text{with}$$

$$s_l = [(k_0 R)^2 - (l + \tfrac{1}{2})^2]^{\frac{1}{2}}/k_0 \qquad (121b)$$

This is very reminiscent of the partial-wave analysis of scattering, and indeed is just the W.K.B. approximation to the phase shifts of the Rayleigh partial wave procedure. That procedure has been used exactly (P1), giving a result somewhat larger than does (121b) at small angles of scattering. A series procedure is also applicable for the evaluation of (121a) directly.

The results of such a calculation are indicated in Fig. 30. The effect of nuclear transparency is to reduce the contribution of the shadow scattering as the transparency increases (or R/l decreases). The graphs show this reduction in the case of a plausible value for the index of refraction, implying some increase in phase velocity within the nucleus.

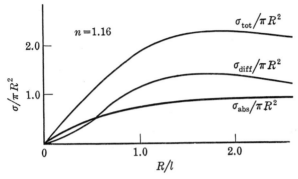

Fig. 30. Cross sections computed from the optical model. The diffraction, absorption, and total cross sections, measured in units of the geometrical cross section, are given as a function of the nuclear radius measured in units of the free path. A particular value, $n = 1.16$, has been chosen for the refractive index. From (F5).

When n is not simply unity, the diffraction scattering may considerably exceed the geometrical limit πR^2 for a black nucleus.

By fitting the data on neutron scattering at 90 Mev to the results of Eqs. (118) and (119), we can choose $n + i\tau$ in such a way that the value of R obtained for a certain choice of $n + i\tau$ fits for all nuclei from Li to U the simple relation $R = r_0 A^{1/3}$, with r_0 chosen at 1.39×10^{-13} cm, a very reasonable value. Suitable values, which are consistent with direct scattering experiments for neutron-proton and proton-proton scattering at this energy are $l = 3.3 \times 10^{-13}$ cm and $n = 1.16$ (F5). For these values the coherent scattering is larger than the geometrical value.

A less empirical evaluation of $n + i\tau$ is possible in two ways. The nuclear material simply acts to change the phase velocity of the waves, and can thus be represented by a potential well of depth V, with the relation $n = k/k_0 = (1 + V/E)^{1/2}$. This works well enough for 90-Mev neutrons, but the same choice by no means satisfies the experiments at higher energy, where the variation of total cross section with energy does not follow the predictions of the simple potential well idea. A much more sophisticated approach has been made (J2) by means of the familiar result of optical dispersion theory, which gives the refractive index in terms of the scattering amplitudes for forward scattering by the individual nucleons. The relation is

$$n - 1 = [a_{n\text{-}n}(0) + a_{n\text{-}p}(0)]\pi\rho/k^2 \qquad (122)$$

where ρ is the density of nucleons in the nucleus, and the a's are the appropriate scattering amplitudes. Use of the empirical cross sections

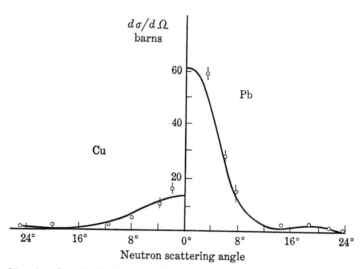

Fig. 31. Angular distributions of elastic scattering computed from the optical model. The differential cross section is shown as a function of scattering angle for two nuclear radii (corresponding to copper and to lead). The experimental points are shown. All this is for 90-Mev neutrons incident. From (F5) and (C10).

is required for l, but it is of course not enough to fix the quantities a in (122) unambiguously. Best fit with the observed total cross sections for a nucleus like Al is found when the real part of the index of refraction is made to go rapidly to unity, $k/k_0 \to 1$—as the energy increases above 100 Mev. Such a scattering amplitude results from a nucleon-nucleon potential consisting of a strong repulsive core surrounded by an attractive well, with a core radius of some 10^{-13} cm. This result can be taken as some confirmation of the view, based on the very flat and strongly isotropic proton-proton cross section above 100 Mev, that some such "hard-core" model of the nucleon-nucleon interaction is at least phenomenologically suitable. With $a_{n\text{-}p} = a_{p\text{-}p}$ the fit for the total cross section to relation (119) is quite good.

The angular distributions are another source of information. In Fig. 31 we show a comparison between theory and experiment for neutrons of about 90 Mev. The diffraction pattern is qualitatively correct, but the experimental peaks are a little sharper, as though the nucleus were somewhat smaller than expected from the constant-density model. Experiments at higher energy show the positions of the successive minima in the diffraction pattern, and indicate that the minima are in fact blurred out, perhaps only slightly in the heaviest nuclei, but beyond recognition in the lightest ones. This is consistent with the results to be expected if we surrender the naive idea of a strictly uniform sphere of nuclear matter and imagine instead that the nucleus has a core of constant density surrounded by a fringe of nuclear matter with a thickness something like the range of nuclear forces within which the density falls gradually to zero. Such a model is of course actually implied by the simple notion of a nuclear surface, as it is for any classical drop of liquid. Taking such a model, and the connection between n and the empirical nucleon-nucleon cross sections given by the dispersion theory, Jastrow (J3) claims a reasonable fit, both to the total cross sections and to the details of the angular distribution of the diffraction scattering, over a wide range of energy and nuclear mass. Much more remains to be done.

D. Processes of Nuclear De-excitation at High Energy

Let us return to the topic first mentioned in this chapter: the detailed course of nuclear disintegration in the region of hundred-Mev energies. In the step-by-step treatment of the cascade, each particle was followed until the kinetic energy it possessed, relative to the bottom of the overall nuclear potential well, fell below a certain limit, some 30 Mev. After this, no single collision between this particle and the nuclear edge is likely to result in the emission of the particle; rather, reflection will occur, and the energy will gradually distribute over the whole of the nuclear system. Not until it is again by chance concentrated on a single nucleon (or in a single well-defined mode of nuclear motion) will emission occur. This is the basis of the compound nucleus treatment which is the main burden of this entire discussion. To place matters in terms of the familiar thermal analogy: excitation of a nucleus by collision with a single nucleon, or a small nucleus, corresponds to heating the nuclear matter very hot indeed in a small spatial region. From this region a nucleon or several may emerge, taking off most of the energy. But the heat will proceed to spread. The time of conduction of energy over the whole, compared with the time it takes a single nucleon or a few nucleons of a cascade to emerge, will determine whether or not the subsequent steps will proceed by thermal evaporation. Our treatment assumes that, after a certain energy loss has been suffered by each fast-recoiling nucleon, all the remaining excitation energy passes into thermal form. Since the spread of energy is mainly through the zero-point motion of the Fermi gas of nucleons, this implies that the statistical treatment will be valuable when the individual nucleon has an excitation *not* large compared to its zero-point energy, well under 20 Mev or so. This limits the process plainly to cases where the whole nucleus is excited by a good deal less than its total binding energy, say by some 5A Mev at the most. We have already seen that such excitations are ample to handle the most frequent cases observed in the bombardments with

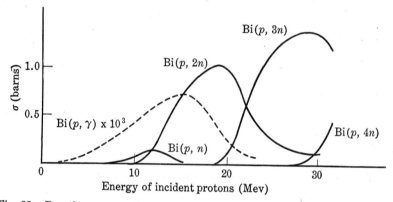

Fig. 32. Reaction cross sections for various proton-induced reactions on bismuth. The competition between the several modes of decay is shown strikingly here; as each new mode becomes energetically possible, it tends to drain away the previously favored decay method. After (K5).

nucleons up to almost 500 Mev in fairly heavy targets, and they cover also, at least in not too small nuclei, the interesting phenomena following upon meson absorption, both π and μ (B12, M6).

The statistical treatment we have used earlier in the low-energy cases implies of course a thermal equilibrium, which will not actually exist in the case of high excitation and the emission of many particles. We can expect that a kind of transient equilibrium will in most cases exist between the successive nucleon emissions which make up the total event. The limit on such an idea is no different from that mentioned just above: the time for rediffusion of the excitation energy after an act of emission, governed by the thermal transport, should be small compared to the delay before the next concentration of energy on a single emitted particle. The typical thermal transport time is under 10^{-21} sec; while the time for nucleon emission up to the highest excitations here considered is ten thousand times as great. The whole division of the process into an immediate cascade and a subsequent evaporation is of course approximate; but within these limits the approximation is successful to a rather high degree, and very instructive.

Of course, the transition from the ordinary statistical treatment of reactions like (n,α) or (n,p) to the large evaporative stars so dramatically revealed in the nuclear emulsion studies is a continuous one. For instance, an elegant series of experiments by Kelly (K6) has carried the simple competition theory of formation of the compound nucleus and its successive decay (see Section 7) through the whole series of reactions with the target nucleus Bi^{209}: (p,n), $(p,2n)$, $(p,3n)$, $(p,4n)$. Excitation energies in this experiment ranged up to about 40 Mev. Figure 32 shows the results obtained, which fit the expected relations of the statistical theory of competition [see Eq. (89)] very well indeed. If we write the ratio of excess energy of excitation over threshold to the temperature as x, the data fit the simple result $\sigma(p,2n)/\sigma_p = 1 - (1 + x)e^{-x}$ very well by adjusting the single parameter, the temperature kT. The value chosen for kT agrees completely with the calculated value for the semi-empirical level density formula, Eq. (31), about 1.1 Mev.

1. Spallation and Evaporation Stars. As the bombarding, and hence in general the excitation energy, continues to rise, we reach a region of higher complexity. Here not only a single product, or a few related competitors, can emerge, but a whole series of successive steps can be taken, each one in many alternative ways. This fact, and the often important fluctuations away from the mean statistical behavior of even such a complex multiple evaporation, is the reason for the absence of any well-codified study of this general subject. So far we can give fairly satisfactory but rather tedious means of calculation, but no compact summary of the possible results.

Two different experimental approaches to the field have led to different nomenclature, and to somewhat different descriptions, of one and the same phenomenon. The radiochemical procedures of separating the various radioactive products from targets bombarded with projectiles at differing energies, and so obtaining yield curves for a whole series of possible products, is one powerful means of study (B4). Here of course only the over-all change is observed; if A and Z change by 20 and 10 say, the event can be described as the emission of 10 neutrons and 10 protons. But the emission of alphas or even other small nuclear fragments in such an event is by no means excluded. Typically a high-energy bombardment yields a bewilderingly large number of product nuclear species. By extension from the idea of the *fission* of a nucleus into two large fragments, with a little neutron spray, the radiochemists have come to call these processes *spallation*, with the implication of the emission of a whole series of small fragments, rather than the cleavage into two big ones familiar in fission.

On the other hand, the cosmic-ray workers, first with their cloud chambers (P4), and more recently with the powerful nuclear emulsion techniques (B9, H3), have typically studied not the statistical residue of millions of disintegrations by identification of the product nuclei, but the ionizing fragments released from each individual nuclear break-up, with the familiar bristle of ionized rays, each marking the trajectory of a single ionizing fragment starting in the central decaying nucleus and ending at the end of the fragment's range. In this method, besides the simple count of the fragments and charge carried off, the energy and angular distribution can also be obtained. But a good statistical sample is tedious to collect, and neutrons are invariably missed. (A few experiments with counters have satisfied us that the invisible neutrons, expected in more or less equal numbers with the visible "prongs," are really emitted.) The typical appearance of the event in the emulsion has led to its designation as a "nuclear star." Star or spallation reaction, the event is the same, but the method of detection, and to some extent the features used for description, differ widely.

In Fig. 33 we present a rather generalized summary of the results of a typical spallation study: the bombardment of a copper target with protons of 340 Mev (B4). The contours in the N,Z plane show the observed yields, with some plausible extrapolations and smoothings. Characteristic is the large number of observed nuclear species, more than thirty having been identified. The biggest yield is for nuclei differing by only a few units in Z and N, plainly due to events in which not much excitation was left behind after a small cascade. There is a strong tendency to stay in the vicinity of the stable valley; it is not likely that the neutron-proton balance will be badly upset by evaporative events in which nearly all the emitted nucleons are protons (or neutrons). This tendency is compelled by the quasi-equilibrium theory, and favored by the energetically advantageous emission of alpha-particles themselves.

The spallation studies have shown one other rather interesting phenomenon (B5). Both by identification of the short-lived isotope Li^8, and by arguments of energy conservation, it has been demonstrated that at least a few events are possible which bridge the gap between simple alpha-emission and straightforward fission. In Section 10, it was pointed out that the splitting-off of small fragments is energetically favorable for a wide range of A because of the balance of Coulomb and surface energy. In spallation experiments, where infrequent events can be detected with relative ease, it has been found that there is indeed a small yield of nuclei of mass far removed from that of the target even for rather low bombardment energies.   For example, 70-Mev protons on Cu give a small yield of Cl^{38}.   The connecting reaction which involves emission of single nucleons and alphas only is the reaction $Cu^{63}(p,6\alpha pn)Cl^{38}$.   But that reaction has a threshold, calculated from mass differences, of some 110 Mev.   The extreme reaction, from the

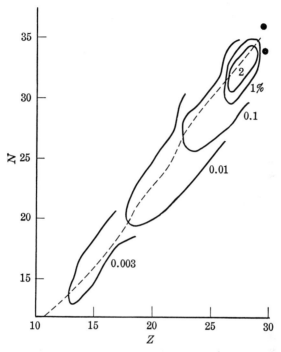

Fig. 33.   A contour map plotting the yield of a spallation reaction in the N,Z plane. The target nuclei are marked with solid circles; copper was bombarded with 340-Mev protons (B5).   The yields center roughly on the line of greatest stability, shown dashed.

point of view of minimizing surface energy, is the three-particle break-up, $Cu^{63}(p,nAl^{25})Cl^{38}$.   The threshold for this rather unlikely course of reaction is about 50 Mev.   It thus seems established that a variety of heavier fragments, of which Li^8 has surely been found, but probably extending over a wide range of masses, up to processes splitting the nucleus into several pieces of approximately equal weight, can in fact take place.   This marks a kind of transition to the case of low-energy fission, and implies that the statistical competition of specialized vibrations of the nucleus leading to massive splits will have to be taken into account in a complete theory of cooling.

2. Evaporative Stars: The Fundamental Process. The study of the energy and angular distribution of observed star prongs enables a rough distinction—allowing considerable overlap—between the cascade and its evaporative consequences. The evaporative prongs are generally marked by: (1) a roughly isotropic angular distribution, (2) a rapid decrease in prong frequency as energy increases. The long tail up to high energies actually observed—so-called "gray" and "sparse black" prongs, named from their low ionization densities in the emulsion (B9)—are regarded as cascade particles. True evaporative particles ought to show a typically quasi-Maxwellian drop-off of number with energy, and no such long tail to energies far beyond any possible mean particle energy. In general, we expect the evaporative process to be sensitive, especially in its last stages, to details of nuclear structure, like the odd-even property and even more refined shell-like behavior.

The thermodynamic treatment of the stars is based on the statistical formula, due to Weisskopf, which connects the probability for disintegration of a compound nucleus with the formation cross section, by the principle of detailed balance. [Compare the discussion in Section 5, Eqs. (51) and (52).] We write

$$P(T)\, dT = \frac{gM}{\pi^2 \hbar^3} \cdot \sigma(T) T\, \frac{\rho(f)}{\rho(i)}\, dT \tag{123}$$

where $P(T)\, dT$ is the probability per unit time for emission of a particle of mass M and spin statistical weight g with kinetic energy in dT; σ is the cross section for capture of the same particle by the residual nucleus f to form the initial nucleus i; and the functions ρ are the level densities of initial and final nucleus as indicated, functions of course of the mass and charge number and of the initial excitation energy, W, and final excitation W'.

In principle, we may now use the function $P_j(T)$ for emission of a particle of type j with mass A_j and charge Z_j from the initial nucleus of given kind and given excitation energy, $W = W' + T + B_j$, with B_j the binding energy, and then simply follow the course of the successive emissions until all the excitation energy has been converted into kinetic and potential energy of the fragments, and into radiation. This implies the solution of the set of coupled equations which can be given, if only formally, as (F13)

$$\frac{\partial y(Z,A,W,t)}{\partial t} = \sum_j \int_{W+B_j}^{\infty} dW'\, y(Z + Z_j, A + A_j, W', t) P_j(W', W' - W)$$

$$- \sum_j y(Z,A,W,t) \int_{B_j}^{W} P_j(W;T)\, dT \tag{124a}$$

Here the yield function $y(Z,A,W,t)$ gives the probability of finding a nucleus with charge Z, mass A, excitation energy W, at time t after the start of the process, which fixes the initial condition:

$$y(Z,A,W,t) = \delta_{AA_0} \delta_{ZZ_0} \delta(W - W_0) \tag{124b}$$

Now from the function y one can learn all the facts about the star, including of course both the mean behavior and fluctuations from it. For example, the total yield of a definite nuclear species is just given by

$$y_{tot}(A,Z) = \int_0^{B_j} y(Z,A,W,t \to \infty) \, dW$$

Naturally such a complete treatment is next to impossible; indeed, fluctuations are generally treated very casually [but see (T1)]. We shall examine a more manageable approximation; perhaps the complete treatment will one day be performed by Monte Carlo technique, which seems very well suited to the task.

3. The Mean Behavior in Cooling. The most satisfactory approach is the study of the mean behavior of the evaporative process. To make this possible in general (F13), several approximations must be made, not all of easily controlled accuracy:

1. In the fundamental formula (123), the cross sections are replaced by very simple forms: usually just the geometrical πR^2 for neutron emission, and a simplified expression like $\sigma = \pi R^2(1 - V'/T)$ for a charged particle with a Coulomb barrier height given by $V' = 0.7(ZZ_je^2/R)$, to take care of penetration effects.

2. The level density is expressed by some one of the results of a particular nuclear model, discussed in Section 3. The detail with which the shell properties are represented may vary greatly.

3. The cooling proceeds usually by the emission of particles whose A_j and Z_j are small compared to those of the initial and residual nucleus. This allows series expansion of functions of A and Z, performed as though A and Z were continuous variables, instead of integers.

First of all we define the relative width (hence probability) for emitting a particle of a given kind, indexed by j. In the typical calculation, it may be worth while to consider half-a-dozen or more types of emitted particle, as proton, neutron, deuteron, H^3 or triton, He^3, He^4 or alpha-particle, and sometimes even heavier fragments. In general, then, the mean emission width is given by the expression

$$\Gamma_j(W) = \int_{V_j'+B_j}^W P_j(W,T) \, dT$$

where P_j is the transition rate given by (123). The approximation of mean cooling is of course just to consider the process as going always proportional to these mean emission rates, and to neglect the different courses of the evaporation which come from the fluctuations about the mean energy and type of decay. Naturally no single act follows the average behavior, and the successive steps in fact depend in turn upon just what particle and energy loss preceded them. These refinements are here neglected. Now we can calculate the mean energy of excitation lost by evaporation of particle j:

$$\overline{\delta W_j} = \bar{\Gamma}_j + B_j = \frac{\int_0^\infty P_j(T) T \, dT}{\int_0^\infty P_j \, dT} + B_j \qquad (125a)$$

and we can express the mean cooling in one way by writing the mean rate of energy loss per nucleon emitted:

$$\frac{\overline{\delta W}}{\overline{\delta A}} = \frac{\sum_j \Gamma_j \overline{\delta W_j}}{\Sigma \Gamma_j \, \delta A_j} \qquad (125b)$$

In a similar way we can write the mean number of particles of type j lost per unit energy loss:

$$\frac{\overline{\delta n_j}}{\overline{\delta W}} = \frac{\Gamma_j}{\Sigma \Gamma_j \overline{\delta W_j}} \qquad (125c)$$

and for the entire cooling from initial to final excitation energy get

$$\overline{\delta n_j} = \int_{V_i' + B_i}^{W_i} \frac{\Gamma_j(W) \, dW}{\sum_j \Gamma_j \overline{\delta W_j}} \qquad (125d)$$

Here there is of course one such equation for each of the values of j, say six or more, and the equations are all coupled. The main coupling is through the effect of the changing neutron-proton ratio, and some reasonably trustworthy solutions have been obtained (neglecting other relations) (L3).

(a) *Cooling Behavior with an Explicit Model.* To gain any insight into the expected behavior of this phenomenon, it is necessary to introduce an explicit nuclear model which can fix the level density and its variation with Z,A, excitation energy, and even finer details like the odd-even effects. In Section 3 we set out a number of expressions from various models for the level density $\rho(W)$. We choose here to use the rather simple model of the Fermi gas, which has some weak experimental support, and can be regarded as the empirical expression of the results for nuclei of middle weight and for energies in the range here studied. With a Fermi energy of 22 Mev, we obtain [compare Eq. (31)]

$$\rho(W) = \frac{e^{S(A,Z,W)}}{\tau(2\pi \, dW/d\tau)^{\frac{1}{2}}} \quad \text{and} \quad S = 0.63 \frac{(AW)^{\frac{1}{2}}}{\text{Mev}} \quad (126)$$

Here the entropy is given as a function of the excitation energy W, and we have introduced the temperature τ, writing $W/\text{Mev} = A\tau^2/10$, and τ is in Mev. With this model the rate of evaporation becomes, neglecting some slowly varying ratios,

$$P(T) \, dT = gM/\pi^2\hbar^3 (T - V')e^{(S_f - S_i)} \, dT \quad (127)$$

and, if we make the approximation, valid for small emitted fragments and $\delta W \ll W_j$, of expanding the function $S(A,W)$, we get $S(A - \delta A_j, W - \delta W) = S_A(W) - \delta W/\tau - \delta A_j\tau/10$ and

$$P(T) \, dT = \text{const} \, (T - V') \exp \frac{-(T - V')}{\tau} \quad (128a)$$

This is the familiar Maxwellian distribution of evaporated fragment energies. The mean kinetic energy taken off by an evaporated particle j is

$$T_j = \tau \frac{\displaystyle\int_0^\infty x^2 e^{-x} \, dx}{\displaystyle\int_0^\infty x e^{-x} \, dx} = 2\tau \quad (128b)$$

and the total width $\Gamma_j(W)$ for emission of j-particles with any energy T is approximately

$$\Gamma_j = \hbar \int_{B_j + V'}^{W} P(\tau, W') \, dW'$$

$$\cong g \frac{\delta A_j}{2\pi} \cdot \frac{A^{\frac{2}{3}}\tau^2}{11 \text{ Mev}} \exp\left(-\frac{\delta A_j\tau}{10} - \frac{B_j + V_j'}{\tau}\right) \quad \tau \text{ in Mev} \quad (129)$$

Both terms in the exponent here depend strongly on the type of particle emitted; they are the effective potential barrier V_j' and the binding energy B_j. Now we must explicitly give the variation of binding energy with A and Z, which will of course determine the nature of the most probable emitted particle. We write a semi-empirical form for the binding energy of a nucleus in its ground state [compare Eq.

(101)], with $\langle (N - Z)/A \rangle$ written for the value of $(N - Z)/A$ which corresponds to the most stable nucleus of a given A:

$$B = \text{const} + c_1 A - c_2 A [(N - Z)/A - \langle (N - Z)/A \rangle]^2$$

Here we can take c_1 about 8.6 Mev, and c_2 about 23 Mev. These numbers are suited for target nuclei in the middle of the table, $A \sim 100$, as in photographic emulsion. Now, if a particle of type j is evaporated, with δn_j neutrons and δZ_j protons, taking off kinetic energy T, the *drop* in excitation is given by differentiating B, and regrouping the terms, to yield

$$\delta W = T + B_j$$

$$B_j = c_1 \, \delta A_j - 2 \left[\frac{N - Z}{A} - \left\langle \frac{N - Z}{A} \right\rangle \right] (c_n \, \delta n_j - c_z \, \delta Z_j) + I_j$$

$$c_n = c_2 \left\{ 1 - A \frac{\partial}{\partial A} \left\langle \frac{N - Z}{A} \right\rangle - \frac{1}{2} \left[\frac{N - Z}{A} + \left\langle \frac{N - Z}{A} \right\rangle \right] \right\} \simeq 0.8 c_2$$

$$c_z = c_2 \left\{ 1 + A \frac{\partial}{\partial A} \left\langle \frac{N - Z}{A} \right\rangle + \frac{1}{2} \left[\frac{N - Z}{A} + \left\langle \frac{N - Z}{A} \right\rangle \right] \right\} \simeq 1.2 c_2$$

$$\text{(130)}$$

and I_j is the *internal* binding energy of the emitted fragment. The energy B_j is of course the threshold energy for emission of the given fragment with zero kinetic energy, which we call the binding energy of the fragment into the initial nucleus. We have considered only nuclei rather near the stable valley—$(N - Z)/A \simeq \langle (N - Z)/A \rangle$—in evaluating c_n and c_z.

Now we can examine at least the general cooling behavior by simply looking at the competition between the various emitted fragments.

(b) *The Competition in Cooling.* Let us look at the ratios of the Γ_j for the various particles. First, note that the statistical and mass factors $g \, \delta A_j$ alone will give relative weights for the six most common products as follows: $p:n:d:T:He^3:\alpha::1:1:3:3:3:2$. Note the increase in statistical probability, especially for the heavy isotopes of hydrogen, which feel a low Coulomb barrier as well.

Much more important, however, than the statistical and mass factors is the exponent in Eq. (129). We write here the expected emission width relative to that for neutron emission, using the energy relations of (130). We can write the effective Coulomb barrier heights for nuclei of the emulsion ($A \sim 90$) as $V_j' = 6 b_j$ Mev, where the values of b_j are estimated to include charge, radius, and mass effects on penetrability, and we get $b_n = 0$; $b_p = 0.7$; $b_d = 0.8 = b_T$; $b_{He^3} = 1.6$. Then the widths, relative to the width for neutron emission, become

$$\Gamma_n/\Gamma_n = 1$$

$$\Gamma_p/\Gamma_n = \exp\left[-(92(\nu - \bar{\nu}) + 4)/\tau\right]$$

$$\Gamma_d/\Gamma_n = 3\exp\left[-\tau/10 - (55(\nu - \bar{\nu}) + 11)/\tau\right]$$

$$\Gamma_T/\Gamma_n = 3\exp\left[-2\tau/10 - (18(\nu - \bar{\nu}) + 14)/\tau\right]$$

$$\Gamma_{He^3}/\Gamma_n = 3\exp\left[-2\tau/10 - (110(\nu - \bar{\nu}) + 19)/\tau\right]$$

$$\Gamma_\alpha/\Gamma_n = 2\exp\left[-3\tau/10 - (74(\nu - \bar{\nu}) + 8)/\tau\right]$$

(131)

The energies involved and the temperature τ are all given in Mev. We have written ν for the quantity $(N - Z)/A$; the value of ν for the most stable nucleus of a given A is written as $\bar{\nu}$. Thus $(\nu - \bar{\nu})A$ = neutron excess − proton excess.

An examination of these ratios alone enables a qualitative discussion of the course of the mean curve of cooling. The most noteworthy features are these:

1. The Coulomb barrier—contributing to the last term of the exponent—of course favors the emission of neutrons over charged particles, and reduces the emission of particles of charge $+2$, as long as it is of any consequence. Since the temperature τ is $\sim(W)^{1/2}$, the effect of the Coulomb barrier on charged-particle emission will be decisive for all excitations up to some critical energy. For higher energies the emission of ions and neutrons will show little difference ascribable to Coulomb effects. The critical energy for proton barrier effect in these middle nuclei is an excitation of from 100 to 150 Mev; for helium isotopes, from 250 to 350 Mev.

2. Apart from the Coulomb barrier, the most striking term in the exponent of the relative emission widths is the symmetry energy, proportional to the fractional neutron excess of the initial nucleus, $(\nu - \bar{\nu})$. Looking, for example, at the proton-neutron ratio, Γ_p/Γ_n, we see that this term favors neutron emission when there are too many neutrons compared to the region of stability, and favors proton emission when the nucleus is neutron deficient. This term has been called a "governor" term (L3), because it prevents great excursions from the region of stable nuclei in the cooling process. It arises of course from the parabolic form of the familiar Heisenberg valley in the nuclear energy surface. In many-particle stars it will more or less insure that more neutrons than protons are emitted.

3. The leading term in the exponent of the relative widths for emission of the complex star fragments—d, α, etc.—grows more negative as the

excitation, and with it the temperature, increases. This term arises from the dependence, not of the energy, but of the entropy itself, on the number of nucleons in the nucleus. It favors the emission of lighter rather than heavier particles, because more ways exist of assembling a nucleus if it contains more nucleons. If it were not for this type of term, the emission of the heavier fragments would become more probable than that of single nucleons because of the purely statistical weights.

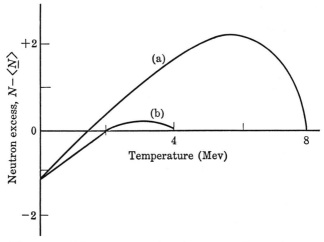

Fig. 34. The course of the neutron number of an evaporating nucleus as a function of nuclear temperature. The neutron excess is plotted; it is the difference between the number of neutrons in the nucleus, N, and the number of neutrons characteristic of the most stable nucleus of the same mass number A. The neutron excess first increases and then decreases as the nucleus cools. The terminal value of $N - \langle N \rangle$ is about -1, implying the subsequent emission of a slow proton, or simply β^+-decay, following the main process of evaporation. See pages 174–177. The curves are drawn for a nucleus with initial $A = 100$, and for two initial temperatures, 4 and 8 Mev. After (L3).

For example, without this term $\Gamma_\alpha/\Gamma_n \to 2$ as τ grows without limit. As star size increased, then, alpha-emission would outweigh proton emission and even neutron emission, a very odd result, and far from what is actually observed. With this entropy term, however, the ratio Γ_α/Γ_n goes through a very flat maximum in the region of 100-Mev excitation. As we have seen, however, in earlier chapters, the variation of level density with A is quite poorly known, and detailed predictions from this simple entropy assumption cannot be expected to agree in detail with experience.

Now we can integrate the simultaneous equations (125) to give the full course of the cooling. This has been done in rather rough approximations, perhaps best by LeCouteur, whose procedure we follow (L3).

In general, we can expect this typical state of affairs: the highly excited nucleus, say with 400 Mev, begins by evaporating neutrons and protons about equally. To begin, it has $\nu - \bar{\nu}$ almost zero—perhaps one or two protons and neutrons have been knocked out of the stable target nucleus in the nuclear cascade. But now the nucleus boils off several protons

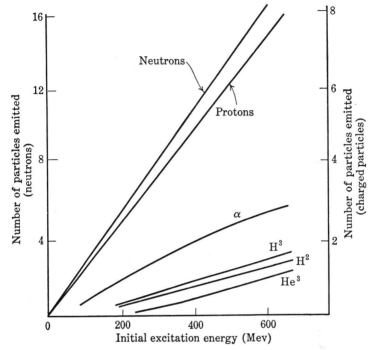

Fig. 35. The number of evaporated particles of several types as a function of initial excitation energy, for an evaporating nucleus of initial $A = 100$. The neutron number scale is at the left; that for charged-particle emission at the right. After (L3).

and several neutrons. By the time it has emitted say four of each, the cooling nucleus has become neutron-rich, with respect to the smoothed-over line of maximum stability, and the "governor" term begins to favor the loss of neutrons. Then the cooling proceeds, somewhat preferentially losing neutrons, until the excitation has dropped below some 100 Mev. From here on, proton loss will be almost prohibited by virtue of the Coulomb barrier, and the excitation energy will fall until no more particles can be emitted. The resultant nucleus is now neutron-deficient by a little less than one neutron on the average, more or less independent of the initial energy of excitation for not too low excitations. We show in Fig. 34 a schematic plot of the neutron number against excitation during the cooling, which follows the course here described.

In Fig. 35, we plot, after LeCouteur, the mean numbers of various emitted particles for different excitation energies, with an initial nucleus of $A = 100$. The virtual independence of the relative yields of various particles upon energy is a feature of the theory; but the calculations have actually been done *neglecting* the small variations actually predicted,

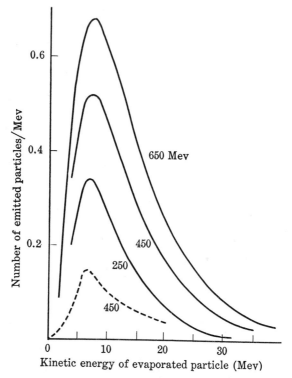

Fig. 36.   Energy spectrum of evaporated particles for several initial excitation energies.   Initial nucleus of $A = 100$.   The solid curves all refer to emission of protons; the dotted curve, to that of alpha-particles.   After (L3). `

and using the relative yields given by equations for an initial excitation of 400 Mev. In Fig. 36 we give the expected kinetic energy distribution of evaporated fragments; it is given by the rough averaged formula, very much as in (127), by

$$P(T)\,dT = \frac{T - V'}{\tau^2}\, e^{-(T - V')/\tau}\, dT \tag{132}$$

Results are given for several excitation energies, and for both singly charged and doubly charged star prongs.

All these results are likely to be acceptable only for fairly large excitations ($W > 150$ Mev), and the theory cannot be taken seriously for A much less than about 60. The actual figures are for a definite $A = 100$.

(c) *The End of the Cooling Process*: *Low-Energy Prongs*. We followed the cooling process down to the point where the temperature is so low that no further nucleon emission is possible energetically. But this threshold of course varies with the type of particle. Moreover, the process has left us with a nucleus which is neutron-poor by about 0.8 neutron. Then the values of the threshold energy are *not* the same as for a stable nucleus, and become, from (130), $B_p \simeq 7$ Mev, $B_n \simeq 10$ Mev, $B_\alpha \simeq 5$ Mev for the three main possibilities. Thus, even though the Coulomb barrier reduces the *rate* of charged-particle emission for such low energies very much indeed, the neutron cannot compete at all, since the binding energy of the neutron in the neutron-poor residual nucleus is higher than normal. De-excitation can go on by gamma-emission, beta-decay, or charged-particle emission. The anticipated lifetime for these slow processes at an excitation of 10 Mev is perhaps 10^{-16} sec or so for the gamma, and some 10^{-2} sec for the beta. Protons emitted through the barrier with kinetic energies of anything above 0.5 Mev will favorably compete with such slow radiative processes.

Alphas and other fragments of mass above one unit will experience a much greater loss in penetrability; since this factor is already 10^{-10}, protons are about the only practical competitors. Thus, if a nuclear particle of any kind, the next-to-the-last to be emitted, leaves the residual nucleus with an excitation of less than 10 Mev and of more than $B_p + 0.5$ or some 7 Mev, a proton will be emitted. If the remaining excitation is below B_p, gamma-rays alone can come off. Thus about 30 percent of all nuclei left with 10 Mev excitation will emit slow protons, far more than would be expected if neutron competition were not excluded by the shift in binding energies due to the neutron deficit. A computation (L3) has shown that there is to be expected in emulsion nuclei about 0.2 proton per star with kinetic energies in the range from 0.5 to ~3 Mev. These very slow protons have apparently been observed (H3). In addition there is a considerable excess of slow alphas observed; this cannot be accounted for by such a mechanism, but is ascribed to a lowering of the effective barrier by processes to be considered in Section 11E (L3).

It will not escape the reader that this type of calculation has overlooked even the most striking features of nuclear shell structure, like the odd-even variation in energy content. This does not affect the previous phenomenon, slow-proton emission, but in general it should have some detailed effects on the closing scenes of the evaporation, when excitations are not large compared with the few Mev which represent shell-closing energies, etc. Moreover, the rather large gamma-ray width which seems to be observed in the neighborhood of 20 Mev excitation may occasionally compete—say one time in ten or a hundred—with the last one or two emitted particles. All these interesting but somewhat fine points await both more systematic experiment and a better theoretical treatment.

(d) *Effects of High Nuclear Temperature.* The calculations of evaporation ought not to neglect the changes in the nuclear properties which arise from the high nuclear temperatures during the earlier stages of the process. In equation (126) and in the binding-energy formulas of (130) we have over-simply considered the nuclei throughout as though they were in their ground state. The work of LeCouteur (see Figs. 34 and 35 which are essentially taken from his work) actually did not leave out this important and complicated circumstance. The effects to be considered are three in number, all closely related to thermal expansion:

1. Depression of the Coulomb barrier, and consequent favoring of emission of low-energy charged particles, as a result of the thermal expansion of the nucleus. An estimate of the thermal expansion of the nucleus due to an actual change in the equilibrium volume energy at high temperature, entirely analogous to the familiar phenomenon on large scale, can be obtained by thermodynamic arguments. We can write the internal energy of a nucleus of given A as $U(V,\tau)$, showing its dependence on temperature and volume. For a definite temperature— actually $\tau = 0$—this internal energy is a minimum at some volume, say V_0. Expanding, we can write

$$U(\tau,V) = U(\tau,V_0) + \frac{\partial U}{\partial V}\bigg|_{V_0,\tau} (V - V_0) + \frac{1}{2}\frac{\partial^2 U}{\partial V^2}\bigg| (V - V_0)^2 + \cdots$$

But the coefficient of the linear term is zero by the definition of V_0. Now the Helmholtz free energy, for negligible external pressure, is just

$$F = U - \tau S = U(\tau,V_0) - \tau S(\tau,V) + \frac{1}{2}\frac{\partial^2 U}{\partial V^2}\bigg| (V - V_0)^2$$

and the actual equilibrium volume at any temperature τ will satisfy the relation $\dfrac{\partial F}{\partial V}\bigg|_{\tau} = 0$ fixing the free energy at a minimum. We have already given the entropy in terms of A (Eq. 126) and we can estimate the entropy as a function of volume by using the relation $V = \frac{4}{3}\pi r_0^3 \cdot A$. This of course is not precise; the entropy depends both on A explicitly, the number of nucleons, and on the volume for fixed A, but it will serve for an estimate. Now we get $S = 0.2A\tau = 0.2 \cdot V/(4\pi r_0{}^3/3) \cdot \tau$, and this yields an expression for the volume change with temperature:

$$V = V_0 + [0.2/(4\pi r_0{}^3/3)] \cdot [\tau^2/(\partial^2 U/\partial V^2|_{\tau,V_0})] \qquad (133)$$

The familiar thermodynamic result $dF = -S\,d\tau - p\,dV$ for small departures from equilibrium yields the relation $\partial F/\partial V\,|_\tau = -p$. But the ordinary isothermal compressibility is defined as $\kappa = -(1/V)\,(\partial V/\partial p)\,|_\tau$. Since $\partial p/\partial V\,|_\tau = 1/(\partial V/\partial p)\,|_\tau$, we have $1/\kappa = V\,\partial^2 F/\partial V^2\,|_\tau$. For low temperatures we can write, closely enough, $\partial^2 F/\partial V^2\,|_\tau \cong \partial^2 U/\partial V^2\,|_\tau$.

An estimate of the nuclear compressibility, $\partial^2 U/\partial V^2$, is easy to obtain in several ways. An application of the virial theorem (78) gives $\partial^2 U/\partial V^2 = kU_{\text{kin}}/V^2$, where the factor k is about 2; direct calculations with models using a Fermi gas and correcting for assumed two-body interaction potentials are in fair accord. Some insight may be had by recalling that the velocity of sound v is given by the relation $v^2 \cong -[V(\partial^2 U/\partial V^2)]/\rho$. If the sound velocity is estimated very roughly as simply the rms velocity of the particles in the Fermi gas, we have $v^2/c^2 = 6E_F/5Mc^2$. Using (133), we can write the relative change in radius upon heating $[R(\tau) - R(0)]/R(0) \cong \frac{1}{6}(\tau^2/E_F) = 0.008\tau^2$ (τ in Mev), a small but not entirely negligible change. Bagge (B1) has pointed out that there is likely to be another, more dynamical, source of reduction of the Coulomb barrier than this uniform volume expansion. Surface vibrations in the excited nuclear drop "wrinkle" the surface; over many cycles, protons in the nuclear surface layers are to be found farther out from the center than in the smooth undisturbed drop at zero temperature. The diagram of Fig. 37 shows the nuclear

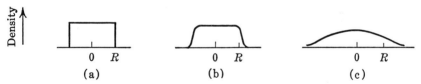

Fig. 37. Schematic plot of density of nuclear matter in a cross-sectional cut through a nucleus. In (a) is shown the abstract model of a uniform sphere without surface effects; in (b), the more realistic version of the Fermi model, with a fringe of gradually falling nucleon density; in (c), the nuclear density in a highly excited and hence much expanded and strongly oscillating nucleus.

density distribution at zero excitation and at high temperature; there is both a lowering of the mean ρ and a wide fringe of nuclear matter as τ increases. An estimate of $\overline{a^2}$, the mean square amplitude of the surface vibration normal modes at a given temperature, has been made by Bagge, who shows that although the number of modes excited is not large, and quantum treatment is necessary, the value of $\overline{a^2}$ is nevertheless very closely proportional simply to the nuclear temperature. This can be described by saying that the surface vibration energy is simply a definite fraction of the total excitation (F14) and that the mean frequency of the modes excited changes slowly. The surface effect appears to be quite important, reducing the barrier in the ratio $V'/V_0 = 1/(1 + \sqrt{\overline{a^2}}/R)$, and a semi-empirical estimate of the effective proton barrier as V_p' $= 4/(1 + 0.15\tau)$ seems to fit the present data reasonably well. With this variation of barrier with temperature, the spectrum of emitted charged particles of course changes, and this reduction of V' is fairly surely observed (B11, B8).

2. The excited nucleus has a different balance between protons and neutrons; at high excitation there is a tendency toward *increasing* the difference of neutron and proton number, $N - Z$. This of course tends to favor the emission of protons from a nucleus already rich in neutrons. The tendency originates from a complex set of causes, most important of which is a new balance between potential and kinetic energy which has to be struck for the now expanded volume of the heated nucleus. A shift in volume decreases the Fermi kinetic energy, and the potential energy will readjust to fix a new minimum total energy, now at a different value of ν from that of the cold nucleus of the same A. The effect has been evaluated by LeCouteur most recently, using a Fermi gas plus interactions. He shows that it leads to an entropy term of the form $+ \text{const} [(N - Z)/A]^2$. It becomes appreciable only for excitations above about 300 Mev. It has only a rather small influence therefore. It more or less corrects the high-energy emission for the fact that stable heavy nuclei in the ground state are neutron-rich, and equalizes the proton-neutron emission at high excitation.

3. The surface tension energy at high temperature decreases. Evidently the nuclear expansion could reach a "critical point" where the nucleons are all excited beyond their binding energies; here the drop would vaporize entirely. The nuclear surface tension will decrease regularly with temperature until the critical temperature, τ_c, is reached. Using the rough Fermi-gas-like relation between excitation and temperature, we can write $W_c = 8A \text{ Mev} = A\tau_c^2/10$, and from this we get $\tau_c = 9$ Mev, independent of A in this approximation. Now let us again take thermodynamics as a guide (G7). If we write down the Gibbs free energy for a surface film, in which the surface tension $-\gamma$, surface force per unit length in the film, takes the place of pressure in the usual case, we have $G_S = U - \tau S - \gamma A$ for an area of film A, with internal energy U and entropy S at temperature τ. Now the partial derivative $-\partial G_S/\partial A|_\tau = \gamma$ gives the surface tension. An isothermal change in

film area will obey the first and second laws: $dU = \tau\, dS + \gamma\, dA$, and we can write $dG_S = -S\, d\tau - A\, d\gamma$. Differentiating, $-\partial\gamma/\partial\tau = (S/A) + (\partial G_S/\partial\tau)$. But, in equilibrium at any τ, the Gibbs free energy of film and bulk liquid are equal for a given mass of nuclear matter. We write $G_S = G_L$. Then $-\partial\gamma/\partial\tau = (S/A) + (1/A)(\partial G_L/\partial\tau) = (S - S_L/A)$. Now we can form $G_S/A = G_L/A = -\gamma + (U/A) - (\tau S/A)$, and we get a differential expression for the surface tension γ as a function of τ:

$$-\gamma + \tau\frac{d\gamma}{d\tau} = \frac{(U - U_L)}{A} \tag{134}$$

The term pV in the liquid-phase free energy is cancelled by that of the surface film, except for thickness changes, which we neglect as usual.

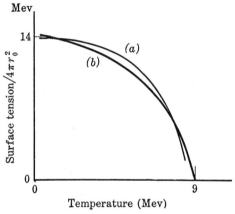

Fig. 38. The nuclear surface tension as a function of nuclear temperature. The curves indicate different models: curve (a) arises from the actual surface energy of a classical liquid drop with surface waves excited by the thermal motion; curve (b) from the simple linear assumption for the integration of the free energy equation of the text. The two are very close. From (Y1).

Now the right-hand side of (134) is the additional energy due to the surface film, measured per unit area of nuclear surface. Using as unit of area just $4\pi r_0^2$, this becomes about 14 Mev for nuclei in their ground states, with $\tau = 0$, as the semi-empirical formula showed in Section 10. As the temperature rises, surface vibrations are excited and the energy increases. Using a liquid drop model, Bethe (B13) has shown that the excess surface energy increases like $\tau^{7/3}/\gamma(\tau)$. As a first approximation we can neglect the change in γ, and write $U - U_L/A = 14 + \text{const } \tau^{7/3}$. We can then solve (134), using as boundary condition the requirement that $\gamma(\tau_c) = 0$. The surface tension then goes to zero, following the law $\gamma(\tau) = 14 + \tau/\tau_c - 15(\tau/\tau_c)^{7/3}$. A numerical integration has been performed by Yamaguchi (Y1) which gives a very similar result. A plot is given in Fig. 38.

The reduced surface tension means that the balance between Coulomb and surface energy is displaced in favor of the Coulomb repulsion. We would expect this, since the Coulomb forces show only a slow change with mean separation, while the surface forces are, of course, of very short range. An expanded nucleus requires little additional energy to undergo fission, for which process the repulsive Coulomb forces overcome the surface tension; the nuclear volume energy can be taken as remaining constant throughout. The familiar Bohr-Wheeler estimate of fission threshold, as given in Eq. (107), is just

$$E_f = 4\pi r_0^2 A^{2/3} \cdot \gamma(\tau) f\left(\frac{Z^2}{A}\right)$$

With this model, Fujimoto and Yamaguchi (F12) have estimated that the silver fission threshold would fall from some 50 Mev for the ground state of the nucleus to half of that value at about 100-Mev excitation, and to only a few Mev at 350-Mev excitation. The fission width can be estimated in the usual way as about $\Gamma_f \simeq (\tau/2\pi)e^{-E_f/\tau}$. This makes such fission a good competitor for really large excitation, 300 to 400 Mev or more. Such heavy spallation fragments are found not infrequently, as we have mentioned above (H3). Of course, fission yielding fragments with much smaller mass is even more favored by the decrease in surface tension, and many reasonably heavy fragments have been seen in high-energy stars, especially the easily recognized unstable ones like Li^8.

The mechanism for fission here described is only a single one which may contribute to fission at high excitation energies. With the heaviest nuclei, and at somewhat lower energies, fission is observed subsequent to the emission of many neutrons, at temperatures below the barrier height for protons. This upsets the Coulomb-surface energy balance as well, and reduces the fission threshold. The mechanism is plainly very different (G4).

It has been observed (F14) that a calculation of the temperature dependence of the surface energy, using the model for surface vibrations which Bagge employed, yields not very different results, and still predicts very easy loss of highly charged fragments at high temperature. Using Bagge's formulas for the mean amplitude of surface waves, but taking into account the variation of surface tension with temperature, it appears that excitations of 300 or 400 Mev would greatly distort the surface shape of nuclei, so much indeed that whole little drops would come off in a kind of spray. $\overline{(a^2)}^{1/2}/R \simeq 1$ describes such a condition. It seems rather likely that the actual situation is more nearly a non-equilibrium local heating, capable of distorting the surface locally enough to pinch off a small drop, but not involving the surface of the entire nucleus in such a way as to give the nearly flat distribution of fission fragment masses which the near-disappearance of the equilibrium surface tension might lead one to expect. The whole phenomenon is clearly of importance, but our present account is too closely classical to trust quantitatively.

4. Fluctuations in Cooling. We have so far described in detail only the average behavior of the cooling nucleus; we have ignored all fluctuations. Obviously, such a complicated process in which only a few, or perhaps a few dozen, particles take part must be subject to important fluctuations in the number, type, energy, and direction of emission of the emitted nucleons. So far this problem is only sketchily understood, but a simple model will serve us at least for orientation (F12).

Consider a nucleus so very hot that we can ignore its cooling, even though it has emitted many nucleons. It is restricted, moreover, to the emission of only one type of particle, with binding energy B, which also remains constant throughout the process. Then the probability of emitting a single nucleon in energy range dT is just $P(T)\,dT = e^{-T/\tau}T\,dT/\tau^2$, where τ is the temperature, taken as constant throughout, and T the kinetic energy. Now the probability that the nucleus will emit n or more nucleons, when it has an initial total excitation W, is given by the multiple integral:

$$P(n,W) = \int \cdots \int dT_1 \cdots dT_{n-1} P(T_1) P(T_2) \cdots P(T_{n-1})$$

$$0 \le \sum_1^{n-1} T_i \le W - nB \tag{135}$$

where the upper limit follows because there must remain at least B Mev of excitation after the loss of $n-1$ nucleons if at least one more is to be emitted, and the lower limit represents the process occurring by the possible route in which each of the first $n-1$ nucleons just manages to dribble out with zero kinetic energy.

It will not seriously distort this rather unrealistic picture to replace the Maxwell distribution in kinetic energy by a Gaussian distribution adjusted to have a mean and a standard deviation equal to the Maxwellian values. We know that $\bar{T} = 2\tau$ and $\overline{(T - \bar{T})^2} = 2\tau^2$, so that we can rewrite

$$P(T)\,dT \doteq e^{-(T-\bar{T})^2/4\tau^2} \frac{d(T - \bar{T})}{2(\pi)^{\frac12}\tau} \tag{136}$$

Now the probability for the multiple emission is a compounding of normal distribution. As in the familiar statistical problem of the chi-square test, we write $\chi^2 = \sum_{1}^{n-1} (T_i - \bar{T})^2/4\tau^2$ and recall that χ^2 is then the square of the radius vector in a hyperspace of $n - 1$ dimensions. In such a space the volume element is proportional to the quantity $\chi^{n-2} d\chi$. The proportionality constant is of course a function of n. If we recall that, as the excitation W grows without limit $P(n,W) \to 1$ for any given value of n, we can evaluate this function of n. Now for not too small values of $(W - nB)/\tau$ and of n, the region of integration, which is bounded by the coordinate axes and a set of planes in the hyperspace, can be replaced without serious error of a sphere of radius say χ_m in the polar coordinate system described by χ. Remembering the required normalization, we obtain

$$P(n,W) = f(n) \int^{\chi_{max}} \chi^{n-2} e^{-\chi^2} d\chi = f(n) \int^{t_{max}} t^{(n-3)/2} e^{-t} dt \quad (137)$$

which we can write $P(n,W) \doteq \gamma[(n - 1)/2,\ t_{max}(W)]/\Gamma[(n - 1)/2]$, where $\gamma(n,x)$ is the incomplete gamma-function defined by

$$\gamma(n,x) = \int_0^x e^{-t} t^{n-1} dt \quad \text{and} \quad \Gamma(n) = \gamma(n,\ x \to \infty)$$

It is important to note that we want the dependence of $P(n,W)$ *not* on the value of W, as in the usual statistical problem, but on the parameter n. We can estimate the distribution in χ^2, for any fixed large value of n, by the familiar saddle-point method, getting a Gaussian distribution given by $e^{-[\chi^2 - (n-1)]^2/4(n-1)^2} d\chi^2$. Now the first approximation to $P(n)$ can be obtained by considering the geometrical interpretation of the integral, and observing that $P(n)$ is unity for any n such that the sharp peak in χ^2 lies within the original region of integration. Taking the original limits, then, and using the hyperplane rather than the sphere boundary, we can estimate that $\overline{\chi^2}(W,\bar{n}) = (W - \bar{n}B)/2\tau$. In the next approximation, the width of the region in which $P(n)$ falls from unity to zero can be estimated from the standard deviation in χ^2. We are led to these results for the mean number of nucleons emitted in the process and for the standard deviation, with an approximately Gaussian distribution in n:

$$\bar{n} \cong \frac{W + 2\tau}{2\tau + B}$$

$$\overline{n^2} - \bar{n}^2 \simeq \frac{8\tau^2}{B^2} \frac{W + 2\tau}{2\tau + B} \qquad (138)$$

The relative rms fluctuation is just $\Delta n/\bar{n} \simeq 3/(\bar{n})^{1/2} \cdot (\tau/B)$. The mean energy loss for the emission of a single Maxwellian particle is $B + 2\tau$, and the many-particle case is seen to give a mean value not very different from what one would get neglecting any correlation, namely $W/(2\tau + B)$. The standard deviation is also not much different from the consequence of a very naive statistical estimate. Some reactions have been observed in which a highly excited nucleus emits a considerable but definite

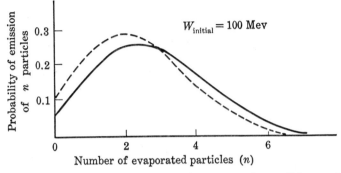

Fig. 39. The probability of emission of exactly n evaporation particles as a function of n. These fluctuations are calculated, on a very much simplified model, for a nucleus of initial $A = 100$ and excitation energy of 100 Mev. The dashed curve comes from an attempt to integrate the coupled equations of evaporation; the solid curve, which is a Poisson distribution, from a still simpler theory. Only qualitative conclusions may be safely drawn from the present theory. From (T1) and (H10).

number of identical nucleons, and the energy spectrum for those emitted particles seems to resemble the statistical energy distribution $P(n,W)$ given above.[1]

The omission of all the complicating effects from this picture is all too clear. A couple of attempts to solve the cascade equations under more realistic assumptions have been made (H10, T1). Even these more elaborate efforts have neglected the change in mass and in binding energy as the cooling proceeds, and have in general neglected the fluctuation in energy taken off with each nucleon. The resulting fluctuations primarily emphasize the choice the cooling nucleus makes between protons and neutrons, with differing mean probabilities and mean energy removal for the two types of nucleons emitted. The results indicate something very close to a Poisson distribution in the number of neutrons or in the number of protons emitted, with the mean being given by the mean cooling behavior we have already considered. In Fig. 39 we plot some consequences of the two methods mentioned. It is fairly clear that most

[1] Private communication from E. Segrè.

of the details of the process have been suppressed in these generalized models. Whether the fluctuations are underestimated or overestimated by these models is not clear. The changes in mass number and energy which have been neglected certainly cause correlations to be more important, but some of the correlations have the effect of stabilizing the process closer to the mean. It is very likely here also that a Monte Carlo procedure will be the first to yield a reliable answer to the problem.

E. Mesons: Virtual and Real

We have come to the end of a sufficiently long, but yet only very summary, account of the theory of nuclear reactions in general. It is appropriate to close with an admonition.

All our considerations have been based on a single picture of the nucleus: physically, as a collection of neutrons and protons with more or less strong interaction; formally, as a system whose Hamiltonian was a sum of kinetic energies of a given number of heavy nucleons plus more or less complicated interaction potential energies. It is clear that this idea, taken either physically or formally, is at best an incomplete model. Looking at the nuclear system in short time intervals, or with fine distance resolution, we would not in fact distinguish an unchanging number of nucleons colliding and shifting position, but fixed in number and type. On the contrary, we know that even the exchange of momentum which is the ordinary force between nucleons, like the exchange of spin and of charge which correspond to more subtle but still phenomologically described interactions is *not* to be understood in this way. The mediation of some kind of field of mesons seems certain. Like all fields whose quanta need relativistic description, that of the mesons within the nucleus cannot be assigned a definite particle count. We have to think of transient states, in which mesons appear and disappear, carrying momentum, charge, and spin back and forth among the heavy nucleons in what may be a very complicated manner. In a way we have used a description of the nucleus whose molecular analogue would be a pair of protons and an oxygen nucleus held together by some given potential, to form a molecule of water. Yet the meson field is still more complicated than that of the atomic electrons, though it contains charges. It is in some ways more closely akin to the essentially relativistic electromagnetic field, in the cases where the photons may have a purely transient existence, as ordinary photons do in fact have within the near-zone field of a radiating dipole. The anomalous nucleon magnetic moments arise from such meson fields. The existence of many-body forces, of velocity-dependent forces, of circulating currents not ascribable simply to orbital motion or to spin flipping of the nucleons is the very least to be expected from the virtual mesons within the nucleus (S1). Suspected are severe changes in the familiar properties of free nucleons themselves due to their immersion in the virtual meson sea (M8). Transient changes in charge—producing doubly charged protons or negative neutrons—changes in spin, even in rest mass, are all probable circumstances of the nuclear matter, looked at sharply enough. And, when energy enough becomes available from outside to satisfy the demands of permanent meson liberation, all sorts of new effects can be seen. Meson absorption, emission, and scattering, where the mesons fly free of the nuclear region to reach our counters or the emulsion grains, are but the most obvious effects. All have been studied, and are in active development. What of the release of mesons, strongly interacting with nucleons as they do, which never leave the nucleus, but are reabsorbed within it to transfer energy, momentum, spin, and charge throughout the nuclear drop? Already it seems that the sharp rise of the deuteron photo-cross-section (B6) in the energy region near and just above the threshold for free meson production involves some such explanations.

All this is far from our simple picture of a closed and tight cluster of Z protons and N neutrons. But it is a picture closer to the truth. It is well to end this account, then, with the clear warning that application of the simpler ideas is reliable at best only in the domain where such long time averages are involved that the transient mesons can usually be replaced by the smooth forces of our picture, and for energies well below the energy at which real mesons can be released, even internally. With that warning not forgotten, the theory of nuclear reactions can yield results valuable for innumerable applications, for the detailed understanding of nuclear structure in a kind of chemist's approximation. One day this theory may serve for the construction of a better and superseding picture, based on deeper knowledge of the fundamental nature of the nucleon itself.

REFERENCES

(A1)   R. Adair, Revs. Modern Phys., **22**, 249 (1950).

(B1)   E. Bagge, Ann. Physik, **33**, 389 (1938).

(B2)   J. Bardeen, Phys. Rev., **51**, 799 (1937).

(B3)   H. H. Barschall et al., Phys. Rev., **72**, 881 (1947); Phys. Rev., **76**, 1146 (1949).

(B4)   R. Batzel, D. Miller, and G. Seaborg, Phys. Rev., **84**, 671 (1951).

(B5)   R. Batzel and G. Seaborg, Phys. Rev., **82**, 607 (1951).

(B6)   T. Benedict and W. Woodward, Phys. Rev., **85**, 924 (L) (1952).

(B7)   P. G. Bergmann, *An Introduction to the Theory of Relativity*, Prentice-Hall, New York, 1st ed., 1942, p. 86.

(B8)   G. Bernardini et al., Phys. Rev., **76**, 1792 (1949).

(B9)   G. Bernardini et al., Phys. Rev., **82**, 105 (L) (1951).

(B10) G. Bernardini, E. Booth, and S. Lindenbaum, Phys. Rev., **80,** 905 (L) (1950).
(B11) G. Bernardini, G. Cortini, and A. Manfredini, Phys. Rev., **79,** 952 (1950).
(B12) G. Bernardini and F. Lévy, Phys. Rev., **84,** 610 (L) (1951).
(B13) H. A. Bethe, Revs. Modern Phys., **9,** 79 (1937).
(B14) H. A. Bethe and M. S. Livingston, Revs. Modern Phys., **9,** 245 (1937).
(B15) J. Blair, Phys. Rev., **75,** 907 (L) (1949).
(B16) J. Blaton, K. Danske, Kgl. Danske Videnskab. Selskab, Mat.-fys. Medd. **24,** n. s., 20, 1 (1950).
(B16a) W. Blocker, R. Kenney, and W. K. H. Panofsky, Phys. Rev., **79,** 419 (1950).
(B17) N. Bohr and F. Kalckar, Kgl. Danske Videnskab. Selskab, Mat.-fys. Medd., **14,** 10 (1937).
(B18) N. Bohr and J. Wheeler, Phys. Rev., **56,** 426 (1939).
(B19) T. Bonner and J. Evans, Phys. Rev., **73,** 666 (1948).
(B20) H. Bradt and D. Tendam, Phys. Rev., **72,** 1117 (L) (1947).
(B21) G. Breit and E. Wigner, Phys. Rev., **49,** 519 (1936).
(B22) E. J. Burge *et al.*, Proc. Roy. Soc. (London), **A210,** 534 (1952).
(B23) S. T. Butler, Proc. Roy. Soc. (London), **A208,** 559 (1951).
(C1)   G. Chew, Phys. Rev., **80,** 196 (1950).
(C2)   G. Chew and M. Goldberger, Phys. Rev., **77,** 470 (1950).
(C3)   G. Chew and G. Wick, Phys. Rev., **85,** 636 (1952).
(C4)   R. Christy, Phys. Rev., **75,** 1464 (A) (1949).
(C5)   R. F. Christy and R. Latter, Revs. Modern Phys., **20,** 185 (1948).
(C6)   E. T. Clarke, Phys. Rev., **70,** 893 (1946).
(C7)   E. Clarke and J. Irvine, Phys. Rev., **70,** 893 (1946).
(C8)   G. Cocconi and V. Cocconi Tongiorgi, Phys. Rev., **84,** 29 (1951).
(C9)   S. Cohen, Phys. Rev., **75,** 1463 (A) (1949).
(C10) L. J. Cook, E. M. McMillan, J. M. Peterson, and D. C. Sewell, Phys. Rev., **75,** 7 (1949).
(C11) E. Courant, Phys. Rev., **82,** 703 (1951).
(D1)   S. Dancoff, Phys. Rev., **72,** 1017 (1947).
(D2)   The first results in any detail are found in S. Dancoff and H. Kubitschek, Phys. Rev., **76,** 531 (1949).
(D3)   S. Devons and M. Hine, Proc. Roy. Soc. (London), **A199,** 56 (1949).
(D4)   S. Devons and G. R. Lindsey, Proc. Phys. Soc. (London), **63,** 1202 (1950).
(D5)   B. Diven and G. Almy, Phys. Rev., **80,** 407 (1950).
(E1)   J. B. Ehrman, Phys. Rev., **81,** 412 (1950).
(F1)   E. Feenberg, Phys. Rev., **55,** 504 (L) (1939).
(F2)   E. Feenberg, Revs. Modern Phys., **19,** 239 (1947).
(F3)   E. Feenberg and G. Goertzel, Phys. Rev., **70,** 597 (1949).
(F4)   E. Fermi and L. Marshall, Phys. Rev., **71,** 666 (1947).
(F5)   S. Fernbach, thesis, University of California (Berkeley), 1951 (UCRL-1382).
(F6)   S. Fernbach, R. Serber, and C. Taylor, Phys. Rev., **75,** 1352 (1949).
(F7)   H. Feshbach, D. C. Peaslee, and V. F. Weisskopf, Phys. Rev., **71,** 145 (1947).
(F8)   H. Feshbach and L. I. Schiff, Phys. Rev., **72,** 254 (L) (1947).
(F9)   W. Fowler *et al.*, Revs. Mod. Phys., **20,** 236 (1948).
(F10) W. Fowler and T. Lauritsen, Phys. Rev., **76,** 314 (L) (1949).
(F11) S. Frenkel and N. Metropolis, Phys. Rev., **72,** 914 (1947).
(F12) Y. Fujimoto and Y. Yamaguchi, Prog. Theor. Phys., **4,** 468 (1949).
(F13) Y. Fujimoto and Y. Yamaguchi, Prog. Theor. Phys., **5,** 787 (1950).
(F14) Y. Fujimoto and Y. Yamaguchi, Prog. Theor. Phys., **5,** 76 (1950).

(G0)   W. M. Garrison and J. G. Hamilton, Chem. Revs., **40**, 237 (1951).

(G1)   S. N. Ghoshal, Phys. Rev., **73**, 417 (L) (1948).

(G2)   S. N. Ghoshal, Phys. Rev., **80**, 939 (1950).

(G3)   R. Goeckermann and I. Perlman, Phys. Rev., **56**, 426 (1939).

(G4)   R. Goeckermann and I. Perlman, Phys. Rev., **73**, 1124 (L) (1948).

(G5)   M. Goldberger, Phys. Rev., **74**, 1269 (1948).

(G6)   H. Goldsmith et al., Revs. Modern Phys., **19**, 259 (1947).

(G7)   E. Guggenheim, *Thermodynamics*, Interscience, New York, 2nd ed., 1950, p. 165.

(H1)   J. Halpern and A. Mann, Phys. Rev., **83**, 370 (1951).

(H2)   A. O. Hanson et al., Revs. Modern Phys., **21**, 635 (1949).

(H3)   J. Harding, S. Lattimore, and D. Perkins, Proc. Roy. Soc. (London), **A196**, 325 (1949).

(H4)   G. H. Hardy and S. Ramanujan, Proc. Math. Soc. (London), **42**, 75 (1918).

(H5)   J. Heidmann, Phys. Rev., **80**, 171 (1950).

(H6)   W. Heitler, *The Quantum Theory of Radiation*, Oxford University Press, 2nd ed., 1947, p. 110.

(H7)   R. Herb et al., Phys. Rev., **75**, 246 (1949).

(H8)   N. Heydenburg et al., Phys. Rev., **73**, 241 (1948).

(H9)   C. Hibdon and C. Muehlhause, Phys. Rev., **76**, 100 (1949).

(H10) W. Horning and L. Baumhoff, Phys. Rev., **75**, 370 (1949).

(H11) W. Hornyak and T. Lauritsen, Revs. Mod. Phys., **20**, 191 (1948).

(H12) W. Hornyak et al., Revs. Modern Phys., **22**, 291 (1950).

(J1)   J. Jackson, Phys. Rev., **83**, 301 (1951).

(J2)   R. Jastrow, Phys. Rev., **82**, 261 (L) (1951).

(J3)   R. Jastrow and J. Roberts, Phys. Rev., **85**, 757 (A) (1952).

(J4)   J. Jungerman and S. Wright, Phys. Rev., **75**, 1470 (1949).

(K1)   F. Kalckar, J. R. Oppenheimer, and R. Serber, Phys. Rev., **52**, 273 (1937).

(K2)   P. L. Kapur and R. Peierls, Proc. Roy. Soc. (London), **A166**, 277 (1938).

(K3)   L. Katz and A. Cameron, Phys. Rev., **84**, 1115 (1951).

(K4)   L. Katz and A. Cameron, Can. J. Phys., **29**, 518 (1951).

(K5)   L. Katz and A. Penfold, Phys. Rev., **81**, 815 (1951).

(K6)   E. Kelly, thesis, University of California (Berkeley) (1950) (UCRL-1044).

(K7)   B. Kinsey, G. Bartholomew, and W. Walker, Phys. Rev., **83**, 519 (1951).

(K8)   E. J. Konopinski and H. A. Bethe, Phys. Rev., **54**, 130 (1938).

(L1)   W. Lamb, Phys. Rev., **55**, 190 (1939).

(L2)   T. Lauritsen and W. Hornyak, Revs. Modern Phys., **20**, 191 (1948).

(L3)   K. LeCouteur, Proc. Phys. Soc. (London), **A63**, 259 (1950).

(L4)   J. Levinger and H. Bethe, Phys. Rev., **78**, 115 (1950).

(M1)   F. Mariani, Nuovo cimento, **8**, 403 (1951).

(M2)   L. Marshall, Phys. Rev., **75**, 1339 (1949).

(M3)   J. Mattauch and S. Flügge, *Nuclear Physics Tables*, Interscience, New York, 1946.

(M4)   J. E. Mayer and M. G. Mayer, *Statistical Mechanics*, John Wiley & Sons, 1st ed., New York, 1940, p. 363.

(M5)   M. G. Mayer, Phys. Rev., **78**, 16 (1950).

(M6)   R. Menon et al., Phil. Mag., **41**, 583 (1950).

(M7)   N. Metropolis and G. Reitwiesner, NP-1980, Technical Information Service (USAEC), Oak Ridge, 1950.

(M8)   H. Miyazawa, Prog. Theor. Phys., **6**, 263 (1951).

(N1)   A. Newton, Phys. Rev., **75**, 17 (1949).

(O1)   J. Oppenheimer and M. Phillips, Phys. Rev., **48**, 500 (1935).

(P1)   S. Pasternack and H. Snyder, Phys. Rev., **80**, 921 (L) (1950).

(P2)   D. Peaslee, Phys. Rev., **74**, 1001 (1948).

(P3)   H. Poss, E. Salant, G. Snow, and L. Yuan, Phys. Rev., **87**, 11 (1952).

(P4)   W. Powell, Phys. Rev., **69**, 385 (1946).

(R1)   L. N. Ridenour and W. J. Henderson, Phys. Rev., **52**, 889 (1937).

(R2)   J. H. Roberts, MDDC, **731**, U. S. Government Printing Office, 1947; also doctoral dissertation, University of Chicago, 1947.

(S1)   R. Sachs and N. Austern, Phys. Rev., **81**, 705 (1951).

(S2)   L. Schiff, Phys. Rev., **70**, 761 (1946).

(S3)   L. I. Schiff, *Quantum Mechanics*, McGraw-Hill Book Co., New York, 1st ed., 1949, pp. 38, 221.

(S4)   T. Schmidt, Z. Physik, **106**, 358 (1937).

(S5)   G. T. Seaborg and I. Perlman, Revs. Modern Phys., **20**, 585 (1948).

(S6)   F. Seidl, Phys. Rev., **75**, 1508 (1949).

(S7)   R. Serber, Phys. Rev., **72**, 1008 (1947).

(S8)   W. Shoupp and J. Hill, Phys. Rev., **75**, 785 (1949).

(S9)   A. J. F. Siegert, Phys. Rev., **56**, 750 (1939).

(S10)   H. Steinwedel and J. H. Jensen, Z. Naturforsch., **5a**, 413 (1950).

(S11)   M. Stern, Revs. Modern Phys., **21**, 316 (1949); and Part V of Volume I of this work.

(T1)   K. Takayanagi and Y. Yamaguchi, Prog. Theor. Phys., **5**, 894 (1950).

(T2)   E. Teller and M. Goldhaber, Phys. Rev., **74**, 1046 (1949).

(T3)   E. Teller and J. A. Wheeler, Phys. Rev., **53**, 778 (1938).

(T4)   D. H. Templeton, J. J. Howland, and I. Perlman, Phys. Rev., **72**, 758, 766 (1947).

(T5)   G. Thomson, Phil. Mag., **40**, 589 (1949).

(T6)   L. Turner, Revs. Modern Phys., **12**, 1 (1940).

(U1)   U. S. National Bureau of Standards, Mathematical Tables Project, *Tables of Spherical Bessel Functions*, Vol. 21, 1947.

(V1)   G. Volkoff, Phys. Rev., **57**, 866 (1940).

(W1)   B. Waldman and M. Wiedenbeck, Phys. Rev., **63**, 60 (1943).

(W2)   S. Watanabe, Z. Physik, **113**, 482 (1939).

(W3)   K. Way, Phys. Rev., **75**, 1448 (1949).

(W4)   K. Way and E. Wigner, Phys. Rev., **73**, 1318 (1948).

(W5)   V. F. Weisskopf, *Lecture Series in Nuclear Physics*, MDDC, **1175**, U. S. Government Printing Office, 1947, pp. 106 *et seq.*

(W6)   V. F. Weisskopf and D. H. Ewing, Phys. Rev., **57**, 472 (1940).

(W7)   E. P. Wigner and L. Eisenbud, Phys. Rev., **72**, 29 (1947).

(W8)   E. P. Wigner and E. Feenberg, Repts. Progr. Phys., **8**, 274 (1942).

(W9)   R. Wilson, Phys. Rev., **72**, 189 (1947).

(W10)   R. Wilson, D. Corson, and C. Baker, Comm. on Nuclear Sci., National Research Council, Report 7, Washington, 1950.

(Y1)   Y. Yamaguchi, Prog. Theor. Phys., **6**, 529 (1951).

(Y2)   C. Yang, Phys. Rev., **74**, 764 (1949).

(Y3)   C. Yang, Phys. Rev., **74**, 764 (1949).

(Y4)   H. York *et al.*, Phys. Rev., **75**, 1467 (1949).

(Y5)   F. L. Yost, J. A. Wheeler, and G. Breit, Phys. Rev., **49**, 174 (1936).

APPENDIX I

In this appendix we have collected graphs which permit the collection of such cross sections as are plotted in text Figs. 12 through 14.   These are mainly graphs auxiliary to the calculation of penetrabilities.   Complete definitions and theory are found in text references (C5, K7, Y5).

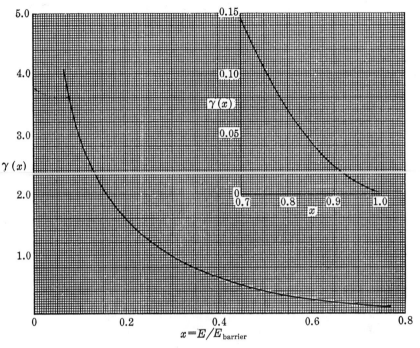

Fig. A-1. Function for computing the penetrability of the Coulomb barrier without angular momentum, P_0, for $l = 0$.   The penetrability P_0 is defined as: $P_0 = e^{-2C_0}$ with $C_0 = g\gamma(x)$. $\gamma(x)$ is here plotted.   Figures 12d and 13a of the text give barrier heights for various nuclei. g is plotted in Figs. A-2a and A-2b.   After (B13).

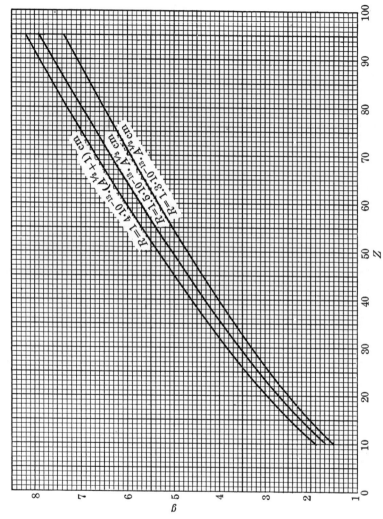

Fig. A-2a.   The characteristic orbital momentum g for protons.   This is the function g which occurs in the penetrability formulas.

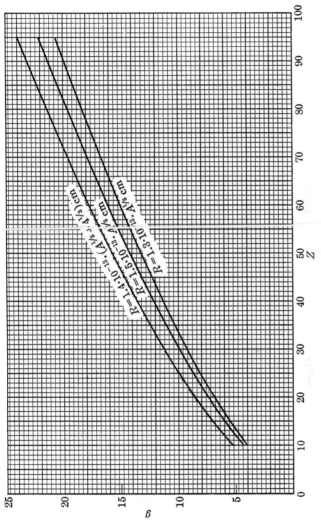

Fig. A-2b.   Characteristic orbital momentum g for alpha-particles.

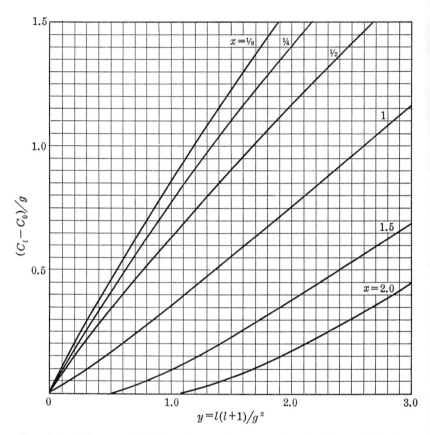

Fig. A-3.　The penetrabilities for angular momenta $l \neq 0$ are defined as $P_l = e^{-2C_l(x,y)}$. The plot gives $(C_l - C_0)/g$, where g is the characteristic orbital momentum plotted in Figs. A-2a and A-2b as a function of two parameters: energy in terms of the barrier height x and parameter $y = l(l + 1)/g^2$. After (K7).

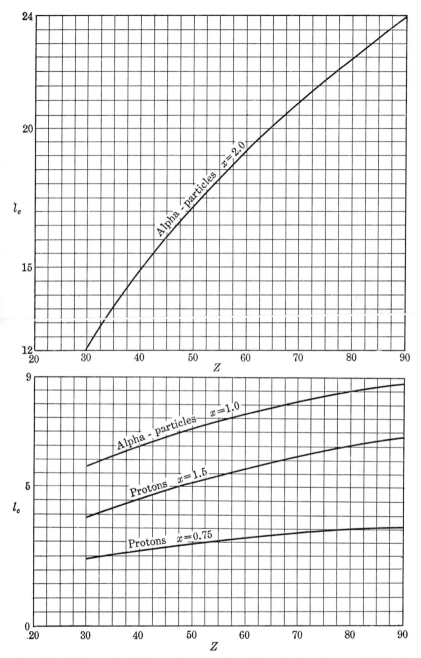

Fig. A-4. Values of orbital angular momentum l_c, such that the contribution to the total cross section for compound nucleus formation, $\sigma = \pi \lambda^2 \sum\limits_{l=0}^{\infty} (2l + 1)P_l$, for all l greater than $\bar{l}_c$, is less than 10 percent. These curves form a guide for stopping the computation of the P_l as l grows.

197

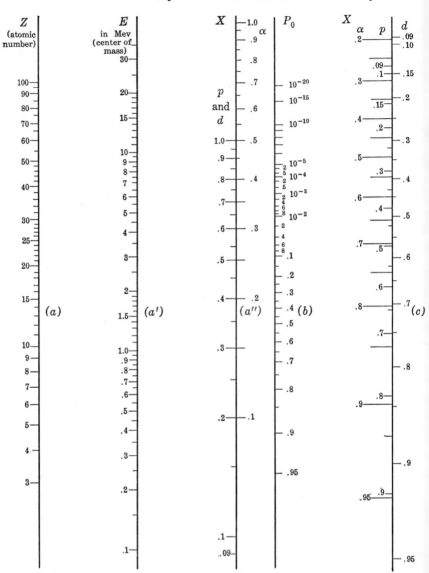

Fig. A-5. Nomogram constructed for the evaluation of the penetrability of the Coulomb barrier, in the case of zero orbital angular momentum, $l = 0$. The penetrability P_0 can be found in two ways, of different accuracy: (1) Using lines (a), (a'), and (a''), the value of the parameter x, which is the energy of the particle measured in terms of the barrier height for a definite Z, can be found directly. The approximation $A = 2Z$ is used for this graph, which is quite rough for the heavy elements, and may lead to P_0 in error by a factor of ~ 5, even where $P_0 \sim 0.1$. With this value of x, connecting points on lines (a), (b), and (c) then gives the penetrability, P_0. (2) The barrier height B may be found, not from the nomogram, but by directly reading off its value from the graphs of Figs. 12c and 13c of the text. Then $x = E/E_s$ can be found, and connecting proper points on (a), (b), and (c) of the nomogram will give P_0 to good accuracy over the whole readable range of the nomogram.

APPENDIX II

We list first a number of theoretical and experimental survey papers of both a general and a more specialized kind.

COMPILATIONS OF EXPERIMENTAL INFORMATION

M. S. Livingston and H. A. Bethe, Revs. Modern Phys., **9**, 245 (1937). List and discussion of all work on reactions up to July, 1937.

J. Mattauch and S. Flügge, *Nuclear Physics Tables*, New York, Interscience, 1946. Some data and references for all reactions up to about 1941.

W. Hornyak, T. Lauritsen, P. Morrison, and W. A. Fowler, Revs. Modern Phys., **22**, 291 (1951). A very full survey up to the middle of 1950 dealing with reactions involving the lightest target nuclei only, from H to Ne.

BOOKS

S. Devons, *The Excited States of Nuclei*, Cambridge University Press, 1949. Excellent account of experimental methods and of theory.

V. F. Weisskopf, in *Lecture Series in Nuclear Physics*, MDDC-1175, U. S. Government Printing Office, 1947, pp. 106 *et seq.* Theory.

J. Blatt and V. Weisskopf, *Theoretical Nuclear Physics*, John Wiley & Sons, New York, 1952. Comprehensive account.

PAPERS OF MORE RESTRICTED SCOPE

(a) Photonuclear Reactions

　Experimental

　　K. Strauch, Phys. Rev., **81**, 973 (1951). Work with ∼300-Mev γ's.

　　A. K. Mann and J. Halpern, Phys. Rev., **82**, 733 (1951).

　　L. Katz and A. S. Penfold, Phys. Rev., **81**, 815 (1951).

　Theoretical

　　J. S. Levinger and H. A. Bethe, Phys. Rev., **78**, 115 (1950).

　　E. P. Courant, Phys. Rev., **82**, 703 (1951).

(b) Theory of Particle Reactions in General

　　V. F. Weisskopf, Helv. Phys. Acta, **23**, 187 (1950). Physical picture.

　　E. P. Wigner, Am. J. Phys., **17**, 99 (1949). Introduction to the general dispersion theory.

　　E. P. Wigner and L. Eisenbud, Phys. Rev., **72**, 29 (1947). Presents the full theory.

　　J. Jackson, Phys. Rev., **83**, 301 (1951). A simplification of the theory.

　　T. Teichmann, Phys. Rev., **77**, 506 (1950).

　　E. Wigner, Phys. Rev., **73**, 1002 (1948).

　　The last two present instructive and useful applications of Wigner's general theory.

(c) Neutron Excitation

　Theoretical

　　E. Fermi and L. Marshall, Phys. Rev., **71**, 666 (1947). Thermal neutrons; includes experimental work.

　　B. T. Feld, Phys. Rev., **75**, 1115 (1949). Fast neutrons.

　　H. Feshbach, D. Peaslee, and V. Weisskopf, Phys. Rev., **71**, 145, 564 (1947). The basis for our version of the theory of dispersion.

Experimental

R. K. Adair, Revs. Modern Phys., **22**, 249 (1950). A comprehensive review.

D. J. Hughes, W. Spatz, and N. Goldstein, Phys. Rev., **75**, 1781 (1949).

(d) Charged Particle Excitation

Theoretical

V. Weisskopf and D. Ewing, Phys. Rev., **57**, 472, 935 (1940).

D. Peaslee, Phys. Rev., **74**, 1001 (1948). Deuterons only.

Experimental

E. L. Kelly, thesis, University of California, Berkeley, UCRL-1044, 1951.

S. N. Ghoshal, Phys. Rev., **80**, 939 (1950).

P. C. Gugelot, Phys. Rev., **81**, 51 (1951).

(e) Nuclear Fission

Theoretical

N. Bohr and J. Wheeler, Phys. Rev., **56**, 426 (1939). General theory, using drop model.

D. Brunton, Phys. Rev., **76**, 1798 (1949).

Experimental

Plutonium Project, Revs. Modern Phys., **18**, 513 (1946).

J. Jungerman and S. C. Wright, Phys. Rev., **76**, 111 (1949).

J. Jungerman, Phys. Rev., **79**, 632 (1950). Alpha- and alpha-induced fission.

(f) High-Energy Nuclear Stars

Theoretical

W. Horning and L. Baumhoff, Phys. Rev., **75**, 370 (1949).

M. L. Goldberger, Phys. Rev., **74**, 1269 (1948).

Y. Fujimoto and Y. Yamaguchi, Prog. Theor. Phys., **4**, 468 (1950).

Experimental

G. Bernardini, E. Booth, and S. Lindenbaum, Phys. Rev., **80**, 905 (1950). 400-Mev protons.

R. Menon, H. Muirhead, and O. Rochat, Phil. Mag., **41**, 583 (1950). Pi-meson-induced stars.

PAPERS ON SPECIFIC REACTIONS

The reactions are grouped by their means of excitation (list closed July, 1951). The references for each reaction are coded according to the first two or three letters in their authors' names and the years the works were published. A star (*) means that work above 100 Mev is reported. Some conventions are worth pointing out:

1. Strictly speaking, gamma-rays often are secondary products of other reactions. These are not separately considered. Only reactions in which gammas are the sole product are listed under "Gamma-rays."

2. Electron-induced reactions in which the electron is in fact captured by inverse beta-decay have not yet been observed. The electron serves to excite the nucleus, and itself passes on. It comes away from the reaction, though it is not in fact a reaction product.

3. Reactions with more than two product particles are listed only once; the order of emission (if known) is not taken into account.

The classification here adopted depends upon the facts: (i) for evident reasons of effectiveness and availability, the incident particles used in almost all nuclear reactions are light nuclei, up to helium (plus photons and electrons, etc.); and (ii) most reactions yield for at least one of the products another light nuclear particle, leaving behind as the second product particle a residual nucleus not far removed from the target nucleus in charge or mass number.

Gamma-rays

(γ, γ) Sc46; Wi45b; Wi45c; Gu41; Gae49.

(γ, meson) *Lax51; *Lit51; *Mo50; *Pet51; *Ste50.

(γ, n) Bal46; *Per49; Mc49; By51; Jo50; Kat51b; Med50; Pri50.

(γ, $2n$) Bal46; *Per48.

(γ, p) Same as (γ, n) Hi47; Cou51; Di50; *Lev51; To51; *Wak51; By51.

(γ; p, n, or d) Bal46; *Per48; By51.

(γ, α) Has51; Mil50; Pr50.

(γ, multiple products) Bal46; *Per48.

(γ, star) *Gae50.

(γ, fission) Ti49; Hax41; Bo39; Ko50; *Su50.

Electrons

(e; e', n) Bl49; Sk48.

(e; e') Wi44; Wi45a; Wi45c; Mul51.

Mesons

(π, π) *Ca51; *Be50.

(π, star) *Be50; *Che50; *Men50; *Ta50.

Neutrons

(n, γ) Fes47; *Kn49; Hug49; Gos47; An50; Cap51; Ham50; He50; Hu51; Mu50; Ki51.

(n, n) Fe47; Fel49; Se49; Fes47; Ad49; Har50; *Pas50; Stt51.

(n, $2n$) Hou46; Ma42; Hey37; Coh51; Fow50; Waf50.

(n, spallation) De48.

(n, p) Coo49; Boo37; Am35; Sa40; Coh51.

(n; p, n, or d) *Kn49; *Bru49; *Chw50; *Ha50; Waf50.

(n; H^3 or He^3) Bru49; Cor41; On40; *Ha50.

(n, α) Sh41; Wu40; *Kn49; Am35; Sa40; Bø46; St50.

(n, stars) *Go48; *Tr50.

(n, fission) Pl46; *Ke48; Ph49; Fra47; Bou50; Ros50.

Protons

(p, γ) Du38; Wal48; Ben46; Fo48; Dev49; Hal50.

(p, π) *Bj50; *Blo51; *Hen51; *Jon50.

(p, n) Wei40; Du38; Del39; Bla51; *Bod51; *Kn51; *Mir51.

(p, $2n$) Te47a.

(p, spallation) *Baz50; *Baz51; *Hy50; *Me51.

(p, p) Fu48; Ba39; Hei47; Bed49; Goh51; Lth50; Rh50.

(p; p, n, or d) Ri46; Pa48; Th49.

(p, α) Th49; Bur49; Bar50; Ch50; Coc49; Ra50; Dev49.

(p, heavy particle) *Mar51; *Wr50.

(p, star) *Tho49; *Cam50; *Fr50; *Hod51; *Pek50.

(p, fission) Ju48; Bo39.

Deuterons

(d, γ) We43.

(d, n) Pe48; Ke49; Cl46b; Ro47; Amm49; Fa49; *Kn51.

(d, $2n$) Ke49; Te47a.

(d, spallation)   Wil48; *Mi48; *Bat50; *Lin50.

(d, p)   Pe48; Pol49; Cl46b; All48; Buw50; Cu50; Hav51; Phi50; Va51.

(d, $p\alpha$)   Cl47.

(d, d)   Gug47; Gr49; Ker51.

(d, H^3)   Kr41; Wi46; Ka49.

(d, α)   Kri49; Li38; Cl46a; In50; Sch50.

(d, αn)   Mad50.

(d, stars)   *Ga49a; *Ho49.

(d, fission)   *Wo49; Ju48; Kr40; *Goe49.

Tritium

    (H^3, n)   Cr51.

    (H^3, p)   Ku48a.

    (H^3, He^3)   Ku47b.

He^3

    (He^3, p)   Al39.

Alpha-particles

    (α, γ)   Ben51.

    (α, mesons)   *Bu49; *Jon51.

    (α, n)   Eg48; Bra47; Rid37; Ric48; Hap49; Tem49.

    (α, $2n$)   Gh48; Te47a; Fi50; Tem49.

    (α, spallation)   *Wo49; *Oc48; *Lin50.

    (α, p)   Bro49; Roy51.

    (α, α)   La39.

    (α; p, $3n$)   Hel46; Ne49; Te47b.

    (α, stars)   *Ga49b.

    (α, fission)   *Oc48; *Wo49; Ju48.

Heavy particles

    (heavy particle, star)   *Bra48; *Bra49.

REFERENCES FOR APPENDIX II

(Ad49)   R. K. Adair, C. K. Bockelman, and R. E. Peterson, Phys. Rev., **76**, 308 (L) (1949).

(Al39)   L. W. Alvarez and R. Cornog, Phys. Rev., **56**, 613 (L) (1939).   (Si)

(All48)   H. R. Allan and C. A. Wilkinson, Proc. Roy. Soc. (London), **A194**, 131 (1948).

(Am35)   E. Amaldi, O. D'Agostino, E. Fermi, B. Pontecorvo, F. Rasetti, E. Segrè, Proc. Roy. Soc. (London), **A149**, 522 (1935).

(Amm49)   P. Ammiraju, Phys. Rev., **76**, 1421 (L) (1949).

(An50)   H. L. Anderson, Phys. Rev., **80**, 499 (1950).

(Ba39)   S. Barnes and P. Aradine, Phys. Rev., **55** (1950).   (In)

(Bal46)   G. Baldwin and G. Klaiber, Phys. Rev., **70**, 259 (1946).   (Excitation survey)

(Bar50)   C. A. Barres, A. P. French, and S. Devons, Nature, **166**, 145 (L) (1950).

(Bat50)   F. O. Bartell, A. C. Helmholz, S. D. Softky, and D. B. Stewart, Phys. Rev., **80**, 1006 (1950).

(Baz50)   R. E. Batzel and G. T. Seaborg, Phys. Rev., **79**, 528 (L) (1950).

(Baz51)   R. E. Batzel and G. T. Seaborg, Phys. Rev., **82**, 607 (1951).

(Be50)   G. Bernardini, E. T. Booth, L. Lederman, and J. Tinot, Phys. Rev., **80**, 924 (L) (1950).

(Bed49)   R. S. Bender, F. C. Shoemaker, S. G. Kaufmann, and G. M. B. Bou-
          vicius, Phys. Rev., **76**, 273 (1949).
(Ben46)   W. E. Bennett, T. W. Bonner, C. E. Mandeville, and B. E. Watt, Phys.
          Rev., **70**, 882 (1946).
(Ben51)   W. E. Bennett, P. A. Roys, and B. J. Toppel, Phys. Rev., **82**, 20 (1951).
(Bj50)   R. Bjorklund, W. E. Crandall, B. V. Moyer, and H. F. York, Phys. Rev.,
          77, 213 (1950).
(Bl49)   J. S. Blair, Phys. Rev., **75**, 907 (L) (1949).
(Bla51)   V. P. Blaser, F. Boehm, P. Marmier, and D. C. Peaslee, Helv. Phys.
          Acta, **24**, 3 (1951).
(Blo51)   M. M. Block, S. Passman, and W. W. Havens, Phys. Rev., **83**, 167 (L)
          (1951).
(Bo39)   N. Bohr and J. A. Wheeler, Phys. Rev., **56**, 426 (1939).   (Fission
          theory liquid drop)
(Bø46)   J. K. Bøggild, Kgl. Danske Videnskab. Selskab, Mat.-fys. Medd., **23**, [4]
          (1946).
(Bod51)   D. Bodansky and N. F. Ramsey, Phys. Rev., **82**, 831 (1951).
(Boo37)   E. T. Booth and C. Hurst, Proc. Roy. Soc. (London), **A161**, 248 (1937).
(Bou50)   C. C. Bounton and G. C. Hanna, Can. J. Research, **28**, 498 (1950).
(Bra47)   H. L. Bradt and D. J. Tendam, Phys. Rev., **72**, 1117 (1947).
(Bra48)   H. L. Bradt and B. Peters, Phys. Rev., **74**, 1828 (1948).
(Bra49)   H. L. Bradt and B. Peters, Phys. Rev., **75**, 1779 (L) (1949).
(Bro49)   J. E. Brolby, Jr., M. B. Sampson, and A. C. G. Mitchell, Phys. Rev.,
          76, 624 (1949).
(Bru49)   K. Brueckner and W. M. Powell, Phys. Rev., **75**, 1274 (L) (1949).
(Bu49)   J. Burfening, E. Gardner, and C. M. G. Lattes, Phys. Rev., **75**, 382
          (1949).
(Bur49)   W. Burcham and W. Freeman, Phys. Rev., **75**, 1756 (1949).
(Buw50)   H. Burrows, W. M. Gibson, and J. Rotblat, Phys. Rev., **80**, 1095 (L)
          (1950).
(By51)   P. R. Byerly, Jr., and W. E. Stephens, Phys. Rev., **83**, 54 (1951).
(Ca51)   M. Camac, D. R. Corson, R. M. Littauer, A. M. Shapiro, A. Silverman,
          R. R. Wilson, and W. M. Woodward, Phys. Rev., **82**, 745 (1951).
(Cam50)   V. Camerini, P. H. Fowler, W. O. Lock, and M. Muirhead, Phil. Mag.,
          41, 413 (1951).
(Cap51)   P. C. Capson and A. J. Verhoeve, Phys. Rev., **81**, 336 (1951).
(Ch50)   C. Y. Chao, Phys. Rev., **80**, 1035 (1950).
(Che50)   W. B. Cheston and L. J. B. Goldfarb, Phys. Rev., **78**, 683 (1950).
(Chw50)   C. F. Chew and M. L. Goldberger, Phys. Rev., **77**, 470 (1950).
(Cl46a)   E. T. Clarke and J. W. Irvine, Jr., Phys. Rev., **69**, 680 (A) (1946).
(Cl46b)   E. T. Clarke, Phys. Rev., **70**, 893 (1946).   (Thick target yield survey)
(Cl47)   E. T. Clarke, Phys. Rev., **71**, 187 (1947).   (Al)
(Coc49)   W. Cochrane and A. H. Hester, Proc. Roy. Soc. (London), **A199**, 458
          (1949).
(Coh51)   B. L. Cohen, Phys. Rev., **81**, 184 (1951).
(Coo49)   J. Coon and R. Nobles, Phys. Rev., **75**, 1358 (1949).   (He³, N¹⁴)
(Cor41)   R. Cornog and W. F. Libby, Phys. Rev., **59**, 1046 (1941).
(Cou51)   E. P. Courant, Phys. Rev., **82**, 703 (1951).
(Cr51)   R. W. Crews, Phys. Rev., **82**, 100 (L) (1951).
(Cu50)   C. D. Curling and J. O. Newton, Nature, **166**, 339 (1950).

(De48)   F. de Hoffmann, B. T. Feld, and P. R. Stein, Phys. Rev., **74**, 1330 (1948). (U^{235})

(Del39)   L. A. Delsasso, L. N. Ridenour, R. Sherr, and M. G. White, Phys. Rev., **55**, 113 (1939).

(Dev49)   S. Devons and M. G. N. Hine, Proc. Roy. Soc. (London), **A199**, 56, 73 (1949).

(Di50)   B. C. Diven and G. M. Almy, Phys. Rev., **80**, 407 (1950).

(Du38)   L. DuBridge, S. Barnes, J. Buck, and C. Strain, Phys. Rev., **53**, 447 (1938).

(Eg48)   D. T. Eggen and M. L. Pool, Phys. Rev., **74**, 57 (1948).

(Fa49)   D. E. Falk, E. Creutz, and F. Seitz, Phys. Rev., **76**, 322 (L) (1949).

(Fe47)   E. Fermi and L. Marshall, Phys. Rev., **71**, 666 (1947).   (Theory and experimental survey)

(Fel49)   B. T. Feld, Phys. Rev., **75**, 1115 (1949).   (Theory and survey)

(Fes47)   H. Feshbach, D. C. Peaslee, and V. F. Weisskopf, Phys. Rev., **71**, 145, 564 (1947).

(Fi50)   R. W. Fink, F. L. Reynolds, and D. H. Templeton, Phys. Rev., **77**, 614 (1950).

(Fo48)   W. A. Fowler, C. C. Lauritsen, and T. Lauritsen, Revs. Modern Phys., **20**, 236 (1948).

(Fow50)   J. L. Fowler and J. M. Slye, Jr., Phys. Rev., **77**, 787 (1950).

(Fr50)   P. Freier and E. P. Ney, Phys. Rev., **77**, 337 (1950).

(Fra47)   S. Frankel and N. Metropolis, Phys. Rev., **72**, 914 (1947).

(Fu48)   H. Fulbright and R. Bush, Phys. Rev., **74**, 1323 (1948).   (Light nuclei)

(Ga49a)   E. Gardner and V. Peterson, Phys. Rev., **75**, 364 (1949).   (d, stars in photoplates exp.)

(Ga49b)   E. Gardner, Phys. Rev., **75**, 379 (1949).   (Stars in photoplates exp.)

(Gae49)   E. R. Gaerttner and M. L. Yeater, Phys. Rev., **76**, 363 (1949).

(Gae50)   E. R. Gaerttner and M. L. Yeater, Phys. Rev., **77**, 714 (L) (1950).

(Gh48)   S. N. Ghoshal, Phys. Rev., **73**, 417 (L) (1948).

(Go48)   M. L. Goldberger, Phys. Rev., **74**, 1269 (1948).   (Heavy nuclei: theory)

(Goe49)   R. H. Goeckermann and I. Perlman, Phys. Rev., **76**, 628 (1949).

(Goh51)   G. Goldhaber and R. M. Williamson, Phys. Rev., **82**, 495 (1951).

(Gos47)   H. H. Goldsmith, H. W. Ibser, and B. T. Feld, Revs. Modern Phys., **19**, 259 (1947).   (Excitation survey)

(Gr49)   G. W. Greenlees, A. E. Kempton, and E. H. Rhoderick, Nature, **164**, 663, (L) (1949).

(Gu41)   E. Guth, Phys. Rev., **59**, 325 (1941).   (Theory)

(Gug47)   K. M. Guggenheim, H. Heitler, and G. F. Powell, Proc. Roy. Soc. (London), **A190**, 196 (1947).

(Ha50)   J. Hadley and H. York, Phys. Rev., **80**, 345 (1950).

(Hal50)   R. H. Hall and W. A. Fowler, Phys. Rev., **77**, 197 (1950).

(Hap49)   I. Halpern, Phys. Rev., **76**, 248 (1949).

(Ham50)   B. Hamermesh, Phys. Rev., **80**, 415 (1950).

(Har50)   S. P. Harris, C. O. Muehlhause, and G. E. Thomas, Phys. Rev., **79**, 11 (1950).

(Has51)   R. N. H. Haslam and H. M. Skarsgard, Phys. Rev., **81**, 479 (L) (1951).

(Hav51)   J. A. Harvey, Phys. Rev., **81**, 353 (1951).

(Hax41)   R. O. Haxby, W. E. Shoupp, W. E. Stephens, and W. H. Wells, Phys. Rev., **59**, 57 (1941).

(He50)   R. L. Henkel and H. H. Barschall, Phys. Rev., **80**, 145 (1950).

(Hei47)   H. Heitler, A. N. May, and C. F. Powell, Proc. Roy. Soc. (London), **A190**, 180 (1947).

(Hel46)   A. C. Helmholz, Phys. Rev., **70**, 982 (L) (1946).

(Hen51)   E. M. Henley and R. H. Huddlestone, Phys. Rev., **82**, 754 (1951).

(Hey37)   F. A. Heyn, Physica, **4**, 1224 (1937).

(Hi47)   O. Hirzel and H. Wäffler, Helv. Phys. Acta, **20**, 373 (1947).

(Ho49)   W. Horning and L. Baumhoff, Phys. Rev., **75**, 470 (1949).   (Theory, d, stars in photoplates)

(Hod51)   P. E. Hodgson, Phil. Mag., **42**, 82 (1951).

(Hou46)   F. G. Houtermans, Nachr. Akad. Wiss. Göttingen, Math.-physik. Kl., **1**, 52 (1946).

(Hu51)   H. Hurwitz, Jr., and H. A. Bethe, Phys. Rev., **81**, 898 (L) (1951).

(Hug49)   D. J. Hughes, W. D. B. Spatz, and N. Goldstein, Phys. Rev., **75**, 1781 (1949).

(Hy50)   E. K. Hyde, A. Ghiorso, and G. T. Seaborg, Phys. Rev., **77**, 765 (1950).

(In50)   D. R. Inglis, Phys. Rev., **78**, 104 (1950).

(Jo50)   H. E. Johns, L. Katz, R. A. Douglas, and R. N. H. Harlan, Phys. Rev., **80**, 1062 (1950).

(Jon50)   S. B. Jones and R. S. White, Phys. Rev., **78**, 12 (1950).

(Jon51)   S. B. Jones and R. S. White, Phys. Rev., **82**, 374 (1951).

(Ju48)   J. Jungerman and S. C. Wright, Phys. Rev., **74**, 150 (1948).

(Ka49)   D. Kahn and G. Groetzinger, Phys. Rev., **75**, 906 (L) (1949).

(Kat51b)   L. Katz, H. E. Johns, R. G. Baker, R. N. H. Harlan, and R. A. Douglas, Phys. Rev., **82**, 271 (L) (1951).

(Ke48)   E. L. Kelly and C. Wiegand, Phys. Rev., **73**, 1135 (1948).

(Ke49)   E. L. Kelly and E. Segrè, Phys. Rev., **75**, 999 (1949).   (Bi)

(Ker51)   K. K. Keller, J. B. Niedner, C. F. Way, and F. B. Shull, Phys. Rev., **81**, 481 (L) (1951).

(Ki51)   B. B. Kinsey, G. A. Bartholomew, and W. A. Walker, Phys. Rev., **82**, 380 (1951).

(Kn49)   W. J. Knox, Phys. Rev., **75**, 537 (1949).   (Light nuclei)

(Kn51)   W. J. Knox, Phys. Rev., **81**, 687 (1951).

(Ko50)   H. W. Koch, J. McElhinney, and E. L. Gasteiger, Phys. Rev., **77**, 329 (1951).

(Kr40)   R. S. Krishnan and T. E. Banks, Nature, **145**, 860 (1940).

(Kr41)   R. S. Krishnan, Nature, **148**, 407 (L) (1941).

(Kri49)   N. Krisberg and M. L. Pool, Phys. Rev., **75**, 1693 (1949).   (Ti)

(Ku47b)   D. Kundu and M. L. Pool, Phys. Rev., **72**, 101 (1947).   (Ag)

(Ku48a)   D. Kundu and M. L. Pool, Phys. Rev., **73**, 22 (1948).   (Rh and Co)

(La39)   K. Lark-Horowitz, J. R. Risser, and R. N. Smith, Phys. Rev., **55**, 878 (1939).   (In)

(Lax51)   M. Lax and H. Feshbach, Phys. Rev., **81**, 189 (1951).

(Lev51)   C. Levinthal and A. Silverman, Phys. Rev., **82**, 822 (1951).

(Li38)   J. Livingood and G. Seaborg, Phys. Rev., **54**, 391 (1938).

(Lin50)   M. Lindner and I. Perlman, Phys. Rev., **78**, 499 (1950).

(Lit51)   R. M. Littauer and D. Walker, Phys. Rev., **82**, 746 (1951).

(Lth50)   C. Levinthal, E. A. Martinelli, and A. Silverman, Phys. Rev., **78**, 199 (1950).

(Ma42)   W. Maurer and W. Raums, Z. Physik, **119**, 602 (1942).

(Mad49) C. E. Mandeville, C. P. Swann, and S. C. Snowdon, Phys. Rev., **76**, 980 (L) (1949).

(Mar51) L. Marquez and I. Perlman, Phys. Rev., **81**, 953 (1951).

(Mc49) J. McElhinney *et al.*, Phys. Rev., **75**, 542 (1949).   (Gamma-excitation survey)

(Mcd50) B. D. McDaniel, R. L. Walker, and M. B. Stearns, Phys. Rev., **80**, 807 (1950).

(Me51) J. W. Meadows and R. B. Holt, Phys. Rev., **83**, 47 (1951).

(Men50) M. G. K. Menon, H. Muirhead, and O. Rochat, Phil. Mag., **41** (4th series), 583 (1950).

(Mi48) D. Miller, R. Thompson, and B. Cunningham, Phys. Rev., **74**, 347 (L) (1948).

(Mil50) C. H. Millar and A. G. W. Cameron, Phys. Rev., **78**, 78 (L) (1950).

(Mir51) R. D. Miller, D. C. Sewell, and R. W. Wright, Phys. Rev., **81**, 374 (1951).

(Mo50) R. F. Mozley, Phys. Rev., **80**, 493 (L) (1950).

(Mu50) C. O. Muehlhause, Phys. Rev., **79**, 277 (1950).

(Mul51) C. J. Mullin and E. Guth, Phys. Rev., **82**, 141 (1951).

(Ne49) A. Newton, Phys. Rev., **75**, 209 (L) (1949).

(Oc48) P. R. O'Connor and G. Seaborg, Phys. Rev., **74**, 1189 (L) (1948).

(On40) R. D. O'Neal and M. Goldhaber, Phys. Rev., **58**, 574 (1940).   (Li)

(Pa48) W. K. Panofsky and R. Phillips, Phys. Rev., **74**, 1732 (L) (1948).

(Pas50) S. Pasternack and H. S. Snyder, Phys. Rev., **80**, 921 (L) (1950).

(Pe48) D. C. Peaslee, Phys. Rev., **74**, 1001 (1948).   (Theory, *d*-excitation)

(Pek50) D. H. Perkins, Proc. Roy. Soc. (London), **203**, 399 (1950).

(Per48) M. Perlman and G. Friedlander, Phys. Rev., **74**, 442 (1948).   (Gamma-excitation survey)

(Per49) M. Perlman, Phys. Rev., **75**, 988 (1949).   (Table)

(Pet51) J. M. Peterson, W. S. Gilbert, and R. S. White, Phys. Rev., **81**, 1003 (1951).

(Ph49) A. Phillips, L. Rosen, and R. Taschek, Phys. Rev., **75**, 919 (1949).

(Phi50) G. C. Phillips, Phys. Rev., **80**, 164 (1950).

(Pl46) Plutonium Project, Revs. Modern Phys., **18**, 513 (1946).   (Fission survey)

(Pol49) E. Pollard, V. Sailor, and L. Wyly, Phys. Rev., **75**, 725 (1949).   (Al)

(Pr50) M. A. Preston, Phys. Rev., **80**, 307 (L) (1950).

(Pri50) G. A. Price and D. W. Kerst, Phys. Rev., **77**, 806 (1950).

(Ra50) J. K. Rasmussen, W. F. Hornyak, C. C. Lauritsen, and T. Lauritsen, Phys. Rev., **77**, 617 (1950).

(Rh50) E. H. Rhoderick, Proc. Roy. Soc. (London), **A201**, 348 (1950).

(Ri46) J. R. Richardson and B. T. Wright, Phys. Rev., **70**, 445 (A) (1946).

(Rid37) L. N. Ridenour and W. J. Henderson, Phys. Rev., **52**, 889 (1937).   (Excitation survey)

(Ric48) H. T. Richards, MDDC 1504.

(Ro47) R. B. Roberts and P. H. Abelson, Phys. Rev., **72**, 76 (1947).

(Ros50) L. Rosen and A. M. Hudson, Phys. Rev., **78**, 533 (1950).

(Roy51) R. R. Roy, Phys. Rev., **82**, 227 (1951).

(Sa40) R. Sagane, S. Kojima, G. Miyamoto, M. Ikawa, Phys. Rev., **57**, 1179 (L) (1940).

(Sc46) L. I. Schiff, Phys. Rev., **70**, 761 (1946).

(Sch50) A. D. Schelberg, M. B. Sampson, and R. G. Cochran, Phys. Rev., **80**, 574 (1950).

(Se49) F. G. P. Seidl, Phys. Rev., **75**, 1508 (1949).

(Sh41) R. Sherr, K. Bainbridge, and H. Anderson, Phys. Rev., **60**, 473 (1941). (Pt, Hg)

(Sk48) L. S. Skaggs, J. S. Laughlin, A. O. Hanson, and J. J. Orlin, Phys. Rev., **73**, 420 (L) (1948).

(St50) A. Stebler, H. Bichsel, and P. Huber, Helv. Phys. Acta, **23**, 511 (1950).

(Ste50) J. Steinberger, W. K. H. Panofsky, and J. Steller, Phys. Rev., **78**, 802 (1950).

(Stt51) P. H. Stetson and C. Goodman, Phys. Rev., **82**, 69 (1951).

(Su50) N. Sugarman, Phys. Rev., **79**, 532 (L) (1950).

(Sz48) A. Szalay and E. Csongor, Phys. Rev., **74**, 1063 (1948).   (Mg)

(Ta50) S. Tamor, Phys. Rev., **77**, 412 (L) (1950).

(Te47a) D. H. Templeton, J. J. Howland, and I. Perlman, Phys. Rev., **72**, 758 (1947).

(Te47b) D. H. Templeton, J. J. Howland, and I. Perlman, Phys. Rev., **72**, 766 (1947).

(Tem49) G. M. Temmer, Phys. Rev., **76**, 424 (1949).

(Th49) R. Thomas, S. Rubin, W. Fowler, and C. Lauritsen, Phys. Rev., **75**, 1612 (L) (1949).

(Tho49) G. Thomson, Phil. Mag., **40**, 589 (1949).

(Ti49) E. W. Titterton and F. K. Goward, Phys. Rev., **76**, 142 (L) (1949).

(Ti51) E. W. Titterton, Phil. Mag., **42**, 109 (L) (1951).

(To51) M. E. Toms and W. E. Stephens, Phys. Rev., **82**, 709 (1951).

(Tr50) J. Tracy and W. M. Powell, Phys. Rev., **77**, 594 (1950).

(Va51) E. M. Van Patler, W. W. Buechner, and H. Sperduto, Phys. Rev., **82**, 248 (1951).

(Waf50) H. Wäffler, Helv. Phys. Acta, **23**, 239 (1950).

(Wak51) D. Walker, Phys. Rev., **81**, 634 (L) (1951).

(Wal48) R. L. Walker and B. D. McDaniel, Phys. Rev., **74**, 315 (1948).

(We43) K. Weiner, M. L. Pool, and J. Kurbatov, Phys. Rev., **63**, 67 (1943).

(Wei40) V. Weisskopf and D. Ewing, Phys. Rev., **57**, 472, 935 (1940).   (Theory and experiment: p, n.)

(Wi44) M. L. Wiedenbeck, Phys. Rev., **66**, 36 (A) (1944).

(Wi45a) M. L. Wiedenbeck, Phys. Rev., **67**, 59 (A) (1945).

(Wi45b) M. L. Wiedenbeck, Phys. Rev., **68**, 1 (1945).

(Wi45c) M. L. Wiedenbeck, Phys. Rev., **68**, 237 (1945).

(Wi46) M. L. Wiedenbeck, Phys. Rev., **70**, 435 (L) (1946).

(Wil48) G. Wilkinson and H. Hicks, Phys. Rev., **74**, 1733 (L) (1948).   (Table, rare earths)

(Wo49) R. D. Wolfe and N. E. Ballou, Phys. Rev., **75**, 527 (L) (1949).

(Wu40) C. S. Wu, Phys. Rev., **58**, 926 (L) (1940).

(Wr50) S. C. Wright, Phys. Rev., **79**, 838 (1950).

PART VII

The Neutron

BERNARD T. FELD

The Massachusetts Institute of Technology

In 1948, when this work was begun, the status of the field of neutron physics was uncertain and rather anomalous. Important progress, which had been made during the war, was known to the great body of physicists only through a few "releases" and through the Smyth report. The main prewar references—the articles of Bethe, Bacher, and Livingston, in *Reviews of Modern Physics*—were hopelessly out-of-date. They had been partially and inadequately replaced by hastily assembled and informally distributed mimeographed notes of a Los Alamos lecture series on nuclear physics (LA-24) and of a series of lectures by Fermi on neutron physics.

By the time the first draft of this work was completed, in June of 1949, the situation was quite a different one. As a consequence of a wise and far-sighted policy on the part of the American, British, and Canadian atomic energy commissions, practically all the basic scientific data, which had been accumulated during the war, appeared in the open literature. As a result of the widespread renewal of interest in the problems of neutron physics, the field has developed, and continues to develop, at a rate which has converted the task of compiler and author into an almost hopeless struggle against obsolescence and has expanded the dimensions of this work far beyond its original conception. The unequal struggle was, quite arbitrarily, concluded as of July 1, 1951. Since then, some changes have been made, mainly as a result of important new developments which have come to the attention of the author, mostly through publication in American journals.

This work is primarily intended for the practicing nuclear physicist. It presupposes a knowledge of the fundamentals of nuclear physics as well as of its terminology. Some of the terms, such as "barn," [1] are of comparatively recent origin, but their use has become widespread.

[1] Barn, a unit of cross section; origin: big as a ———. (1 barn = 10^{-24} cm^2.) This unit is said to have been invented by the nuclear physicists at Purdue University, around 1941 or 1942, to describe nuclear cross sections which are relatively easy to measure.

Although an attempt has been made to present herein a complete summary of the major aspects of neutron physics, some important applications have, perforce, received inadequate treatment or been omitted completely.   Thus, no attention has been paid to the role of neutrons in biophysics; nor has any space been devoted to the many interesting problems concerning the effects of neutron interactions on the macroscopic physical properties of matter.   Also, and regretfully, omitted is a discussion of the fascinating problems of the origin of the elements, in which the properties of neutron interactions may have played a decisive role.   [The interested reader is referred to an excellent summary of this field by Alpher and Herman, Revs. Mod. Phys., **22**, 153 (1950).]

It would be impossible to give a complete list of the many individuals to whom I am indebted for aid, encouragement, information, discussion, and criticism during the progress of this work.   My colleagues at M.I.T., Brookhaven, and elsewhere, especially H. Feshbach, M. Goldhaber, G. Placzek, and V. F. Weisskopf, have been unusually generous in this respect.   I owe a special debt to E. Amaldi, of the University of Rome, not only for congenial and informative discussions but for having generously allowed me access to an unpublished work on neutron physics by G. C. Wick and himself.

In memory of many pleasant hours, during which the outline of this article achieved shape and substance, I respectfully dedicate this work to my teacher and friend, the late H. H. Goldsmith.

SECTION 1. PROPERTIES AND FUNDAMENTAL INTERACTIONS

A. Discovery

The discovery of the neutron is one of the most dramatic chapters in the history of modern physics. It started in Germany, in the last month of 1930, with the report by Bothe and Becker (B50) of a penetrating radiation resulting from the bombardment of certain light elements by polonium alpha-particles. They bombarded many substances, using a Geiger point-counter as a detector of the resulting radiation. Most of the elements investigated (Pb, Ag, Ca, N, C, O, Ne) yielded no detectable radiation; two (Mg, Al) showed a slight effect. Lithium, boron, and fluorine gave appreciable amounts of radiation capable of affecting the counter, and beryllium yielded a comparatively tremendous amount. Bothe and Becker concluded that the radiation consisted of gamma-rays, more penetrating than any that had been observed up to that time.[1]

Curie and Joliot (C36, J10) immediately undertook a study of the properties of this penetrating radiation. They had available a much stronger polonium source (100 millicuries, as compared to the 3–7 available to Bothe and Becker) and were able to measure the absorption of the radiation in lead. They observed, for the radiation from beryllium, an exponential attenuation with an absorption coefficient of 0.15 cm^{-1}. (The radiations from boron and lithium had lead absorption coefficients of 0.2 and 1.7 cm^{-1}, respectively.)

So far, there was nothing to contradict the suggestion—and, indeed, this was universally assumed—that the radiations were very penetrating gamma-rays. (We know now that an absorption coefficient in lead of 0.15 cm^{-1} is smaller than that of the most penetrating gamma-rays.) However, in January of 1932, Curie and Joliot (C37) reported the following interesting observations: They investigated the effects of placing thin screens of various materials in front of the ionization chamber, which was being used to detect the radiations. For most of the screens nothing noteworthy occurred. However, when the screens contained hydrogen, the current in the ionization chamber went up.

Curie and Joliot inferred that the increased ionization was due to the ejection of protons from the screen by the primary radiation. They strengthened this theory by the following set of observations: (1) The application of a magnetic field in the region between the screen and the ionization chamber did not decrease the effect; it would have, if the ejected particles had been slow electrons. (2) The effect vanished when 0.2 mm of aluminum was placed between the screen and the chamber. This was sufficient to absorb protons, but not fast electrons. (3) Cloud chamber photographs of the tracks of particles ejected by the radiation

---

[1] The conclusions of Bothe and Becker, as well as the observations upon which they were based, turn out, in retrospect, to be completely valid. The Geiger point-counter, used as a detector by these investigators, was not sensitive to neutrons; thus, Bothe and Becker could not have observed neutrons in their experiments. It was only with the introduction of ionization chambers, proportional counters, and cloud chambers as detectors that the neutrons became observable in subsequent investigations. The measurements of the gamma-ray energies ($\sim$3 Mev from boron and $\sim$5 Mev from beryllium), reported by Bothe and Becker, have subsequently been confirmed. Indeed, the important discovery by Bothe and Becker of artificial excitation of nuclear gamma-radiation, reported in their 1930 paper, has unfortunately been almost completely obscured by the drama associated with the discovery of the neutron. For a more complete discussion of the significance of the observations of Bothe and co-workers, the reader is referred to an article by Fleischmann (F32).

from hydrogen-containing screens showed ionization consistent with that of protons, but inconsistent with that of electrons (C38).

Curie and Joliot first hypothesized that the ejection of protons from the screens was due to Compton scattering of the incident gamma-radiation by the hydrogen nuclei. From the observed range (energy) of the (recoil) protons, they estimated the energy of the photons from beryllium to be 50 Mev. Curie and Joliot recognized a number of serious difficulties in connection with their hypothesis; they could conceive of no source of such high-energy photons in a reaction of alpha-particles on beryllium, and they felt (erroneously) that photons of such high energy should be even more penetrating than the observed radiation. But, while they decided that the ejection of protons (and other light nuclei) was by a new type of gamma-ray interaction (C38), it remained for Chadwick, working at the Cavendish Laboratory in England, to reject the gamma-ray hypothesis and take the bold step of postulating a new particle.

Chadwick was very quick to follow up the researches reported from the Institut du Radium. Only slightly more than a month after the report discussed above he was publishing data (C5), obtained with counters and cloud chambers, showing that the radiations from beryllium bombarded with alpha-particles were capable of conferring high speeds not only upon protons, but also upon the nuclei of other light elements (He, Li, Be, B, C, N, O, A). From the observed ranges of the light nuclei, and using the then current range-energy relationships, Chadwick showed that the Compton recoil hypothesis of Curie and Joliot was inconsistent with the data. The data could, however, be explained if the light nuclei were assumed to be recoils from elastic collisions with a neutral (to explain the great penetrability) particle of approximately protonic mass.

To obtain the mass of this particle (called by Chadwick the neutron) Chadwick (C6) used the available data on the maximum range (velocity) of the proton recoils, and the results of Feather (F2) on the maximum range of the nitrogen recoils, observed in a cloud chamber. (If these were due to Compton recoils, they would have required gamma-ray energies of 55 and 90 Mev, respectively.) By application of the law of conservation of momentum, Chadwick derived that the particles responsible for these recoils had a mass of 1.15 times the proton mass, with an uncertainty such that "it is legitimate to conclude that the mass of the neutron is very nearly the same as the mass of the proton."

Another estimate of the mass of the neutron was made by Chadwick from observations on the neutron-producing reaction $B^{11} + He^4 \rightarrow N^{14} + n^1$. On the assumption that the maximum-energy neutrons (obtained from the maximum range of proton recoils) correspond to leaving N^{14} in its ground state, and from the values of the masses of the three nuclei involved, previously determined by Aston, Chadwick deduced the value of 1.0067 atomic mass units for the mass of the neutron.

Within a short time, immediately following upon the series of announcements described above, a large number of investigators in many lands were conducting experiments on the properties of the neutron and its interactions. Although it is not the author's intention to continue this historical survey much beyond the discovery stage, it is of some interest to review briefly the advances made within only a year after the appearance of Chadwick's papers. For a more detailed discussion of the early history, the reader should refer to the original papers and to excellent review articles (written in 1933) by Chadwick (C7) and Darrow (D4).

It was soon ascertained that the neutrons resulting from the bombardment of beryllium and boron by polonium alpha-particles had a rather wide energy spread (F2, M21, C39) including many neutrons of energy considerably below 1 Mev (A36), with the neutron energy strongly dependent on the direction of emission, with respect to the alpha-particle direction, as well as on the energy of the alpha-particle. Gamma-rays were also shown to be emitted in the neutron-producing reaction (B51, C39).

The yield of neutrons from beryllium and boron was found to decrease rapidly with decreasing alpha-particle energy (R7, C40, C7).

By placing considerable quantities of lead next to the neutron-detecting ionization chamber (but not directly in the beam) (B70) or by surrounding the cloud chamber with copper (A36), the number of neutrons detected was appreciably increased, thus indicating a large neutron scattering by these substances.

In the nitrogen gas of the cloud chamber, used in the experiments of Feather (F2), a number of events were observed which could be ascribed to the transmutation $N^{14} + n^1 \rightarrow B^{11} + He^4$, the reverse of the reaction on boron which had been observed to produce neutrons. He also observed transmutations in oxygen and carbon (F3). Transmutations were observed in nitrogen, oxygen, and aluminum by Meitner and Philipp (M21), and in nitrogen by Harkins, Gans, and Newson (H37) and by Kurie (K27).

At first, it was generally assumed that the neutron is probably a closely bound combination of a proton and an electron,[1] especially since

----

[1] As early as 1920, Rutherford (R27) published an interesting and prophetic speculation: "Under some conditions . . . it may be possible for an electron to combine much more closely with the H nucleus [than in the neutral hydrogen atom], forming

the first estimates indicated that its mass is less than that of the proton. The first suggestion that the neutron should be regarded as a fundamental particle appears to have come from Iwanenko (I3), and it soon became clear, mainly on the basis of quantum-mechanical arguments involving the spin and statistics of light nuclei, that the neutron, like the proton, probably has a spin of $\frac{1}{2}$ and obeys Fermi-Dirac statistics (M21, C7). Thus, with the discovery of the neutron and the recognition of its properties, the currently accepted picture of nuclei, as consisting of protons and neutrons, soon emerged.

Since 1933 the development of the field has proceeded with rapidly increasing intensity. We therefore abandon, at this point, the historical survey. Instead, we shall summarize and discuss the present knowledge of the properties of neutrons and their interactions. We shall, however, in discussing each aspect, attempt to include some of the historical background. It must be emphasized that, although, in the relatively short time that has elapsed since the discovery of the neutron, tremendous progress has been made in understanding and utilizing it, there is still much to be done before the neutron can be said to be completely understood. Many important and crucial experiments are in the process of being performed, while others are still in the future.

B. Properties

Since the neutron is one of the constituents of atomic nuclei, a knowledge of its properties is fundamental for the understanding of nuclei. In addition, the properties of the neutron determine, to a large extent, the interactions between neutrons and nuclei, and between neutrons and conglomerations of nuclei (matter). In this section we summarize these properties from the point of view of the neutron as a fundamental particle.

Wherever possible, we shall discuss the experimental evidence on which the conclusions as to the nature of the neutron are based. However, the understanding of many of these experiments depends on a detailed knowledge of the interaction of neutrons with matter. In such cases, the results of the experiments will simply be stated, and the discussion of the experiments reserved for subsequent sections.

---

a kind of neutral doublet. Such an atom would have very novel properties. Its external field would be practically zero, except very close to the nucleus, and in consequence it should be able to move freely through matter. Its presence would probably be difficult to detect by the spectroscope, and it may be impossible to contain it in a sealed vessel. On the other hand, it should enter readily the structure of atoms, and may either unite with the nucleus or be disintegrated by its intense field, resulting possibly in the escape of a charged H atom or an electron or both."

Before proceeding with the discussion of the neutron, a few points should be noted in justification of devoting so much attention to the neutron as compared to other nuclear particles. The neutron is unmatched among atomic and nuclear particles as a tool for the investigation of nuclear properties. The distinguishing feature of neutrons is the absence of electric charge; thus, the interaction of neutrons with matter is primarily determined by purely nuclear properties.

In the fifty or so years since its beginnings, nuclear physics has made large contributions to the development of the other sciences (chemistry, geology, biology, medicine) and to technology. Since its discovery the neutron has assumed a most important role in furthering this progress. Were there no other reason, the importance of the neutron for the nuclear chain reaction might constitute sufficient justification for assigning to it a position of special significance among the tools of modern science.

1. Charge. The neutron is usually assumed to have no net charge. This assumption is consistent with all the observed properties and interactions of neutrons. However, the observations do not preclude the possibility that the neutron may have a net charge so small as to have heretofore eluded detection. It is therefore of interest to derive from the available evidence an upper limit for the magnitude of the possible neutron charge.

The most direct evidence on the neutron's neutrality comes from the experiments of Dee (D6), reported at the same time as Chadwick's announcement of the discovery of the neutron. He investigated the ionization produced in air in a cloud chamber irradiated by fast neutrons and concluded that, if the neutron interacts with atomic electrons at all, this process produces not more than one ion pair per 3 meters of the neutron's path in air. From these data it may be concluded (F36) that the charge of the neutron is less than $\frac{1}{700}$ of the proton charge.

A somewhat less direct determination of an upper limit to the neutron charge may be obtained from considerations involving the observed neutrality of atoms throughout the periodic table. Since the ratio of neutrons to protons in atomic nuclei increases from zero in hydrogen to 1.6 in uranium, this neutrality implies both that the difference between the proton and electron charges is small and that the neutron charge is small. An estimate of the possible magnitude of the neutron charge depends on the accuracy with which we know atoms to be neutral. Rabi [1] and co-workers have observed that the molecule CsI (108 protons and electrons and 152 neutrons) has a net charge less than 10^{-10} of

---

[1] Private communication.

the electron charge. From this observation it is possible to draw a number of conclusions: (1) The smallness of the charge of CsI may be due to an accidental cancellation of the neutron charge and the proton-electron charge difference. In this case, which is exceedingly unlikely, the magnitude of these charges can only be determined by another observation on some other atom or molecule, with a different neutron-proton ratio. In any event, both the neutron charge and the proton-electron charge difference would have to be quite small to account for the neutrality of atoms, say $< 10^{-5}e$. (2) Either the neutron charge or the proton-electron charge difference is zero (or considerably less than 10^{-12} electron charges), in which case the non-zero charge is less than 10^{-12} electron charges. (3) The neutron charge and the proton-electron charge difference are both finite, and very small. Thus, if they were equal and opposite, the neutron charge would have to be less than 2×10^{-12} electron charges. It seems quite reasonable to conclude, from this evidence, that the net charge on the neutron is exceedingly small, probably less than 10^{-12} electron charges.

Despite the electrically neutral character of the neutron, there is a very small electromagnetic interaction between neutrons and charged particles arising out of the magnetic dipole moment of the neutron (to be discussed). In addition, it should be pointed out that, according to currently prevailing theories, the neutron should not strictly be regarded as a fundamental particle, but rather as having a complex structure involving equal numbers of $+$ and $-$ charged particles (mesons). Such a structure is certainly required for the understanding of the magnetic moment of the neutron. The complex nature of the neutron would lead to a small, purely electrical interaction between neutrons and electrons; the existence and magnitude of such a neutron-electron interaction is being investigated and is discussed further on.

Two other points are worth noting as having a bearing on the possible charge of the neutron: (1) The observation of the decay of the neutron into a proton, an electron, and a neutrino (discussed in Section 1B3) implies that (a), if the proton and electron charges are equal and opposite, the neutron and the neutrino have the same charge, if any; or (b), if the neutrino is uncharged, the neutron charge is equal to the proton-electron charge difference; or (c) some combination of (a) and (b). In this connection, de Broglie has pointed out (B69) that hypothesis (a) would be consistent with the neutrality of atoms if there were both positively and negatively charged neutrinos and, correspondingly, neutrons, so that heavy nuclei could contain approximately equal numbers of neutrons of the two charges. (2) The smallness of the neutron-electron interaction (Section 1C3) implies that the charge on the neutron must be exceedingly small. In particular, the observation by Fermi and Marshall (F23) that the scattering of thermal neutrons by xenon atoms is spherically symmetrical to better than 1 percent allows us to set an upper limit on the possible net charge of the neutron of $\sim 10^{-18}$ electron charges.

2. Mass.[1] ·The most accurate determination of the neutron mass is obtained, indirectly, from observations on nuclear transmutations in which all the masses and energies, except the mass of the neutron, are known. Thus, the estimate of Chadwick, quoted above, was obtained from consideration of the $B^{11}(\alpha,n)N^{14}$ reaction (C7). In the same paper Chadwick observed that a more direct determination of the neutron mass could be obtained if the binding energy of the deuteron, the nucleus consisting of a neutron and a proton, were known, since the masses of the proton and deuteron had both been determined by mass-spectroscopic means.

Soon afterward Chadwick and Goldhaber (C8) observed that the deuteron can be decomposed into a neutron and a proton by the absorption of a gamma-ray from ThC″ (2.614_8 Mev). From the energy of the resulting proton they obtained a value of 2.1 Mev for the deuteron binding energy. Until recently the accepted neutron mass was obtained from accurate measurements of the threshold gamma-ray energy for the photodisintegration of the deuteron.

However, quite recently Bell and Elliott (B16) have accurately measured the energy of the gamma-rays resulting from the capture of neutrons, of negligible kinetic energy, by protons (the reverse of the photodisintegration). Using their value of 2.230 ± 0.007 Mev for the gamma-ray energy, and other data, Bainbridge (Volume I, Part 5) gives the value $M = 1.008982$ atomic mass units for the neutron mass.

3. Instability. With the first relatively accurate determination of the neutron mass (C8), which showed that it exceeds the mass of the hydrogen atom, Chadwick and Goldhaber ventured the prediction that the neutron should be unstable against beta-decay, according to the reaction neutron $\rightarrow$ proton $+ \beta^- +$ neutrino. The maximum beta-ray kinetic energy for the decay of neutrons of negligible kinetic energy is given by the $n - H$ mass difference, which we take to be equivalent to 782 ± 1

---

[1] That the neutron mass behaves in the conventional fashion with respect to gravitation has been directly verified by McReynolds (M19), who measured the "free fall" of slow neutrons.

kev (T16).[1] Assuming that the decay of the neutron follows the empirical laws of beta-decay, being an allowed transition with a log ft value of ~3.5, the half-life of the neutron should be ~20 min.

Recent experiments in two laboratories have established that the neutron does decay, as per the above predictions. In the first ones, performed at the Oak Ridge National Laboratories by Snell, Miller, Pleasonton, and McCord (S43, S44), the neutron decay has been observed through the simultaneous (coincidence) detection of the beta-particle

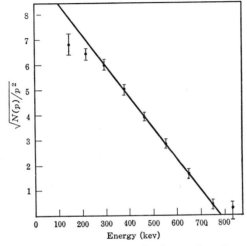

Fig. 1. Fermi plot of the negatrons from the decay of neutrons, due to Robson (R15). The deviations from the allowed shape, below 300 kev, are instrumental.

and proton, resulting from the decay of neutrons in an intense beam passing through an evacuated chamber containing the particle detectors. Control experiments were performed to establish that the coincidences occurred only in the presence of the neutron beam, and that the beta-particles were of roughly the expected energy. These experiments are consistent with "a half-life in the range 10–30 minutes."

Robson (R15) at the Chalk River Atomic Energy Project, in Canada, has not only observed the neutron decay and measured its half-life but, in an experiment of exemplary care and ingenuity, has also succeeded in measuring the spectrum of the decay electrons. He first observed the positive heavy particles resulting from the decays (in a highly sensitive mass spectrometer) and established that they are protons. He then

---

[1] Actually, in the decay of a neutron at rest the emission of a β-particle and a neutrino requires, for the conservation of momentum, that some energy be given to the proton. However, for the emission of a β-ray of the maximum possible energy, the kinetic energy of the recoil proton is only 0.43 kev.

succeeded in obtaining coincidences between the protons and their associated beta-particles, detected in a magnetic lens electron spectrometer in which he simultaneously measured the energy of the beta-particles. The beta-spectrum obtained in this manner is shown in Fig. 1, a conventional allowed-transition Fermi plot. The end point corresponds to a maximum beta-ray kinetic energy of 782 ± 13 kev. From an (experimental plus computational) evaluation of the geometrical efficiency of proton detection and a measurement of the neutron density in the beam (only $\sim 10^4$ neutrons/cm³), Robson deduced the half-life of 12.8 $\pm$ 2.5 min for the decay of the neutron.

Other experiments have been suggested for the observation of the decay of the neutron and the measurement of its half-life. Among the most interesting is the following: A sealed, evacuated, thin-walled container of material with low neutron absorption, say glass, is placed in a region of high neutron density. After some time has elapsed, the accumulation of hydrogen gas in the container is measured. The container acts as a semi-permeable membrane, permitting the free entry of neutrons but preventing the escape of hydrogen formed by neutron decay in the container. For a neutron density of about 0.5×10^{10} neutrons/cm³ (corresponding to a thermal neutron flux of $\sim 10^{15}$ neutrons·cm⁻²·sec⁻¹, of average velocity $\sim 2 \times 10^5$ cm/sec) a hydrogen pressure of $\sim 10^{-4}$ mm of Hg would be developed in the container in approximately one month; such an accumulation of hydrogen gas should be easily observable. The difficulties of this experiment involve the attainment of sufficiently high neutron fluxes (see Section 3), possible production of hydrogen through (n,p) reactions in the walls of the container, and the necessity for complete removal of hydrogen from the container (walls) prior to irradiation.

4. Spin and Statistics. Like the electron and the proton, the neutron has a spin of $\frac{1}{2}$ and obeys Fermi-Dirac statistics. The evidence for the spin value of $\frac{1}{2}$ is quite conclusive, although it involves a combination of experimental observations and the theoretical deductions therefrom. Some of these experiments involve the interaction between neutrons and protons and the properties of the deuteron; they will be further discussed in Section 1C.

The most important evidences for the value of $\frac{1}{2}$ for the spin of the neutron are: (1) the cross section and energy dependence of the scattering of neutrons by protons, taken in conjunction with the evidence concerning the neutron-proton force, derived from the binding energy and spin of the deuteron; (2) the values of the magnetic moments of the deuteron, proton, and neutron; (3) the coherent scattering of neutrons by hydrogen, as evidenced in experiments involving the scattering by hydrogen-containing crystals, total reflection from hydrogen containing "mirrors," and the scattering by ortho- and para-hydrogen; (4) the polarization of neutrons by scattering in ferromagnetic materials and, in particular, by total reflection from magnetic mirrors. The results of these experiments, coupled with the success of the semi-empirical theory of nuclear forces in explaining the observed properties of the deuteron and many of the properties of light nuclei, constitute a most convincing argument for the correctness of the assignment to the neutron of a spin of $\frac{1}{2}$.

As a particle of odd half-integral spin, the neutron is expected to obey Fermi-Dirac statistics. All the available evidence supports this expectation. The most important arguments concerning the statistics obeyed by the neutron involve (1) properties of the light nuclei—in particular, the fact that the deuteron and alpha-particle are known to obey Bose-Einstein statistics—which can be qualitatively understood only by use of the exclusion principle (in a fashion closely analogous to its application to the qualitative understanding of the periodic table), and (2) the saturation of nuclear forces, as manifested in the constant density of nuclear matter (the proportionality of the nuclear radius to $A^{1/3}$).

5. Magnetic Moment.[1] The first strong indication that the neutron has an intrinsic magnetic dipole moment came from the observation that the moments of the proton and deuteron are very different: $\mu_d < \mu_p$ by ~ 2 nuclear magnetons. Since the deuteron is known to have spin $I = 1$, it is expected, on the basis of the simplest reasonable deuteron structure (a neutron and a proton in a $^3S_1$ state), that $\mu_d = \mu_p + \mu_n$.

---

[1] The neutron, having spin $\frac{1}{2}$, cannot show any moments higher than a dipole moment. Although the possibility of the existence of an electric dipole moment of the neutron is usually dismissed, on the basis of theoretical arguments involving the concepts of symmetry and parity, it has recently been pointed out by Purcell and Ramsey (P32) that the assumptions on which these arguments are based are still not completely proved. Thus, for example, "if the nucleon should spend part of its time asymmetrically dissociated into opposite magnetic poles of the type that Dirac has shown to be theoretically possible, a circulation of these magnetic poles could give rise to an electric dipole moment." Although the detection of a possible electric dipole moment of the neutron is experimentally rather difficult, the above authors suggested that it could be observed in a modification of the experiment of Alvarez and Bloch (A13); they proposed to detect a shift of the neutron precession frequency, caused by the application of a strong electric field. However, such an experiment by Purcell, Ramsey, and Smith (S40) yielded a negative result and placed an upper limit, on the neutron's electric dipole moment, of two opposite electron charges separated by a distance of $5 \cdot 10^{-21}$ cm.

The magnetic moment of the neutron has been measured by an ingenious modification of the Rabi-type molecular beam magnetic resonance experiment (R1). In this experiment the usual polarizing and analyzing (focusing) inhomogeneous magnetic fields are replaced by slabs of magnetized iron whose property of preferentially transmitting neutrons of one direction of polarization is used in a manner completely analogous to an optical polarimeter. (The polarization of neutrons by transmission through magnetized iron, the Bloch effect, will be discussed in Section 5D.)

Early measurements of the neutron magnetic moment (F47, P28) gave a value of ~ -2 nuclear magnetons. The *negative sign*, which was definitely established by observing the *direction* of precession of neutrons in a known magnetic field, means that the neutron angular momentum and its magnetic moment are oppositely directed.

The first accurate measurement of the neutron moment, by Alvarez and Bloch (A13), yielded the value $| \mu_n | = 1.935 \pm 0.02$ nuclear magnetons. More recent experiments (A34, B39, R16) have measured, with high precision, the ratio of the neutron moment to the proton moment. These measurements, when combined with the latest value of the proton moment, yield (M1)

$$\mu_n = -1.91280 \pm 0.00009 \text{ nuclear magnetons}$$

6. Wave Properties. In accordance with the laws of quantum mechanics we expect that the neutron should, under the appropriate experimental conditions, exhibit wave properties. Associated with neutrons of kinetic energy E (velocity v, momentum p) there is a wavelength

$$\lambda = \frac{h}{p} \cong \frac{h}{(2ME)^{1/2}} \qquad \text{(for } v \ll c) \qquad (1)$$

Table 1 gives the neutron wavelengths corresponding to an assortment of neutron energies. The energy is expressed both in electron volts and in degrees Kelvin, the temperature T corresponding to a given energy E being defined by the relationship

$$E = kT \qquad (2)$$

where E is expressed in ergs and k is Boltzmann's constant, $k = 1.3803 \times 10^{-16}$ erg/°K. Also included in Table 1 is the "Dirac wavelength," $\lambdabar \equiv \lambda/2\pi$, which is frequently the form in which the neutron wavelength enters into the expressions with which we shall be concerned. The classification of neutrons into types, according to their energy, will be described in Section 1B7.

TABLE 1

WAVELENGTHS ASSOCIATED WITH VARIOUS NEUTRON ENERGIES

E (ev)	T (°K)	v (cm/sec)	λ (cm)	$\lambdabar$ (cm)	Type
0.001	11.6	4.37×10^4	9.04×10^{-8}	1.44×10^{-8}	Cold
0.025	290	2.19×10^5	1.81×10^{-8}	2.88×10^{-9}	Thermal
1.0	1.16×10^4	1.38×10^6	2.86×10^{-9}	4.55×10^{-10}	Slow (reso- nance)
100	1.16×10^6	1.38×10^7	2.86×10^{-10}	4.55×10^{-11}	Slow
10^4	1.16×10^8	1.38×10^8	2.86×10^{-11}	4.55×10^{-12}	Intermediate
10^6	1.16×10^{10}	1.38×10^9	2.86×10^{-12}	4.55×10^{-13}	Fast
10^8	1.16×10^{12}	1.28×10^{10}	2.79×10^{-13}	4.43×10^{-14}	Ultrafast
10^{10}	1.16×10^{14}	2.99×10^{10}	1.14×10^{-14}	1.81×10^{-15}	Ultrafast (relativis- tic)

For the purpose of rapid calculation it is convenient to note the following relationships:

$$T(\text{in °K}) = 1.16 \times 10^4 E$$

$$v(\text{in cm/sec}) = 1.38 \times 10^6 E^{\frac{1}{2}}$$

$$\lambda(\text{in cm}) = 2.86 \times 10^{-9} E^{-\frac{1}{2}}$$

$$\lambdabar(\text{in cm}) = 4.55 \times 10^{-10} E^{-\frac{1}{2}}$$

where E is always given in electron volts:

$$1 \text{ ev} = 1.602 \times 10^{-12} \text{ ergs}$$

These expressions hold only in the non-relativistic energy region, i.e., for kinetic energies well below the energy corresponding to the neutron rest mass,

$$Mc^2 = 939.5 \text{ million electron volts (Mev)}$$

As can be seen from Table 1, the relativistic effects (on the connection between v, or λ, and E) are already evident, albeit still small, at a kinetic energy of 100 Mev.

In general, the importance of the wave characteristics of the neutron is determined by the magnitude of the ratio between the neutron (Dirac) wavelength and the dimensions of the system with which the neutron is interacting. For neutrons of wavelength large compared to nuclear dimensions, the wave properties are of primary importance in determining the nature of the interaction between neutrons and nuclei. Since nuclear radii fall in the range 2×10^{-13} to 10^{-12} cm, the wave properties of the neutron are seen to be important for energies up to the fast neutron region; for fast neutrons, the wave properties are of comparatively lesser significance.

The wavelengths of thermal neutrons are of the same order as the interatomic distances in solid matter. Thus, we would expect neutrons of these energies to show interference effects in their passage through, and scattering by, ordered materials. Such interference phenomena were predicted by Elsasser (E5) and by Wick (W24) in 1936–37, and soon indicated by Preiswerk and von Halban (P29) and by Mitchell and Powers (M33). Indeed, thermal neutrons have been found to behave very much like x-rays under similar circumstances, with the important difference that the scattering and absorption of neutrons are nuclear phenomena, whereas the corresponding properties of x-rays arise from their interaction with atomic electrons. Neutron diffraction and interference phenomena will be discussed in detail in Section 5.

It is worth observing that, although wave effects are relatively less important for fast neutrons, they may possibly become significant again for ultrafast neutrons. In this energy range the neutron wavelengths are of the order of the distance between nucleons in the nucleus, and the scattering from the nucleons within a nucleus can exhibit interference effects. Indeed, it is possible that, with the development of techniques for studying such effects, investigations of the "form factor" in nuclear scattering may provide important information on nuclear structure.

7. Classification according to Energy. In the subsequent discussion we shall find it convenient to refer to neutrons of different kinetic energies according to the following system of classification:

I. Slow neutrons: $0 < E < 1000$ ev

II. Intermediate neutrons: 1 kev $< E < 500$ kev

III. Fast neutrons: 0.5 Mev $< E < 10$ Mev

IV. Very fast neutrons: 10 Mev $< E < 50$ Mev

V. Ultrafast neutrons: 50 Mev $< E$

Although the dividing lines between these categories are quite arbitrary, this system of classification can be justified on two grounds. In the first place, the interactions of the different classes of neutrons with nuclei and with matter in bulk involve, in general, different reactions and types of phenomena. Secondly, the methods of producing and detecting the different classes of neutrons are quite different.

(a) *Slow Neutrons.* The behavior of neutrons in this energy range has been more extensively investigated than in any of the other ranges. The interaction of slow neutrons with heavy nuclei is characterized by sharp absorption resonances and large absorption cross sections for very low-energy neutrons. This is also the region in which crystal effects are important.

Of particular importance to the study of the slow neutron region is the fact that a number of instruments, known as monochromators, have been developed whereby neutrons of a given energy may be singled out and their properties studied. Monochromators in the slow neutron region are characterized by high resolving power, so that the dependence of a particular effect on the neutron energy can be ascertained to high accuracy.

The slow neutron range is conveniently subdivided into a number of sub-ranges, of which the most important are:

(1) Cold Neutrons. These constitute a special category of slow neutrons of energy less than ~ 0.002 ev; they exhibit an anomalously large penetrability through crystalline or polycrystalline materials.

(2) Thermal Neutrons. In diffusing through materials with relatively small neutron absorption, slow neutrons tend to assume a velocity distribution of the Maxwellian form

$$dn(v) = Av^2 e^{-Mv^2/2kT} \, dv \tag{3}$$

The peak of the Maxwellian distribution is at an energy $E_0 = kT$, where T is the absolute temperature of the medium through which the neutrons are diffusing. Neutrons having such a velocity distribution are referred to as thermal neutrons.

Frequently the neutrons diffusing through a given medium are not in thermal equilibrium with the medium. This results in a rather greater preponderance of high-energy (slow) neutrons than is given by the Maxwell distribution function. Slow neutrons originating from such a source, generally of energy above ~ 0.5 ev, are often referred to as epithermal neutrons.

In much of the work on slow neutrons the thermal neutrons are separated from neutrons of higher energy (say epithermal) by taking advantage of their strong absorption in relatively thin layers of cadmium. Those neutrons in a given distribution which are absorbed by a cadmium layer are sometimes called C-neutrons; the neutrons which penetrate cadmium (energy > 0.3–0.5 ev) are, correspondingly, called epicadmium neutrons.

(3) *Resonance Neutrons.* This classification refers to slow neutrons of energy between ~1 and ~100 ev; it is based on the large number of distinct, sharp, absorption resonances which have been observed in the interaction of neutrons, in this energy range, with heavy nuclei.

(*b*) *Intermediate Neutrons.* In the intermediate range the predominant type of neutron reaction is elastic scattering. Until fairly recently this region has been the least extensively studied, mainly because of the lack of suitable neutron sources and detectors. Recently a number of techniques have been developed for the study of this energy range. These techniques are now being extensively exploited.

(*c*) *Fast Neutrons.* The fast-neutron region is characterized by the appearance of many nuclear reactions which are energetically impossible at lower neutron energies, of which the most important is inelastic scattering. This region has been fairly extensively investigated, although the available techniques have been rather crude as compared to those used in the slow-neutron range.

(*d*) *Very Fast Neutrons.* This energy interval is distinguished from the preceding by the appearance of nuclear reactions involving the emission of more than one product, such as the $(n,2n)$ reaction. It is a relatively unexplored energy range, mainly because of the comparatively small number of suitable neutron sources.

(*e*) *Ultrafast Neutrons.* The development of ultrahigh energy particle accelerators has resulted in the possibility of producing ultrafast neutrons and studying their properties. Before the advent of these machines, this region was accessible only through the utilization of the neutrons in the cosmic radiation. A distinguishing feature of nuclear reactions in this energy range comes from the relatively small interactions of neutrons with nuclei, resulting in a partial transparency of nuclei to ultrafast neutrons. Also, for these high energies, "spallation reactions"—in which the bombarded nucleus emits many fragments—are observed.

C. Fundamental Interactions

Of primary importance for the understanding of nuclear forces is the study of the interaction between neutrons and other nucleons—neutrons and protons—and between neutrons and the lighter particles (electrons, mesons). There have been many experimental and theoretical investigations which shed light on the nature of nuclear forces. Among the most important are the scattering of neutrons (and protons) by protons, the capture of neutrons by protons, the static and dynamic properties of the deuteron, the scattering of neutrons by hydrogen molecules, and some of the properties of heavy nuclei. Since most of these results have already been discussed in Part IV of Volume I, they will merely be presented here in summary form.

However, since a number of aspects of the neutron-proton interaction are of primary importance for the understanding of the interaction of neutrons with matter, such aspects will be discussed more fully. Thus, the scattering and capture of neutrons by protons will be covered in some detail. The discussion of the scattering of neutrons by hydrogen molecules, involving as it does the wave properties of neutrons, will be reserved for Section 5.

1. The Neutron-Proton Interaction. (*a*) *Properties of the Deuteron.* (1) Static Properties. The ground state of the deuteron is essentially a $^3S_1$ configuration.[1] From the known binding energy of the deuteron, conclusions can be drawn concerning the force (potential) between the neutron and proton in this state, in which the neutron and proton spins are aligned in the same direction (total spin = spin of the deuteron = 1). The static properties of the deuteron give no information concerning the neutron-proton potential in the singlet state (total spin = 0) (B22).

(2) Photodisintegration. The deuteron can be disintegrated into a neutron and a proton by the absorption of an amount of energy greater than its binding energy, 2.23 Mev. Although this can be accomplished through the bombardment of deuterons by a variety of particles, the disintegration of the deuteron was first observed (C8) in bombardment by gamma radiation. This process, the so-called photodisintegration of the deuteron, has been most extensively investigated, and has yielded much useful information concerning the neutron-proton interaction (B22).

Immediately after its discovery, Bethe and Peierls (B20) and Massey and Mohr (M6) propounded the theory of the disintegration of the deuteron by a photoelectric effect. Soon afterward, Fermi (F15) suggested a second mechanism which contributes to the disintegration: a photomagnetic process. In the photoelectric disintegration the electric field of the gamma-radiation acts on the instantaneous electric dipole moment of the deuteron (the average electric dipole moment is, in the

---

[1] The deuteron has a small electric quadrupole moment, which fact implies that the ground-state wave function contains, in addition to the predominant $^3S_1$ function, a small admixture of $^3D_1$ form. The implications of this fact, especially with regard to the tensor nature of nuclear forces, has been discussed in detail in Part IV of Volume I.

ground state, zero). After separation of the proton from the neutron, through the action of the electric field, the spins of the neutron and proton remain parallel; thus, the photoelectric effect involves only the properties of the neutron-proton interaction in the triplet state. In the second process the magnetic field of the radiation interacts with the magnetic dipole moments of the neutron and proton, the effect of the interaction being to "flip" the spin of one of the particles with respect to that of the second; thus, the photomagnetic process also involves the properties of the neutron-proton potential in the singlet state.

The contributions of the two processes can be separated experimentally, since they result in different angular distributions of the emerging particles with respect to the direction of the incident gamma-ray. These angular distributions can be understood in terms of a rough, semi-classical model of the deuteron as a neutron and proton separated by a fixed distance and having equal probability for all possible orientations of the connecting line. Thus, in the case of photoelectric disintegration, the effect is greatest when the deuteron's dipole moment is in the direction of the electric field vector of the gamma-ray beam, which is perpendicular to the direction of motion of the photon. This leads to a distribution of recoil neutrons and protons (in the center-of-mass coordinate system) proportional to the square of the sine of the angle between the incident photon and the recoils.

In the photomagnetic disintegration, on the other hand, the effect is produced by the difference between the action of the photon's magnetic field on the neutron and the proton, which is due to the difference between the magnetic dipole moments of the two particles [-1.91280 and $+2.79255$ nuclear magnetons, respectively (M1)]. This difference is independent of the orientation of the deuteron, and hence the recoils, which are due to the photomagnetic disintegration, are spherically symmetrically distributed in the center-of-mass coordinate system.[1]

In addition to the different angular distributions, the cross sections for the photoelectric and photomagnetic disintegrations have different dependences on the gamma-ray energy. The cross sections start out at zero at the photodisintegration threshold, rise to maxima for values of

[1] This difference in the angular distributions of the recoil products follows from simple quantum-mechanical considerations. Thus, in the photoelectric effect the final state of the separated neutron and proton must be a P state to satisfy the selection rule for electric dipole radiation, $\Delta L = \pm 1$; also, since the electric field does not act, in first order, on the nucleon spins, $\Delta S = 0$. The transitions occur from the state of the deuteron for which $m = \pm 1$ (with respect to the direction of the incident photon); hence the $\sin^2 \theta$ distribution of the recoils. Correspondingly, the magnetic dipole transition requires $\Delta L = 0$, $\Delta S = \pm 1$. Thus, the final state is a $^1S_0$ state, with a spherically symmetrical distribution of the recoils.

$E_\gamma = -2.2$ Mev of approximately twice the binding energies (of the triplet and singlet states, respectively), and then fall off with increasing gamma-ray energy.[1] For photon energies close to the threshold, the two effects are comparable in importance. For photon energies large compared to the binding energy of the deuteron, the photomagnetic effect is negligible compared to the photoelectric effect. Thus, the angular distribution of the recoils can be described by the expression $a + b \sin^2 \theta$, with a and b both energy-dependent, and a falling off much more rapidly than b with increasing gamma-ray energy. For photon energies considerably above the threshold, the simple considerations described above are no longer completely applicable; other effects, such as the tensor nature of the neutron-proton interaction, come into play (R6).

Since the early attempts to observe the cross section and angular distribution of the recoils in the photodisintegration of the deuteron (C10), the techniques of measurement have been considerably improved. More recent results (B30, G28, W44) confirm the theoretical predictions and provide important information concerning the nature of the neutron-proton interaction.

(b) *The Capture of Neutrons by Protons.* Although, for neutrons of most energies, the most important effect in the neutron-proton interaction is the scattering process, discussed in (c) below, it was soon observed (W18, D19, A20) that neutrons are appreciably absorbed in hydrogen-containing substances. This absorption is attributable to a radiative capture (n,γ) process, a reaction to be expected, since the combination of a neutron and a proton into a deuteron is energetically preferred. The gamma-rays accompanying this process were first observed by Lea (L10). The radiative capture reaction, $n + p \rightarrow d + \gamma$, is the inverse of the photodisintegration of the deuteron, and the calculation of its cross section follows directly from the photodisintegration calculations (B22).

Such a calculation indicates that capture of a slow neutron by a photoelectric process (emission of an electric dipole gamma-ray) has a negligible cross section (B20); this result is easily understood, since photoelec-

---

[1] If $\epsilon_3 \cong 2.2$ Mev and $|\epsilon_1| \cong 0.065$ Mev are the absolute values of the binding energies in the triplet and singlet states (the singlet state is actually unbound) and $E = E_\gamma - \epsilon_3$, then the simple theory gives (B22)

$$\sigma_{el} \simeq \frac{8\pi}{3} \frac{e^2}{\hbar c} \frac{\hbar^2}{M} \frac{\epsilon_3^{1/2} E^{1/2}}{(E + \epsilon_3)^3}$$

$$\sigma_{mag} \simeq \frac{2\pi}{3} \frac{e^2}{\hbar c} \frac{\hbar^2}{M} \frac{(\mu_p - \mu_n)^2}{Mc^2} \frac{(\epsilon_3^{1/2} + |\epsilon_1|^{1/2})^2 \epsilon_3^{1/2} E^{1/2}}{(E + \epsilon_3)(E + |\epsilon_1|)}$$

tric capture requires that the neutron-proton system be, initially, in a
P state, which is highly improbable for a slow neutron. Indeed, it was
the observation of an appreciable neutron-proton capture cross section
which led Fermi (F15) to postulate a photomagnetic capture process
and its inverse, the photomagnetic disintegration. Since the photomagnetic capture involves only S states ($^1S_0 \rightarrow {}^3S_1$), the resulting
cross section has a $1/v$ dependence on the neutron energy and therefore
becomes quite appreciable for thermal neutrons. Fermi showed that
the photomagnetic capture is indeed strong enough to account for the
relatively rapid absorption of thermal neutrons in hydrogenous materials.

The precise experimental determination of the neutron-proton (n,γ)
cross section is difficult, since capture represents only a small fraction
of the total neutron-proton cross section at even the smallest available
neutron energies and, further, it leads to a non-radioactive end product.
Thus, none of the usual methods of measuring cross sections (Section 3)
is easily applicable. Its value can, however, be inferred from measurements involving the diffusion of thermal neutrons in hydrogen-containing materials (Section 4), since the average distance traveled, before
absorption, by a thermal neutron depends on the capture as well as on
the scattering cross section (A20). Or, equivalently, the mean life of a
thermal neutron in a hydrogenous material is inversely proportional to
the capture cross section, so that a measurement of the mean life can
yield a value for $\sigma(n,\gamma)$ (A18, M4).

The most accurate value of the (n,γ) cross section has been obtained
from a direct comparison of slow neutron-proton absorption with the
absorption of boron, which also has a $1/v$ energy dependence (R8, W19).
Whitehouse and Graham (W19) obtained

$$\frac{\sigma_B}{\sigma_H} = 2270 \pm 68$$

Using the value $\sigma_B = 710 \pm 21$ barns for neutrons of velocity $v = 2200$ m/sec (R20), this yields

$$\sigma_H(n,\gamma) = 0.313 \pm 0.013 \text{ barns}$$

Since the photomagnetic capture and disintegration processes involve
the properties of the neutron-proton interaction in the singlet state, the
magnitudes of the cross sections can be used to infer the strength of this
interaction. In particular, different cross-section values are predicted,
depending on whether the singlet state is bound or unbound (B22). In
the case of the photodisintegration experiments, the cross-section determinations are not sufficiently accurate to allow an unambiguous choice
between the two possibilities (G28).

The neutron-proton radiative capture cross section is measured with sufficient accuracy. Rosenfeld (R19) calculates the cross section, for neutrons of energy 0.026 ev, to be 0.32 or 0.16 barn for the cases, respectively, of an unbound or a bound singlet state. The experiments strongly favor the conclusion that the $^1S_0$ state of the deuteron is unbound. "But [chiefly because of the neglect of the exchange effect] the calculation is not sufficiently accurate to allow us to regard this evidence as entirely conclusive."

The conclusion is, however, completely borne out by the measurements on the scattering cross sections for ortho- and parahydrogen (see Section 5).

(c) *The Scattering of Neutrons by Protons.* (1) Cross Section. Since the first investigations of Chadwick (C7), there have been many measurements, at various neutron energies, of the cross section for the scattering of neutrons by protons. The results are summarized in Fig. 2,

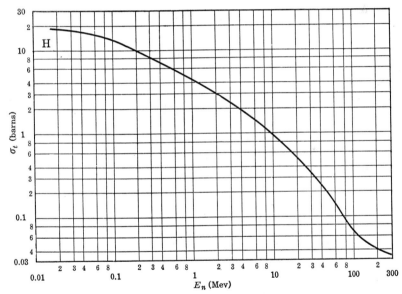

Fig. 2. Cross section for the scattering of neutrons by free protons *vs.* kinetic energy of the neutron, in the range 0.01–300 Mev, from the compilation of Adair (A2). Additional data, in the ultrafast range, are given in (T3) and (D12).

in which the neutron-proton scattering cross section is plotted as a function of the neutron energy, between 0.01 and 300 Mev.

The quantum-mechanical treatment of neutron-proton scattering was first given by Wigner (W27), who showed that the cross section as a function of neutron kinetic energy E is given (in the limit of neutron wavelength large compared to the range of the neutron-proton force) by the expression

$$\sigma(n\text{-}p) = \frac{4\pi\hbar^2}{M(\frac{1}{2}E + |\epsilon|)} \tag{4}$$

where ϵ is the binding energy of the neutron-proton system (deuteron). The above expression must be corrected for the finite range of the neutron-proton force (B22); however, this correction is independent of E and need not be considered for the purposes of the arguments which follow. The above expression was found to agree with the observed cross sections for neutrons of ~ 1 Mev and greater.

When applied to slow neutrons, the above expression yields a value of ~ 3 barns. The early experiments (D19) gave a value, very much greater, of ~ 35 barns. (The cross section for the scattering of neutrons by free protons has, in fact, been determined to be ~ 20 barns.)

This serious discrepancy was explained by Wigner [1] under the assumption that the force between a neutron and proton depends on the relative orientation of their spins. Since in a fourth of the cases the neutron-proton scattering takes place in the singlet state, the cross section should be given by the expression

$$\sigma(n\text{-}p) = \frac{4\pi\hbar^2}{M}\left(\frac{3}{4}\frac{1}{\frac{1}{2}E + |\epsilon_3|} + \frac{1}{4}\frac{1}{\frac{1}{2}E + |\epsilon_1|}\right) \tag{5}$$

where ϵ_3 and ϵ_1 refer, respectively, to the binding energies of the triplet and singlet states of the deuteron. To fit a slow-neutron cross section of 20 barns, $|\epsilon_1| \cong 0.065$ Mev.

From the neutron-proton scattering, it is impossible to determine the sign of ϵ_1. Actually, we know from other evidence that the singlet state of the deuteron is unbound. Thus, although the term "binding energy" has no meaning for this state, ϵ_1 represents a certain combination of the constants which describe the neutron-proton interaction in the singlet state (B22).

Early measurements of the slow neutron-proton scattering cross section (D19, W18, A20) showed a wide variation, outside the experimental uncertainties. The reason for these variations was given by Fermi (F17), who ascribed them to the effect of the binding of the pro-

---

[1] Although it is universally acknowledged throughout the literature (F5, B22) that Wigner originated the idea of the spin dependence of the neutron-proton force to explain the large neutron-proton scattering cross section for slow neutrons, he has not, to our knowledge, published these considerations.

tons in the material—molecule, liquid, or solid—used as a neutron scatterer. Such effects are, of course, negligible for neutron energies considerably greater than the binding energy of the proton in the system under consideration. They are most important for neutron energies less than the lowest excitation energy of the system in which the proton is bound. The proton behaves like a particle of infinite mass when bound in solids or liquids, or like a particle of the total mass of the molecule involved in the case of neutron scattering by gaseous materials. It can be shown that the scattering cross section of slow neutrons by bound protons varies directly as the *square of the reduced mass* of the neutron, the scattering being spherically symmetrical in the center-of-mass coordinate system. Thus, the scattering cross section of infinitely slow (zero energy) neutrons by protons in solids or liquids should approach four times the free proton cross section, or about 80 barns.

The variation of the neutron-proton cross section in the energy range in which the proton is neither free nor completely bound (energy greater than the lowest excitation energy but less than the binding energy of the protons) depends on the specific properties of the proton-containing material under consideration and is rather difficult to compute. Disregarding interference effects due to the crystalline properties of the solid under consideration or to the order introduced by the molecular structure (see Section 5), the cross section can be shown to decrease monotonically from the bound proton to the free proton cross section as the neutron energy increases from 0 to several electron volts (A31, M27).

Thus, the free proton scattering cross section for slow neutrons can be obtained from measurements on neutrons in the resonance energy range. As a result of such measurements (C18), the slow neutron-free proton scattering cross section was determined to be slightly less than 21 barns. However, binding effects still have a small influence for neutrons with energy of a few electron volts. In the most recent experiments (M24), the neutron-proton cross section has been measured as a function of the neutron energy, and theoretical considerations (P19) were used to extrapolate to a free proton neutron-proton scattering cross section of 20.36 ± 0.10 barns for neutrons of zero kinetic energy.

Effects of nuclear binding are, of course, present in the scattering of neutrons by heavier nuclei, although their importance decreases rapidly with increasing mass number A of the scattering nucleus. In general, for nuclei bound in solids or liquids,

$$\sigma_{\text{bound}} = \left(\frac{A+1}{A}\right)^2 \sigma_{\text{free}} \tag{6}$$

Thus, for deuterons bound in solid material, $\sigma_{\text{bound}} = 2.25\sigma_{\text{free}}$, while, for the scattering of slow neutrons by carbon, $\sigma_{\text{bound}} = 1.17\sigma_{\text{free}}$.

(2) Angular Distribution. It was first pointed out by Wigner (W27) and by Wick (W22) that the angular distribution, in the scattering of

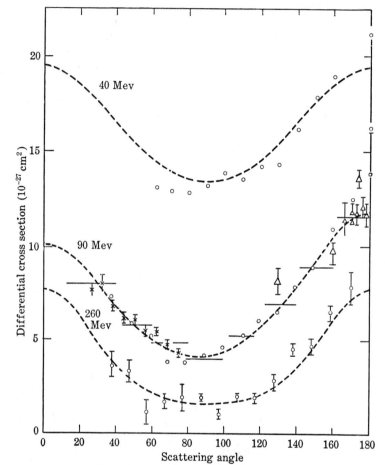

Fig. 3. Angular distributions in the scattering of ultrafast neutrons by protons. The figure is from a paper by Kelly, Leith, Segrè, and Wiegand (K9).

fast neutrons by protons, should provide information concerning the neutron-proton interaction in states of higher angular momentum (P, D, etc). The scattering of slow neutrons by protons involves only the state of zero angular momentum (S state) and is therefore spherically symmetrical in the center-of-mass coordinate system. The energies at which higher angular momentum scatterings set in measure the strengths of the interaction in these states, while the form of the angular distribution leads to inferences concerning the nature of the potential.

A number of experiments using $d + d$ neutrons (2.4 to 2.7 Mev) show that, at these energies, the neutron-proton scattering is spherically symmetrical in the center-of-mass system (R19). While the scattering is still essentially spherically symmetrical at 14 Mev (B10), some of the experiments in the 9–14-Mev neutron energy range (L7, P24) show indications of a slight asymmetry, corresponding to a preferential scattering of protons in the forward direstion. This asymmetry is quite pronounced for neutrons of energy 27 Mev (B71). Such an effect is to be expected on the basis of a theory of a neutron-proton interaction of the exchange type; exchange forces are required to explain the "saturation" of nuclear forces, since they lead to a repulsive force at short distances and thus tend to prevent the collapse of heavy nuclei and to maintain a constant density of nuclear matter.

Neutron-proton scattering experiments with 40-, 90-, and 260-Mev neutrons show large deviations from spherical symmetry; their results are plotted in Fig. 3. The most interesting characteristic of these results is the rough symmetry about 90° (in the c.m. system) of the differential neutron-proton scattering cross section. Serber has pointed out that these results indicate a neutron-proton interaction involving approximately equal proportions of forces of the ordinary and exchange type.

Christian and Hart (C15) have discussed the type of neutron-proton interaction which is required to fit both the low-energy and the high-energy data. They use an interaction potential of the Serber type, choosing the radial dependence to obtain the best possible fit, and also taking into account the tensor form of the interaction, required by the electric quadrupole moment of the deuteron.

The Serber interaction, a mixture of equal parts ordinary and exchange forces, has the property that all terms which correspond to odd orbital angular momentum quantum numbers vanish; the observed symmetry of the high-energy neutron-proton scattering about 90° is, of course, the decisive evidence in favor of the Serber interaction, since any appreciable interaction in a state of odd orbital angular momentum would destroy this symmetry. However, the terms of odd angular momentum are precisely those which lead to a strong repulsion between the neutron and proton for small distance of separation and, therefore, are required for the "saturation" of nuclear forces. Indeed, it appears doubtful whether a nucleon-nucleon interaction of the Serber type is consistent with the saturation of nuclear forces in heavy nuclei.

2. The Neutron-Neutron Interaction. (a) *Experimental Evidence.*
(1) Low Energies. Since the highest available neutron densities are
still far from appreciable (below 10^{10} neutrons/cm³), it is manifestly impossible to obtain information about the neutron-neutron interaction
through observation of the scattering of neutrons by free neutrons; our
knowledge of the force between two neutrons must, perforce, be inferred
from other information. In considering the available information, it is
useful to bear in mind the following general considerations: (1) Experiments involving neutrons of kinetic energy below ~20 Mev yield information only about the neutron-neutron forces in the singlet S state since,
at these energies, states of higher angular momentum are not appreciably
excited, and the exclusion principle prevents the neutron-neutron system
from existing in a triplet S state. Experiments with ultrafast neutrons
can, on the other hand, yield information about the neutron-neutron
interaction in both the singlet and triplet states. The same arguments
hold, of course, for the proton-proton interaction. (2) Since there is
some reason to expect that the purely nuclear interaction between two
nucleons should be independent of whether they are neutrons or protons (see further on), the evidence on the proton-proton interaction can
be considered to have some bearing on the problem of the neutron-
neutron interaction. In any event, we shall herein review, briefly, the
available information on the interaction between two nucleons, irrespective of their charge.[1]

The strongest evidence concerning the charge symmetry of nuclear
forces (equality of the nuclear neutron-neutron and proton-proton
forces) is derived from the observed energy differences between mirror-
image nuclei (nuclei which can be obtained from one another by inter-
changing the neutrons and protons). The energy differences between
such nuclei, as measured by the maximum energy of the beta-rays
emitted in the decay of one of the pair into the other, can be completely
accounted for by the neutron-proton mass difference and the difference
in the electrostatic energies of the two nuclei. In addition, mirror nuclei
are similar with respect to their observed level structure. From this
evidence, we conclude that the purely nuclear neutron-neutron and
proton-proton forces are essentially equal. Actually the evidence on
nuclear level structure lends strong support to the stronger hypothesis
of charge independence (equality of the neutron-neutron, neutron-
proton, and proton-proton forces in the same states), since nuclear isobars are observed to exhibit markedly similar level patterns.

[1] A much more complete discussion of these points is contained in Part IV of Volume I.

The purely practical restrictions, which prevent the performance of neutron-neutron scattering experiments, do not obtain in the case of proton-proton scattering. Many such experiments have been performed for proton energies up to ~15 Mev. From these it can be concluded that within the experimental uncertainty (and taking into account the effect of the Coulomb interaction) the nuclear neutron-proton and proton-proton forces in the $^1S_0$ state appear to be equal.

Thus, the available evidence supports the idea of the charge independence of the nuclear forces between two nucleons.

(2) On the Possible Existence of a Stable Di-Neutron. The strength of the neutron-neutron interaction in the $^1S_0$ state determines whether or not there can be a stable system consisting of two neutrons. (There is no possibility for a stable two-nucleon state of higher orbital angular momentum.) The existence of such a stable "di-neutron" is, until now, experimentally neither proved nor disproved. If the nucleon-nucleon interaction is completely charge independent, the di-neutron will be unstable, since the $^1S_0$ neutron-proton system is unstable by about 65 kev; however, this is so close to being stable that it would require only a rather small increase of the neutron-neutron interaction over the corresponding neutron-proton interaction to lead to a stable di-neutron.

A stronger argument against the existence of a stable di-neutron can be derived from the equality of the low-energy neutron-neutron and proton-proton forces, as evidenced by the properties of the mirror-image nuclei. Analysis of low-energy proton-proton scattering (J1) proves, conclusively, that the ^1S proton-proton interaction is not strong enough to lead to a bound state (even in the absence of the Coulomb repulsion).

Although the weight of available evidence does not favor the existence of a stable di-neutron, it is, nevertheless, of interest to consider some of the possible consequences of its existence. Feather (F4) has pointed out that it is possible to obtain an upper limit to the binding energy of the di-neutron from the observation that the nucleus He^6 does not decay according to the reaction $He^6 \rightarrow He^4 + n^2$. From the masses of the nuclei involved, he concludes that the binding energy of the di-neutron is less than 0.7 ± 0.2 Mev. He also points out that the di-neutron would be beta-unstable, $n^2 \rightarrow H^2 + \beta^- + \nu$, with a mean life (assuming an allowed transition) of $1 < \tau < 5$ sec.

If the di-neutron should exist as a stable configuration, and if it should be possible to obtain it in sufficient numbers, it could easily be detected in experiments involving scattering by nuclei. For the two neutrons would be scattered coherently, and the interference effects would persist to considerably higher energies than do the normal coherence effects in slow-neutron scattering, since the di-neutron would be a compact system, of dimensions $\sim 10^{-12}$ cm. Thus, the scattering of di-neutrons by hydrogen atoms would be the same as the scattering of cold neutrons by parahydrogen molecules (see Section 5), for which the cross section is ~ 4 barns, as compared to ~ 20 barns for the free neutron-proton scattering cross section.

Furthermore, as pointed out by Feather, capture of a di-neutron would, as compared to ordinary neutron capture, result in a different compound nucleus and in characteristic radioactivities.

The difficulty in observing such effects would, if the di-neutron were stable, arise from the difficulty of obtaining an appreciable source of di-neutrons. Such a source would have to be obtained from a suitable nuclear reaction, in which di-neutrons are emitted. It could not be obtained by neutron-neutron collisions in a region of high slow-neutron density (even if neutron densities of sufficient magnitude were available) because the required reaction, $n + n \rightarrow n^2 + \gamma$, would be highly forbidden, since it would involve the transition $^1S_0 \rightarrow {}^1S_0$. Although a di-neutron could, if stable, be produced in a collision involving three neutrons, such collisions would be exceedingly improbable.

Fenning and Holt (F11) have attempted to detect the presence of di-neutrons in the Harwell pile, by looking for alpha-particles from the reaction

$$ \text{Bi}^{209} + n^2 \rightarrow \text{AcC}^{211} \xrightarrow[2.16\,\text{min}]{\alpha} \text{AcC}'' \xrightarrow[4.8\,\text{min}]{\beta} \text{Pb}^{207} $$

(They were investigating the possibility that di-neutrons might be emitted in slow-neutron fission.) They exposed bismuth to a flux of $\sim 10^{12}$ neutrons$\cdot$cm$^{-2}\cdot$sec^{-1}, but could detect no activity attributable to AcC, from which they established an upper limit of 1.5×10^{-21} sec^{-1} for the product of the di-neutron flux and the cross section for its absorption in bismuth.

In considering the possible effects of the di-neutron on nuclear reactions, it should be noted that such effects might exist even if the di-neutron is not stable, for the dynamics of a reaction involving two neutrons would be quite different if the two neutrons were absorbed or emitted as a single unit than if they behaved independently (C19). Thus, Kundu and Pool (K25) consider the characteristics of the excitation of (H^3,p) reactions on rhodium and cobalt as "probable evidence of the di-neutron." Another, and more favorable, reaction in which effects of a di-neutron might be observed involves the two possibilities

$$ \text{H}^3 + \text{H}^3 \rightarrow \text{He}^4 + 2n + Q_1 $$
$$ \rightarrow \text{He}^4 + n^2 + Q_2 $$

If the two neutrons are emitted independently, their energies, and that of the recoil alpha-particle, will vary over a rather wide range (for a given energy of the bombarding triton), as is to be expected in a three-particle reaction. If, on the other hand, the two neutrons are emitted as a single particle, the energies of the di-neutron and of the alpha-particle are uniquely determined, for a given angle of emission, by the laws of conservation of energy and momentum. The weight of available evidence favors the first of the two above-mentioned reactions (L22, A9, L14).

Perhaps the most striking evidence concerning the di-neutron is derived as a by-product of the experiments of Panofsky, Aamodt, and Hadley (P3) on the absorption of negative pi-mesons by deuterium in the reaction $\pi^- + d \rightarrow 2n + \gamma$. In interpreting the observed gamma-ray energy distribution, Watson and Stuart (W6) point out that the shape is strongly dependent on the degree of correlation in the directions of emission of the two neutrons; indeed, if the neutrons were always emitted as a di-neutron, the gamma-ray spectrum would be monochromatic. The observations are sufficiently accurate to show that there is a strong interaction (attraction) between the two neutrons; they are not sufficiently precise, as yet, to allow more than an upper limit of $\sim$200 kev to be placed on the binding energy of the di-neutron. The properties of the meson-producing reaction, $\gamma + d \rightarrow 2n + \pi^+$, might also throw some light on the di-neutron.

(3) High Energies. For neutrons with kinetic energies in the ultrafast range, it becomes possible to observe the neutron-neutron interaction somewhat more directly in the scattering of neutrons by deuterium nuclei. If the wavelength of the neutron is much less than the average separation between the neutron and proton in the deuteron, the two nucleons should scatter neutrons independently; the cross section for the scattering of neutrons by neutrons, $\sigma(n\text{-}n)$, should then be given by the difference between the scattering cross section of deuterium and that of hydrogen,

$$\sigma(n\text{-}n) = \sigma(n\text{-}d) - \sigma(n\text{-}p) \tag{7}$$

Unfortunately, there are still appreciable effects of the structure of the deuteron in the scattering of neutrons of a few hundred Mev, since the neutron wavelength is not negligible compared to the internucleon distance. Another way of expressing this difficulty is to note that the nucleons in the deuteron are moving with kinetic energies of internal motion as high as $\sim$25 Mev; the velocity, corresponding to this kinetic energy, is only $\sim\frac{1}{2}$ of the velocity of a 100-Mev neutron.

A possible way out of this difficulty has been suggested by Segrè.[1] Since it is feasible to measure, directly, both $\sigma(n\text{-}p)$ and $\sigma(p\text{-}p)$, a meas-

[1] Private communication.

urement of $\sigma(p\text{-}d)$ should determine the magnitude of the effect, on the cross section, of the structure of the deuteron. This correction could then be applied to the measurement of $\sigma(n\text{-}d)$ in order to extract the neutron-neutron cross section.

The interpretation of neutron-deuteron scattering for ultrafast neutrons has been considered by a number of authors, e.g., De Hoffman (D8), Gluckstern and Bethe (G9), and Chew (C14). It turns out that, in addition to the expected contributions from neutron-proton and neutron-neutron scattering (both averaged over the momentum distributions of the nucleons in the deuteron), there is a cross term due to interference between the two scattering centers and depending in detail on the nature of the interactions. As a result, the simple additivity relationship of Eq. (7) cannot even be applied at energies of a few hundred Mev.

The most extensive attempt at interpretation of neutron-deuteron and proton-deuteron scattering experiments in the ultrafast energy range has been carried out by Chew (C14). He has treated the problem by the "impulse approximation," in which the scattering nucleon is assumed to behave in a relatively independent fashion during the time of the impact. This approximation appears to be appropriate for the treatment of some aspects of the neutron-deuteron scattering problem, e.g., the dissociation, by neutron impact, of the deuteron; however, other aspects, such as elastic neutron scattering or proton "pick-up," cannot be treated in this fashion. From the available data, Chew concludes that there is "no evidence for a difference between neutron-neutron and proton-proton interactions."

The results of measurements, on the cross sections for scattering of ultrafast neutrons by protons and deuterons, are summarized in Table 2.[1]

TABLE 2

TOTAL CROSS SECTIONS OF PROTONS AND DEUTERONS FOR ULTRAFAST NEUTRONS

E_n (Mev)	$\sigma(n\text{-}d)$ (barns)	$\sigma(n\text{-}p)$ (barns)	Difference (barns)	Reference
42	0.289 ± 0.013	0.203 ± 0.007	0.086 ± 0.015	H61
85	0.117 ± 0.005	0.083 ± 0.004	0.034 ± 0.006	C25
95	0.104 ± 0.004	0.073 ± 0.002	0.031 ± 0.004	D9
270	0.057 ± 0.003	0.038 ± 0.002	0.019 ± 0.003	D10
280	0.049 ± 0.005	0.033 ± 0.003	0.016 ± 0.006	F41

(b) *Some Comments Pertaining to the Meson Theory of Nuclear Forces.* On the basis of the observed properties of the forces between two nucleons (in particular, the short range), Yukawa predicted the existence

[1] For results of $p\text{-}p$ scattering measurements see Volume I, Part IV, Section 2A.

of a particle of mass intermediate between that of the electron and the proton. According to his idea the force between two nucleons is regarded as resulting from the interchange of such particles, called mesons, between nucleons, in much the same way that purely electrical forces may be regarded as resulting from the interchange of photons between charged particles. There have been developed, since Yukawa's suggestion, a number of different types of meson theories of nuclear forces; these differ in the properties of the assumed mesons and in the type and strength of the assumed coupling between the meson and the nucleon fields (P7).

Yukawa's prediction was soon followed by the discovery of such a particle in the cosmic radiation. This particle, the mu-meson or muon, has a mass of $\sim$210 electron masses, may be either positive or negative, and is unstable, decaying into an electron and two neutral particles of negligible rest mass (presumably neutrinos) with a mean life of 2.15 $\times$ 10^{-6} sec. However, subsequent investigation has shown that the muon has a very weak interaction with nucleons, a fact which eliminates it from the role of nuclear binding material.

There is, however, another type of meson, the pi-meson or pion, which appears to be more directly associated with the nuclear forces. It has a mass of $\sim$275 electron masses, and decays into a muon and (presumably) a neutrino, with a mean life of 2.6 $\times$ 10^{-8} sec. Pions have been produced in the interaction between two nucleons, or between a nucleon and a gamma-ray, when there is enough energy available to supply the rest mass. In addition to charged pions of both sign, there have also been observed neutral pions (whose mass appears to be slightly less than the mass of the charged pion) which decay into two gamma-rays, with a very short mean life ($\sim$$10^{-15}$ sec). Finally, there is evidence for the existence of one or more types of still heavier meson. Very little is known concerning their interactions with nuclei.

Of the various types of mesons which have been observed, it is the pion which most probably plays the role of nuclear binding agent. It is produced directly in the interaction between two nucleons, and between nucleons and gamma-rays; the cross section for its production is of an order of magnitude which indicates that it interacts strongly with nucleons—strongly enough to account for the strength of nuclear forces. Indeed, recent work on the production of pions, through the use of ultrahigh-energy machines, and on the interaction of pions with nucleons and nuclei provides the strongest arguments for the fundamental validity of the meson theory of nuclear forces.

Although meson theories have, so far, been unable to account in detail for the nuclear forces, they do provide a qualitative basis for understanding the properties of nucleons (like, say, the anomalous magnetic moments of the neutron and proton) and of nuclear forces. The evidence on meson production at high energies together with the evidence on the charge independence of the nucleon-nucleon forces favor a symmetrical meson theory, in which charged mesons of both sign, as well as neutral mesons, play a comparable role. The exchange of charged mesons leads to the neutron-proton force, while neutral mesons are exchanged in the neutron-neutron and proton-proton interactions.

3. The Neutron-Electron Interaction. From the observation that the neutron has an intrinsic magnetic moment, it may be inferred that the neutron is a complex particle whose structure contains, at least for part of its existence, some moving charges. Indeed, according to current meson theories, the neutron can dissociate, spontaneously, into a tightly bound system of proton and negative pion, according to the reaction

$$n \rightleftarrows p + \pi^-$$

During the fraction of its existence as a neutron proper, it can be regarded as truly neutral; in the proton-pion state, however, the neutron has a charge structure corresponding to a relatively concentrated positive charge surrounded, at a somewhat greater distance (of the order of a few times 10^{-13} cm), by a cloud of equal negative charge. The fraction of the time during which the neutron is in this dissociated state is variously estimated in the different meson theories to lie somewhere in the range ~ 0.1 to 0.5.

As a consequence of this structure, there is an electromagnetic interaction between neutrons and electrons, the predominant aspects of which can be described in terms of the interaction between two magnetic dipoles (that of the electron and that of the neutron). This magnetic dipole-dipole interaction is, of course, strongly dependent on the relative orientations of the spins of the particles. It has been investigated extensively in studies of the scattering of slow neutrons by paramagnetic and ferromagnetic materials; these phenomena will be discussed in detail in Section 5.

A magnetic interaction of the dipole-dipole type would, because of its spin-dependent character, vanish for the case of a neutron interacting simultaneously with an even number of electrons which are in a $^1S_0$ state. Nevertheless, it has been observed that there is a small, spin-independent neutron-electron interaction. Such an interaction follows from meson-theoretic descriptions of the structure of the neutron, and its observed magnitude is in rough agreement with theoretical expectations (to be discussed later in this section). The strength of the interaction is such that it leads to a (spin-independent) cross section for the scattering of neutrons by a single bound electron of $\sigma_e \sim 5 \times 10^{-7}$ barns.

Although the value of σ_e is exceedingly small as compared to the cross sections for scattering of neutrons by nuclei ($\sim$ a few barns), effects of this scattering are, nevertheless, detectable in the scattering of slow neutrons by some heavy atoms. The possibility of observing such effects was first suggested and discussed by Condon (C24). This possibility results from the interference between the elastic scattering of sufficiently slow neutrons by the nucleus and by all the electrons in the atom.

Let us consider the scattering of a beam of slow neutrons, wavelength of the same order as the atomic dimensions, by a single atom containing Z electrons. The differential scattering cross section is

$$\frac{d\sigma}{d\Omega} = \left| a_0 + Za_eF(\theta) \right|^2 \tag{8}$$

where a_0 and a_e are, respectively, the amplitudes for scattering of a neutron by the nucleus and by a single bound electron,[1] i.e., $\sigma_e = 4\pi a_e^2$. $F(\theta)$ is the atomic electron form factor, which can be computed from the electron distribution or, alternatively, obtained from data on the scattering of x-rays (C22). Since $\sigma_0 = 4\pi a_0^2 \gg \sigma_e$, we may write

$$4\pi \frac{d\sigma}{d\Omega} = \sigma_0 \left[1 \pm 2ZF(\theta) \left(\frac{\sigma_e}{\sigma_0} \right)^{\frac{1}{2}} \right] \tag{8a}$$

For neutrons of wavelength large compared to the atomic dimensions, $F(\theta) \rightarrow 1$, while, as the neutron wavelength becomes small compared to the distance between the electrons, $F(\theta) \rightarrow 0$. To observe a possible neutron-electron interaction of the magnitude expected, it is absolutely necessary to take advantage of the interference between the neutron scattering by the nucleus and that by the atomic electrons.

For an estimate of the magnitude of possible effects, let us assume a set of arbitrary, but reasonable, values, $\sigma_0 \approx 5$ barns, $\sigma_e \approx 5 \times 10^{-7}$ barns, $ZF \approx 50$. Then

$$\frac{\Delta\sigma}{\sigma_0} = 2ZF \left(\frac{\sigma_e}{\sigma_0} \right)^{\frac{1}{2}} \sim 3 \text{ percent}$$

---

[1] Strictly speaking, a_0 refers only to the coherent portion of the nuclear scattering amplitude. When there is, in addition, an incoherent contribution to the nuclear scattering, the above expression for the differential atomic scattering cross section requires the addition of an incoherent term, a_1^2, where the total nuclear scattering cross section is $\sigma_s = 4\pi(a_0^2 + a_1^2)$. Although, for the discussion of this section, we shall assume that $a_1 = 0$, all the expressions to be derived can easily be modified if the nuclei exhibit any incoherent scattering.

Although it should be possible to measure an effect of this magnitude, it is necessary to devise some means of distinguishing it from the purely nuclear scattering, whose cross section is seldom known to an accuracy of 3 percent. One possibility is the method devised by Fermi and Marshall (F23). They compared the scattering of thermal neutrons by gaseous xenon atoms, into a given solid angle, at angles of 45° and 135°. Such a difference would arise from two sources: (1) the difference in the electron form factor which was, for the neutrons employed, $F(45°)$ $- F(135°) = 0.261$; (2) an asymmetry in the scattering due to the center-of-mass motion of the scattering system, since the angles were fixed in the laboratory system. In order to compute the magnitude of this effect, it is necessary to take into account the thermal motion of the xenon atoms (Doppler effect), as well as the energy distribution in the slow-neutron beam and the variation of the sensitivity of the detector with neutron energy.

Fermi and Marshall observed a definite asymmetry in the scattering of ~2 percent which, however, became much less than the experimental uncertainty of 0.85 percent after they applied the Doppler effect correction. Thus, although the accuracy of their measurement is insufficient to confirm the existence of the neutron-electron scattering, their results set an upper limit to the neutron-electron interaction. If the interaction is described in terms of a fictitious square well potential of depth V_0 and range equal to the classical electron radius, $r_0 = e^2/mc^2$ $= 2.8 \times 10^{-13}$ cm, the experiment of Fermi and Marshall gives $| V_0 |$ $\lesssim 5000$ ev. (Compare with $V \sim 25 \times 10^6$ ev for the neutron-proton potential.) [1]

The method of Fermi and Marshall has been reapplied by Hamermesh, Ringo, and Wattenberg [2] (H28) with, however, significant improve-

---

[1] The spin-independent neutron-electron interaction is, if it is of mesonic origin, a short-range interaction. Consequently, the value of σ_e for slow neutrons depends only on the volume integral of the interaction potential, rather than on any details of its shape. The Born approximation yields

$$\sigma_e = \frac{M^2 b^2}{\pi \hbar^4}$$

where M is the neutron mass and

$$b = 4\pi \int V(r) r^2 \, dr = - \left(\frac{4\pi}{3}\right) V_0 r_0^3$$

for the fictitious square well potential of range r_0. A value of $V_0 = 5000$ ev corresponds to $\sigma_e = 4.3 \times 10^{-7}$ barns. It should be noted that a negative b (attractive potential) corresponds to a negative a_e, while the nuclear scattering amplitude, a_0, is usually positive.

[2] I am indebted to Dr. A. Wattenberg for advance communication and discussion of these results.

ments in the geometry and a large increase in the number of neutrons counted. They have obtained the value

$$V_0 = 4100 \pm 1000 \text{ ev}$$

This value is based on measurements of the scattering of krypton as well as of xenon; measurements were also performed on argon to check the correction for the center-of-gravity motion. Of the uncertainty of ± 1000 ev, quoted by these investigators, half is statistical and half is their estimate of possible systematic errors. Their result is in good agreement with the previous measurement of Havens, Rabi, and Rainwater (H46, H47).

The method of observing the neutron-electron interaction, devised by Havens, Rabi, and Rainwater, is based on observation of the total cross section

$$\sigma = \int d\sigma \, (\theta) = \sigma_0 \pm 2Z\bar{F}(\sigma_0\sigma_e)^{\frac{1}{2}} \tag{9}$$

They distinguish the effect of the coherent electron scattering by observing the variation of σ with neutron energy for wavelengths of the order of the atomic dimensions. For a neutron source of variable energy, they employed the Columbia velocity selector; as scattering materials, they used liquid lead and bismuth. Their method suffers from the difficulty that it is necessary to apply rather large corrections to the observed cross section vs. energy curve before the effect of the neutron-electron interaction can be ascertained. These corrections arise from a number of causes: (1) In addition to the nuclear scattering there is, for lead and bismuth, a small nuclear absorption whose cross section varies with the neutron velocity as $1/v$. This correction can be applied with good accuracy. (2) Since they were dealing with atoms bound in a liquid, rather than with free atoms, it is necessary to take into account the effects of the binding (see page 231) on the variation of the cross section with energy. Although such effects (which include, of course, a Doppler effect for the motion of the atoms in the liquid) depend, to a certain extent, on the details of the binding mechanism, it has been shown by Placzek (P19) that they can be evaluated with the requisite accuracy. (3) There are, in the scattering of neutrons by liquids, effects due to interference between the scattering by different atoms. Although such effects are relatively small, since the experiments involve neutrons with wavelengths of the order of atomic dimensions and hence somewhat smaller than the interatomic distances, they cannot be neglected in comparison with the effects of the neutron-electron scattering. The liquid coherence effects can be shown to vary as λ^2, in the energy region of interest, and the coefficient of the λ^2 term can be evaluated by a general method for systems of high density and small compressibility, as shown by the calculations of Placzek, Nijboer, and van Hove (P21). (4) Although the three effects discussed above, all of which arise from nuclear causes, can be taken into account in a satisfactory fashion, there is a possible electronic effect which must be taken into consideration. Even though the ground states of atomic lead and bismith are $^1S_0$, and Fermi and Marshall (F23) have proved that scattering due to the neutron magnetic moment is negligible for such atoms, small magnetic scattering effects might possibly be present when these atoms are in the liquid state.

The results upon which Havens, Rabi, and Rainwater base their value of the neutron-electron interaction were obtained by careful analysis of data on the scattering of monoenergetic slow neutrons by liquid bismuth; they lead to

$$V_0 = 5300 \pm 1000 \text{ ev}$$

Of the quoted uncertainty, 650 ev is statistical in origin, the rest being an estimate of possible systematic errors.[1]

Although a detailed meson-theoretic discussion of the spin-independent neutron-electron interaction is outside the province of this review (even assuming that an adequate theory were available), the phenomena which can give rise to such an interaction are, however, susceptible of relatively simple physical interpretation.[2] Actually, there are two distinct types of interaction which, together, can probably account for the observed effect. The first may be regarded as an electrostatic interac-

---

[1] D. J. Hughes has reported (at the February 1952 meeting of the American Physical Society) a measurement of the neutron-electron interaction by observation of the critical angle for total reflection of cold neutrons from a liquid oxygen-bismuth interface (see Section 5). His preliminary results are in excellent argeement with the measurements of Havens, Rabi, and Rainwater and of Hamermesh, Ringo, and Wattenberg. However, this method appears to be capable of yielding the most accurate value of the strength of the neutron-electron interaction. Using this method, Harvey, Hughes, and Goldberg have obtained $V_0 = 4250 \pm 400$ ev (private communication, October 1952).

[2] Purcell and Ramsey (P32), in their discussion of the possible existence of a neutron electric dipole moment, point out that the observed neutron-electron interaction could, alternatively, be accounted for by the assumption of a small electric dipole moment of the neutron. The magnitude required to account for the observed interaction is that of two opposite electron charges separated by a distance of 3×10^{-18} cm. Since the experiments of Purcell, Ramsey, and Smith (S40) have yielded an upper limit of two electron charges separated by 5×10^{-21} cm for the electric dipole moment of the neutron, the explanation of the observed neutron-electron interaction lies, in all likelihood, along the meson-theoretic lines indicated below.

tion which arises from the fact that the neutron is not a strictly neutral particle but behaves, at least during an appreciable fraction of its existence, as a positive charge surrounded by a negative meson cloud. Thus, when the neutron and electron are separated by a distance less than the extent of the meson distribution (which is of the order of the classical electron radius r_0) they will interact electrostatically. The predicted magnitude of this effect depends on the form of the meson theory used in its calculation and, in any event, has only been calculated approximately (i.e., by perturbation techniques, to first order in the coupling constant).   Such calculations have been carried out by Slotnick and Heitler (S39), by Case (C2), by Dancoff and Drell (D2), and by Borowitz and Kohn (B48).   These calculations predict effects of the order of, but somewhat smaller than, the observed interaction. Thus, for instance, Case (C2) obtained an attractive interaction which, when expressed as a square well potential of range r_0, yields $V_0 \cong 300(f^2/2\pi)$ ev; $f^2/2\pi$, for this case (the coupling constant for a pseudoscalar meson with pseudoscalar coupling), is ≈ 5, giving $V_0 \approx 1500$ ev.

The second effect arises, as was pointed out by Foldy (F37), as a direct consequence of the anomalous magnetic moment of the neutron.   It can, in fact, be computed, without specification of the form of the meson theory,[1] by assuming that the neutron obeys the Dirac equation with the additional "Pauli terms" (P7) in the Hamiltonian, $-\mu_n(e\hbar/2Mc)(\beta\boldsymbol{\sigma}\cdot\mathbf{H} - i\beta\boldsymbol{\alpha}\cdot\mathbf{E})$. ($\mu_n \cong -1.91$ is the neutron moment in nuclear magnetons.)   The $\boldsymbol{\sigma}\cdot\mathbf{H}$ term leads to the spin-dependent, magnetic dipole-dipole interaction between the neutron and the electron. The second term leads to an interaction of the form $-\mu_n(e\hbar^2/4M^2c^2)\beta$ div $\mathbf{E}$ which corresponds, for the field of a point electron, to an attractive interaction with

$$V_0 = -\left(\frac{3\mu_n}{4}\right)\left(\frac{\hbar c}{e^2}\right)^2 \left(\frac{m}{M}\right)^2 mc^2 = 4100 \text{ ev} \qquad (10)$$

Thus, the Foldy term alone appears almost sufficient to account for the observed interaction.   A more accurate measurement of the strength of the neutron-electron interaction should, indeed, eventually lead to an evaluation of the magnitude of the electrostatic interaction and permit a check on the applicability of specific meson theories.

[1] Since the fact that the neutron has an anomalous magnetic moment is, itself, a consequence of meson theories, it could not be said that this effect is of non-mesonic origin.   Indeed, some of the meson-theoretic calculations (S39, D2) include the effect. However, since no existing theory is capable of yielding the observed value of the neutron magnetic moment, it appears more reasonable to follow the method of Foldy, which assumes the observed neutron moment, and to compute this effect by a phenomenological treatment.

The two effects described above are susceptible of relatively simple, order-of-magnitude computations. The strength of the electrostatic neutron-electron interaction has been estimated by Fermi and Marshall (F23), who considered a model of a point proton (charge g^2e) surrounded by a negative meson cloud of charge density

$$\rho(r) = -\left(\frac{g^2e}{2\pi ar^2}\right)\exp\left(-\frac{2r}{a}\right) \tag{11}$$

This expression is suggested by Yukawa's original (scalar) theory of the meson field, according to which the extent of the meson wave function is essentially determined from the uncertainty principle,

$$a \simeq \hbar/\kappa c \tag{12}$$

where κ is the pion mass (≈ 275 electron masses). $g^2 \sim 0.1$ to 0.5 is the is the fraction of time during which the neutron exists in the proton-meson state.

The potential energy $U(r)$ of interaction of the above charge distribution with a point electron can be obtained by solution of the Poisson equation, and the strength of the neutron-electron interaction is given by

$$b = 4\pi \int_0^\infty U(r)r^2\,dr = -\left(\frac{\pi}{3}\right)g^2e^2a^2 \tag{13}$$

Assuming a potential well of radius r_0 and depth V_0, we obtain

$$V_0 = -\frac{3b}{4\pi r_0{}^3} = \left(\frac{g^2}{4}\right)\left(\frac{m}{\kappa}\right)^2\left(\frac{\hbar c}{e^2}\right)^2 mc^2 \approx 3 \times 10^4 g^2 \text{ ev} \tag{14}$$

Considering that the computation is classical and, furthermore, modeled on a meson theory which is known to be inadequate, the agreement with the meson-theoretic computations, quoted in the preceding, is quite satisfactory.

It is somewhat more difficult to give a simple physical interpretation of the interaction which arises from the neutron's magnetic moment. However, Weisskopf [1] has suggested a rather ingenious derivation of the Foldy term: The assumption that the neutron obeys the Dirac equation leads to a *zitterbewegung* in the motion of the neutron, such that its path is a spiral whose radius is of the order of the neutron's Compton wavelength, $R \approx \hbar/Mc$. The neutron travels with the velocity of light, c, in this spiral path whose pitch is such as to give a transport velocity equal to the velocity v of the neutron. (The intrinsic spin angular momentum of the neutron can be interpreted as arising from this spiral motion.) Accordingly, when the neutron is within a distance

---

[1] Private communication.

R of the electron, which, we assume, behaves like a point charge, there is a magnetic spin orbit interaction between the electron current and the neutron's intrinsic magnetic moment whose energy is, neglecting numerical factors,

$$E \approx \mu_n \left(\frac{e\hbar}{Mc}\right)\left(\frac{e}{R^2}\right) = \mu_n \left(\frac{e^2}{\hbar c}\right) Mc^2 \tag{15}$$

Since this interaction has a range of $\sim R$, we obtain

$$V_0 \approx \frac{-ER^3}{r_0{}^3} \approx -\mu_n \left(\frac{\hbar c}{e^2}\right)^2 \left(\frac{m}{M}\right)^2 mc^2 \tag{10a}$$

which is, aside from the factor $\frac{3}{4}$, the result of the calculation of Foldy. Since the interaction depends only on the electron's charge, it is easily seen to be spin-independent.

SECTION 2. INTERACTION WITH NUCLEI

A. Introduction

The experiments through which the existence of the neutron was established and in which its properties were first elucidated very soon indicated that neutrons are capable of inducing nuclear transmutations. Some of these early investigations have been discussed in Section 1. In these the neutron-induced transmutations were observed in cloud chambers. Although the cloud chamber is a very effective instrument for observing nuclear transmutations, its use imposes serious restrictions on the types of nuclear reactions which can possibly be detected: The target nuclei must be capable of being introduced, as an appreciable constituent, into the cloud chamber; the transmutation products must be charged and have sufficient energy (range) to leave observable and identifiable tracks. With relatively few exceptions, cloud chamber techniques can only be applied to the study of nuclear transmutations induced in light elements by fast neutrons.

With the announcement by Curie and Joliot (C41), in January 1934, of the production of artificially radioactive nuclei, an entirely new field of neutron investigation became available.[1] Their discovery prompted

---

[1] The discovery by Curie and Joliot was made in experiments involving the bombardment of boron, magnesium, and aluminum by polonium alpha-particles. They first reported the reaction

$$Al^{27} + \alpha \rightarrow P^{30} + n$$

$$P^{30} \rightarrow Si^{30} + e^+$$

and proved that the reaction product is an isotope of phosphorus, decaying by positron emission, with a half-life of 3.25 min.

Fermi to investigate the possibility of producing artificial radioactivity by neutrons, and he soon announced (F13) that the bombardment of aluminum and fluorine by neutrons does indeed induce such radioactivity. Within a short time, Fermi and his co-workers at the University of Rome succeeded in inducing artificial radioactivity in a variety of elements through neutron bombardment (F12). In the next few years the Rome group played a leading role in the investigation of neutron-induced nuclear reactions.

A significant step forward in the study of neutron reactions resulted from the observation by Fermi, Amaldi, Pontecorvo, Rasetti, and Segrè (F14) that the neutron-induced radioactivity in silver can be significantly increased by interposing, between the source of fast neutrons and the silver detector, a slab of paraffin. This effect was correctly ascribed to the slowing down of the neutrons by collisions with hydrogen nuclei, and it indicated that the probability of neutron capture increases with decreasing neutron energy. This conjecture was confirmed by the observation, by Moon and Tillman (M35), of an effect of the temperature of the moderator on the neutron capture. The slowing down of neutrons in hydrogen-containing materials will be discussed subsequently. For the purpose of this summary it is, however, important to note that the recognition of the strong dependence of neutron capture probability on the neutron velocity was a significant step toward the understanding of neutron reactions and that, for many years, sources of neutrons slowed down in paraffin were the main tool for the investigation of neutron-induced nuclear reactions.

The fact that radioactivity can be induced by neutrons in the heaviest elements is already a strong indication that the reactions responsible for their production probably do not involve the emission of charged particles since, for heavy nuclei, the Gamow barrier is a very strong deterrent to charged particle emission. Furthermore, in many cases the radioactive nuclei were shown to be isotopes of the bombarded nuclei (F12). In particular, the ~ 15 hr half-life β^- activity resulting from neutron capture by Na^{23}, discovered by Bjerge and Westcott (B32), was identified as an isotope of sodium by Amaldi, D'Agostino, and Segrè (A16); the fact that the decay involves emission of β^- particles was interpreted to imply that the radioactive isotope is Na^{24} (rather than Na^{22}), indicating an (n,γ) reaction. The observation that the probability of producing radioactivities in heavy nuclei increases with decreasing neutron velocity represents an even stronger argument for the contention that the reaction involved is that of radiative capture (n,γ)—capture of a neutron followed by gamma-ray emission. That this is indeed the case was shown by Amaldi, D'Agostino, Fermi, Pontecorvo, Rasetti, and

Segrè (A19), who proved that the capture of slow neutrons by cobalt, cadmium, chlorine, iridium, silver, and mercury is accompanied by gamma-ray emission.[1] For slow neutrons, radiative capture is usually the most important reaction. However, in the case of the capture of slow neutrons by light nuclei, charged particle emission may be much more probable. Thus, Chadwick and Goldhaber (C9) and, independently, Amaldi, D'Agostino, Fermi, Pontecorvo, Rasetti, and Segrè (A17) showed that the strong capture of slow neutrons by lithium and boron is due to an (n,α) reaction. Somewhat later Burcham and Goldhaber (B75) demonstrated that the capture of slow neutrons by nitrogen is due to an (n,p) reaction.

Perhaps the most important advance in the study of neutron reactions was the discovery of slow-neutron resonances—the preferential capture of neutrons of specific energies by certain nuclei. The first indication of resonance effects was obtained in the experiments of Bjerge and Westcott (B33), soon followed by the work of Moon and Tillman (M35, T9), which established the resonance nature of some slow-neutron interactions. There then followed a period of rapid development of techniques for studying the properties of slow-neutron resonances. Among the most important of these were: the use of cadmium difference and self-indication methods by Fermi and Amaldi (F16) and by Szilard (S64); the measurement of neutron slowing down lengths in paraffin using, as a detector, the resonance in question, by Amaldi and Fermi (A20); the use of boron absorption techniques for the measurement of resonance energies by Frisch and Placzek (F45) and by Weeks, Livingston, and Bethe (W11); the development of the first slow-neutron velocity selector by Dunning, Pegram, Fink, Mitchell, and Segrè (D20). These techniques, their development and extension, will be discussed in detail in Section 3. Among the most significant of the early studies was the proof, by Dunning, Pegram, Fink, and Mitchell (D19), that the very large interaction of thermal neutrons with cadmium cannot be due to neutron scattering and must, therefore, be assumed to result from the radiative capture process.

The study of slow-neutron resonance capture received great impetus from the theoretical considerations of Bohr (B44) on the role of the compound nucleus in nuclear reactions. On the basis of Bohr's arguments, it became possible to understand the existence of slow-neutron capture resonances, and to interpret their observed properties in terms of the Breit-Wigner formula (B60) (previously derived on the basis of very

---

[1] The emission of gamma-radiation in the capture of neutrons by hydrogen had previously been observed by Lea (L10).

general considerations) for the energy dependence of the nuclear cross section in the neighborhood of a resonance.

In addition to the work mentioned above, some of the investigations which were important in confirming the theoretical ideas concerning neutron resonances include those of Preiswerk and Halban (P30), Frisch (F46), and Goldsmith and Rasetti (G19). The experiments and theory of slow-neutron resonances, up to 1937, are summarized by Bethe (B24), by Bohr and Kalckar (B45), and by Moon (M36). The theory and observation of slow-neutron resonances, up to 1940, are discussed by Peierls (P10).

While the most important advances in neutron physics were made in the study of the properties of slow neutrons, the investigation of fast neutron reactions was not completely neglected. Of the artificial radio-activities induced, by neutrons from Rn-Be sources, in light elements, the pioneering work of Fermi and co-workers (F12) showed, by chemical separation of the radioactive nuclei, that the responsible reactions were mainly (n,p) and (n,α). In the case of the heavy elements, the radio-active products appeared, in most cases, to be isotopes of the target nuclei. Fermi and co-workers advanced two alternative reaction possi-bilities: radiative capture, or the ejection of a neutron from the target nucleus by a neutron-neutron collision, i.e., the $(n,2n)$ reaction. The dependence of the probability of most neutron reactions on the neutron velocity, discussed above, led to the assumption of the first hypothesis, confirmed by the observations on sodium (B32, A16) and other ele-ments (A19). However, in 1936, Heyn (H56) proved that, for neutrons of sufficiently high energy, the $(n,2n)$ reaction could also be induced.

In the meanwhile, Dunning and co-workers at Columbia University (D18, D19) were studying the reactions of fast neutrons with nuclei, using Ra-Be sources. In addition, with the discovery, by Szilard and Chalmers (S63), of the photodisintegration of beryllium by the gamma-rays from radium and its products, there became available neutron sources in the intermediate-energy range. These were exploited by a number of investigators (M22, L13, G25) for the study of neutron reac-tions in the 0.1 to 1 Mev range. Of primary importance in the study of fast-neutron reactions was the discovery, in 1933, of the possibility of producing strong fast-neutron sources by the use of particle accelera-tors through (d,n) reactions (Crane, Lauritsen, and Soltan, C30), and (p,n) reactions (Crane and Lauritsen, C31). Of special significance in this respect is the $d + d$ reaction (Oliphant, Harteck, and Rutherford, O3), which can be used with relatively low-voltage accelerators.

Among the early results of fast-neutron studies was the observation by Lea (L11) of the excitation of gamma-rays by the passage of fast neutrons through matter. Lea showed that the production of gamma-rays increased with the atomic number of the material traversed, and that the observed effects were not due to a neutron capture process; he ascribed them to the excitation of nuclei in the inelastic scattering of fast neutrons, followed by nuclear de-excitation through gamma-ray emission. Similar results were obtained by Kikuchi, Aoki, and Husimi (K12). It was shown, by Danysz, Rotblat, Wertenstein, and Zyw (D3), by Ehrenberg (E2), and by Collie and Griffiths (C20), that fast neutrons are indeed slowed down, far in excess of what could be accounted for by elastic scattering, in their passage through heavy elements.

The last of the significant new neutron reactions to be uncovered was neutron fission, discovered by Hahn and Strassman (H4) early in 1939. This discovery was the result of a long series of investigations which attempted to understand and interpret the results of the neutron bombardment of uranium, first reported by Fermi et al. (F12). Immediately after the announcement by Hahn and Strassman that isotopes of barium, lanthanum, and cerium are certainly among the products of the capture of slow neutrons by uranium, Meitner and Frisch (M23) showed that a fission reaction (division into two fragments of roughly equal mass) was to be expected from energetic considerations; such a reaction, they observed, is highly exoergic. Physical evidence for the expulsion of high-speed nuclear fragments in the slow-neutron fission of uranium was soon obtained by Frisch (F49) and by Joliot (J11). The history of the discovery and early investigation of the fission reaction has been reviewed by Turner (T17).

B. General Considerations

Given a complete knowledge of the law of force between nucleons and of the law of motion (quantum mechanics) which governs their mutual interaction, it is conceivably possible to set up a program of computing the static properties of all nuclei and the detailed characteristics of the interactions between neutrons and nuclei. Actually, this program is still in its preliminary stages, if indeed the goal is at all attainable for any but the lightest nuclei. In the first place, the law or laws of force are not yet sufficiently well established. In the second place, their application to complex, heavy nuclei would involve the solution of the equations of motion for the many-body problem, in which the components are closely spaced and strongly interacting (so that the approximation methods, which are so useful in problems involving the electrons in an atom, may not be applicable to nuclei). Finally, it is by no means certain that specifically many-body forces (not detectable in or predictable from a study of the nucleon-nucleon interaction) do not come into play in the interaction of the nucleons in a nucleus.

Nevertheless, a number of attempts have been made to understand the properties of nuclear (especially neutron) interactions in terms of approximations in which the nucleons in the nucleus are assumed to behave as more-or-less independent particles (A19, B11, B21, P11). The predictions of such models were soon found to be at strong variance with experimental observations, especially with regard to the properties of slow-neutron resonances; for, while these models predict strong thermal neutron capture cross sections and slow-neutron resonances, the widths of the levels and the spacing of levels, as predicted, were far in excess of those observed. Furthermore—and most significant—the independent particle models were unable to account for the predominance of radiative capture over scattering in most slow-neutron resonances.

To overcome these difficulties Breit and Wigner (B60) introduced the idea that the slow-neutron capture process must involve more than one of the nuclear constituents; their arguments were based mainly on an analogy with certain atomic and molecular phenomena. The conceptual and theoretical groundwork for the understanding of nuclear reactions was laid by Bohr (B44) in a work of classic and far-reaching significance. Bohr emphasized the necessity of going to the opposite extreme from the independent particle picture, and of recognizing that the nucleons in the nucleus interact very strongly with each other. Thus, a neutron, on entering the nucleus, very rapidly loses its identity as bombarding particle, sharing its energy among all the constituents of the nucleus. Accordingly, a nuclear reaction must be regarded as taking place in two distinct and separable stages. In the first, the incident particle is incorporated into a *compound nucleus*, sharing its energy—kinetic and binding—with the rest of the nucleus. In the second stage, the compound nucleus gives up its excitation energy by any one of the possible means at its disposal. These means include radiation, particle emission, and neutron re-emission. In this competition among the various (energetically) possible de-excitation processes, radiation can compete very favorably with particle emission, especially in heavy nuclei, since particle emission (including neutron re-emission) requires the concentration of a large fraction of the excitation energy into one particle, a process which is relatively improbable. Furthermore, because of the sharing of the excitation energy among the nuclear constituents, the compound nucleus has a relatively long lifetime, which results in comparatively sharp resonances. These ideas lend themselves to quantitative development in terms of a statistical theory of nuclear energy levels and of nuclear reactions (B45, B23, F43, W16, L2); they provide the basis for many theoretical investigations of the properties of slow-neutron resonances (B25, K2, S37, B61, W29, F27, F28, A6). In their extreme form, they suggest the liquid drop model of heavy nuclei, which has been so useful in understanding the dynamics of the fission process (B46).

So successful were the ideas of Bohr, and their quantitative development, in understanding, correlating, and predicting the properties of nuclear reactions, as well as some of the general features of the stable nuclei (binding energies, curve of stability) that the independent particle model was completely discredited. There remained, however, certain features of nuclear behavior which, although they could be fitted into the general framework of the statistical model, required concessions in the direction of the independent particle model; thus, it was necessary to treat somewhat differently nuclei with odd and with even numbers of nucleons. Furthermore, the success of the independent particle model, as applied by Schmidt (S5), in correlating nuclear magnetic moments indicated that the ground states, at least, of nuclei require such a treatment.

The accumulation of nuclear data has recently led to the recognition by Mayer (M7) that many nuclear phenomena indicate the existence of a nuclear shell structure, first predicted by Elsasser (E4), thereby reviving the independent particle model. The particular stability of nuclei containing 2, 8, 20, 28, 50, 82, or 126 neutrons or protons is borne out by a large number of nuclear data. A number of forms of the independent particle model have been invoked to derive the above "magic numbers" (F6, N2), of which the most successful has involved the assumption of a strong spin-orbit coupling, by Haxel, Jensen, and Suess (H49) and by Mayer (M8). Table 3 (after Mayer, M9) partially summarizes the predictions of this model.

While the statistical model and the independent particle model represent opposite extremes, it appears necessary nevertheless to recognize that both points of view are applicable, each in its domain, and that the two approaches are complementary. Thus, the independent particle picture appears to be required for the understanding of the ground and low-lying excited states of nuclei, whereas the statistical model is more appropriate for phenomena involving relatively large nuclear excitation, as is the case in almost all neutron reactions. Weisskopf (W17) has pointed out that the nuclear situation seems analogous to that of the electrons in a metal, where the electrons can be described in terms of an independent particle model for the states of small excitation because of the effects of the Pauli principle, despite the fact that they are interacting very strongly with each other.

TABLE 3

ORDER OF ENERGY LEVELS OBTAINED FROM THOSE OF A SQUARE WELL
POTENTIAL BY SPIN-ORBIT COUPLING

(After Mayer, M9)

Oscillator Number	Square Well Level	Spin Term	Number of States	Number in Shell	Total Number
0	$1s$	$1s_{1/2}$	2	2	2
1	$1p$	$1p_{3/2}$	4		
		$1p_{1/2}$	2	6	8
2	$1d$	$1d_{5/2}$	6		(14)
	$2s$	$2s_{1/2}$	2		
		$1d_{3/2}$	4	12	20
3	$1f$	$1f_{7/2}$	8	8	28
	$2p$	$2p_{3/2}$	4		
		$1f_{5/2}$	6		
		$2p_{1/2}$	2	(12)	(40)
4	$1g$	$1g_{9/2}$	10	22	50
	$2d$	$2d_{5/2}$	6		
		$1g_{7/2}$	8		
		$2d_{3/2}$	4		
		$3s_{1/2}$	2		
5	$1h$	$1h_{11/2}$	12	32	82
	$2f$	$2f_{7/2}$	8		
	$3p$	$3p_{3/2}$	4		
		$2f_{5/2}$	6		
		$3p_{1/2}$	2		
		$1h_{9/2}$	10		
6	$1i$	$1i_{13/2}$	14	44	126
	$2g$	$2g_{9/2}$			
	$3d$				
	$4s$				

Nevertheless, it is necessary to observe that neither model provides a complete description of nuclear phenomena in any energy region; the strong interaction undoubtedly influences the properties of the low-lying nuclear levels, while (as we shall have many occasions to observe) the shell structure has important effects on the characteristics of neutron reactions, even at relatively high levels of excitation.

The properties of nuclear reactions have been discussed in Part VI. In this section we shall review these properties as they apply to neutron reactions, and summarize the status of the present knowledge of the interactions of neutrons with nuclei. The available data on neutron cross sections have been compiled by Goldsmith, Ibser, and Feld (G20) (October 1947), by Adair (A2) (July 1950), and by an AEC Committee (A0) (1952). The discussion here will lean heavily on these compilations, in which references are given to the original investigations.

1. Energetics of Neutron Reactions. When a neutron of kinetic energy E is captured by the target nucleus, the product (compound) nucleus acquires an excitation of energy $E' = E + \epsilon$. ϵ is the binding energy of the neutron in the product nucleus. This excitation makes possible a variety of nuclear reactions, depending on the particle or particles whose emission from the compound nucleus requires less than the energy E'. The characteristics of the reactions observed depend on the properties of the compound nucleus at the excitation energy E', and on the competition between the possible modes of de-excitation of the compound nucleus.

Clearly, for neutrons of kinetic energy $E \ll \epsilon$, the characteristics of the observed reactions will be critically dependent on the value of ϵ. The variation of ϵ with Z and A may be summarized as follows: For nuclei of $A \gtrsim 20$, ϵ exhibits large (periodic) fluctuations from nucleus to nucleus. For nuclei of $A \gtrsim 20$, the values of ϵ, *on the average*, increase slowly from ~ 8 Mev to ~ 8.5 Mev at $A \simeq 130$, and then decrease slowly to ~ 7.5 Mev for the heaviest nuclei. However, these values apply to the stable nuclei; the capture of a neutron by a stable nucleus usually results in a radioactive product nucleus for which the neutron binding energies are somewhat smaller than for the stable nuclei. Thus, the values of ϵ, for captured neutrons, average ~ 7–8 Mev for A between 20 and 150, falling slowly to ~ 6 Mev for neutrons captured by the heaviest nuclei.

However, neutron binding energies fluctuate significantly from nucleus to nucleus. The capture of a neutron by a nucleus with an odd number of neutrons results in a greater (by ~ 1–2 Mev) release of energy than capture by adjacent nuclei of even neutron number. Quite large deviations from the average may also occur in the vicinity of neutron magic numbers; thus, the value of ϵ for a neutron captured in a nucleus lacking but one neutron for a closed shell will be anomalously high, while ϵ for a neutron captured by a nucleus already having a completed neutron shell is anomalously low. Furthermore, such magic number effects appear to persist for neutron numbers ranging considerably to either side of a magic number (K23).

In those (relatively rare) cases in which the masses of the target and product nuclei are known, the neutron binding energy can be computed:

$$\epsilon = 931.16\{M(\mathrm{X}^A) + M(n) - M(\mathrm{X}^{A+1})\} \quad \text{in Mev} \quad (16)$$

For light nuclei the masses of the nuclei involved are, in general, available and the above computation can be made. For nuclei of $A \gtrsim 30$ the masses are usually not known, and it is then necessary to resort to the general considerations described above, if it is desired to estimate the value of ϵ.

From the above expression for ϵ, it may be seen that it is not necessary to know the absolute value of the nuclear masses in order to compute ϵ, but only the mass difference, $M(\mathrm{X}^{A+1}) - M(\mathrm{X}^A)$. Nuclear mass differences are frequently known as a result of measurements of the energies of reactions involving the two nuclei in question, even when the absolute values of the masses are unknown. Thus, in the region of the naturally radioactive nuclei, neutron binding energies can be computed with the aid of the observed energies of alpha- and beta-emission (W9).

For a few nuclei the energy release accompanying slow-neutron capture has been measured directly by observation of the energy of the gamma-radiation emitted when the excited compound nucleus decays to its ground state. In this fashion, Bell and Elliott measured the binding energy of the deuteron (B16). Unfortunately, for nuclei more complicated than the deuteron the radiative de-excitation of the compound nucleus is usually achieved by the emission, in cascade, of a number of gamma-rays. Since there are usually a large number of energy levels of the compound nucleus available to such cascade gamma-ray emission, the capture gamma-ray spectrum is quite complicated. However, in certain favorable cases the emission of a single gamma-ray, carrying away all the excitation energy, occurs in a reasonably large fraction of the decays; the energy of this gamma-ray gives, directly, the value of ϵ. Such direct transitions to the nuclear ground states have been observed in a number of nuclei by Kinsey, Bartholomew, and Walker (K15).

In general, the nuclear reactions in which we are interested can be represented symbolically as

$$_0n^1 + {}_z\mathrm{X}^A \rightarrow ({}_z\mathrm{X}^{A+1})^* \rightarrow {}_z x^a + {}_{z-z}\mathrm{Y}^{A+1-a} + Q \quad (17)$$

[For many light nucleus reactions the intermediate (compound) nucleus step should be omitted, since it has no independent existence.] The reaction is frequently abbreviated as $X^A(n,x)Y^{A+1-a}$, or simply as $X^A(n,x)$. The Q value of the reaction is determined by the masses of the nuclei involved:

$$Q = 931.16\{M(n) + M(X) - M(x) - M(Y)\} \quad \text{in Mev} \quad (18)$$

or, conversely, a measurement of the Q value can be used to determine one of the masses, if the other three are known, or the mass difference $M(X) - M(Y)$, from the masses of the neutron and the ejected particle. A positive Q value indicates an exoergic reaction, i.e., a reaction that can take place (from the point of view of available energy) with neutrons of zero kinetic energy; a negative Q value means that the reaction is endoergic and is not possible for neutrons of kinetic energy less than a certain threshold value:

$$E_t = - \left\{ \frac{[M(X) + M(n)]}{M(X)} \right\} Q \cong - \left\{ \frac{(A+1)}{A} \right\} Q \quad (19)$$

The factor in brackets arises from the conservation of momentum, which requires that some of the neutron kinetic energy be expended in providing for the center-of-mass motion of the system. The possibility that a given reaction can be initiated by thermal neutrons depends on having $Q > 0$. Two reactions are, however, always possible for thermal neutrons: (1) elastic scattering (or re-emission) of a neutron (n,n), for which $Q = 0$; (2) radiative capture (n,γ), for which $Q = \epsilon$.

2. Theory of Neutron Reactions; the Compound Nucleus. According to the Bohr model, most neutron reactions can be regarded as taking place in two distinct stages—the formation of an excited compound nucleus, and its subsequent decay. In our survey of the theoretical consequences of these ideas, we lean heavily on the schematic theory of nuclear reactions developed by Weisskopf and co-workers (F27, F28, W17). This theory is based on some general assumptions regarding the structure of nuclei: that the nucleus has a well-defined surface, which is a sphere of radius R, outside of which the interaction with neutrons is negligible; that, once inside the nucleus, the neutron interacts very strongly with the nuclear constituents, rapidly sharing its excitation energy among them.

Because of the saturation property of nuclear forces, the average distance between nuclear constituents is independent of their number,

A. Thus, the volume V of a nucleus is proportional to A, and its radius can be approximated by the relationship

$$R = r_0 A^{1/3} \tag{20}$$

with r_0 between 1.3 and 1.5 $\times$ 10^{-13} cm.

A neutron of kinetic energy E will, on penetrating the nuclear surface, suddenly find itself in a region where its kinetic energy is $E' \cong E + \varepsilon$, where ε is the average kinetic energy of a nucleon inside the nucleus. Such a sudden change of kinetic energy results, from wave-mechanical considerations, in a reflection; the probability for penetration of the surface is given by

$$P = \frac{4kK}{(k + K)^2} \tag{21}$$

where

$$k^2 = \frac{2ME}{\hbar^2} = \frac{1}{\lambda^2} \tag{22a}$$

for the incident neutron, and

$$K^2 = \frac{2M(E + \varepsilon)}{\hbar^2} = k^2 + K_0^2 \qquad K_0^2 = \frac{2M\varepsilon}{\hbar^2} \tag{22b}$$

for the neutron inside the nucleus. (K and k are the wave numbers associated with the neutron inside and outside the nucleus, respectively.)

The value of K_0 can be computed on the assumption that the nucleons in the nucleus obey Fermi-Dirac statistics, distributing themselves among the various possible states of momentum, spin, and isotopic spin (charge) so that no state is occupied by more than one nucleon, giving

$$\varepsilon = \left(\frac{4\pi^2\hbar^2}{2M}\right)\left(\frac{3A}{16\pi V}\right)^{2/3} \cong 20 \text{ Mev}$$
$$K_0 \cong 1.0 \times 10^{13} \text{ cm}^{-1} \tag{23}$$

for $r_0 = 1.5 \times 10^{-13}$ cm. For slow neutrons, $k \ll K \cong K_0$, and

$$P \cong \frac{4k}{K_0} \ll 1 \tag{24}$$

Despite the smallness of P for slow neutrons, the probability of neutron capture to form a compound nucleus may be quite large since slow neutrons have a large extent (wavelength). The capture probability depends critically on the proximity of the excitation energy ($E' = E + \varepsilon$) to one of the energy levels of the compound nucleus, being essentially a resonance phenomenon. We postpone the discussion of the formation of the compound nucleus to the next section and confine ourselves, at this point, to consideration of what happens after the compound nucleus has been formed.

Once a neutron has entered the target nucleus, it very rapidly shares its energy among the nuclear constituents, forming a compound nucleus in an excited state. Furthermore, owing to the smallness of P (which works both ways), the neutron has a very small probability of re-emerging, even if it should find itself in the relatively improbable circumstance of possessing all the excitation energy. Consequently, the lifetime of the compound nucleus is very long compared to the time required for its traversal by a nucleon. In fact, for slow neutrons captured in nuclei containing a relatively large number of constituents (say $A \gtrsim 100$) the most favorable mechanism for de-excitation of the compound nucleus is usually the emission of gamma-radiation, which is itself a relatively improbable process.

These considerations can be made somewhat more quantitative. The compound nucleus, formed in an excited state, may have a number of (energetically) possible modes of decay which always include radiation (n,γ), neutron re-emission (n,n), and may also include the emission of one or more particles (n,a), (n,b), etc. These compete freely with each other, each mode of decay being characterized by a mean-life, τ_i (the lifetime which the excited state would have if all other possible modes of decay were turned off). The mean-life of the excited state

$$\frac{1}{\tau} = \sum_i \frac{1}{\tau_i} \tag{25}$$

is associated, according to the uncertainty principle, with a finite width (energy spread) of the excited state of the compound nucleus:

$$\Gamma = \frac{\hbar}{\tau} \tag{26}$$

Correspondingly, we can define a partial width for the ith mode of decay:

$$\Gamma_i = \frac{\hbar}{\tau_i} \tag{27}$$

so that

$$\Gamma = \sum_i \Gamma_i \tag{28}$$

The characteristics of the compound nucleus decay are determined by the relative values of the partial widths for the various possible modes of decay. For the case of gamma-ray emission, the entire excitation energy is available to the gamma-radiation. Since, for slow neutrons, $\epsilon \gg E$ and $E' \approx \epsilon$, the probability of gamma-ray emission is essentially independent of the energy of the incident neutron. However, $\Gamma_\gamma \approx$ constant may be expected to depend to a certain extent on the angular momentum properties of the state involved, so that the constant will not be the same for all the states of the compound nucleus.

For particle emission, however, the situation is quite different. In this case, in addition to kinetic energy, the emerging particle must also be supplied with its binding energy. Since the excitation energy is shared among the many particles in the compound nucleus, the possibility of emission of a particle depends on the concentration of sufficient energy into this particle to allow it to escape. Let T_a be the average time between such rearrangements of the nuclear constituents as would permit the emission of particle a. The frequency of emission of the particle a ($1/\tau_a$) is then given by the product of the frequency of such favorable configurations ($1/T_a$) and the probability that the particle a, given the requisite amount of energy, can penetrate through the nuclear surface:

$$\frac{1}{\tau_a} = \frac{P_a}{T_a} \tag{29}$$

Hence

$$\Gamma_a = \frac{\hbar}{\tau_a} = \frac{\hbar P_a}{T_a} \tag{30}$$

According to the previous considerations, and assuming that the kinetic energy of the emerging particle is small compared to its energy in the nucleus, and that it has zero angular momentum,

$$P_a \cong \frac{4k_a}{K_0} G_a \tag{31}$$

where G_a is the Gamow barrier for particle a; $G_n = 1$ for neutrons. Thus

$$\Gamma_a \cong \frac{4\hbar G_a}{K_0 T_a} k_a = \gamma_a G_a E_a{}^{\frac{1}{2}} \tag{32}$$

The above relationship applies only to the emission of particles of zero angular momentum. It involves the kinetic energy of the emerging particle, E_a, through the factor $E_a{}^{\frac{1}{2}}$ and through the energy dependence of the Gamow factor, G_a, when the particle is charged. It involves the properties of the compound nucleus through the factor K_0, which is essentially independent of the nucleus involved, and the periodicity T_a. The last factor depends quite critically on the specific nucleus involved and on the excitation energy of the compound nucleus state; this dependence on the properties of the compound nucleus is through the nuclear level spacing, at the excitation energy involved, as indicated by the following simplified considerations, due to Weisskopf (W17): Assume that the energy levels of the compound nucleus are equally spaced,

$$E_n = E_0 + nD \tag{33}$$

Owing to the strong interaction, the nuclear wave function is given by a linear combination:

$$\Psi = \sum_{n=0}^{N} a_n \phi_n \exp \frac{-iE_n t}{\hbar} = \exp \frac{-iE_0 t}{\hbar} \sum_{n=0}^{N} a_n \phi_n \exp \frac{-inDt}{\hbar} \tag{34}$$

The periodicity T, which is defined as the time required for the nucleus to return to a previous configuration, is given by the condition

$$\left| \Psi(t + 2\pi\hbar/D) \right| = \left| \Psi(t + T) \right| = \left| \Psi(t) \right| \tag{35}$$

whence

$$T = \frac{2\pi\hbar}{D} \tag{36}$$

Although the level spacing in the compound nucleus is far from uniform, the above relationship nevertheless holds approximately for our case, where D_a is the average level spacing (of the levels which are capable of decaying through emission of the particle a in a state of given angular momentum) in the energy region of the excitation energy. Combining Eqs. (32) and (36),

$$\Gamma_a \approx \frac{2G_a D_a}{K_0 \pi} k_a = C D_a G_a E_a^{\frac{1}{2}} \tag{37}$$

for the emission of particles of zero angular momentum. The above is a much simplified derivation of a well-known relationship between level spacing and level width (B21, B46, F27), which is borne out by the observed neutron widths for slow neutrons (W31, B34).

The $E^{\frac{1}{2}}$ dependence of the particle width on its kinetic energy also follows from very general considerations involving the density of momentum states available to the outgoing particle, in the case of emission of zero angular momentum particles. For the emission of particles of higher angular momentum, l, there is an additional energy dependence, which can be expressed as follows:

$$\Gamma_{al} = (2l + 1) C D_{al} G_{al} E_a^{\frac{1}{2}} v_{al} \tag{38}$$

where $v_{al} = v_l(k_a R)$, R being the nuclear radius. Expressions for $v_l(x)$ are (F27, B34)

$$v_0 = 1$$

$$v_1 = \frac{x^2}{(1 + x^2)}$$

$$v_2 = \frac{x^4}{(9 + 3x^2 + x^4)}$$

$$v_3 = \frac{x^6}{(225 + 45x^2 + 6x^4 + x^6)}$$

(39)

These have the limiting values

$$v_l \rightarrow \frac{x^{2l}}{[1 \cdot 3 \cdot 5 \cdots (2l - 1)]^2} \qquad \text{for } x \rightarrow 0$$

$$v_l \rightarrow 1 \qquad \text{for } x \rightarrow \infty$$

(40)

Thus, for the emission of low-energy particles ($k_a R \ll 1$), we need concern ourselves only with $l = 0$. At sufficiently higher energies, states of $l > 0$ come into play.

Because of the selection rules associated with angular momentum changes, the absorption and emission of particles of different angular momenta usually involve different energy levels of the compound nucleus. For a given energy level of the compound nucleus, the emission of a given particle in different states of angular momentum can usually be treated on the same basis as the competition for the emission of different particles.

So far, the spacing of the levels in the compound nucleus, D, has entered our considerations only as a parameter in the level width formulas. Clearly, the level spacing is also of primary importance in the formation of the compound nucleus, since the probability of neutron absorption depends on the proximity of the nuclear excitation energy to one or more of the levels of the compound nucleus.

On the basis of the Bohr model, it is possible to obtain a rough, semiquantitative picture of the dependence of the level spacing of the nucleus on the excitation energy. For low excitation energies (of a few Mev or less) the possible modes of excitation of the compound nucleus are few, and the energy levels are widely spaced. The excitation of the low-lying levels will involve only one or a few nucleons, and the details of the low-lying levels will depend on the nucleus involved, being strongly influenced by such phenomena as magic numbers. As the energy of excitation is increased, it becomes possible to excite more modes, involving a greater number of nuclear constituents, and the levels become more closely spaced. For large excitation energies (say $\sim$10 Mev) an expression for the spacing of energy levels may be obtained from thermodynamic considerations, and is of the form

$$\omega(E') = C \exp 2(aE')^{\frac{1}{2}} \tag{41}$$

$\omega(E') = 1/D$ is the level density (number of levels per unit energy interval) at the excitation energy E'. Typical values of C and a, for a number of odd values of A, are given in Table 4; the level densities for even A nuclei appear to be somewhat lower.

TABLE 4

CONSTANTS DETERMINING THE LEVEL SPACINGS OF SOME ODD A NUCLEI, EQ. (41)

(Derived by Blatt and Weisskopf, B34, from available data)

A	C (Mev^{-1})	a (Mev^{-1})
27	0.5	0.45
55	0.33	1.3
115	0.02	6.5
201	0.005	12

Figure 4a is a schematic energy level diagram for two nuclei, $A \cong 55$ and $A \cong 201$. Aside from the details, which depend on the nucleus involved, the general characteristics of the level scheme for the heavier nucleus can be derived from that of the lighter by a contraction of the energy scale. This feature is qualitatively expected from the Bohr model since the heavier the nucleus, the more particles are available to participate in the excitation, and the greater the level density at a given excitation energy. Figure 4b shows the same level diagrams greatly magnified in the region of excitation corresponding to the absorption of a neutron.

As implied by Fig. 4b, the level spacing of interest, in considering reactions involving neutron capture, is that which corresponds to the excitation $E' = E + \epsilon$ of the compound nucleus. At first glance it might be expected that, for neutrons of moderate energy, this would be primarily determined by the binding energy, ϵ. However, evidence has recently been presented by Harris, Muehlhause, and Thomas (H40) and by Hurwitz and Bethe (H81) that this is not the case. Thus, Harris *et al.* have presented data which indicate that the level densities at E'

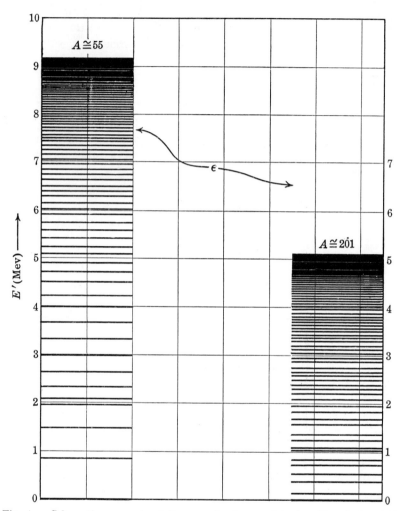

Fig. 4a. Schematic energy level diagrams for two nuclei, $A \approx 55$ and $A \approx 201$. The average level spacings are according to the statistical theory (Eq. 41), and the constants are from Table 4. The details of the structure, i.e., the relative positions of adjacent levels and the fluctuations in level spacing, are entirely fictitious, corresponding to no known nucleus. They are intended to illustrate the possibility of large deviations from the average.

≈ ϵ, for capture of neutrons by odd proton-even neutron and by even proton-odd neutron nuclei, are essentially the same (for nuclei of roughly the same A) although ϵ is considerably smaller for the former than for

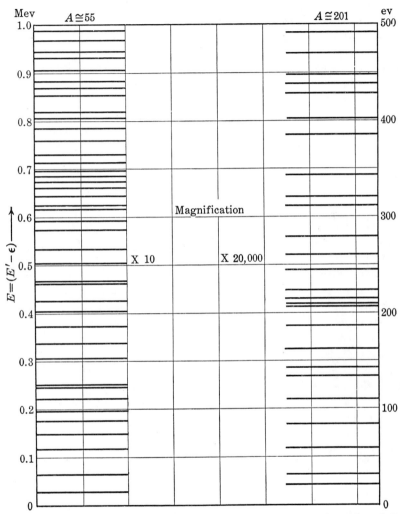

Fig. 4b. Energy level diagrams of Fig. 4a greatly magnified in the region of the neutron binding energy.

the latter (by ~1 Mev). They ascribe the difference in ϵ to a lowering of the ground-state energy of the compound nucleus of even Z-even N, as compared to that of odd Z-odd N; the level densities corresponding to ϵ are, however, the same for both types. Hurwitz and Bethe concur and present arguments for the hypothesis that the level density of the compound nucleus, at $E' \approx \epsilon$, is determined primarily by the binding energy of the *target* nucleus (rather than by that of the compound nucleus); target nuclei with high binding energy (e.g., even-even or magic number nuclei) result in compound nuclei with low level spacing. Data of Hughes and co-workers [1] on the radiative capture of fast neutrons, however, appear to be in disagreement with this point of view.

In any event, it should be pointed out that the effect of the apparent validity of the independent particle model at low excitation energies will be to invalidate the applicability of Eq. (41) to excitation energies of a few Mev. Available evidence, mainly from inelastic scattering and (p,n) reactions, indicates that level densities at low excitation energies are rather smaller than predicted by Eq. (41), and that the exponential behavior does not really set in until values of $E' \gtrsim$ 3–5 Mev are achieved. The constants of Table 4 should be regarded as applying, roughly, to energies $E = E' - \epsilon \sim$ 0–2 Mev.

The compound nucleus theory of nuclear reactions, outlined above, will be expected to break down at very high excitation, for at high enough energies the probability of escape of the incident neutron after a single traversal may be quite large, i.e., the nucleus is more or less transparent to high-energy neutrons. Thus, the incident neutron may not have sufficient opportunity to share its energy among the nuclear constituents before it (or one of the other nucleons) escapes. In this respect, it is to be expected that the absorption of a charged particle by a heavy nucleus will, even for high incident energies, be more likely to lead to a true compound nucleus, since the escape of the charged particle from the nucleus is impeded by the Gamow barrier.

3. Formation of the Compound Nucleus; Resonances and the Breit-Wigner Formula. In accordance with the two-stage picture of neutron reactions (formation of a compound nucleus; subsequent emission of a), the (n,a) cross section is

$$\sigma(n,a) = \sigma_c \frac{\Gamma_a}{\Gamma} \tag{42}$$

The first factor, σ_c, is the cross section for the absorption of the incident neutron into an excited compound nucleus; the second factor represents the relative probability for the de-excitation of the compound nucleus through the emission of a.

The cross section for the formation of the compound nucleus depends critically on the proximity of the excitation energy $(E + \epsilon)$ to one or

[1] Private communication.

more of the energy levels of the compound nucleus. In the case where only one level of the compound nucleus is involved (all other levels being far enough removed from the value of the excitation energy so that their influence on σ_c may be neglected), the energy dependence of σ_c is given by a characteristic resonance formula,

$$\sigma_c = \pi\lambda^2 f \frac{\Gamma_n\Gamma}{(E - E_r)^2 + \Gamma^2/4} \tag{43}$$

whence

$$\sigma(n,a) = \pi\lambda^2 f \frac{\Gamma_n\Gamma_a}{(E - E_r)^2 + \Gamma^2/4} \tag{44}$$

Equation (44) is the well-known Breit-Wigner one-level formula; the symbols have been previously defined, except for E_r, which is the neutron kinetic energy for which the excitation energy is equal to the difference between the ground state and the energy of the compound nucleus level involved in the reaction, and f, a statistical weighting factor which depends on the neutron spin, $s = \frac{1}{2}$; its orbital angular momentum, $l\hbar$; the total neutron angular momentum quantum number $j = l \pm \frac{1}{2}$; the spin of the target nucleus, I; and the spin of the compound nucleus level involved, $J = I + j, I + j - 1, \cdots, |I - j|$:

$$f_l = \frac{(2J + 1)}{(2I + 1)(2s + 1)} = \frac{(2J + 1)}{2(2I + 1)} \tag{45}$$

The factor f is simply a measure of the probability that the neutron angular momentum, $j\hbar$, and that of the target nucleus, $I\hbar$, either or both assumed oriented at random (unpolarized), will have a relative orientation appropriate to the necessary total angular momentum, $J\hbar$, required for the formation of the compound nucleus level involved in the resonance. For slow neutrons, $l = 0$, $j = \frac{1}{2}$, and $J = I \pm \frac{1}{2}$; whence for $I \pm 0$,

$$f_0 = \frac{1}{2}\left[1 \pm \frac{1}{(2I + 1)}\right] \cong \frac{1}{2} \quad \text{for large } I \tag{45a}$$

and

$$f_0 = 1 \quad \text{for } I = 0$$

For neutrons of $l > 0$ there are two possible "channel" spins, $j = l \pm \frac{1}{2}$, each of which combines with the target nucleus spin I to give the possible compound nucleus spin values J. Some of these can be formed through only one channel; for these, the statistical factor, $f_l(J)$, is unambiguously given by Eq. (45). Other J values can be formed through both channels; for such levels the question arises as to whether the proper value of the statistical factor is $f_l(J)$ or $2f_l(J)$.

Let us consider a specific example: Assuming a P-resonance ($l = 1$) for a target nucleus of $I = \frac{1}{2}$, the possible J values of a compound nucleus state are

$$J = 2,1 \qquad \text{for } j = \tfrac{3}{2}$$

$$J = 1,0 \qquad \text{for } j = \tfrac{1}{2}$$

The statistical weights are, from Eq. (45),

$$f_1(2) = \tfrac{5}{4}$$

$$f_1(1) = \tfrac{3}{4}$$

$$f_1(0) = \tfrac{1}{4}$$

For levels of $J = 2$ or $J = 0$, there is no ambiguity. The $J = 1$ state illustrates the possible ambiguity. On the one hand, a given $J = 1$ level may be such that it interacts only with one of the two possible channel spins (or one of two possible orthogonal linear combinations of $J = \frac{3}{2}$ and $j = \frac{1}{2}$); under these circumstances, the statistical factor $f_1(1) = \frac{3}{4}$. On the other hand, the interaction might be completely independent of j, depending only on the l value, which is the same for both channels. In this case, $f_1(1) = 2 \times \frac{3}{4} = \frac{3}{2}$.

In either event, the ambiguity disappears if many levels of the compound nucleus are involved in a given interaction, since the sum of the statistical factors, over all possible J and j values, is $\sum_{J,j} f_1(J) = 3$. This is a special instance of the general relationship

$$\sum_{J,j} f_l(J) = (2l + 1) \qquad (45b)$$

The situation with regard to the statistical factor is even more complicated if the same compound nucleus state can be formed by different neutron orbital angular momenta (I2). However, this added complication is seldom of practical importance, since the neutron widths will be very different for different values of l, which fact usually effectively eliminates the influence of all but the lowest possible l value. In addition, for a given compound nucleus state the parities of both the initial and the final states are well defined. Hence, the choice of possible l values is even further limited, adjacent values not being simultaneously available.

According to Eqs. (43) and (44), neutron capture and the accompanying reactions are characterized by sharp resonances for incident neutron energies $E = E_r$, with the maximum (peak) cross section

$$\sigma_{olc} = \frac{4\pi\lambda^2 f_l \Gamma_{nl}}{\Gamma} \tag{46}$$

$$\sigma_{ol}(n,a) = \frac{4\pi\lambda^2 f_l \Gamma_{nl} \Gamma_a}{\Gamma^2} \tag{47}$$

and (full) width at half maximum

$$\Delta E = \Gamma = \frac{\hbar}{\tau} \tag{48}$$

Equation (44) applies to the case of elastic scattering as well as to the case of emission of some other particle. However, in addition to the scattering which involves the formation of a compound nucleus (so-called capture scattering) there is a second type of elastic scattering process known as potential scattering. Potential scattering results from the small penetrability of the nucleus to slow neutrons (Eq. 24) and can usually be described in terms of the scattering of an impenetrable sphere, for which the scattering cross section would be

$$\sigma_p = \pi\lambda^2 \sum_l (2l+1)\left| e^{2i\xi_l} - 1 \right|^2 = 4\pi\lambda^2 \sum_l (2l+1) \sin^2 \xi_l \tag{49}$$

ξ_l is the phase shift of the scattered partial wave of orbital angular momentum $l\hbar$. For slow incident neutrons, $R \ll \lambda = 1/k$ and

$$\xi_0 = kR \qquad \xi_{l>0} \ll \xi_0 \tag{50}$$

whence

$$\sigma_p \cong \sigma_{p0} = 4\pi\lambda^2 \sin^2 kR \cong 4\pi R^2 \tag{49a}$$

The phase shifts corresponding to scattering by a rigid sphere can be obtained from the following general expression (F27, L23), with $kR = x$

$$\xi_l(x) = -\tan^{-1}\frac{J_{l+\frac{1}{2}}(x)}{N_{l+\frac{1}{2}}(x)} \tag{50a}$$

where J and N are, respectively, the Bessel and Neumann functions.

$$
\begin{aligned}
\xi_0 &= x \\
\xi_1 &= x - \frac{\pi}{2} + \cot^{-1} x \\
\xi_2 &= x - \pi + \cot^{-1}\frac{x^2 - 3}{3x} \\
\xi_3 &= x - \frac{3\pi}{2} + \cot^{-1}\frac{x(x^2 - 15)}{6x^2 - 15}
\end{aligned}
\tag{50b}
$$

For $x \ll 1$,

$$\xi_0 = x$$

$$\xi_1 \approx \frac{x^3}{3} - \frac{x^5}{5} + \frac{x^7}{7} \cdots$$

$$\xi_2 \approx \frac{1}{9} \left(\frac{x^5}{5} - \frac{x^7}{21} \cdots \right)$$

(50c)

$$\xi_3 \approx \frac{1}{225} \left(\frac{x^7}{7} - \frac{x^9}{3} \cdots \right)$$

A more useful approximation is, in the limit $x \ll |\, 2l - 1\,|$,

$$\xi_l \approx \tan^{-1} \frac{x^{2l+1}}{1 \cdot 3 \cdot 5 \cdots (2l + 1) \cdot 1 \cdot 1 \cdot 3 \cdot 5 \cdots (2l - 1)} \qquad (50d)$$

At the other extreme, for $x \gg l^2$,

$$\xi_l \approx x - \frac{l\pi}{2} \qquad (50e)$$

Values of the phase shifts *vs.* x have been tabulated by Lowan, Morse, Feshbach, and Lax (L23).

Equation (49) applies to the general case of scattering by an arbitrary potential (as well as to scattering by a rigid sphere):

$$\sigma_{sc} = 4\pi \lambdabar^2 \sum_l (2l + 1) \sin^2 \beta_l \qquad (49')$$

The phase shifts, β_l, are obtained from the asymptotic behavior of the radial functions, u_l, in terms of which the wave function of the system is written:

$$r\psi(r,\theta) = \sum_l u_l(r) P_l(\cos \theta) \qquad (49'')$$

The functions u_l satisfy the radial Schrödinger equations:

$$u_l'' + \left[\left(\frac{2M}{\hbar^2} \right) (E - V) - \frac{l(l + 1)}{r^2} \right] u_l = 0 \qquad (49''a)$$

For slow and intermediate neutrons, $\lambdabar \gg R$ and only $l = 0$ scattering need be considered; i.e., $\beta_{l>0} \ll \beta_0$, and $\sigma_{sc} \cong 4\pi\lambdabar^2 \sin^2 \beta_0$.

The value of β_0 depends, of course, on the form of the scattering potential V (in Eq. 49''a, with $l = 0$). A number of possibilities are illustrated in Fig. 5 in which u_0 is plotted in a number of hypothetical cases.

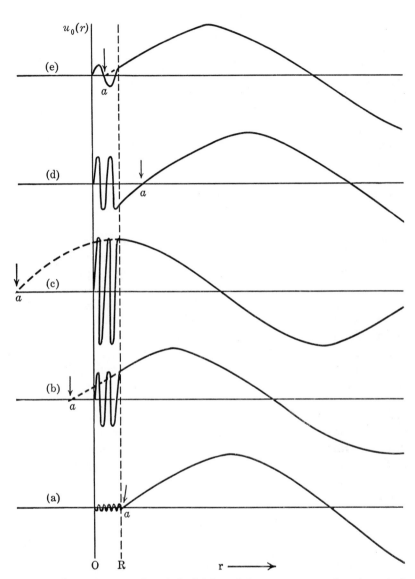

Fig. 5. Illustrative examples of the joining of the neutron wave functions at the nuclear boundary, leading to different phase shifts and scattering lengths. Case (a) applies far from a resonance, on the assumption of a "rigid sphere" nuclear model. Cases (b), (c), and (d) represent resonance scattering. Case (e) is intended to illustrate scattering by a finite potential well.

It is assumed that the potential V acts only in the range $0 - R$; for $r > R$, $u_0(r > R) = \sin(kr + \beta_0)$. The intercept a of $u_0(r > R)$ on the r axis, indicated with an arrow in each case, determines $\beta_0 = -a/\lambda$. a is called the scattering length or scattering amplitude; according to convention, positive a will be assumed to mean that the intercept is on the right—cases (a), (d), and (e)—i.e., a negative phase shift, β_0.

Figure 5a illustrates the case of scattering far from a resonance; it is seen that $a \cong R$, $\beta_0 \cong -R/\lambda \ll 1$, and $\sigma_{sc} \cong 4\pi R^2$. (Figure 5 greatly exaggerates the magnitude of R; for slow neutrons, R, the nuclear radius, is $\sim 10^{-12}$ cm and λ is $\sim 10^{-8}$ cm.) This case is essentially the same as scattering by a rigid sphere, for which $u_0(r < R) = 0$.

Cases (b), (c), and (d) represent various stages of scattering near and at resonance. It is seen that the resonance condition (case c) corresponds to $a \cong \pm\lambda/4$, $\beta_0 \cong \pm\pi/2$, and $\sigma_0 \cong 4\pi\lambda^2$.

Case (e) is supposed to represent the class of scatterings by a finite potential well, rather than by a rigid sphere (e.g., neutron-proton scattering). Under such circumstances, the scattering length depends in detail on the depth and range of the potential. In particular, if we consider scattering by a potential of fixed depth but continuously increasing range, the value of a will go through "resonances" (involving both large magnitude and change in sign) at certain values of R. Such "nuclear size resonances" have recently been invoked by a number of authors (F38, M40, S33) to explain large variations in the potential scattering of adjacent nuclei.

For neutron energies far from a resonance, potential scattering is the most important scattering process. In the region of a resonance, capture scattering predominates. However, for the scattering of a neutron of given l, the capture and potential scattering are coherent and interfere with each other. Thus, the Breit-Wigner formula must, in the case of elastic scattering, be modified to

$$\sigma(n,n) = \pi\lambda^2 f_l \left| \frac{i\Gamma_{nl}}{(E - E_r) + i\Gamma/2} + e^{2i\xi_l} - 1 \right|^2 + \sigma_p' \qquad (51)$$

where σ_p' is the incoherent part of the potential scattering,[1]

$$\sigma_p' = \sigma_p - \pi\lambda^2 f_l \left| e^{2i\xi_l} - 1 \right|^2 \qquad (49b)$$

For most observed neutron resonances, the neutron kinetic energy is sufficiently low so that we have only to concern ourselves with $l = 0$ interactions. Furthermore, except for the light nuclei ($A \lesssim 25$), the

[1] Note that the usual coefficient $(2l + 1)$ is contained in the statistical factor f_l.

only reactions of significance in the region of observed resonances are (n,n) and (n,γ). For such resonances (with $kR \ll 1$),

$$\Gamma = \Gamma_n + \Gamma_\gamma$$

$$\sigma(n,\gamma) = \pi\lambda^2 f_0 \frac{\Gamma_n \Gamma_\gamma}{(E - E_r)^2 + \Gamma^2/4} \tag{52}$$

$$\sigma(n,n) = \pi\lambda^2 f_0 \left| \frac{\Gamma_n}{(E - E_r) + i\Gamma/2} + 2kR \right|^2 + 4\pi R^2 (1 - f_0)$$

The radiative capture resonance is of the symmetrical Breit-Wigner form (Eqs. 43 and 44). Because of the interference between capture and potential scattering, the scattering resonance is not symmetrical about E_r. Instead, it goes through a minimum at an energy below E_r and falls off less rapidly on the high-energy side. The position of the scattering minimum is given by

$$E_r - E_{\min} \cong \frac{\Gamma_n \lambda}{2R} \cong \frac{D}{\pi K_0 R} \tag{53}$$

and the cross section at the minimum is

$$\sigma_{\min}(n,n) \cong 4\pi R^2 \left(1 - f_0 + \frac{f_0 R^2 \Gamma^2}{\lambda^2 \Gamma_n^2} \right) \tag{54}$$

(assuming $\Gamma_n \lambda / R \ll \Gamma$ and using Eqs. 37 and 52). Figures 6a and 6b show typical shapes of scattering resonances for the case of target nuclei of spin 0 and spin $\frac{9}{2}$ (indium). For the latter case, it must be kept in mind that the capture scattering involves a definite, single J value of the compound nucleus, while the potential scattering occurs for both possible J values of the system (in this case $J = \frac{9}{2} \pm \frac{1}{2} = 5$ or 4), resulting in a finite scattering at the minimum. In addition, Fig. 6b corresponds to a case where $\Gamma \approx \Gamma_\gamma \gg \Gamma_n$, and the presence of the radiative capture process also prevents the scattering minimum from going to zero.

Another situation of interest is when $\Gamma \approx \Gamma_{nl} \gg \Gamma_\gamma$, which is frequently encountered in nuclei of $A \gtrsim 50$ for intermediate-energy neutrons. In this case, application of Eq. (51) gives, for the position of the scattering minimum,

$$E_r - E_{\min} = \frac{\Gamma}{2} \operatorname{ctn} \xi_l \tag{53a}$$

and, for the minimum cross section,

$$\sigma_{\min}(n,n) = \sigma_p' \tag{54a}$$

In addition, the maximum of the resonance is shifted toward higher energies:

$$E_{max} - E_r = \frac{\Gamma}{2} \tan \xi_l \qquad (55)$$

and the peak cross section is

$$\sigma_0(n,n) = 4\pi\lambdabar^2 f_l + \sigma_p' \qquad (55a)$$

For a scattering resonance involving a target nucleus of $I = 0$ and S scattering only $(\xi_{l>0} \ll \xi_0)$ the scattering cross section will be zero at

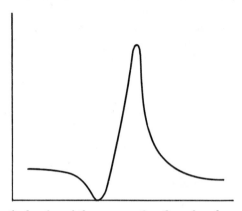

Fig. 6a.   Schematic drawing of the cross section through a slow-neutron scattering resonance for $l = 0$ neutrons, for a target nucleus of spin 0. A spin $I \neq 0$ of the target nucleus would change this curve by multiplying it by $f_0(J)$ and adding to it a constant cross section $[1 - f_0(J)]4\pi R^2$.

the minimum (Fig. 6a). For $I > 0$ or $l > 0$ or both, the minimum will not fall to zero, since the potential scattering for angular momenta not associated with the resonance does not interfere with the capture scattering.

Returning, now, to slow-neutron reactions in heavy nuclei (Eqs. 52), we note that the properties of a given resonance are completely determined in terms of four parameters, E_r, Γ_n, Γ_γ, and f_0. These can, in turn, be ascertained from four measured quantities: (1) the resonance energy, E_r; (2) the resonance width, $\Gamma = \Gamma_n + \Gamma_\gamma$; and (3), (4) the peak capture (or total) and scattering cross sections, $\sigma_0(n,\gamma)$ and $\sigma_0(n,n)$. (We assume that R is given by $r_0 A^{1/3} \times 10^{-13}$ cm.) Of these, $\sigma_0(n,n)$ is usually most difficult to measure, since (for $\Gamma_\gamma \gg \Gamma_n$) it is only a small fraction of the total. Thus, in a study of the 0.176-ev $Cd^{113}(I = \frac{1}{2})$ resonance, Beeman (B12) has been able to extract all the parameters, and to show that the level of the compound nucleus has the spin $J = 1$.

In the absence of a measurement of $\sigma_0(n,n)$, it is only possible to determine the product $f_0\Gamma_n$.

For pure scattering resonances ($\Gamma \approx \Gamma_n \gg \Gamma_\gamma$) the statistical factor f is immediately determined from the difference between the peak cross section and the minimum cross section, since $\sigma_0 - \sigma_{\min} = 4\pi\lambda^2 f$.

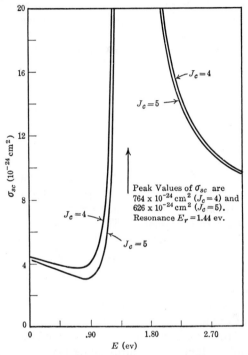

Fig. 6b. The scattering cross section of indium ($I = \frac{9}{2}$) for the 1.44 = ev resonance. The curves are computed from the known constants of the (capture) resonance and for the two possible values of $J = 5$ or 4. From Feshbach, Peaslee, and Weisskopf (F27).

So far, we have discussed the case of a single resonance, neglecting the effects of all the other resonances. This approximation is valid in the vicinity of a single resonance when the level spacing D is large as compared to the level width Γ. If this is not the case, the levels can interfere with each other, provided they belong to the same class (same l, J, and parity).[1] Interference between levels has been discussed by a number of authors (B25, B24, P10, B61, S37, W29).

Assuming, still, that there is only one resonance affecting the energy region in which we are interested, the cross sections far from the reso-

[1] This statement applies only to the total cross section. Interference effects can always occur in the angular distribution of the reaction products provided, *only*, that the levels overlap.

nance, $|E - E_r| \gg \Gamma$, are

$$\sigma(n,a) = \frac{\pi\lambda^2 f \Gamma_n \Gamma_a}{(E - E_r)^2} \qquad (56)$$

$$\sigma(n,n) \cong 4\pi R^2 \qquad (57)$$

These are of especial interest in the thermal neutron energy region when the first resonance falls appreciably above or below thermal energies ($|E_r| \gg E_{th}$). In this case

$$\sigma_{th}(n,a) = \frac{\pi\lambda^2 f \Gamma_n \Gamma_a}{E_r^2} \qquad (58)$$

Recalling that $\lambda \sim E^{-\frac{1}{2}}$ and, from Eq. (37), that $\Gamma_n \sim E^{\frac{1}{2}}$, we have, provided that Γ_a is constant over the range of thermal energies,

$$\sigma_{th}(n,a) = \sigma^* \left(\frac{E^*}{E}\right)^{\frac{1}{2}} = \sigma^* \left(\frac{v^*}{v}\right) \qquad (59)$$

where σ^* is the cross section at a specific (arbitrary) energy E^* (velocity v^*). This is the well-known $1/v$ law for slow-neutron reaction cross sections far from a resonance. Deviations from the $1/v$ law will result from too close proximity to a resonance; Eq. (56) shows that the effect of a close positive energy resonance ($E_r > 0$) is that the cross section falls less rapidly than $1/v$, while a too-close negative resonance results in a thermal neutron réaction cross section which falls faster than $1/v$.

The thermal neutron scattering cross section will, on the other hand, be constant if the first resonance is sufficiently far removed. However, in the case of scattering, the effects of interference between the potential scattering and the resonance will extend to considerable distances (Figs. 6a and 6b), so that even a far-away resonance can have an appreciable effect on the thermal neutron scattering.

At the other extreme, we are frequently concerned with observations of cross sections which represent an average over many energy levels; this will be the case when the energy spread of the neutrons, used in the measurement, is large compared to the level spacing of the compound nucleus at the excitation energy involved. Assuming that λ, Γ_n, Γ_a are essentially constant over the energy spread of the neutron source, the average over Eq. (44) and sum over $J = I \pm \frac{1}{2}$ yield

$$\overline{\sigma(n,a)} = \frac{2\pi^2 \lambda^2 \Gamma_n \Gamma_a}{D\Gamma} \qquad (60)$$

If states of $l > 0$ are possible, the above average must be summed over all possible l values, each with its appropriate f_l and appropriate neutron width Γ_{nl} and level spacing D_l.

If we consider heavy nuclei and $l = 0$ interactions only, there are two regions of interest: (1) $\Gamma \approx \Gamma_\gamma \gg \Gamma_n$; here, as for thermal neutron capture, $\sigma(n,\gamma) \propto 1/v$; (2) $\Gamma \approx \Gamma_n \gg \Gamma_\gamma$; in this range, $\sigma(n,\gamma) \propto 1/E$. The total cross section, however, has a more complicated energy dependence, since it is now necessary to take into account the potential scattering as well as the capture scattering and radiative capture (F28).

The more general approach developed by Weisskopf and co-workers (F27, F28, W17, B34) gives, for the cross section for the formation of the compound nucleus,

$$\sigma_c \approx \pi(\lambdabar + R)^2 P \tag{61}$$

The factor $\pi(\lambdabar + R)^2$ is a measure of the area of interaction of the neutron and the target nucleus; P is the probability that the neutron will penetrate the nuclear surface. In the resonance region, P is a sharply varying function of the neutron energy, being the resonance factor. In terms of the simple picture which we have used, the incident neutron wave, of wavelength $\lambdabar = 1/k$, must join smoothly on to the neutron wave, $\Lambda = 1/K$, at the surface of the nucleus. Since (for slow and intermediate neutrons) $K \gg k$, the amplitude of the neutron wave inside the nucleus will, in general, be very small, except for certain exceptional values of the neutron energy at which the amplitude of the incoming wave at the nuclear surface has the maximum value. These special cases (energies) correspond to the resonances, for which the joining of the wave functions was schematically represented in Fig. 5.

We have previously (Eq. 21) given an expression for P which can be interpreted as the average (over many resonances) probability for the neutron to penetrate the target nucleus. Hence, the average reaction cross section is

$$\overline{\sigma_c} \cong \frac{4\pi(\lambdabar + R)^2 kK}{(k + K)^2} \tag{62}$$

For slow and intermediate neutron energies, $\lambdabar = 1/k \gg R$, $K \cong K_0 \gg k$, whence

$$\overline{\sigma_c} \cong \frac{4\pi\lambdabar^2 k}{K_0} = \frac{4\pi}{kK_0} \approx \frac{500}{E^{1/2}} \text{ barns} \tag{62a}$$

(for E in electron volts). Thus, the average cross section for the formation of the compound nucleus also follows a $1/v$ law in these energy ranges. Introducing the connection between neutron energy and neutron width from Eq. (37),

$$k = \frac{\pi\Gamma_n K_0}{2D} \tag{37a}$$

the average cross section for the formation of the compound nucleus becomes

$$\bar{\sigma}_c \cong \frac{2\pi^2 \lambdabar^2 \Gamma_n}{D} \tag{63}$$

Since the cross section $\overline{\sigma(n,a)} = \bar{\sigma}_c \Gamma_a / \Gamma$, Eqs. (63) and (60) are seen to be equivalent, thereby confirming the interpretation of P (Eq. 21) as the average over many resonances of the penetrability.

4. Summary; Energy Dependence of Neutron Cross Sections. In the preceding discussion we have outlined the basic considerations which determine the interactions of neutrons with nuclei. We have observed that the reactions of neutrons of a given energy with a given nucleus depend on the level structure of the compound nucleus, at the excitation energy resulting from the neutron capture. Although we are, at the present state of our knowledge, incapable of predicting the details of the nuclear level structure, a great deal can, nevertheless, be said concerning the average behavior of nuclei.

In referring to neutron energies, we shall continue to use the classification of Section 1B7:

    I. Slow neutrons: $E < 1000$ ev
    II. Intermediate neutrons: 1 kev $< E < 0.5$ Mev
    III. Fast neutrons: 0.5 Mev $< E < 10$ Mev
    IV. Very fast neutrons: 10 Mev $< E < 50$ Mev
    V. Ultrafast neutrons: 50 Mev $< E$

In addition to the dependence of nuclear level properties on the kinetic energy of the incident neutron, the nuclear level spacing is very different for nuclei of widely different atomic weight, A. It is therefore convenient to classify nuclei according to the following system:

    I. Light nuclei: $A < 25$
    II. Medium nuclei: $25 < A < 80$
    III. Heavy nuclei: $80 < A$

These dividing lines are, of course, not to be considered sharp boundaries.

While we shall return, in a subsequent section, to the experimental evidence on the question of the compound nucleus level spacing as a function of the nuclear atomic weight, it is useful to bear in mind the following summary of the average level spacing of the compound nucleus:

(1) Light Nuclei. For slow and intermediate neutrons, the levels are very widely spaced, being ~ 1–0.1 Mev apart, on the average. Thus,

very few levels are encountered, and these are relatively broad and easily resolved. In the fast and very fast neutron energy region, the levels are closer, but still separate and resolvable.

(2) Medium Nuclei. For slow and intermediate neutrons, the levels are ~100–1 kev apart. Hence, few levels are encountered in the slow-neutron range, but many in the intermediate region. For fast neutrons the level spacing rapidly decreases, and the levels begin to overlap. For very fast neutrons the compound nucleus has a continuum of levels.

(3) Heavy Nuclei. In the slow and intermediate neutron ranges, the level spacing is ~1000–5 ev. Many levels are observed for slow neutrons; the levels are no longer resolved in the intermediate range; for fast and very fast neutrons the compound nucleus has a continuum of levels.

For ultrafast neutrons and for all nuclei, the compound nucleus picture requires considerable modification.

(a) *The Total Cross Section*, σ_t. Most neutron cross section measurements involve the determination of the fraction of a given neutron beam transmitted through a known thickness of material; such measurements usually determine the total cross section, the sum of the cross sections for all processes (absorption, scattering) which remove neutrons from the beam,

$$\sigma_t = \sum_a \sigma(n,a) \tag{64}$$

For a neutron flux of ϕ_0 (neutrons·cm^{-2}·sec^{-1}) incident on a slab of material of density N(nuclei/cm^3) and thickness t(cm), the emerging, undeviated flux ϕ is

$$\phi = \phi_0 \exp(-Nt\sigma_t) \tag{65}$$

Figure 7 shows typical slow-neutron total cross sections for the three categories of elements. The cross section of carbon exhibits thermal neutron interference effects due to the crystal structure of the graphite used in the measurement. Above ~1 ev, the cross section becomes and remains constant. The cross section of cobalt shows a scattering resonance at 120 ev. The cross section in the thermal neutron region has a $1/v$ component due to radiative capture. The indium and iridium cross sections show many resonances and large $1/v$ capture cross sections for thermal neutrons. Owing to the close spacing of the levels, the neutron width is small (Eq. 37) compared to the radiation width, so that radiative capture predominates in the observed resonances.

For intermediate and fast neutrons individual levels have been well resolved only in light and medium nuclei; for these relatively large level spacings, the neutron widths are much larger than the gamma-ray

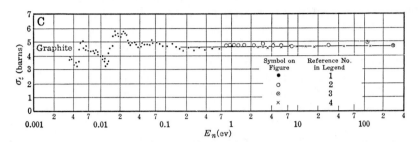

(1) Columbia Velocity Selector (unpublished).   (2) W. W. Havens, Jr., and L. J. Rainwater, Phys. Rev., **75**, 1296 (1949).   (3) C. T. Hibdon and C. O. Muehlhause, Phys. Rev., **76**, 100 (1949).   (4) W. B. Jones, Jr., Phys. Rev., **74**, 364 (1948).

(a)

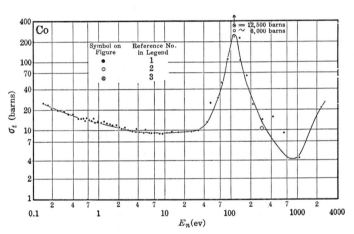

(1) Wu, Rainwater, and Havens, Phys. Rev., **71**, 174 (1947).   (2) C. T. Hibdon and C. O. Muehlhause, Phys. Rev., **76**, 100 (1949).   (3) F. G. P. Seidl, Phys. Rev., **75**, 1508 (1949).

(b)

Fig. 7. Typical total cross section *vs.* energy curves for slow neutrons, from Adair (A2). (a) Carbon, a light element. In this case, $\sigma_t = \sigma_{sc}$. The variations, below ~0.04 ev, are interference effects due to the polycrystalline structure of the sample (see Section 5). (b) Cobalt, a medium element. Again, $\sigma_t \approx \sigma_{sc}$, except in the thermal neutron range. Effects of scattering resonances at 120 ev and >2000 ev are evident.

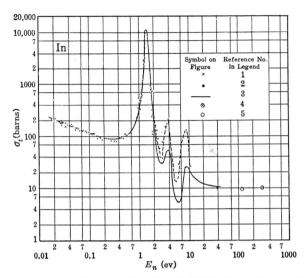

(1) Borst, Ulrich, Osborne, and Hasbrouck, Phys. Rev., **70**, 557 (1946).   (2) Havens, Wu, Rainwater, and Meaker, Phys. Rev., **71**, 165 (1947).   (3) B. D. McDaniel, Phys. Rev., **70**, 832 (1946).   (4) E. Fermi and L. Marshall (unpublished).   (5) C. T. Hibdon and C. O. Muehlhause, Phys. Rev., **76**, 100 (1949).

(c)

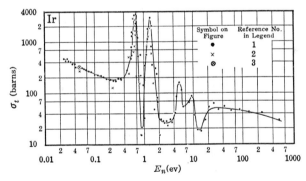

(1) Rainwater, Havens, Wu, and Dunning, Phys. Rev., **71**, 65 (1947).   (2) Sawyer, Wollan, Bernstein, and Peterson, Phys. Rev., **72**, 109 (1947).   (3) Powers, Goldsmith, Beyer, and Dunning, Phys. Rev., **53**, 947 (1938).

(d)

Fig. 7 (Continued).   (c) Indium, a heavy element. The famous resonance, at 1.44 ev, is well resolved. There are probably many unresolved resonances above 10 ev. (d) Iridium, a heavy element. The first two capture resonances are fairly well resolved. There are probably many unresolved resonances above 20 ev.

widths, and the observed resonances are due to scattering. We postpone the discussion of scattering resonances and consider, instead, the
average behavior of the total cross section for intermediate and fast
neutrons. The average total cross section, according to the theory of
Feshbach and Weisskopf (Eqs. 49, 61, 62), depends on the properties of
the nucleus involved only through the nuclear radius, R.[1]

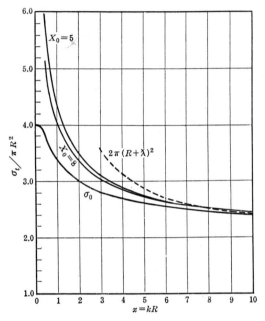

Fig. 8.   Total cross sections (averaged over resonances) as a function of $x = kR$,
for $X_0 = K_0R = 5$ and 8. σ_0 is the total cross section for an impenetrable sphere
of radius R.   The broken curve gives the approximate behaviors for large x.   From
Feshbach and Weisskopf (F28).

Figure 8 is a plot of the expected average total cross section *vs.* neutron
energy.   The cross section is given in units of πR^2, and the energy in
units of

$$x = kR = 0.222RE^{1/2} \tag{66}$$

where R is in units of 10^{-13} cm and E in Mev.   The curves are plotted
for two values of $X_0 = K_0R$: $X_0 = 5$ ($A \approx 40$) and $X_0 = 8$ ($A \approx 160$).
The curve labeled σ_0 is the total cross section of an infinitely repulsive

[1] The parameter $K_0 \approx 1 \times 10^{-13}$ cm, the wave number of a neutron in the nucleus,
is assumed to be the same for all nuclei; this is not strictly true, but the variations
in K_0 are expected to be small.

sphere of radius R. For large values of x, the curves are approximately fitted by the broken curve,

$$\sigma_t \approx 2\pi(R + \lambdabar)^2 \tag{67}$$

It is important to note that, while the value of the total cross section approaches $2\pi R^2$ for $\lambdabar \ll R$, the deviations from this asymptotic value are quite appreciable, even for very fast neutrons; thus, for $E = 50$ Mev, $\lambdabar = 0.64 \times 10^{-13}$ cm, which cannot be neglected.

In Fig. 9 the experimental values of the total cross section are compared with the theory for a number of elements: (a) iron, $A \approx 56$; (b) silver, $A \approx 108$; (c) antimony, $A \approx 122$; and (d) lead, $A \approx 207$. The measurements employed relatively poor resolution, and as a result the averaging process was, to a large extent, performed experimentally. The agreement with theory is seen to be excellent, except in the case of antimony, where the observed cross section falls considerably below the theoretical value at low energies.[1]

(b) *Cross Section for Formation of a Compound Nucleus*, σ_c. The cross section for the formation of a compound nucleus includes all reactions, except elastic scattering in which the quantum state of the nucleus is unchanged. It is usually defined as

$$\sigma_c = \sigma_t - \sigma_{el} \tag{68}$$

While this definition does not accurately take into account the effects of interference between capture and potential scattering, such effects are essentially eliminated when the cross section is averaged over many resonances.

For light and medium nuclei, σ_c for slow and intermediate neutrons is mainly due to capture scattering (except for thermal and slower neutrons). For heavy nuclei, in these energy regions, σ_c is almost entirely due to radiative capture. For fast and very fast neutrons, elastic scattering contributes little to the value of σ_c, the other possible reactions —inelastic scattering, (n,p), (n,α), $(n,2n)$, etc.—predominating.

The energy dependence of σ_c (averaged over resonances) is described by Eqs. (61), (62), (62a) and plotted in Fig. 10. (The method of plot-

---

[1] This "anomalous" type of behavior has been found, by the Wisconsin group (M31), to occur with unanticipated frequency. Furthermore, extension of the total cross section measurements to 3.2 Mev has brought to light, for the heavier elements, the frequent existence of a broad maximum in σ_t which appears to move to higher energies with increasing mass number. These phenomena are strongly suggestive of the scattering by a finite potential, and could possibly be interpreted as supporting an "independent particle" model for fast neutron scattering. It is, at present, difficult to see how these results can be reconciled with the apparent widespread applicability of statistical models.

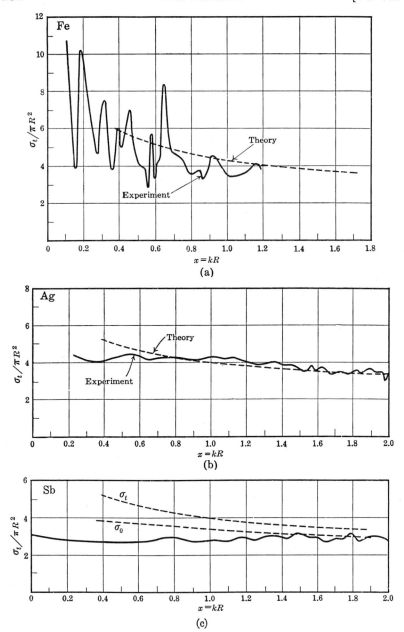

Fig. 9.   Comparison of the theory of Feshbach and Weisskopf (F28) with measured total cross sections for a number of elements.   The measurements are due to Barschall and co-workers (references in F28).   (a) Iron, $A \approx 56$.   (b) Silver, $A \approx 108$. (c) Antimony, $A \approx 122$.   In the case of antimony the observed cross section is in better agreement with the prediction of scattering from a rigid sphere.

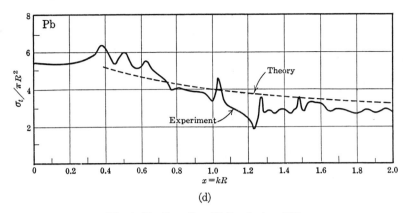

Fig. 9 (Continued).   (d) Lead, $A \approx 207$.

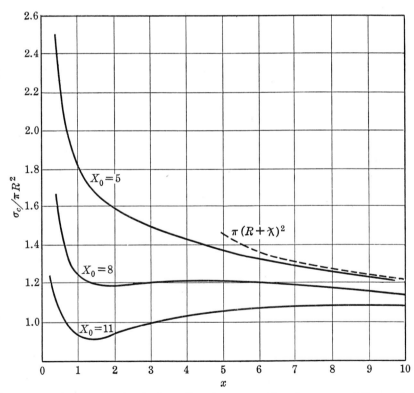

Fig. 10.   Cross section for the formation of a compound nucleus *vs.* $x = kR$, according to Feshbach and Weisskopf (F28).   The solid curves are for $X_0 = K_0 R = 5$, 8, and 11.   The broken curve, appropriate to large x, is $\sigma_c \approx \frac{1}{2}\sigma_t \approx \pi(R + \lambda)^2$.

ting is the same as that employed in Figs. 8 and 9.) As seen from Eq. (62), $\sigma_c \rightarrow \pi(R + \lambda)^2$ for $x \gg X_0$; the deviation of σ_c from $\pi(R + \lambda)^2$ depends on the value of x/X_0, being ≈ 11 percent for $x = X_0$ and ≈ 4 percent for $x = 2X_0$. For large values of x, $\sigma_c \approx \frac{1}{2}\sigma_t$ and, since capture elastic scattering is negligible for large x, $\sigma_c \approx \sigma_{el}$; i.e., for large x, the total cross section divides into approximately equal parts elastic scattering and capture.

C. Types of Neutron Reactions

In the previous section, we have discussed the general properties of neutron reactions and the formation of the compound nucleus. Although it has been observed that the nature of the compound nucleus de-excitation is governed by the competition between the various possible modes of decay, the properties of this competition have been treated in the most general way. This section is devoted to the anatomy of neutron reactions—to the details of the competition between the various possible neutron reactions, as they are influenced by the properties of the nuclei involved and by the energy of the impinging neutrons.

The relative probability of a given neutron reaction (n,a)—neutron in, particle a out—is defined in terms of the cross section $\sigma(n,a)$. For a (pure) material containing NV nuclei in a neutron flux ϕ, the number of (n,a) reactions per second is $NV\phi\sigma(n,a)$.

1. Scattering (n,n). Neutron scattering is one of the two reactions which are energetically possible for all nuclei at all neutron energies. (The other is radiative capture.) The observed elastic scattering is, in general, the result of a superposition of the potential scattering and the capture scattering (Eq. 51). However, this superposition is such that it is coherent (addition of amplitudes, interference effects) for the capture scattering and that part of the potential scattering which involves the same neutron orbital angular momentum, $l\hbar$, and the same total angular momentum state, J. The remainder of the potential scattering is observed as an incoherent background (addition of cross sections) to the scattering, as described by Eq. (51).

(a) Slow Neutrons. In the slow-neutron energy range, the neutron wavelength is very much larger than any nuclear radius. Hence, neutrons can react (with appreciable probability) only in the $l = 0$ state. Thus, the potential scattering cross section is $4\pi R^2$ (Eq. 49a), and the scattering cross section reduces to Eq. (52).

In the absence of nuclear resonances, the slow-neutron (potential) scattering cross section would be expected to increase with atomic number as $A^{2/3}$. Table 5 is a compilation of observed slow-neutron scattering cross sections together with the corresponding values of $4\pi R^2$, computed on the assumption $R = 1.47A^{\frac{1}{3}} \times 10^{-13}$ cm. The scattering cross sections, in many cases, deviate considerably from $4\pi R^2$, being both larger and smaller. These deviations are too large to be ascribed to fluctuations in R. An additional, noteworthy fact is that the deviations occur, with comparable frequency, at all values of the atomic number.

These fluctuations in σ_{sc} can be ascribed to the effect of a nearby resonance, being the result of the interference between the potential and the resonance scattering. A value of $\sigma_{sc} > 4\pi R^2$ indicates that the closest resonance is at an energy lower than that at which the cross section was measured (frequently $E_r < 0$), while $\sigma_{sc} < 4\pi R^2$ indicates a resonance at a higher energy.

The probability that a scattering measurement, made at a given (arbitrary) neutron energy, will fall on a resonance is inversely proportional to the level spacing. That is, the average distance of a given energy from a resonance is proportional to the level spacing; thus, the larger the level spacing, the farther, on the average, from the closest level. However, the region over which interference effects are important is also proportional to the level spacing (Eq. 53). Hence, the probability that a scattering measurement will give a cross section different from $4\pi R^2$ is essentially independent of the level spacing and, therefore, of the atomic number of the scatterer.

TABLE 5

SLOW NEUTRON SCATTERING CROSS SECTIONS FOR FREE NUCLEI

Element	A †	σ_{sc} ‡ (barns)	$4\pi R^2$ § (barns)	$E \parallel$ (ev)	References ¶
$_1\mathrm{H}^1$		20.36		0	W10, M24
$_1\mathrm{H}^2$		3.3		th	S33
$_2\mathrm{He}^4$		1.4	(0.2)	th	H41
$_3\mathrm{Li}^7$		~1.5	0.99	th	S33
$_4\mathrm{Be}^9$		6.1	1.17	th	S33
			(0.8)		
$_5\mathrm{B}$	11, 10	3.9	1.33	C	W10
			(1.5)		
$_6\mathrm{C}^{12}$		4.70	1.42	th	W10
			(1.8)		
$_7\mathrm{N}^{14}$		9.96	1.58	10–200	W10, M25
$_8\mathrm{O}^{16}$		3.73	1.70	15–1000	W10, M25
			(2.3)		
$_9\mathrm{F}^{19}$		3.3	1.93	0.25–40	W10, R5

TABLE 5 (*Continued*)

SLOW NEUTRON SCATTERING CROSS SECTIONS FOR FREE NUCLEI

Element	A †	σ_{sc} ‡ (barns)	$4\pi R^2$ § (barns)	E ‖ (ev)	References ¶
$_{10}$Ne	20	2.4	2.01	*th*	H41
$_{11}$Na^{23}		3.3	2.20	1–800	H58
$_{12}$Mg	24, 26, 25	3.9	2.28	*th*	S33
			(2.5)		
$_{13}$Al^{27}		1.35	2.44	*th*	W10
			(2.7)		
$_{14}$Si	28	2.2	2.51	1–100	W10, R5
$_{15}$P^{31}		∼3.3	2.68	1–10	G20
$_{16}$S	32	∼1.2	2.74	10–400	A2
			(2.1)		
$_{17}$Cl	35, 37	14.2	2.93	*th*	H59
			(2.8)		
$_{18}$A	40	0.8	3.17	*th*	H41
$_{19}$K	39	∼2	3.13	*th*	S33
$_{20}$Ca	40	3.3	3.18	*th*	S33
$_{21}$Sc^{45}		12.8	3.44	*th*	H40
$_{22}$Ti	48	6	3.58	*th*	S33, F27, G12
$_{23}$V^{51}		5.02	3.73	*th*	H26
$_{24}$Cr	52	3.7	3.78	*th*	S33
$_{24}$Cr^{53}		8.4	3.83	*th*	H40
$_{25}$Mn^{55}		2.1	3.93	*th*	S33
$_{26}$Fe^{54}		2.4	3.88	*th*	S33
$_{26}$Fe^{56}		12.5	3.97	*th*	S33
$_{26}$Fe^{57}		2	4.02	*th*	S33
$_{26}$Fe	56	11.3	3.97	*th*	S33
		11.1	(3.9)	1.44	F27, H36
$_{27}$Co^{59}		5	4.12	*C*	F27, B57
$_{28}$Ni^{58}		27	4.07	*th*	S33
$_{28}$Ni^{60}		1.0	4.16	*th*	S33
$_{28}$Ni^{62}		9	4.25	*th*	S33
$_{28}$Ni	58, 60	16.7	4.10	*th*	S33
$_{29}$Cu	63, 65	7.6	4.33	*th*	S33
		8.3	(3.8)	1.44	F27, H36
$_{30}$Zn	64, 66, 68	4.1	4.41	*th*, 1.44	S33, F27, H36
			(4.4)		
$_{30}$Zn^{67}		7	4.48	*th*	H40
$_{31}$Ga	69, 71	3	4.60	*th*	W10
$_{32}$Ge	74, 72, 70	8.3	4.71	*th*	S33
$_{33}$As^{75}		∼7	4.83	*th*	S33

TABLE 5 (*Continued*)

SLOW NEUTRON SCATTERING CROSS SECTIONS FOR FREE NUCLEI

Element	A †	σ_{sc} ‡ (barns)	$4\pi R^2$ § (barns)	E ‖ (ev)	References ¶
$_{34}$Se	80, 78	10	5.00 (5.0)	C	F27, G12
$_{35}$Br	79, 81	5.9	5.04	*th*	S33
$_{36}$Kr	84, 86, 82, 83	7.2	5.20	*th*	H41
$_{37}$Rb	85, 87	5.4	5.27	*th*	S33
$_{38}$Sr	88	9.3	5.36	*th*	S33
$_{39}$Y^{89}		3.9	5.41	*th*	H40
$_{40}$Zr	90, 94, 92, 91	~7	5.50	*th*	S33
$_{41}$Nb^{93}		6.1	5.58	*th*	S33
$_{42}$Mo	98, 96, 95, 92	7.3	5.69	*th*	S33
$_{44}$Ru	102, 104, 101, 99, 100	6	5.92	C	F27, G12
$_{45}$Rh^{103}		3.5	5.96	*th*	H40
$_{46}$Pd	106, 108, 105, 110	4.7 4.4	6.11	*th* C	S33 F27, G12
$_{47}$Ag^{107}		10	6.12	*th*	S33
$_{47}$Ag^{109}		6	6.20	*th*	S33
$_{47}$Ag	107, 109	7	6.15 (5.8)	*th*	S33
$_{48}$Cd	114, 112, 111, 110, 113	5.3	6.32 (6.5)	5–100	G20
$_{49}$In	115	2.2	6.42	*th*	W10
$_{50}$Sn	120, 118, 116	4.8	6.56 (6.9)	*th*	S33
$_{51}$Sb	121, 123	4.1	6.67 (6.7)	*th*, 0.1–2	S33, G20
$_{52}$Te	130, 128, 126	5	6.88	C	G12
$_{53}$I^{127}		3.7	6.86	*th*	S33
$_{54}$Xe	132, 129, 131, 134	4.3	7.02	*th*	H41
$_{55}$Ce^{133}		~7	7.08	*th*	S33
$_{56}$Ba	138, 137	8	7.23	C	G12
$_{59}$Pr^{141}		7.9	7.35	*th*	H40
$_{62}$Sm	152, 154, 147, 149, 148	23	7.68	*th*	H40
$_{63}$Eu	153, 151	29.7	7.73	*th*	H40
$_{64}$Gd	158, 160, 156, 157, 155	26	7.90	*th*	H40

TABLE 5 (*Continued*)

SLOW NEUTRON SCATTERING CROSS SECTIONS FOR FREE NUCLEI

Element	A †	σ_{sc} ‡ (barns)	$4\pi R^2$ § (barns)	E ‖ (ev)	References ¶
$_{72}$Hf	180, 178, 177, 179	25.7	8.61	*th*	H40
$_{73}$Ta^{181}		6.9	8.69	*th*	S33
$_{74}$W	184, 186, 182, 183	5.6	8.78	*th*	S33
$_{74}$W^{186}		23	8.84	*th*	H40
$_{76}$Os	192, 190, 189, 188	~10	8.98	C	G20, G12
$_{78}$Pt	195, 194, 196	11.1	9.14	*th*	S33
$_{79}$Au^{197}		~9	9.19 (7 1)	*th*	S33
$_{80}$Hg	202, 200, 199, 201, 198	15	9.30	0.1–10	G20
		21.5	(9.7)	*th*	H60
$_{81}$Tl	205, 203	9.6	9.42	0.1–1	F27, G20
$_{82}$Pb	208, 206, 207	11.5	9.51	*th*	S33
		12.4	(7.6)	1–10	F27, G20
$_{83}$Bi^{209}		9.2	9.56	5–10	F27, G20
		10	(7.8)	*th*	S33
$_{92}$U	238	8.2	10.5	*th*	U2

† When more than one isotope is involved, this column lists the most important isotopes, of relative abundance greater than 10 percent, in the order of abundance.

‡ The cross sections are for free nuclei. Most observations have been made on bound nuclei; these have been corrected according to the relationship

$$\sigma_{\text{free}} = \left(\frac{A}{A+1}\right)^2 \sigma_{\text{bound}}$$

§ Measured nuclear radii, taken from the collection of Blatt and Weisskopf (B34), are given in parentheses. Otherwise they are computed on the basis of

$$R = 1.47A^{\frac{1}{3}} \times 10^{-13} \text{ cm}$$

‖ The symbols have the following meanings: *th*, a thermal Maxwell distribution of neutrons at a temperature of ~300°K; C, those neutrons, in a thermal distribution, capable of penetrating through appreciable thicknesses of cadmium. (These have energies above the cadmium cut-off, ~0.5 ev.)

¶ This compilation leans heavily on the previous compilations of Shull and Wollan (S33), Way *et al.* (W10), and Feshbach, Peaslee, and Weisskopf (F27), in which references are given to the original investigations.

However, the curves of σ_{sc} vs. E will be very different for nuclei of widely different atomic number, since the number of resonance and their characteristics depend strongly on the level spacing.

(1) **Light Nuclei.** In general, the main reaction of slow neutrons with light nuclei is elastic scattering. There are four exceptions—Li^6 and B^{10}, for which the main reactions are (n,α); He^3 and N^{14}, for which there is an appreciable slow-neutron (n,p) cross section. Aside from these, $\sigma_{sc} = \sigma_t$ (see Fig. 7a).

(2) **Medium Nuclei.** With regard to the scattering of slow neutrons, medium nuclei are similar to light nuclei, except that resonances are sometimes encountered. These are primarily scattering resonances since the level spacing is quite large. For this case $\Gamma \sim \Gamma_n > \Gamma_\gamma$, the peak cross section

$$\sigma_0(n,n) \cong 4\pi\lambdabar_r^2 f = \frac{2.6f}{E_r} \times 10^6 \text{ barns} \qquad (55a')$$

(E_r is in electron volts.) The 120-ev resonance in·cobalt (Fig. 7b) is an example of such a scattering resonance. The peak cross section for this resonance should be $\sim$13,000 barns since, for Co^{59}, $I = \frac{7}{2}(f \sim \frac{1}{2})$. The smallness of the peak cross section in Fig. 7b, as well as the absence of the expected interference between the resonance and potential scattering, is due to the poor resolution of the measurement. Since the

TABLE 6

Properties of Some Neutron Scattering Resonances

Target Nucleus	Spin I	E_r (ev)	Γ_n (ev)	Γ_n/Γ	Compound Nucleus Spin J	Observed σ_0 (barns)	$4\pi\lambdabar_r^2 f$ (barns)	References
$_{11}Na^{23}$	$\frac{3}{2}$	3,300	340	$\sim$0.999	2	550	540	H58, †
$_{16}S^{32}$	0	111,000	18,000	$\sim$1	$\frac{1}{2}$	21.5	23.4	A1
$_{17}Cl^{35}$	$\frac{3}{2}$	-75	2.63 ‡	0.90 ‡	(2)			H59
$_{25}Mn^{55}$	$\frac{5}{2}$	345	20	0.990	3	4–5,000	4,400	S17, H40, H43
$_{27}Co^{59}$	$\frac{7}{2}$	123	$\approx$4	0.94	(4)	12,500	12,200	H38, S17, H40, †
$_{33}As^{75}$	$\frac{3}{2}$	46	0.11	0.72			$\sim$28,000	†
$_{59}Pr^{141}$	$\frac{5}{2}$	$(\sim 10?)$		0.93			$(\sim$130,000)	H40
$_{62}Sm^{152}$	0	8.2	$\sim$0.3	0.66	$\frac{1}{2}$	320,000	H40
$_{74}W^{186}$	0	19.25	0.25	0.62	$\frac{1}{2}$	$\sim$90,000	135,000	H39, H40, S19
$_{81}Tl^{(203)}$	$\frac{1}{2}$	260	$\approx$3.2	0.52	(1)		7,500	H40
$_{83}Bi^{209}$	$\frac{9}{2}$	770	3.5	$\sim$1			$\sim$1,700	†

† Some of the original data in this table have been revised in the light of recent measurements by the Harwell time-of-flight velocity selector group (M26) and by the Argonne fast chopper group (whose members included L. M. Bollinger, R. R. Palmer, and S. P. Harris). We are grateful to these groups for private communications of their results.
‡ These values are at $E = |E_r| = 75$ ev.

recognition, by Goldhaber and Yalow (G14), that the resonance of manganese at $\sim$300 ev is a scattering resonance, many such resonances have been observed and investigated in medium (and some heavy) nuclei. Table 6 summarizes the properties of a number of scattering resonances.

(3) Heavy Nuclei. In heavy nuclei, with their relatively small level spacings, the gamma-ray width is generally larger than the neutron

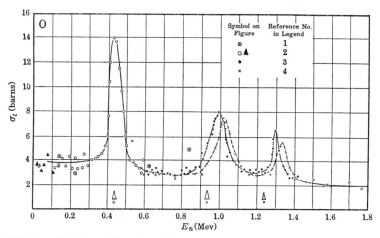

(1) Fields, Russell, Sachs, and Wattenberg, Phys. Rev., **71**, 508 (1947). (2) Adair, Barschall, Bockelman, and Sala, Phys. Rev., **75**, 1124 (1949). (3) Bockelman, Miller, Adair, and Barschall, Phys. Rev., **84**, 69 (1951). (4) Freier, Fulk, Lampi, and Williams, Phys. Rev., **78**, 508 (1950).

Fig. 11. Total (scattering) cross section of O^{16} for intermediate and fast neutrons, showing well-resolved P-wave resonances at 0.440, 1, and 1.3 Mev; from Adair (A2). Measurements from $\sim$1.8 to 4 Mev have exhibited additional resonances whose angular momenta and parities have been deduced by Baldinger, Huber, and Proctor (B5) by means of accurate measurements of the angular distributions of the elastically scattered neutrons.

width, $\Gamma \sim \Gamma_\gamma > \Gamma_n$. Accordingly, the peak scattering cross section is small compared to the peak radiative (and total) cross section,

$$\sigma_0(n,n) = \frac{\Gamma_{nr}}{\Gamma_\gamma} \sigma_0(n,\gamma) \tag{47a}$$

The resonance scattering of cadmium (B12) is an example of this case.

Owing to fluctuations in the nuclear level spacing, and to the differences in neutron binding energies, levels are sometimes encountered in heavy nuclei for which $\Gamma_n \gtrsim \Gamma_\gamma$. The broad resonance of W^{186} at 19 ev has been found to be such a scattering resonance (H39).[1]

[1] The existence of broad, scattering resonances for slow neutrons on heavy nuclei might be additional evidence for the necessity, under certain circumstances, of regarding neutron reactions from the independent particle point of view.

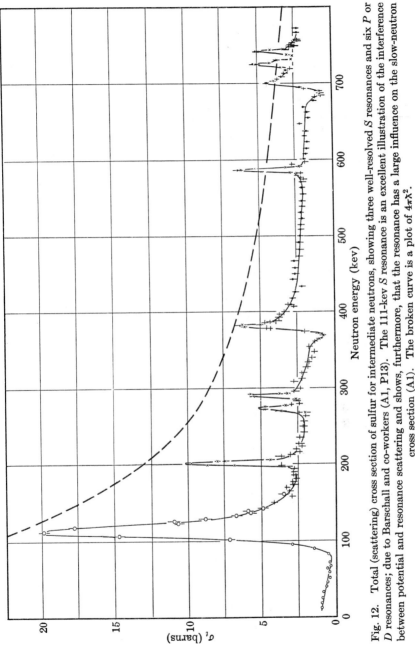

Fig. 12. Total (scattering) cross section of sulfur for intermediate neutrons, showing three well-resolved S resonances and six P or D resonances; due to Barschall and co-workers (A1, P13). The 111-kev S resonance is an excellent illustration of the interference between potential and resonance scattering and shows, furthermore, that the resonance has a large influence on the slow-neutron cross section (A1). The broken curve is a plot of $4\pi\lambda^2$.

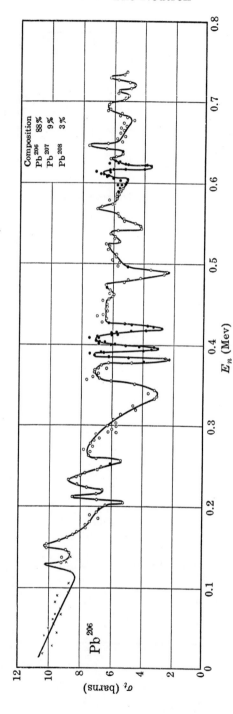

(a) Pb²⁰⁶—a magic number nucleus

Fig. 13a. Scattering cross section for intermediate-energy neutrons of Pb²⁰⁶—a magic number nucleus; data of Peterson, Adair, and Barschall, Phys. Rev., **79**, 935 (1950). Note similarity in behavior to cross sections in Figs. 13b and 13c.

(b) *Intermediate Neutrons.* The intermediate neutron energy region is, with respect to the interaction of neutrons with nuclei, a transition region. At the low-energy end, the neutron wavelength is still large

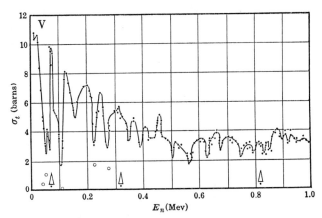

Fig. 13b. Scattering cross section for intermediate-energy neutrons of V^{51}; data from Blair and Wallace, Phys. Rev. **79**, 28 (1950).

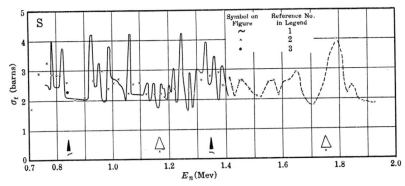

(1) Peterson, Barschall, and Bockelman, Phys. Rev., **79**, 593 (1950).   (2) Freier, Fulk, Lampi, and Williams, Phys. Rev., **78**, 508 (1950).   (3) Fields, Russell, Sachs, and Wattenberg, Phys. Rev., **71**, 508 (1947).

Fig. 13c. Scattering cross section of S^{32} in the fast-neutron region; from Adair (A2).

compared to nuclear radii; at the upper end, the neutron wavelength is comparable with (and, for heavy nuclei, smaller than) nuclear dimensions. In this region, the character of the neutron scattering process slowly changes.

(1) Light Nuclei. Figure 11 shows the scattering cross section of oxygen ($I = 0$) in the intermediate (and lower end of the fast) energy range. The cross section is constant up to the resonance at 440 kev.

This resonance must be ascribed to capture of $l = 1$ neutrons (P reso-nance), since its peak cross section (14 barns) is greater than $4\pi\lambda_r^2 = 6$ barns, and since it shows none of the interference properties associated with S resonances. The value of the peak cross section is consistent with a value $J = \frac{3}{2}$ ($f_1 = 2$) for the compound nucleus; i.e., $\sigma_0(n,n)$ $= 8\pi\lambda_r^2 + \sigma_p' \cong 12 + 4 = 16$ barns. The resolution of the measure-ment is excellent ($\sim$10 kev), but its finite value is sufficient to account for the difference of $\sim$2 barns between the observed and expected peak cross sections.

(2) Medium Nuclei. In Fig. 12 is plotted the total (scattering) cross section for sulfur ($A = 32$). This curve is especially interesting, since it illustrates many of the features of scattering resonances which we have previously discussed. The broken curve is a plot of $4\pi\lambda^2$. The three S-wave resonances, at 111 kev, 375 kev, and 700 kev, have peak cross sections close to $4\pi\lambda^2$, indicating the excellent resolution of the measurements. They show very well the interference between the po-tential and resonance scattering. The other six resonances appear to be due to $P(l = 1)$ or $D(l = 2)$ neutrons, and are incompletely resolved. Of these, the 585-kev resonance can be ascribed to a $J = \frac{3}{2}$ state of the compound nucleus, S^{33} (P13).

(3) Heavy Nuclei. For heavy nuclei in the intermediate-energy re-gion, the resonances are usually much more closely spaced than the resolution of the best available measuring devices. At the low-energy end the resonances are still primarily due to radiative capture ($\Gamma_\gamma > \Gamma_n$), while at the upper end the neutron width has caught up with the gamma-ray width, and scattering predominates. Toward the high-energy end of the intermediate region inelastic scattering starts to compete as a possible reaction, but we postpone the discussion of this reaction.

For certain of the heavy nuclei, the level spacing of the compound nucleus, at the excitation energy corresponding to neutron capture, is anomalously large. Such appears to be the case for the magic number or near magic elements lead and bismuth, owing either to an anomalously small neutron binding energy, or to an intrinsically large level spacing, or both. The cross section of Pb^{206} is shown in Fig. 13a. As an interesting comparison, we also plot the cross section of V^{51} in the intermediate region (Fig. 13b), and that of S^{32} in the fast-neutron region (Fig. 13c). All of these show approximately the same level spacings.

The curves of Fig. 13 can be used to illustrate some other interesting possibilities in scattering resonances. If the resonances are still resolva-ble at relatively large values of $x = kR \gtrsim 1$ (due either, as in S^{32}, to large spacing for fast neutrons or, as in Pb^{206}, to a large nuclear radius), $l = 1$ potential scattering becomes appreciable, and P-wave resonances are no longer expected to be symmetrical. Thus, the 1055-kev sulfur resonance must, because of the large peak cross section, be ascribed to neutrons of $l > 0$; however, it also shows a definite interference minimum, due to the P-wave potential scattering. It is therefore a $P_{3/2}$ resonance.

Another interesting anomaly occurs in the region $\xi_0 = x \approx \pi/2$. ($\xi_{l>0} \approx \pi/2$, for which the same considerations apply, requires neutrons of much greater energy.) For an S-wave resonance in this energy region, application of Eqs. (53a) and (55) indicates that the minimum cross section, $\sigma_{min} = \sigma_p'$, occurs at $E_{min} = E_r$, while the maximum disappears (i.e., $E_{max} \rightarrow \infty$). This leads to cross-section curves which have the appearance of inverted resonances, as observed in the Pb^{206} cross section of Fig. 13a.

(c) *Fast Neutrons.* Of the total cross section for fast neutrons, approximately half involves the formation of a compound nucleus; the rest is due to elastic (potential) scattering, in which the neutron passes close to, but not into, the target nucleus.

I. Capture Scattering and Inelastic Scattering

With the exception of a few light nuclei (and the heaviest nuclei) the most probable result of fast-neutron capture is neutron re-emission. As long as the incident neutron energy is less than the energy of the first excited state of the target nucleus, the neutrons will be re-emitted with their incident energy (minus, of course, the energy lost to the recoil nucleus to conserve momentum). As soon as the incident neutron energy exceeds the energy required for the excitation of the lowest level of the target nucleus, it becomes possible for the product nucleus to be left in the excited state; correspondingly, the emitted neutron will have a smaller kinetic energy than the incident neutron. This process is known as inelastic scattering.

From the point of view of the excited compound nucleus, decay to the ground state (capture elastic scattering) and to the various energetically possible excited states (inelastic scattering) of the product nucleus are competing processes. Each mode of decay is characterized by a partial width, Γ_i, which is a measure of its relative probability. However, from the experimental viewpoint, there are, in addition to the difference in energy of the elastically and inelastically scattered neutrons, two distinguishing features between the two processes: (1) Capture elastic scattering and potential scattering are coherent processes, and the elastic scattering cross section can therefore exhibit interference effects of the type previously discussed. (2) Inelastic scattering leaves the product nucleus in an excited state, from which it decays by the emission of one or more gamma-rays. Indeed, it was through the observation of this gamma-radiation that the inelastic scattering process was discovered (L11, K12). There have been a number of subsequent investigations of inelastic scattering by the observation of the resulting gamma-radiation (A29, S12, B13, G27); however, all but the most recent of these have been too crude to permit detailed interpretation.

The most useful information concerning inelastic scattering has been derived from experiments involving the observation of the energy distribution of inelastically scattered neutrons. The interpretation of such experiments has been discussed by Feld (F9).

In the ideal inelastic scattering measurement, a monoenergetic neutron beam would be scattered from a thin target of the element under investigation; the scattered neutrons would have a line spectrum, each line corresponding to the excitation of a given level of the target nucleus. The energies of the inelastically scattered neutron groups would give the positions of these energy levels, and the relative strengths of the groups would be a measure of the relative values of the partial widths for the corresponding compound nucleus decay. In addition, the angular distribution of a given group of inelastically scattered neutrons (with respect to the direction of the incident neutrons) would yield valuable information concerning the angular momentum and parity properties of the levels involved. Finally, each group of inelastically scattered neutrons is accompanied (in coincidence) by one or more gamma-rays; the correlation between the direction of emission of the neutrons and gamma-rays would yield further information concerning the angular momentum and parity properties of the levels.

An experiment of the type outlined above is, in practice, exceedingly difficult, since it requires, in addition to a monoenergetic neutron source, a fast-neutron detector of high resolution. Most attempts to measure the energy distribution of inelastically scattered neutrons have employed "threshold" detectors, i.e., a detector sensitive only to neutrons of energy above a fixed value, E_t. Since, in most cases, the sensitivity function of the detector is not well known, such experiments are usually difficult to interpret unambiguously.

Many inelastic scattering measurements have employed heteroenergetic neutron sources, such as the Ra-α-Be or Ra-α-B source, and threshold detectors. Owing to the extreme difficulty in interpreting such experiments (S65), they will be omitted from this discussion.

(1) Light Nuclei. The low-lying levels of light nuclei are very widely spaced ($\sim$0.5–5 Mev). Hence, fast neutrons can excite few levels. In many cases, for neutrons of a few Mev, only one level of the target

nucleus will be available for excitation. The inelastic scattering cross section will depend in detail on the properties of this level, according to the following general considerations: Let σ_c be the cross section for the formation of a compound nucleus.[1] The cross section for the excitation of the level (through inelastic scattering) is

$$\sigma_1 = \frac{\sigma_c \Gamma_1}{\Gamma} \tag{42a}$$

Γ_1, the partial width for inelastic neutron emission, is given by Eqs. (37) to (40):

$$\Gamma_1 \approx (2l + 1)CD_l E_1^{\frac{1}{2}} v_l(k_1 R) \tag{38a}$$

in which the symbols have their usual meanings; E_1 and k_1 are the energy and wave number of the (inelastically) scattered neutron:

$$E_1 \cong E - D_1 \tag{33a}$$

(E is the incident neutron energy; D_1 is the excitation energy of the target nucleus level involved.)   The total width

$$\Gamma = \Gamma_0 + \Gamma_1 + \Gamma_a + \Gamma_b + \cdots \tag{28a}$$

includes the width for elastic neutron re-emission, Γ_0, and the widths for decay by emission of any other particles, Γ_a, Γ_b, etc.

In the expression for σ_1 (Eq. 42a) all the factors are, to a greater or lesser extent, energy dependent. However, in the immediate neighborhood of the threshold ($E \approx D_1$), the main energy dependence arises through the factor $E_1^{\frac{1}{2}} v_l(k_1 R)$ in Γ_1. (It is clear that, for energetic reasons, $\Gamma_1 = 0$ for $E < D_1$.) If we consider a region close to the threshold, such that $E_1 \ll E$, the factors σ_c and Γ are essentially constant. For inelastic scattering in which S-wave ($l = 0$) neutrons are emitted, the cross section will have an $E_1^{\frac{1}{2}}$ energy dependence near the threshold; for emission of $l > 0$ neutrons, the cross section near threshold will increase as $E_1^{(l+\frac{1}{2})}$.

The angular momentum of the emitted neutrons is determined by the values of the spins and parities of the initial (compound nucleus) and final (product nucleus) states. In many cases these values are such that neutrons of only a single, definite angular momentum can be emitted. In some cases, however, the spin values are such that angular momentum conservation could be satisfied in a number of alternative modes of decay, i.e., more than one l value is possible for the emitted neutron.

[1] The energy dependence of σ_c has been discussed on page 283. It should, however, be borne in mind that the general considerations, used to derive Fig. 10, are of questionable validity for light nuclei in the fast-neutron range.

In such cases the parity selection rule further limits the number of possible l values; e.g., if the parity of the initial state is the same as that of the final state, neutrons can be emitted only with even l values; for states of opposite parity, only odd l values are permitted. Consequently, and also because of the strong energy dependence of Γ_l, one—the lowest—of the possible l values of emitted neutrons will be predominant in most cases.

When the angular momentum of the emitted neutrons has a definite value and if, furthermore, the absorption of the incident neutrons to form the compound nucleus state involves a single l value, the inelastically scattered neutrons will have a definite and predictable angular distribution with respect to the direction of the incident neutrons. The angular distributions, in a number of possible cases, have been given by Hauser and Feshbach (H44).

As an example of the type of angular distribution that could be encountered, we give the result for a specific (hypothetical) case:

$$\text{Target nucleus:} \quad I = \tfrac{1}{2}$$
$$\text{Compound nucleus:} \quad J = 3$$
$$\text{Product nucleus:} \quad I' = \tfrac{3}{2}$$
$$\text{Incident neutron:} \quad l = 2$$
$$\text{Scattered neutron:} \quad l' = 1$$

The resulting angular distribution of (inelastically) scattered neutrons is

$$W(\theta) = 1 + \tfrac{3}{2}\tfrac{6}{3} \cos^2 \theta$$

(θ is the angle between the incident and scattered neutrons.)

Similar information concerning the three states involved could be obtained by observation of the angular correlation between the inelastically scattered neutrons and the gamma-radiation which follows the inelastic scattering. In the example given above, the transition $\Delta I = 1$ with parity change would be achieved through the emission of an electric dipole (or magnetic quadrupole) gamma-ray. Angular correlations in successive particle gamma-ray emission are discussed in Part IX of Volume III.

As previously indicated, many cases of inelastic scattering will be considerably more complicated than the example discussed above. For instance, it may be possible for the incident neutrons to excite more than one compound nucleus state, requiring a number of incident neutron l values. Correspondingly, the decay of the compound nucleus to the excited product nucleus can also involve a number of different angular momenta, and the angular distributions for the different l values can interfere. If this situation prevails, the calculation of the angular distribution of the inelastically scattered neutrons requires further knowledge of the details of the competition. Some of these possibilities have been considered by Hauser and Feshbach (H44) and by Wolfenstein (W38):

There has been very little experimental investigation of the inelastic scattering of fast neutrons by light nuclei. The work of Beghian, Grace, Preston, and Halban (B13, G27), on the inelastic scattering of 2.5-Mev neutrons by beryllium, carbon, fluorine, magnesium, sulfur, chromium, iron, and copper is of interest in connection with the above considerations. They detected the inelastic scattering by observing the resulting gamma-radiation and used the intensity of the gamma-rays as a measure of the cross section. In the cases of carbon and beryllium they were unable to detect any gamma-radiation. For the other elements they observed a single (monoenergetic) gamma-ray in the first four cases, indicating that only a single level of the target nucleus was involved; the last two yielded complex gamma-ray spectra. These results are summarized in Table 7a.

The observed cross sections, when combined with a knowledge of σ_c, yield values of the relative probability for inelastic scattering Γ_1/Γ (Eq. 42a). These are shown for fluorine, magnesium, and sulfur in Table 7b, together with the data from which they were derived. The values of σ_c have been estimated from the available data (A2, W32). In the last column of the table, we also give theoretical values of Γ_1/Γ, based on the assumption that only elastic and inelastic scattering are of importance ($\Gamma = \Gamma_0 + \Gamma_1$), and that both types of scattering involve only $l = 0$ neutrons.

In the case of magnesium the inelastic scattering has been observed directly by Little, Long, and Mandeville (L20). They scattered 2.5-Mev neutrons (from a D-D source) in a block of magnesium and measured the energy distribution of the scattered neutrons by observing proton recoils in a cloud chamber. In addition to the elastically scattered group, they observed a single group of inelastically scattered neutrons whose energy corresponds to an excited state of magnesium at 1.30 Mev (compare Table 7a). From the strengths of the two groups, they computed values of ~ 1.6 barns and ~ 0.6 barn for the elastic and inelastic scattering cross sections, respectively, in excellent agreement with the result of Grace et $al.$ and the measured value of $\sigma_t \approx 2.2$ barns. The value of Γ_1/Γ, shown in parentheses in Table 7b, is computed from their value of $\sigma_1 \approx 0.6$ barn.

TABLE 7

(a) *Results of Grace, Beghian, Preston, and Halban* (B13, G27) *on Inelastic Scattering of 2.5-Mev Neutrons, from Observation of the Resulting Gamma-Radiation*

Element	Atomic Weight	Observed E_γ (Mev)	Observed σ_1 (barns)
Be	9		<0.014
C	12		<0.006
F	19	1.3 ± 0.1	0.52 ± 0.18
Mg	24(77%), 25(12%), 26(11%)	1.4 ± 0.1	0.75 ± 0.23
S	32	2.35 ± 0.15	0.38 ± 0.1
Cr	52(84%), 53(10%), 50(4%), 54(2%)	1.4 ± 0.1	1.2 ± 0.4
Fe	56(92%), 54 (6%), 57(2%), 58(0.3%)	0.8 ± 0.1 2.2 ± 0.2	1.8 ± 1.3 0.14 ± 0.05
Cu	63(69%), 65(31%)	1.1 ± 0.1 2.2 ± 0.1	1.2 ± 0.6 0.34 ± 0.12

(b) *Interpretation*

Element	σ_t (barns)	Reference	Estimated σ_c (barns)	Γ_1/Γ Experiment	Γ_1/Γ Theory
F	2.7	W32	1.2	0.4	0.41
Mg	2.2	G20, A2	1.5	0.5 (0.4)	0.40
S	2.8	G20, A2	2	0.2	0.19

(2) Medium Nuclei. In the scattering of fast neutrons by medium nuclei, the product nucleus can be left in any one of many (energetically) available excited states; correspondingly, many groups of inelastically scattered neutrons will be emitted by the compound nucleus. The considerations applied in the previous section for a single level can easily be generalized to the case of many levels. Let σ_i be the cross section for the excitation, through inelastic scattering, of the ith level of the target nucleus (excitation energy D_i):

$$\sigma_i = \frac{\sigma_c \Gamma_i}{\Gamma} \tag{42b}$$

The partial width Γ_i is obtained by the substitution of the subscript i for 1 in Eqs. (38a) and (33a).

Since, for intermediate nuclei and fast neutrons, neutron re-emission is usually predominant over all other processes, the total width is

$$\Gamma = \Gamma_0 + \Gamma_1 + \cdots + \Gamma_i + \cdots + \Gamma_n = \sum_{i=0}^{n} \Gamma_i \qquad (28b)$$

in which the first term is the width for elastic re-emission and the succeeding terms correspond to inelastic scattering in which all possible levels (up to the highest for which $D_n \leq E$) of the target nucleus are excited.

As in the case of one-level excitation, the value and energy dependence of a specific Γ_i are determined by the angular momentum properties of the emitted neutrons which, in turn, derive from the spins and parities of the levels involved. Since, for medium compound nuclei formed by the capture of fast neutrons, many levels involving many angular momenta are likely to be excited, decay to a given product nucleus state will be possible through the emission of neutrons of a number of different angular momenta. In the ensuing competition, $l = 0$ emission when possible, will usually predominate. However, for some levels, $l = 0$ emission will be impossible, and these will usually be less strongly excited. For a complete description it is, of course, necessary to take into account all the possible l values of the emitted neutrons.

Nevertheless, for purposes of illustration it is of interest to consider the energy dependence of the inelastic scattering cross sections under the assumption of S-wave scattering only. The values of the first few σ_i vs. E are shown in Fig. 14; in addition to the assumption of S-wave scattering, we have also assumed uniform level spacing for the product nucleus, i.e., $D_1 = D$, $D_i = iD$. The uppermost curve, labeled σ_{oc}, is the relative cross section for capture elastic scattering. At a given value of the incident neutron energy E, the total cross section for inelastic scattering is

$$\sigma_{in} = \sum_{i=1}^{n} \sigma_i = \sigma_c - \sigma_{oc} \qquad (68')$$

The data on the inelastic scattering of fast neutrons by intermediate nuclei are meagre. Barschall, Battat, Bright, Graves, Jorgensen and Manley (B8) have measured the energy distribution of 3.0 and 1.5 Mev neutrons scattered by iron, using, as an energy-sensitive detector, proton recoil proportional counters with different "bias" values. Although the resolution of these measurements was rather crude, the results can be satisfactorily understood in terms of the theory outlined above and the (three) known levels of Fe^{56} of excitation energy less than 3 Mev (F9). The results of Grace et al. (G27), shown in Table 7a, are in fair agreement with those of Barschall et al. for iron.

(3) Heavy Nuclei. In the scattering of fast neutrons by heavy nuclei a large number of energy levels of the target nucleus are available for excitation. Separate groups of inelastically scattered neutrons will, in general, not be observed, both because of the limited resolving power of

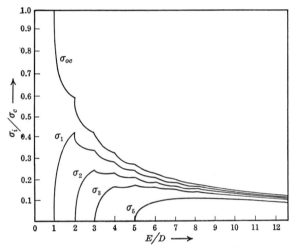

Fig. 14. Cross sections, σ_i, for the excitation of the low-lying levels of the target nucleus as a function of the incident neutron energy, E. The curves are based on the assumptions: (1) constant level spacing; (2) S scattering only; (3) $\Gamma_i = C(E - E_i)^{1/2}$, with C constant over all levels.

all fast-neutron detectors and because the separation of levels in the product nucleus is usually smaller than the spread in energy of available fast-neutron sources. The inelastically scattered neutrons will appear to have a continuous spectrum (except, possibly, for the elastically scattered and a few adjacent high-energy groups) ranging from zero to the incident energy E.

Because of the large number of levels involved, it is no longer fruitful to attempt to interpret such experiments in terms of a theory involving the properties of individual levels. Instead, it is possible to apply a statistical theory, as developed by Weisskopf (W16, B34). The statistical theory predicts an energy distribution of the inelastically scattered neutrons which is of the Maxwellian form

$$d\sigma(\varepsilon,E) \cong \sigma_c \frac{\varepsilon}{T^2} e^{-\varepsilon/T} d\varepsilon \tag{69}$$

In the above, $d\sigma(\varepsilon,E)$ is the cross section for the scattering of a neutron of initial energy E into the energy between ε and $\varepsilon + d\varepsilon$. The constant T, referred to as the nuclear temperature, is a measure of the excitation of the *product nucleus* after the emission of the inelastically scattered neutron. Strictly speaking, it is not energy independent but rather a function of the excitation energy of the residual nucleus, $E - \varepsilon$. However, for most cases of interest, $T \ll E$, and the major part of the spectrum of inelastically scattered neutrons is in the energy region $\varepsilon \ll E$; for this part of the spectrum, T may be regarded as essentially constant, and roughly corresponding to the full possible excitation energy of the product nucleus. However, for the high-energy portion of the spectrum, for which $\varepsilon \sim E$, Eq. (69) is not a good approximation to the inelastically scattered neutron energy distribution.

The energy dependence of Eq. (69) can be understood in terms of two opposing factors in the competition between the various possible modes of de-excitation of the compound nucleus through neutron re-emission: (1) The energy dependence of the neutron scattering width favors the emission of high-energy neutrons. This effect is responsible for the first factor ε in Eq. (69) when proper account is taken of the emission of neutrons in all possible angular momentum states. (If neutrons were emitted only in the $l = 0$ state, the factor would be $\varepsilon^{1/2}$.) (2) The number of available levels of the product nucleus increases rapidly with the excitation energy, thus favoring the emission of low-energy neutrons. This effect leads to the exponential factor in Eq. (69).

The competition between the two factors results in a maximum, in the scattered neutron energy distribution, at an energy intermediate between 0 and E. T, the temperature of the product nucleus, is a measure of its level density at the excitation energy remaining after the emission of the inelastically scattered neutron. From statistical-mechanical considerations, it can be shown that (B34)

$$\frac{1}{T(E')} = \frac{\partial}{\partial E'}[\ln \omega(E')] \tag{70}$$

where $\omega(E')$ is the nuclear level density at the excitation energy $E' = E - \varepsilon$. For an exponential energy dependence of the nuclear level density, as given by Eq. (41),

$$T(E') \approx \left(\frac{E'}{a}\right)^{1/2} \tag{70a}$$

In heavy nuclei, the very rapid increase of nuclear level density with increasing excitation energy has the effect that the maximum of the scattered neutron energy distribution is at relatively low energies; correspondingly, the excitation energy of the product nucleus is, for the major fraction of the inelastic scattering, at an energy close to the maximum possible excitation energy, $E' \sim E$. [This rapid increase in level density corresponds to large values of the constant a (Table 4) and

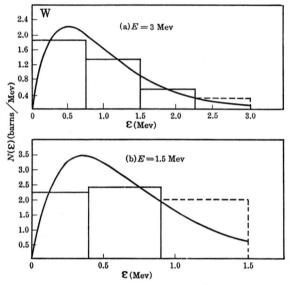

Fig. 15. Energy distribution of inelastically scattered neutrons from wolfram. The experimental results of Barschall *et al.* (B8) are plotted as histograms. The smooth curves are derived from the statistical theory and Eq. (69) (F9).

hence to small values of the nuclear temperature, $T \ll E$.] Thus, over the largest part of the spectrum, the nuclear temperature can be closely approximated by

$$T \approx T(E) \approx \left(\frac{E}{a}\right)^{\frac{1}{2}} \tag{70b}$$

which is independent of the energy of the scattered neutrons. It is in this approximation that Eq. (69) is valid.

The observations of Barschall *et al.* (B8), on the inelastic scattering of 1.5 and 3.0 Mev neutrons by wolfram (tungsten), can be interpreted in terms of the statistical theory and Eq. (69) (F9). The results of their measurements on the energy distribution of the inelastically scattered neutrons are plotted as histograms in Fig. 15, together with the predictions of the theory (smooth curves). The theoretical curves have been computed on the assumption of $T = 0.5$ and 0.35 Mev for $E = 3.0$ and 1.5 Mev, respectively, corresponding to $a = 12$ Mev^{-1}, in good agreement with Table 4.

Table 8 is a collection of integral inelastic scattering cross sections and temperatures for medium and heavy nuclei. The measurements are represented by the cross section for the scattering of a neutron of incident energy E to an energy $\varepsilon \overline{<} E_t$,

$$\sigma_{in}(E,E_t) = \int_0^{E_t} d\sigma(E,\varepsilon) \tag{69a}$$

and by the temperature corresponding to the emitted neutron distribution. Only those measurements have been included for which the incident neutron energy and the detector threshold are relatively well defined. Some of these are amenable to interpretation along the lines outlined above in the discussion of the results for wolfram. For most, the energy sensitivity of the threshold detector used is not sufficiently well known to permit more quantitative conclusions.

However, these measurements do give an indication of the energy distribution of the inelastically scattered neutrons. In particular, they show that, also with regard to inelastic scattering, the magic number nuclei lead and bismuth behave in an anomalous fashion; their scattering is much more similar to that of medium nuclei than to that of heavy nuclei. The importance of this observation is that it relates to the relatively *low-lying level spacings of the target nuclei*, which appear, from these observations, to be anomalously large for lead and bismuth. The previously mentioned evidence on the small capture cross sections and absence of slow-neutron resonances for these nuclei reflect a wide *level spacing of the compound nucleus*.

In addition to the direct observation of inelastically scattered neutrons or the resulting gamma-radiation, there is another method of detecting inelastic scattering, applicable only to certain special nuclei. These are nuclei which have a metastable (long half-life) level at an energy less than that of the incident neutrons; when excited, the metastable state can be detected by the resultant radioactivity. The metastable state of In^{115} (energy 340 kev, half-life 4.5 hr) was first observed by Goldhaber, Hill, and Szilard (G13) as resulting from the inelastic scattering of fast neutrons.

A metastable state can be induced either by direct excitation (the product nucleus is left in the metastable state), or indirectly, through the excitation, by inelastic scattering, of a higher state of the product nucleus, which subsequently decays (by gamma-ray emission) to the metastable state. In the first case, Eqs. (42a) and (38a) determine the

TABLE 8

(a) *Measured Values of Integral Inelastic Scattering Cross Sections,* $\sigma_{in}(E,E_t)$

Ele-ment	E (Mev)	E_t (Mev)	Detec-tor †	$\sigma_{in}(E,E_t)$ ‡ (barns)	Refer-ence	σ_c (barns) (Fig. 10)
Be	2.5	2.5	γ	<0.014	G27	
	14	~3	Al	0.16 ± 0.07	P15	
		~11	Cu	0.82 ± 0.03	P15	0.79
B	14	~3	Al	0.24 ± 0.04	P15	
		~11	Cu	0.69 ± 0.10	P15	0.64
C	2.5	2.5	γ	<0.006	B13	
	14	~11	Cu	0.85 ± 0.02	P15	0.74
F	2.5	2.5	γ	0.52 ± 0.18	G27	1.4
Mg	2.5	2.5	γ	0.75 ± 0.23	G27	1.10
		~2.5	cc	~0.6	L20	
Al	14	~3	Al	0.62 ± 0.07	P15	
		~11	Cu	1.06 ± 0.05	P15	0.93
S	2.5	2.5	γ	0.38 ± 0.1	G27	0.90
Cr	2.5	2.5	γ	1.2 ± 0.4	G27	1.47
Fe	1.5	~0.5	pc	0	B8	
		~0.9	pc	0.6	B8	1.58
	2.5	2.5	γ	1.9 ± 1.3	G27	1.52
	3.0	~0.75	pc	0.3	B8	
		~1.50	pc	0.7	B8	
		~2.25	pc	1.1	B8	1.50
	14	~2	P	0.78 ± 0.03	P15	
		~3	Al	1.21 ± 0.03	P15	
		~11	Cu	1.45 ± 0.02	P15	1.34
Co	1.5	~0.5	pc	(0)	B8	
		~0.9	pc	(0.2)	B8	
		~1.3	pc	(0.8)	B8	1.62
Ni	1.5	~0.5	pc	(0)	B8	
		~0.9	pc	(0.1)	B8	
		~1.3	pc	(0.6)	B8	1.62

TABLE 8 (*Continued*)

(a) *Measured Values of Integral Inelastic Scattering Cross Sections,* $\sigma_{in}(E,E_t)$

Element	E (Mev)	E_t (Mev)	Detector †	$\sigma_{in}(E,E_t)$ ‡ (barns)	Reference	σ_c (barns) (Fig. 10)
Cu	1.5	∼0.5	pc	(0.3)	B8	
		∼0.9	pc	(0.6)	B8	
		∼1.3	pc	(0.9)	B8	1.65
	2.5	2.5	γ	1.5 ± 0.7	G27	1.62
	3.0	∼0.75	pc	(0.6)	B8	
		∼1.50	pc	(1.3)	B8	
		∼2.25	pc	(1.5)	B8	1.61
Cd	14	∼2	P	1.14 ± 0.04	P15	
		∼3	Al	1.66 ± 0.07	P15	
		∼11	Cu	1.89 ± 0.06	P15	1.85
Ta	1.5	∼0.5	pc	(1.4)	B8	
		∼0.9	pc	(2.0)	B8	
		∼1.3	pc	(2.7)	B8	2.57
W	1.5	∼0.5	pc	0.9	B8	
		∼0.9	pc	2.1	B8	2.57
	3.0	∼0.75	pc	1.4	B8	
		∼1.50	pc	2.4	B8	
		∼2.25	pc	2.8	B8	2.63
Au	3.0	∼0.75	pc	(2.1)	B8	
		∼1.50	pc	(2.8)	B8	
		∼2.25	pc	(3.0)	B8	2.69
	14	∼2	P	1.47 ± 0.10	P15	
		∼3	Al	2.06 ± 0.09	P15	
		∼11	Cu	2.51 ± 0.04	P15	2.69
Pb	1.5	∼0.5	pc	0	B8	
		∼0.9	pc	0.4	B8	2.81
	2.5	∼1	U	0.55	S65	
		∼2.5	cc	1.3 ± 0.5	D17	2.77
	3.0	∼0.75	pc	0.7	B8	
		∼1.50	pc	1.2	B8	
		∼2.25	pc	1.6	B8	2.76
	14	∼2	P	0.91 ± 0.06	P15	
		∼3	Al	2.29 ± 0.04	P15	
		∼11	Cu	2.56 ± 0.05	P15	
		12	pp	<2.6	W21	2.77
	14.5	∼3	Al	2.20 ± 0.17	G6	
		∼11	Cu	2.29 ± 0.12	G6	2.76

TABLE 8 (*Continued*)

(a) *Measured Values of Integral Inelastic Scattering Cross Sections*, $\sigma_{in}(E,E_t)$

Element	E (Mev)	E_t (Mev)	Detector †	$\sigma_{in}(E,E_t)$ ‡ (barns)	Reference	σ_c (barns) (Fig. 10)
Bi	2.5	~1	U	0.64	S65	2.77
	14	~2	P	1.03 ± 0.11	P15	
		~3	Al	2.28 ± 0.08	P15	
		~11	Cu	2.56 ± 0.05	P15	
		12	pp	<3.3	W21	2.78

(b) *Temperatures for Observed Distributions of Inelastically Scattered Neutrons* (*Eq.* 69)

Element	E (Mev)	Range of ε (Mev)	$T(E)$ (Mev)	Reference
B	11	>4	2.3 ± 0.3	G31 §
		1–4	0.9 ± 0.1	G31
Al	15	>1	1.1 ± 0.1	S53
Si	10.6	>2	1.3 ± 0.1	G31
Fe	1.5	$\lesssim 0.9$	none ‖	B8, F9
	3.0	<2.25	none	B8, F9
	15	>1	0.6 ± 0.1	S53
Co	10.5	>2	0.95 ± 0.1	G31
Pd	14	>2	0.85 ± 0.1	G31
W	1.5	<0.9	0.35	B8, F9
	3.0	<2.25	0.50	B8, F9
Au	3.0	<2.25	(0.33)	B8, F9
Hg	14.6	>2	0.8 ± 0.1	G31
Pb	1.5	<0.9	none	B8, F9
	2.5	>1	none	D17, F9
	3.0	<2.25	none	B8, F9
	4.3	>1	none	M2

TABLE 8 *(Continued)*

(b) *Temperatures for Observed Distributions of Inelastically Scattered Neutrons*
(Eq. 69)

Element	E (Mev)	Range of ε (Mev)	$T(E)$ (Mev)	Reference
	14	1–3	~0.8	W21
	14.3	>2	0.78 ± 0.1	G31
	15	>1	0.7 ± 0.1	S53
Bi	4.3	>1	none	M2
	14	1–5	~0.9	W21

† The symbols have the following meanings:

γ = direct detection of gamma-rays from the product nucleus
P = $P^{31}(n,p)$ reaction
Al = $Al^{27}(n,p)$ reaction
Cu = $Cu^{63}(n,2n)$ reaction
pc = detection in a biased proton recoil proportional counter
pp = detection by proton recoils in a photographic emulsion
cc = detection by proton recoils in a cloud chamber
U = detection by U^{238} fission in an ionization chamber

‡ Values in parentheses have not been corrected by the authors (B8) for effects of multiple scattering in the target.

§ Reference (G31) is to measurements of Gugelot on neutron distributions from (p,n) reactions. In these cases, the element given is that of the product nucleus and the energy (second column) is the maximum neutron energy, i.e., the proton kinetic energy plus the reaction Q value.

‖ "None" means that the inelastic scattering cannot be treated by the statistical theory. Instead, individual levels must be considered.

behavior of the cross section for the excitation of the metastable level; in the second case, the partial cross section for the production of the metastable state through the excitation of the ith level is given by the product of Eq. (42a) and a factor representing the relative probability for the decay of the ith level to the metastable state. The excitation function (total cross section *vs.* neutron energy) is the sum of the partial cross sections. It will exhibit discontinuities at the energies corresponding to the inception of excitation of those product nucleus levels which have an appreciable probability of decaying to the metastable level.

The cross section for the excitation of the metastable state of In^{115} by neutrons of energy up to ~4 Mev has been measured by Cohen

(C17). The resolution of his measurements was too crude to detect the effects of individual levels of the product nucleus. More recently Ebel (E1) has measured the excitation function for In^{115*} with good resolution. He observes a threshold at 600 kev (no direct excitation of the metastable level) and discontinuities corresponding to additional product nucleus levels at 960 and 1370 kev. Ebel has also measured the cross section for the excitation of the 540-kev metastable level (half-life 7 sec) of Au^{197}. This level can be directly excited, and also excited through levels at 1.14 and 1.44 Mev.

Since the metastable state is characterized by a large difference in spin from the ground state, the levels of the product nucleus which are involved in its excitation are, perforce, those whose spins differ appreciably from that of the ground state. The shape and magnitude of the cross section for excitation of the metastable state can be used to determine (within limits) the spins and parities of the states involved in its excitation (E1).

II. DIFFRACTION OR SHADOW (NON-CAPTURE) ELASTIC SCATTERING

In the previous discussions, we have considered the total cross section as consisting of two parts: (1) that portion which leads to the formation of a compound nucleus, σ_c, and (2) that portion corresponding to processes in which the incident neutron merely changes its direction, without ever effecting a change in the quantum state of the target nucleus; [1] this elastic scattering, σ_{el} (see Eq. 68), is variously referred to as diffraction or shadow scattering.

For slow and intermediate neutrons ($\lambda > R$) capture and diffraction scattering are intimately connected because of the interference between resonance and potential scattering. For fast neutrons ($\lambda < R$) the two processes separate in a natural fashion. In the first place, the position (extent) of the neutron is relatively well defined. Those neutrons which strike the nucleus have a high probability of penetrating its surface, whereupon they are captured into a compound nucleus. While a certain fraction (relatively large for light nuclei, small for medium and heavy nuclei) may be re-emitted with the full energy, these (capture) elastically scattered neutrons can, except for interference effects in the

---

[1] The target nucleus, initially at rest, will of course receive momentum and kinetic energy as a result of the scattering, and the neutron will, correspondingly, lose energy. However, by the term "quantum state" we refer to the state of internal motion of the target nucleus, which is unaffected unless the incident neutron penetrates the nuclear surface.

neighborhood of a resonance, be separated from the diffraction scattered neutrons by virtue of their different angular distribution.

Shadow scattering, on the other hand, results from the diffraction of those neutrons which pass close by, but not into, the nucleus. Thus, despite the fact that we are considering the energy range for which $\lambda < R$, in which neutrons may be expected to exhibit a minimum of wave properties, it is precisely the wave nature of the incident neutron beam which leads to the phenomenon of shadow scattering. Furthermore, while the angular distribution of the diffraction elastically scattered neutrons depends on the value of the nuclear radius (specifically, on $kR = R/\lambda$), the nature of the diffraction scattering process is independent of the nuclear atomic number.

To a good approximation, shadow scattering is analogous to the diffraction of a plane wave (say light) by a spherical obstacle, for wavelengths small compared to the size of the obstacle. The scattered neutrons are confined to within a relatively small angle,

$$\theta_0 \approx \frac{\lambda}{R} \tag{71}$$

An expression for the angular distribution of the scattered neutrons was first derived by Placzek and Bethe (P17) on the basis of the optical analogy. Recently, Hauser and Feshbach (H44) have derived a more accurate formula,

$$\frac{d\sigma(\theta)}{d\Omega} \cong \frac{(R + \lambda)^2}{4} \cot^2\left(\frac{\theta}{2}\right) \{J_1[k(R + \lambda) \sin \theta]\}^2 \tag{72}$$

for the cross section per unit solid angle for scattering of neutrons into the angle θ; J_1 is the Bessel function of the first kind. The cross section has a maximum at $\theta = 0$, falls to zero at $k(R + \lambda) \sin \theta = 3.83$, and then goes through a series of subsidiary maxima and minima.

For very small wavelengths, $\lambda \ll R$, the cross section for shadow (elastic) scattering is

$$\sigma_{el} = \int d\sigma(\theta) \approx \pi(R + \lambda)^2 \tag{73}$$

At this extreme, $\sigma_t \approx 2\pi(R + \lambda)^2$ (Eq. 67), so that diffraction elastic scattering accounts for approximately half of the total cross section for fast, very fast, and ultra fast neutrons.

The experiments of Amaldi, Bocciarelli, Cacciapuoti, and Trabacchi (A21) on the angular distribution of the elastic scattering of 14-Mev

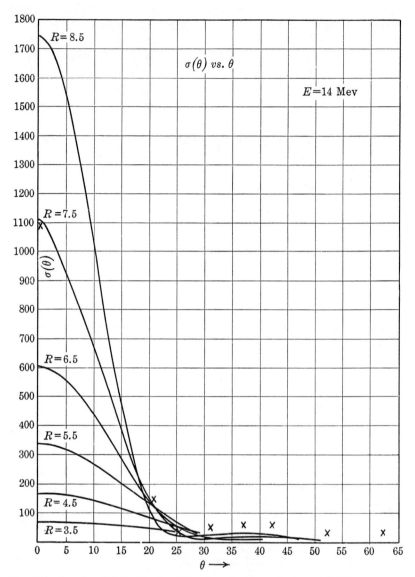

Fig. 16. Angular distribution in diffraction elastic scattering of 14-Mev neutrons for a number of nuclear radii (given in units of 10^{-13} cm). The curves are according to the theory of Hauser and Feshbach (H44). The crosses are from the measurements of Amaldi and co-workers on lead (A21).

neutrons by lead are in excellent agreement with the theory. In addition to the general shape of the scattered neutron distribution, they have observed subsidiary maxima at approximately the expected angles. The theoretical predictions for $E = 14$ Mev and a number of values of the nuclear radius are shown in Fig. 16. Also plotted are the experimental points of Amaldi and co-workers (A21).

III. ANGULAR DISTRIBUTION OF SCATTERED NEUTRONS; THE TRANSPORT CROSS SECTION σ_{tr}

The angular distribution of the scattered neutrons, with respect to the direction of the incident neutrons, is usually described in terms of a differential scattering cross section, $\sigma_{sc}(\theta)$, the cross section for scattering into unit solid angle at the angle θ, in the laboratory system,

$$\sigma_{sc} = \int \sigma_{sc}(\theta) \, d\Omega \qquad (73a)$$

Deviations from spherical symmetry result from a number of possible causes, some of which have previously been discussed. Since the angular distributions are determined by the nature of the scattering process, measurement of $\sigma_{sc}(\theta)$ can sometimes lead to useful nuclear information.

The angular distribution of scattered neutrons is also important in determining the rate of diffusion of neutrons through matter (to be discussed in a subsequent section). In such problems, the important quantity is the transport cross section,

$$\sigma_{tr} = \sigma_t - \int \sigma_{sc}(\theta) \cos \theta \, d\Omega \qquad (74)$$

σ_{tr} determines the rate at which the neutron loses its forward momentum (or the memory of its original direction). Under certain special assumptions concerning the nature of the scattering process simple expressions for σ_{tr} can be derived.

(1) Light Nuclei. In the scattering of fast neutrons by light nuclei, elastic scattering is the most important process. Furthermore, the scattering is (except at the highest energies) mainly S-wave scattering, i.e., spherically symmetrical in the center-of-mass coordinate system (c.m.s.). Neglecting all processes but S-wave elastic scattering, the angular distribution of the scattered neutrons is still not symmetrical in the laboratory system (l.s.), owing to the forward motion of the center of mass.

Thus, for a neutron scattered through the angle φ, in the c.m.s., by a nucleus of atomic weight A, the angle in the l.s. is given by

$$\cos \theta = \frac{(1 + A \cos \varphi)}{(A^2 + 1 + 2A \cos \varphi)^{\frac{1}{2}}} \tag{75}$$

The energy in the l.s. of the elastically scattered neutron, of initial energy E, is

$$E' = \left[\frac{(A^2 + 1 + 2A \cos \varphi)}{(A + 1)^2} \right] E \tag{75a}$$

the difference $(E - E')$ going to the recoil nucleus. The energy of the scattered neutron varies between a maximum, $E_{max}' = E$, for $\varphi = \theta = 0$, and a minimum,

$$E_{min}' = \left[\frac{(A - 1)}{(A + 1)} \right]^2 E \equiv \alpha E \tag{75b}$$

for $\varphi = 180°$. For S-wave scattering (in the c.m.s.) the scattered neutrons are distributed uniformly in energy between E and αE. Correspondingly, under the above assumptions,

$$\sigma_{tr} = \sigma_t - \frac{2}{3A} \sigma_{el} \tag{74a}$$

(2) *Medium and Heavy Nuclei.* It is evident from Eq. (74a) that the effect of the motion of the c.m.s. can be neglected for medium and heavy nuclei. On the other hand, elastic scattering is no longer spherically symmetrical, owing to diffraction effects. Most of the capture leads to inelastic scattering, and the resulting neutrons are not necessarily symmetrically distributed, especially if only a few levels are involved (medium nuclei). However, for most purposes, it is reasonable to treat the inelastic scattering as though it were spherically symmetrical, and to substitute σ_{el} for σ_{sc} in Eq. (74). With this assumption the theory of Feshbach and Weisskopf (F28) can be used to predict the energy dependence of σ_{tr}. The results are shown in Fig. 17, together with the experimental values of Barschall *et al.* (B8).

(d) *Very Fast Neutrons.* So far as neutron scattering is concerned, the very fast-neutron energy range does not differ in any significant respect from the fast-neutron range. Most of the preceding discussion applies equally well to very fast neutrons; indeed, many of the experimental results quoted were for neutrons of energy > 10 Mev. However, in the extension of the previous considerations into the very fast-neutron region, the following points must be kept in mind: (1) Since many levels of the target nucleus can be excited by very fast neutrons, except for a few of the lightest nuclei, the inelastic scattering must be treated according to the statistical theory. (2) Because of the large excitation energy, the compound nucleus has, in addition to neutron re-emission, other possible modes of decay. Thus, for light and some medium nuclei, (n,p), (n,α), etc., reactions compete favorably with neutron re-emission. For medium and heavy nuclei, these reactions are also possible, but the $(n,2n)$ reaction is the most probable competing process. Although we postpone the detailed discussion of this reaction, it is important to note

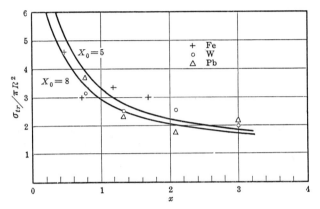

Fig. 17. σ_{tr} vs. $x = kR$ for nuclei of $X_0 = K_0R = 5$ and 8; according to Feshbach and Weisskopf (F28). The points, for iron, wolfram, and lead, are from the measurements of Barschall et al. (B8).

that its presence has a strong effect on the observed energy distribution of the emerging neutrons. Experiments designed to measure the energy distribution of inelastically scattered neutrons must, in the very fast-neutron range, take into account the deviations from Eq. (69) brought about by the presence of the $(n,2n)$ reaction (S53).

The upper end of the very fast-neutron range is characterized, for all nuclei, by $\lambdabar \ll R$. Thus at these energies $\sigma_t \approx 2\pi(R + \lambdabar)^2$ and $\sigma_c \approx \sigma_{el} \approx \pi(R + \lambdabar)^2$.

(e) *Ultrafast Neutrons.* In the ultrafast-energy region, the character of neutron reactions undergoes a gradual change. The simple picture of neutron capture into a compound nucleus, as developed in the previous sections, is no longer applicable. Instead, as pointed out by Serber (S21), the nucleons in the nucleus must be treated as relatively independent particles, since their energy of internal motion and of binding is smaller than the energy of the bombarding neutron. Furthermore, owing to the rapid decrease of the primary $(n-p)$ and $(n-n)$ cross sections with increasing neutron energy—roughly as $1/E$ in the energy range 50 to 250 Mev—the incident neutron has an appreciable probability of passing through the nucleus without undergoing any collisions, i.e., the nucleus is partially transparent to ultrafast neutrons, the more so the lighter the nucleus.

Under these circumstances the probability of a nuclear reaction can be described in terms of an absorption coefficient (reciprocal mean free path) of nuclear matter for neutrons,

$$\kappa = \frac{3A\sigma}{4\pi R^3} \text{ cm}^{-1} \tag{76}$$

where

$$\sigma = \frac{Z\sigma(n\text{-}p) + (A - Z)\sigma(n\text{-}n)}{A} \tag{76a}$$

[In Eq. (76a) $\sigma(n\text{-}p)$ and $\sigma(n\text{-}n)$ are appropriate averages over the spectrum of relative energies of the incident neutron and the nucleons in the nucleus, appropriately reduced to take into account the effect, due to the exclusion principle, that not all energies are available to the recoiling nucleons.] Defining σ_a as the cross section for a collision of the incident neutron inside the nucleus, integration over a spherical nucleus of radius R yields

$$\sigma_a = \pi R^2 \left\{ 1 - \frac{1 - (1 + 2\kappa R)e^{-2\kappa R}}{2\kappa^2 R^2} \right\} \tag{77}$$

The nuclear transparency also influences the diffraction elastic scattering of ultrafast neutrons, both in the magnitude of $\sigma_d = \sigma_{el}$ and in the angular distribution of the scattered neutrons. These effects have been considered in the calculations of Fernbach, Serber, and Taylor (F25). They have derived the diffraction scattering of a partially transparent sphere, characterized by the propagation vector $k + k_1 = [2m(E + V)]^{1/2}/\hbar$. ($V$ is the effective nucleon potential inside the nucleus; $k = 1/\lambda$ is the incident neutron wave number.) The results of these calculations, for the special case $k_1/\kappa = 1.5$, are shown in Fig. 18, in which σ_d, σ_a, and $\sigma_t = \sigma_a + \sigma_d$ are plotted against κR. For large values of κR (complete opacity) $\sigma_a \approx \sigma_d \to \pi R^2$.

Fernbach, Serber, and Taylor have compared their calculated values of σ_t with the measurements of Cook, McMillan, Peterson, and Sewell (C25), for $E \approx 85$ Mev. They find excellent agreement, assuming $R = 1.37A^{1/3} \times 10^{-13}$ cm, $\kappa = 2.2 \times 10^{12}$ cm^{-1}, and $k_1 = 3.3 \times 10^{12}$ cm^{-1} ($V = 30.8$ Mev). The measurements of σ_t at $E \approx 95$ Mev, by DeJuren and Knable (D9) are also in good agreement with theory. These investigators have, in addition, determined σ_a for two elements (carbon and copper), by a "poor geometry" attenuation measurement, and obtained values in good agreement with the theory.

The angular distributions of 84-Mev neutrons elastically scattered by aluminum, copper, and lead have been measured by Bratenahl, Fernbach, Hildebrand, Leith, and Moyer (B59). The results are shown in Fig. 19 in which the dotted curves are the predictions of the theory of Fernbach, Serber, and Taylor.

Measurements of the total cross sections of a number of elements have been carried out at 280 Mev by Fox, Leith, Wouters, and MacKenzie (F41), and at 270 Mev by DeJuren (D10), who also obtained lower

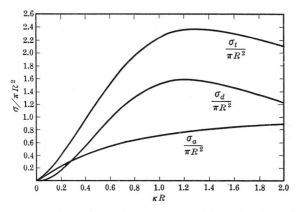

Fig. 18. Absorption, diffraction, and total cross sections as functions of the nuclear radius, measured in mean free paths for the incident neutron. The curves are for $k_1/\kappa = 1.5$, corresponding to neutrons of $E \approx 90$ Mev (F25).

limits for σ_a of carbon, copper, and lead by "poor geometry" attenuation measurements. The above-mentioned measurements of σ_t are included in the compilation of Adair (A2). Cross sections of some representative elements have been measured at a number of intermediate energies—between 110 and 240 Mev—by DeJuren and Moyer (D12). A rather interesting common feature of all the observed σ_t vs. E curves is their comparative independence on energy above $\sim$160 Mev. Another point of interest is the relative constancy of the ratio σ_t (270 Mev)/σ_t (95 Mev); its value is 0.57 between beryllium and tin and then rises slowly to 0.67 for uranium.

The last feature is difficult to reconcile with the partially transparent nucleus model, which predicts considerably greater nuclear opacities for the heavier nuclei.[1] Indeed, for the 270-Mev data, it is only possible

---

[1] This peculiar behavior of σ_t for neutron energies >200 Mev may possibly be associated with the inception of meson production. While the threshold for pion creation is $\sim$275 Mev in a nucleon-nucleon collision, meson production is observed at considerably lower energies for the bombardment of nuclei by nucleons. This is due to the internal motion of the nucleons in the nucleus.

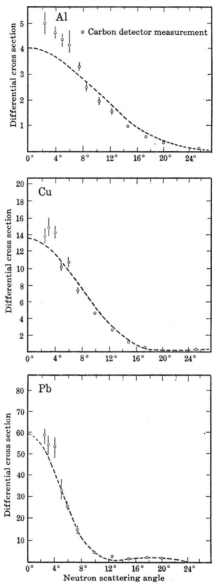

Fig. 19. Differential cross sections for elastic scattering of 84-Mev neutrons by aluminum, copper, and lead, due to Bratenahl, Fernbach, Hildebrand, Leith, and Moyer (B59). The curves are the predictions of the theory of Fernbach, Serber, and Taylor (F25).

"to obtain a reasonable fit . . . [if] the potential change experienced by the bombarding neutron when entering a nucleus [is] dropped to zero" (D10).

2. Radiative Capture (n,γ). The excited compound nucleus, produced by neutron capture, can decay to its ground state through the emission of one or more gamma-rays. The (n,γ) reaction competes with neutron re-emission (always possible) and with any other mode of decay which is energetically permitted. The relative probability of the (n,γ) reaction is determined by the value of the gamma-ray width, Γ_γ, as compared to the widths for all other possible modes of decay:

$$\sigma(n,\gamma) = \frac{\sigma_c \Gamma_\gamma}{\Gamma} \qquad (42')$$

At the excitations corresponding to neutron binding energies, the emission of a gamma-ray takes place in a time of $\sim 10^{-14}$ sec; correspondingly (Eq. 27) $\Gamma_\gamma \sim 0.1$ ev. This value is relatively independent of the atomic weight of the nucleus involved and of the incident neutron energy (at least for slow and intermediate neutrons), although considerable fluctuations, from nucleus to nucleus and from level to level in the same compound nucleus, are to be expected. The above lifetime refers, of course, only to the emission of the first gamma-ray, after which the compound nucleus is usually committed to radiative decay, not having sufficient residual energy to decay by any other mode. In some cases, successive gamma-ray emission leads to a metastable (isomeric) state of the compound nucleus. Usually, however, the gamma-ray emission leads, either directly or through a cascading descent, to the ground state of the compound nucleus.

The study of the energy distribution of the capture gamma-radiation is of considerable interest, since it yields information on the level structure of the compound nucleus, on the nature of the gamma-ray emission process, and on neutron binding energies. Furthermore, knowledge of the capture gamma-ray spectrum is of practical importance in the problem of shielding neutron chain reactors. However, since further discussion of these problems at this point would lead us too far afield, we shall be content merely to point out that the observation of the capture gamma-radiation is one means of detecting the (n,γ) reaction.

In many (n,γ) processes the product nucleus is a stable isotope of the target, e.g., $Cd^{113}(n,\gamma)Cd^{114}$; in such cases, the capture gamma-rays are the only reaction products. However, for most nuclei, radiative capture leads to an unstable (radioactive) product nucleus. The reaction can then be detected and identified by observing the resulting radio-activity. Since these radioactive nuclei are most likely to have an excess of neutrons, they usually decay by negative beta-ray emission. There are a few cases, e.g., $Cu^{63}(n,\gamma)Cu^{64}$, in which the product nucleus can decay by positron emission or K capture.

Most of the factors which determine the energy dependence of $\sigma(n,\gamma)$ have previously been described, both in the general discussion of the cross section for compound nucleus formation, σ_c, and in Section 2C1 on neutron scattering. In the following, we summarize the main features of the radiative capture process.

(a) *Slow Neutrons.* The value of $\sigma(n,\gamma)$ at a given slow-neutron energy is determined by two factors:

(1) The position and characteristics of the closest resonance or, if the energy is far from any one resonance ($| E - E_{ri} | \gg \Gamma_i$), the positions of the closest resonances and their possible interference effects at the energy under consideration. The last aspect has been discussed by Wigner and co-workers (W29, W30, T5). The behavior of $\sigma(n,\gamma)$ in the vicinity of a resonance has been considered in detail (Section 2B3, especially Eqs. 52, 56, 58, and 59).

(2) The relative value of the gamma-ray width, Γ_γ, to the total width, $\Gamma = \Gamma_\gamma + \Gamma_n + \Gamma_a + \cdots$; in all but a few light nuclei only the first two terms, in the above expression for Γ, differ from zero. Since Γ_γ is, as per the previous discussion, essentially fixed, the competition between radiative capture and neutron scattering is primarily determined by the value of Γ_n, which, in turn, is a function of the neutron energy and the compound nucleus level spacing, according to Eqs. (37) and (38).

From these considerations it is clear that the importance and the character of the slow neutron (n,γ) cross section depend on the atomic weight of the target nucleus. In light, medium, and some heavy nuclei, levels are widely spaced, $\Gamma_n \gg \Gamma_\gamma$, and radiative capture plays a minor role. In most heavy nuclei, on the other hand, levels are closely spaced, $\Gamma_\gamma \gg \Gamma_n$, and radiative capture is the predominant resonance reaction. The properties of a number of slow-neutron resonances are summarized in Table 9. The values of the resonance energy and level widths are given, as well as the deduced values of the level spacings, derived from Eq. (37a), for comparison with the observed (average) spacing between levels.

Of particular interest in the study and use (to produce artificially radioactive nuclei, for instance) of radiative capture is the so-called thermal neutron capture cross section, $\sigma_{th}(n,\gamma)$. This cross section has been variously defined, sometimes in a not very precise fashion. We

TABLE 9

PROPERTIES OF SOME SLOW-NEUTRON RESONANCES—MAINLY CAPTURE †

Target Nucleus	E_r (ev)	Γ_γ (ev) ‡	$f\Gamma_n$ (10^{-3} ev) §	D^* (ev) ‖	D_{obs} (ev)
$_{17}Cl^{35}$	-75	0.3	1.64×10^3	2,200	
$_{25}Mn^{55}$	345	0.2	12×10^3	7,700	10,000
$_{27}Co^{59}$	123	0.3	2.4×10^3	2,800	10,000
$_{30}Zn$	520		$5\text{--}25 \times 10^3$	2–8,000	>500
$_{31}Ga^{(69, 71)}$	98	(0.3)	130	90	<100
$_{32}Ge$	95		3–900	2–600	
$_{33}As^{75}$	46	0.05	110	120	50
$_{35}Br^{(85, 87)}$	36	(0.1)	35	86	30
$_{42}Mo^{95}$	46	(0.1)	450	1,000	50
$_{45}Rh^{103}$	1.26	0.20	0.45	6	
$_{46}Pd^{108}$	25	0.14	~40	~60	>10
$_{47}Ag^{107}$	15.9	~0.11	~5	~10	~20
$_{47}Ag^{109}$	5.17	0.16	8.2	34	~20
$_{48}Cd^{113}$	0.176	0.115	0.46	10	~25
$_{49}In^{115}$	1.45	0.08	1.2	14	6
	3.86	(0.08)	0.2	2	6
	9	(0.08)	0.5	5	6
$_{51}Sb^{(121, 123)}$	5.8	(0.1)	~0.3	~2	7
	15	(0.1)	~2	~8	7
$_{52}Te^{123}$	2.2	(0.1)	8	70	~1
$_{53}I^{127}$	19.4	0.45	0.38	1.2	15
$_{62}Sm^{149}$	0.096	0.074	0.31	13	2

TABLE 9 (*Continued*)

PROPERTIES OF SOME SLOW-NEUTRON RESONANCES—MAINLY CAPTURE †

Target Nucleus	E_r (ev)	Γ_γ (ev) ‡	$f\Gamma_n$ (10^{-3} ev) §	D^* (ev) ‖	D_{obs} (ev)
$_{63}Eu^{151}$	−0.011	0.081	0.004	0.5	∼3
$_{63}Eu^{153}$	0.47	0.20	0.9	18	∼3
$_{64}Gd^{157}$	0.028	0.12	0.4	30	
$_{66}Dy^{(161, 163)}$	1.74	(0.1)	3	30	∼3
$_{72}Hf^{177}$	1.08	0.12	0.9	12	2
	2.34	0.16	2.8	26	2
$_{72}Hf^{178}$	7.6	(0.1)	56	150	
$_{73}Ta^{181}$	6.1		0.0007	0.04	5
	10.3	0.2	0.85	3.8	5
	13.6	(0.1)	0.45	1.8	5
	20	(0.1)	0.7	2.2	5
$_{74}W^{182}$	4.15	0.07	1.1	4	∼20
$_{74}W^{183}$	7.8	(0.1)	1.0	5.3	20
$_{74}W^{(184)}$	∼200	(0.1)	∼400	∼200	∼100
$_{74}W^{186}$	19.25	0.15	250	400	∼150
$_{75}Re^{185}$	4.4		0.3	2	5
	11	(0.1)	3.5	15	5
$_{75}Re^{187}$	2.15	0.14	0.43	4.2	3
	5.9		0.09	0.5	3
	7.2		0.40	2.1	3
$_{76}Os^{(189)}$	6.5	(0.1)	1.6	9	6
	8.8	(0.1)	7.5	36	6
$_{77}Ir^{(191, 193)}$	0.64	0.10	0.2	4	2
$_{77}Ir^{193}$	1.27	∼0.15	0.4	5	2

TABLE 9 (*Continued*)

PROPERTIES OF SOME SLOW-NEUTRON RESONANCES—MAINLY CAPTURE †

Target Nucleus	E_r (ev)	Γ_γ (ev) ‡	$f\Gamma_n\,(10^{-3}\,\text{ev})$ §	D^* (ev) ‖	D_{obs} (ev)
$_{78}\text{Pt}^{(195)}$	11.5	(0.1)	6.5	27	10
	18.2	(0.1)	5.5	19	10
$_{79}\text{Au}^{197}$	4.87	0.15	21	136	~50
$_{80}\text{Hg}^{(199,\,201)}$	−2.0	(0.1)	25	250	~15
	35.5	(0.1)	80	190	~15
$_{92}\text{U}^{238}$	~11	~0.20	~8.6	~20	

† This table represents a complete re-evaluation of the data available in the open literature up to the summer of 1952. The measurements, upon which the constants are based, are so numerous that we have not attempted to include references to them in the table. Instead, the reader is referred to previous compilations, of which the most complete are those of Blatt and Weisskopf (B34), of Wigner (W31), and of Teichmann and Wigner [Phys. Rev., **87**, 123 (1952)]. Special attention is called to the most recent neutron cross section compilation prepared by the AEC Neutron Cross Section Advisory Group and issued by the U. S. Department of Commerce, Office of Technical Services, as document AECU-2040 (May 15, 1952). We gratefully acknowledge private communications of unpublished results by the Harwell time-of-flight velocity selector group (M26) and by the Argonne fast chopper group (whose members include L. M. Bollinger, R. R. Palmer, and S. P. Harris). Other data, pertaining to scattering resonances, can be found in Table 6.

‡ The values enclosed in parentheses have been assumed in order to compute $f\Gamma_n$ from the measured value of $\sigma_0\Gamma^2$.

§ The numbers quoted are at the resonance energy, except for the negative energy resonances, where the neutron width is for the energy $E = |E_r|$.

‖ D^* is computed from Eq. (37a): $D^* = \pi K_0 \Gamma_n / 2k$. When the statistical factor f is not known, it is assumed to be 1 for even-even target nuclei and $\frac{1}{2}$ for odd-A target nuclei.

shall define it as the average, over a neutron flux with a Maxwellian energy distribution (Eq. 3), of the slow neutron (n,γ) cross section,

$$\sigma_{th}(n,\gamma) = \frac{\int_0^{E'} \sigma(n,\gamma)\, d\phi(E,E_0)}{\int_0^{E'} d\phi(E,E_0)} \qquad (78)$$

The cut-off energy, E', is chosen to be sufficiently large so that only a very small fraction of the Maxwell distribution is at energies $E > E'$. (Most frequently, the cadmium cut-off, $E' \sim 0.3$–0.5 ev is used; for $E_0 = \frac{1}{40}$ ev, less than 10^{-4} of the neutrons have $E > E'$.) The cut-off is introduced for purely practical reasons, since (1) the cross sections above ~ 1 ev, which frequently show many resonances, are not well known, and (2) most methods for producing thermal neutrons give spectra which, above ~ 1 ev, have a $1/E$ "tail" superimposed on the Maxwell distribution. Unless otherwise specified, thermal neutron cross sections are taken to correspond to the Maxwell distribution at a temperature of $\sim 300°K$ ($E_0 = \frac{1}{40}$ ev, $v_0 = 2.2 \times 10^5$ cm/sec).

If $\sigma(n,\gamma)$ is a known function of E, σ_{th} can be computed in a straight-forward fashion. For nuclei in which the first resonance is relatively far from thermal energies, the (n,γ) cross section obeys the $1/v$ law,

$$\sigma(n,\gamma) = \frac{\sigma_0 v_0}{v} \qquad (59a)$$

and

$$\sigma_{th} = \frac{\sigma_0 v_0 \int_0^{E'} v^2 e^{-v^2/v_0^2}\, dv}{\int_0^{E'} v^3 e^{-v^2/v_0^2}\, dv} = \frac{\pi^{1/2}}{2} \sigma_0 \qquad (79)$$

The thermal neutron (n,γ) cross section may deviate from the $1/v$ law in a spectacular fashion if a resonance happens to fall in the thermal region. The cross section of cadmium, shown in Fig. 20a, is a case in point. However, even if the closest resonance does not fall in the thermal region, it may still cause serious deviations from a $1/v$ behavior for thermal neutrons. The cross sections of iridium (Fig. 7d) and of mercury (Fig. 20b) show, respectively, the effects of a close positive-energy ($E_r > 0$) and negative-energy ($E_r < 0$) resonance. Because of such effects, considerable care must be taken in interpreting measurements of σ_{th} in terms of σ_0.

Table 10 is a collection of thermal neutron (n,γ) capture cross sections.

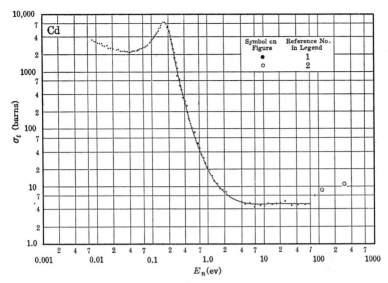

(1) Rainwater, Havens, Wu, and Dunning, Phys. Rev., **71**, 65 (1947).   (2) C. T. Hibdon and C. O. Muehlhause, Phys. Rev., **76**, 100 (1949).   Also see W. H. Zinn, Phys. Rev., **71**, 575 (1947); Sawyer, Wollan, Bernstein, and Peterson, Phys. Rev., **72**, 109 (1947).

(a)

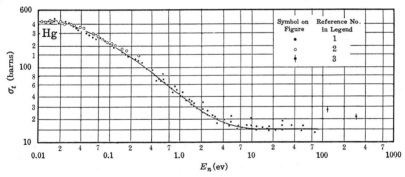

(1) W. W. Havens, Jr., and L. J. Rainwater, Phys. Rev., **70**, 154 (1946).   (2) L. B. Borst *et al.* (unpublished).   (3) C. T. Hibdon and C. O. Muehlhause, Phys. Rev., **76**, 100 (1949).

(b)

Fig. 20.   Slow-neutron cross sections showing the effects of a resonance at or near thermal energies; from Adair (A2).   (a) Cadmium, $E_r = 0.176$ ev.   Note the sharp cut-off at ~0.3–0.5 ev.   (b) Mercury, $E_r = -2.0$ ev, showing the influence of a close negative-energy resonance.

TABLE 10

RADIATIVE CAPTURE CROSS SECTIONS FOR SLOW NEUTRONS

Element	A †	$\sigma(n,\gamma)$ ‡ (barns)	Neutron Energy §	E_r for Closest ‖ Observed Resonance (ev)	References ¶
$_1$H	1	0.313 ± 0.013	v_0		R20
	2	0.00032	P		R20
$_3$Li	7	0.033	th		W10, H68
$_4$Be	9	0.0085	v_0	620,000	R20
$_5$B	11	<0.05	th	430,000	W10
$_6$C		0.0045	th	~4,000,000	R20
	13	~0.1	th		W10
	14	<200	th		W10
$_7$N	15	0.000024	th		††
$_8$O		0.00028 ± 0.00022	P	440,000	R20
	18	0.00022	th		W10, S22
$_9$F	19	0.0094 ± 0.0015	P	32,000	R20, S24
$_{10}$Ne		<2.8	P		††
$_{11}$Na	23	0.50	th, P	3,000	R20, H42, P23, C21
$_{12}$Mg		0.057	P	230,000	W10, H42, P23, C21
	24	0.033	P		‡‡
	25	0.27	P		‡‡
	26	0.05	th, P		S24, ‡‡
$_{13}$Al	27	0.22	P	2,300	W10, H42, P23, C21
$_{14}$Si		0.13	P, th	600,000	W10, H42, P23, T14, C21
	28	0.08	P		‡‡
	29	0.27	P		‡‡
	30	0.12	th, P		S24, ‡‡
$_{15}$P	31	0.17	P		W10, P23, C21
$_{16}$S		0.49 ± 0.05	v_0	111,000	R20
	34	0.26	th		W10, S24
	36	0.14	th		W10
$_{17}$Cl		32	P		W10, H42, P23, C21
	35	42	th	−75	H59
	37	0.6	th	1,800	W10, S24
$_{18}$A		0.77	v_0	>1,000	R20
	40	1.2	P		W10
$_{19}$K		2.0	P	65,000	W10, H42, C21, P23
	39	~3	th		W10, H31
	41	1.0	th		W10, S24

TABLE 10 (*Continued*)

RADIATIVE CAPTURE CROSS SECTIONS FOR SLOW NEUTRONS

Element	A †	$\sigma(n,\gamma)$ ‡ (barns)	Neutron Energy §	E_r for Closest ‖ Observed Resonance (ev)	References ¶
$_{20}$Ca		0.41	P	~200,000	W10, H42, P23, C21
	44	0.6	*th*		W10, S24
	48	1	P		††
$_{21}$Sc	45	12	P		W10, P23
	(20 s)	10	P		W10, G17
	(85 d)	12	P, *th*		W10, S24, ††
$_{22}$Ti		5.6	P		W10, H42, C21, P23
	46	0.57	P		‡‡
	47	1.62	P		‡‡
	48	7.98	P		‡‡
	49	1.80	P		‡‡
	50	0.14	P, *th*		W10, S24, ‡‡
$_{23}$V		4.7	P		W10, H42, C21, P23
	51	4.5	*th*	2,700	W10, S24
$_{24}$Cr		2.9	P	4,200	W10, R20, H42, C21, P23
	50	16.3	P		W10, ‡‡
	52	0.73	P		W10, ‡‡
	53	17.5	P		W10, ‡‡
	54	0.006	P, *th*		W10, S24
$_{25}$Mn	55	12.6	P	345	W10, H42, C21, P23
$_{26}$Fe		2.43	P	~10,000	W10, H42, C21, P23
	54	2.1	P		P22
	56	3.1	P		P22
	57	0.5	P		P22
	58	0.36	*th*		W10, S24
$_{27}$Co	59	35	P	120	W10, H42, C21, P23
	(10.7 m)	0.66	*th*		W10, S24
	(5.3 y)	22	*th*		W10, S24
$_{28}$Ni		4.5	P	3,600	W10, H42, C21, P23
	58	4.23	P		P22
	60	2.70	P		P22
	61	1.8	P		W10, ‡‡
	62	15	P		W10, ‡‡
	64	~2	*ih*		W10, S24
$_{29}$Cu		3.6	P	~500	W10, H42, C21, P23
	63	4.29	P		W10, ‡‡
	65	2.11	P		W10, ‡‡
$_{30}$Zn		1.06	P	480	W10, H42, C21, P23
	64	0.5	*th*		W10, S24
	68 (13.8 h)	0.9	*'h*		W10, H72
	(52 m)	0.1	*th*		W10, H72
	70	0.085	*h*		W10, H72

TABLE 10 (*Continued*)

RADIATIVE CAPTURE CROSS SECTIONS FOR SLOW NEUTRONS

Element	A †	$\sigma(n,\gamma)$ ‡ (barns)	Neutron Energy §	E_r for Closest ‖ Observed Resonance (ev)	References ¶
$_{31}$Ga		2.9	P	100–500	W10, H42, P23
	69	1.4	th		W10, H72
	71	3.4	th		W10, S24
$_{32}$Ge		2.4	P	95	W10, H42, P23
	70	3.3	P		W10, ‡‡
	72	0.94	P		‡‡
	73	13.7	P		‡‡
	74	0.60	P, th		‡‡, S24
	76	0.35	P		‡‡
	(59 s)	0.03	P, th		A33, ††
	(12 h)	0.2	P, th		S24, ††
$_{33}$As	75	4.2	P		W10, H42, P23, C21, ††
$_{34}$Se		12.0	P		W10, H42, C21, P23
	74	44	P		‡‡, S24
	76	82	P		‡‡, A33
	77	40	P		‡‡
	80 (17 m)	0.5	th		W10, S24
	(59 m)	0.03	th		W10, S24
	82 (67 s)	0.05	th		W10, A33
	(25 m)	0.004	th		W10, A33
$_{35}$Br		6.5	P	36	W10, H42, P23, C21
	79 (18 m)	8.5	th		W10, H72, ††
	(4.4 h)	2.9	th		W10, H72, ††
	81	2.3	th		W10, S24
$_{36}$Kr		28	P		††
	78	0.3	th		W10, ††
	80	95	P		††
	82	45	P		††
	83	205	P		††
	84 (4.4 h)	0.1	th		W10, ††
	(10 y)	0.06	th		W10, ††
	86	0.06	th		W10, ††
	87 *	<470	th		W10, ††
$_{37}$Rb		0.70	P		W10, P23
	85	0.7	th		W10, S24
	87	0.12	th		W10, S24
	88 *	<200	th		W10
$_{38}$Sr		1.2	P		W10, H42, P23, C21, ††
	86	1.3	th		W10, S24
	88	0.005	th		W10, S24
	89 *	<110	P		W10
	90 *	~1	P		W10
$_{39}$Y	89	1.4	P		W10, P23

TABLE 10 (*Continued*)

RADIATIVE CAPTURE CROSS SECTIONS FOR SLOW NEUTRONS

Element	A †	$\sigma(n,\gamma)$ ‡ (barns)	Neutron Energy §	E_r for Closest ‖ Observed Resonance (ev)	References ¶
$_{40}$Zr		0.20	P, th		W10, R20, H42, P23, C21
	90	~0.1	P		W10, ‡‡
	91	1.52	P		W10, ‡‡
	92	~0.25	P		W10, ‡‡
	94	~0.08	P		W10, ‡‡
	96	~0.1	P		W10, ‡‡
$_{41}$Nb	93	1.1	P		W10, H42, C21, P23, ††
$_{42}$Mo		2.4	P		W10, H42, P23, C21, ††
	92	<0.001	th		W10, S24
	95	13.4	P		W10, ‡‡
	96	1.2	P		W10, ‡‡
	97	2.1	P		W10, ‡‡
	98	~0.38	P, th		W10, S24, ‡‡
	100	~0.5	P, th		W10, S24, ‡‡
$_{44}$Ru		2.5	P	9.4	W10, H42, P23, ††
	96	0.01	th		W10, ††
	102	1.2	th		W10, S24
	104	0.7	th		W10, S24
$_{45}$Rh	103	150	P	1.3	W10, H42, P23
	(44 s)	137	th		W10, S24
	(4.3 m)	12	th		W10, S24
$_{46}$Pd		8	P		W10, H42, P23, C21
	108	11	th	24	W10, S24
	110	0.4	th		W10, S24
$_{47}$Ag		60	P, th		R20, H42, P23, ††
	107	30	P	45	P22
	109	84	P	5.1	P22
	(22 s)	~100	th		W10, S24, ††
	(225 d)	2.3	th		W10, S24, ††
$_{48}$Cd		2,400	v_0		R20, ††
		3,500	P		P23
	106	1	th		††
	110	0.2	th		W10, G17
	113	19,500	v_0	0.18	W10, M39, D22, ††
	114 (2.3 d)	1.1	th		W10, S23
	(43 d)	0.14	th		W10, S23
	116	1.4	th	~100	W10, S23
$_{49}$In		190	v_0, P		R20, P23
	113 (72 s)	2.0	th	3.8	W10, G17
	(50 d)	56	th		W10, S24
	115 (13 s)	52	th	1.44	W10, S24
	(54 m)	145	th		W10, S24

TABLE 10 (*Continued*)

RADIATIVE CAPTURE CROSS SECTIONS FOR SLOW NEUTRONS

Element	A †	$\sigma(n,\gamma)$ ‡ (barns)	Neutron Energy §	E_r for Closest ‖ Observed Resonance (ev)	References ¶
$_{50}$Sn		0.65	P, v_0		H42, P23, C21, R20
	112	1.1	*th*		W10, S24
	118 (279 d)	0.01	*th*		W10, M29, B55
	120	0.22	*th*		W10, S24
	122 (40 m)	0.30	*th*		W10, S24
	124 (10 m)	0.6	*th*		W10, S24
	(10 d)	0.15	*th*		W10, S24
$_{51}$Sb		6.4	P	5.8	W10, H42, P23, C21
	121	6.8	*th*		W10, S24
	123 (1.3 m)	0.03	*th*		W10, D13, ††
	(21 m)	0.03	*th*		††
	(60 d)	2.5	*th*		W10, S24
$_{52}$Te		4.5	P	>300	W10, H42, P23, ††
	120	68	P		‡‡
	122	2.7	P		W10, H62, ‡‡
	123	390	P		‡‡
	124	6.5	P		W10, H62, ‡‡
	125	1.5	P		‡‡
	126 (9.3 h)	0.8	*th*		W10, S24
	(90 d)	0.07	*th*		W10, S24
	128 (72 m)	0.13	*th*		W10, S24
	(32 d)	0.015	*th*		W10, S24
	130 (25 m)	0.22	*th*		W10, S24
	(30 h)	<0.008	*th*		W10, S24
$_{53}$I	127	6.7	P	20	W10, H42, P23, C21
	129 *	~10	*th*		W10, ††
	131 *	~600	*th*		W10, ††
$_{54}$Xe		31	*th*		R20
	128	<5	P		††
	129	~45	P		††
	130	<5	P		††
	131	120	P		††
	132	0.2	*th*		W10, ††
	134	0.2	*th*		W10, ††
	135 *	3.5×10^6	P		U2
	136	0.15	*th*		W10, ††
$_{55}$Cs	133	29	P		W10, H42, P23, R20, ††
	(3h)	0.016	*th*		W10, S24
	(2.3 y)	26	*th*		W10, S24
	135 *	~15	*th*		W10, S57
	137 *	<2	*th*		††
$_{56}$Ba		1.2	P		W10, H42, C21, P23
	130	~3	*th*		W10, K3, ††
	132 (>20 y)	~6	*th*		W10, K3, ††
	138	0.5	*th*		W10, S24
	139 *	4	*th*		W10, Y1, ††

TABLE 10 (*Continued*)

RADIATIVE CAPTURE CROSS SECTIONS FOR SLOW NEUTRONS

Element	A †	$\sigma(n,\gamma)$ ‡ (barns)	Neutron Energy §	E_r for Closest ‖ Observed Resonance (ev)	References ¶
$_{57}$La		8.9	P		W10, H42, P23
	139	8.4	th		W10, S24
	140 *	~3	th		W10, K3
$_{58}$Ce		0.8	P		W10, H42, P23
	138	~0.4	th		††
	140	0.27	th		W10, K3, ††
	142	0.85	th		W10, K3, ††
$_{59}$Pr	141	11.2	P	(~10?)	W10, P23
$_{60}$Nd		44	P		W10, H42, P23, ††
	142	<12	P		W10, H55
	143	240	P		W10, H55
	144	<15	P		W10, H55
	145	<30	P		W10, H55
	146	1.8	th		W10, B54, ††
	148	3.7	th		W10, B54, ††
	150	<45	P		W10, H55
$_{61}$Pm	147 *	~60	th		W10, P4
$_{62}$Sm		6,500	v_0		R20
		10,000	P		W10, H42, P23
	149	~50,000	P	0.096	W10, ††
	151	~7,000	P		††
	152	150	th	10	W10, S24, B54, ††
	154	5.5	th		W10, S24
$_{63}$Eu		4,200	P		W10, P23
	151	~9,000	P	−0.011	W10, H50, ††
	(9 h)	1,400	th		W10, S24
	152 *	5,500	P		W10, H50, ††
	153	420	P	0.465	W10, H50, ††
	154 *	1,500	P		W10, H50, ††
	155 *	14,000	P		W10, H50, ††
$_{64}$Gd		36,000	P	0.03	W10, H42, C21, P23
	152	<125	th		W10, S24
	155	70,000	P		W10, L4
	157	120,000	P		W10, L4, ††
	158	~4	th		W10, B77, ††
	160	~0.15	th		W10, B77, ††
$_{65}$Tb	159	44	P		W10, P23
$_{66}$Dy		890	P	−1.01; 1.74	P23
		1,150	v_0		W10, B65
	164 (1.3 m)	3,000	th		W10, ††
	(2.4 h)	2,600	th		W10, S24, ††
	165 *	5,000	th		W10, K10

TABLE 10 (*Continued*)

RADIATIVE CAPTURE CROSS SECTIONS FOR SLOW NEUTRONS

Element	A †	$\sigma(n,\gamma)$ ‡ (barns)	Neutron Energy §	E_r for Closest ‖ Observed Resonance (ev)	References ¶
$_{67}$Ho	165	64	P		W10, P23
$_{68}$Er		166	P	~0.5	W10, P23
	170	>7	th		W10, B54
$_{69}$Tm	169	118	P		W10, P23
$_{70}$Yb		36	P		W10, P23
	168	30,000	th		W10, A35, ††
	174	60	th		W10, A35, ††
	176	6.5	th		W10, A35, ††
$_{71}$Lu		108	P		W10, P23
	175 (3.7 h)	25	th		W10, S24, ††
	176	4,000	th		W10, S24, ††
$_{72}$Hf		120	P	~1.0	W10, H42, P23, C21
	177	500	P		††
	180	10	th		W10, S24
$_{73}$Ta	181	21	P	4.1	W10, H42, P23, C21
	(16 m)	0.030	th		W10, S24, ††
	(117 d)	21	th		W10, S24
$_{74}$W		19	P		W10, H42, P23, C21
	180	~2	th		L19
	182			4	
	183			7.4	
	184	2.1	th		W10, S24
	186	40	th	19.5	W10, S24, ††
	187 *	~80	th		L19
$_{75}$Re		84	P	2.3	W10, P23, ††
	185	100	th		††
	187	75	th		††
$_{76}$Os		14.7	P	6.5	W10, P23
	184	~20	th		L19
	190	8	th		W10, S24
	192	1.6	th		W10, S24
	193 *	~190	th		L19
$_{77}$Ir		440	P	0.64	W10, H42, P23
	191 (1.5 m)	260	th		W10, G15, ††
	(70 d)	740	th		W10, S24, ††
	193	130	th	(1.3)	W10, S24
$_{78}$Pt		8.1	P	11.5	W10, H42, P23, C21, ††
	192	90	th		W10, S24, ††
	196 (18 h)	1.1	th		W10, S24
	(82 d)	0.055	th		††
	198	3.9	th		W10, S24

TABLE 10 *(Continued)*

RADIATIVE CAPTURE CROSS SECTIONS FOR SLOW NEUTRONS

Element	A †	$\sigma(n,\gamma)$ ‡ (barns)	Neutron Energy §	E_r for Closest ‖ Observed Resonance (ev)	References ¶
$_{79}$Au	197	95	*P, th*	4.8	W10, H42, P23, S24, ††
	198 *	~16,000	*th*		††
$_{80}$Hg		400	v_0		G20
		340	*P*	−2.0	W10, H42, P23, ††
	196	3,100	*P*		W10, I1
	199	2,500	*P*		W10, I1
	200	<60	*P*		W10, I1
	201	<60	*P*		W10, I1
	202	3.0	*th*		W10, S24, ††
	204	0.43	*th*		W10, S24, ††
$_{81}$Tl		3.3	*P*	260	W10, H42, P23
	203	8	*th*		W10, S24, ††
	205	0.10	*th*		W10, S24, ††
$_{82}$Pb		0.17	*P*		W10, H42, P23, C21, ††
	206			130,000	
	208	0.0006	*th*	350,000	W10, ††
$_{83}$Bi	209	0.032	*P*		W10, H42, ††
	(5 d)	0.017	*th*		W10, S24, ††
$_{90}$Th	232 *	7.0	*P, th*		R20, ††
$_{92}$U		3.5	v_0		U2
	235 *	101	v_0		U2
	238 *	2.80	v_0	11	U2
$_{94}$Pu	239 *	361	v_0		U2
$_{95}$Am	241 *	890	*P*		H29
	(16 h)	570	*P*		H29

† The atomic number A refers to the target nucleus. When more than one activity results from the radiative capture the half-life of the particular activity, to which the figures in that row pertain, is shown in parentheses. An asterisk indicates that the target nucleus is itself radioactive.

‡ Unless otherwise indicated, the uncertainty can be assumed to be in the last significant figure.

§ The symbols have the following meanings:

v_0 = neutrons of velocity 2200 m/sec ($E = \frac{1}{40}$ ev)

P = pile neutrons, usually indicating measurement by the "danger coefficient" method

th = thermal neutron distribution for a temperature of ~300°K (usually indicates measurement by the "activation" technique)

‖ The closest observed resonance is not necessarily the closest resonance, since most elements have not been carefully investigated above ~10 ev. Negative resonances are shown when known.

¶ This compilation leans heavily on the excellent and complete collection of nuclear data by Way and co-workers (W10). The compilation of Ross and Story (R20), although unfortunately somewhat out of date, has been most useful.

†† This table has been checked against a preliminary version of the extensive collection of the A.E.C. Cross Sections Committee, D. J. Hughes, Chairman. A number of values from that table have been added to this one. Furthermore, we have inclined somewhat to the choices, between alternative values, made by that committee. The responsibility for the choices, however, rests on our shoulders. We gratefully acknowledge our indebtedness to D. J. Hughes and his committee.

‡‡ We are grateful to H. Pomerance of the Oak Ridge National Laboratory for making available unpublished measurements of his group based on the "danger coefficient" method (P23)

(b) *Intermediate Neutrons.* For light and medium nuclei, (n,γ) cross sections for intermediate neutrons are very small, since $\Gamma_\gamma \ll \Gamma_n$. In heavy nuclei, the radiative capture cross sections are still quite appreciable in this energy range. The average (over many resonances) cross section is given by Eqs. (60), (62), (62a), and (63):

$$\overline{\sigma(n,\gamma)} = \frac{2\pi^2 \lambdabar^2 \Gamma_n \Gamma_\gamma}{D\Gamma} \cong \left(\frac{500}{E^{1/2}}\right)\left(\frac{\Gamma_\gamma}{\Gamma}\right) \text{ barns} \qquad (60a)$$

(E is in ev). Thus, the cross section follows a $1/v$ law at low energies, and a $1/E$ law at high energies, the transition occurring when $\Gamma_n \approx \Gamma_\gamma$; for heavy nuclei, this occurs in the intermediate region.

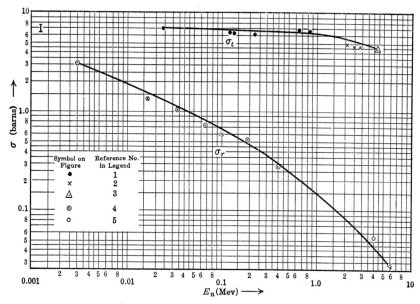

Symbol on Figure	Reference No. in Legend
•	1
×	2
△	3
⊗	4
○	5

(1) R. Fields *et al.*, Phys. Rev., **71**, 508 (1947).   (2) H. Aoki, Proc. Phys.-Math. Soc. Japan, **21**, 232 (1939).   (3) J. R. Dunning *et al.*, Phys. Rev., **48**, 265 (1935).   (4) E. Segrè *et al.* (unpublished).   (5) J. Marshall and L. Szilard (unpublished).

Fig. 21.   Radiative capture cross section, $\overline{\sigma(n,\gamma)}$, for iodine in the intermediate-neutron energy range. Also shown is the total cross section, σ_t. From Goldsmith, Ibser, and Feld (G20).

(n,γ) cross sections for intermediate neutrons have not been so extensively investigated as those for slow neutrons. Among the light and medium elements, fluorine, aluminum, and vanadium have been studied by Barschall and co-workers (see the compilation of Adair, A2); the $\sigma(n,\gamma)$ *vs.* E curves show the expected resonances; the magnitude of

$\sigma(n,\gamma)$ is small—of the order of millibarns. Curves of $\overline{\sigma(n,\gamma)}$ vs. E have been obtained, for a number of heavy elements, by Segrè and co-workers; their results are included in the compilation of Goldsmith, Ibser, and Feld (G20). One of these, for iodine, is reproduced in Fig. 21. The cross section shows the expected behavior (see Eq. 60a). Measurements on fifteen isotopes, using Sb-Be neutrons ($E \approx 35$ kev), have been reported by Hummel and Hamermesh (H77).

(c) *Fast Neutrons.* In the fast-neutron energy region, the behavior of $\sigma(n,\gamma)$ will differ from that described in the previous section for two main reasons: (1) With the inception of the possibility of inelastic scattering, the competition in the de-excitation of the compound nucleus becomes even less favorable to the radiative process. (2) For fast neutrons the possibility of compound nucleus formation by neutrons of $l > 0$ becomes appreciable, so that relationships such as Eq. (62b), based upon $l = 0$ capture only, are no longer strictly valid. This factor tends to compensate for the decrease of radiative capture due to inelastic scattering, since the inelastic re-emission of $l > 0$ neutrons is energetically unfavored.

Hughes, Spatz, and Goldstein (H72) have made a systematic survey, covering 32 isotopes, of (n,γ) cross sections at an energy of ~ 1 Mev. Their results are summarized in Fig. 22. The most significant features of these results are: (1) a rapid increase of $\sigma(n,\gamma)$ with A (roughly exponential), from ≈ 1 millibarn at $A \approx 35$ to ≈ 200 mb at $A \approx 110$; (2) roughly constant (n,γ) cross sections, of ~ 100 mb, for $A \gtrsim 120$; (3) marked deviations from the norm for target nuclei containing neutron closed shells (e.g., Ba^{138}, 82 neutrons; Pb^{208} and Bi^{209}, 126 neutrons). These magic number nuclei have anomalously small (n,γ) cross sections of ~ 2–3 mb. Since the radiative capture cross sections at ~ 1 Mev are essentially inversely proportional to the compound nucleus level spacing at the excitation energy $(\epsilon + 1)$ Mev (see Eqs. 60a and 37, with $\Gamma \approx \Gamma_n \gg \Gamma_\gamma$), the general dependence on atomic number is in reasonable agreement with expectation. The anomalous behavior of the magic number nuclei reflects their small binding energies for an additional neutron and, possibly, large level spacing.

Hughes *et al.* (H72) have also surveyed the available data on the dependence of $\sigma(n,\gamma)$ upon neutron energy, for energies between ~ 0.1 and ~ 10 Mev. While the results of the different investigators are in rather poor agreement with regard to the absolute values of $\sigma(n,\gamma)$, the relative values seem to follow, roughly, a $\sim 1/E$ law. There are, however, a number of unexplained exceptions, notably In^{115}, in which $\sigma(n,\gamma)$ appears to be constant over the energy range 0.1 to 1 Mev.

There are almost no data available on radiative capture in the very fast- and ultrafast-neutron regions. At these energies, $\sigma(n,\gamma)$ is expected to be very small for all nuclei.

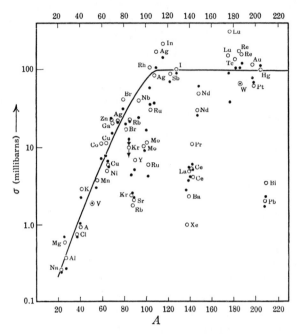

Fig. 22. Activation (n,γ) cross sections for fission neutrons (~1 Mev, average energy) *vs.* atomic weight, A. The points lying appreciably below the smooth curve all correspond to neutron numbers near or at one of the "magic" values—50, 82, 126. We are indebted to Hughes, Garth, and Eggler (private communication) for this figure. Earlier results are reported and discussed by Hughes, Spatz, and Goldstein (H72).

3. Charged Particle Reactions. After the capture of a neutron, the compound nucleus can sometimes decay by emission of a charged particle. Among the possible reactions, (n,p) and (n,α) are most frequently encountered. The energy dependence of a charged particle reaction is governed by Eq. (42): $\sigma(n,a) = \sigma_c \Gamma_a / \Gamma$.

(*a*) *Slow Neutrons.* For a charged particle reaction to take place with slow neutrons, it is necessary that the reaction be exoergic $(Q > 0)$. Furthermore, if the reaction is to compete favorably, the available energy must be sufficiently great to allow appreciable penetration of the Coulomb barrier (the factor G_a in Eqs. 32 and 37). These considerations limit the observable slow-neutron (n,p) and (n,α) reactions to light nuclei. The properties of the most important slow-neutron charged particle reactions are summarized in Table 11. The cross sections in the third column refer to the isotopes involved in the reaction; these must be multiplied by the relative abundances (fifth column) to obtain the cross sections of the normal elements.

TABLE 11

PROPERTIES OF EXOERGIC (n,p) AND (n,α) REACTIONS

Reaction	Q Value (Mev)	Isotopic Cross Section at $v_0 = 2.2 \times 10^5$ cm/sec (barns)	References	Relative Abundance of Isotope in Normal Element (%)
$He^3(n,p)H^3$	0.7637	5060 ± 200	T16, C26, K14	$1 - 10 \times 10^{-5}$
$Li^6(n,\alpha)H^3$	4.785	910 ± 100	T16, R20	7.4
$B^{10}(n,\alpha)Li^7$	2.791	3770 ± 110 †	T16, R20	18.83
$N^{14}(n,p)C^{14}$	0.626	1.76 ± 0.05	T16, C26	100
$Cl^{35}(n,p)S^{35}$	0.62	~0.3	W10	75.4

† A more recent value of the $B^{10}(n,\alpha)$ cross section is 3990 b (AEC Neutron Cross Section Advisory Group, AECU-2040, U. S. Department of Commerce, May 15, 1952). This cross section is of special significance since a majority of the quoted thermal neutron absorption cross sections, in this and in Table 10, are based on a comparison with boron absorption. Thus a change in the accepted value of this cross section is directly reflected in a change, of equal fractional magnitude, in many of the other values quoted.

The cross sections are given at a single neutron energy, 0.025 ev. Since these reactions fully satisfy the conditions for Eqs. (58) and (59), they can be assumed to follow the $1/v$ law in the slow-neutron range. Owing to the large level spacings of such light nuclei, the first resonances occur well into the intermediate- or even the fast-neutron region. Furthermore, owing to the large Q values (available charged particle energy) of these reactions, the reaction widths are essentially constant over a wide energy range. Thus, these reactions obey the $1/v$ law over a comparatively broad energy region which, for the $B^{10}(n,\alpha)$ reaction, for instance, extends to $>10^4$ ev.

(b) *Intermediate Neutrons.* For intermediate neutrons, charged particle reaction cross sections depart from the $1/v$ law because (1) resonances are present in or close to the intermediate-energy region, and (2) the particle width, Γ_a, is no longer independent of the neutron energy. A resonance in the cross section for the formation of the compound nucleus is, of course, also a resonance in the reactions involved in the compound nucleus decay, including the charged particle reactions (see, for instance, the compilation of Adair, A2, figures 8, 9, and 12).

An interesting example of charged particle reaction resonances is N^{14}, which has been investigated with good resolution for neutron energies between ~ 0.2 and 2 Mev, and is shown in Fig. 23. In addition to the (n,p) reaction, previously discussed, the $N^{14}(n,\alpha)B^{11}$ reaction is also in evidence. This reaction is slightly endoergic ($Q \cong -0.26$ Mev), and does not have an appreciable cross section below ~ 1 Mev.

One of the most striking features of Fig. 23 is the apparent separation of the resonances (corresponding to the decay of the same compound nucleus) into predominantly (n,p)—e.g., 1.4 Mev—and (n,α)—1.8 Mev—resonances. Although at first glance this may appear to be in contradiction to the ideas of the compound nucleus picture—upon which we have leaned so heavily—the observations are, as will be seen from the following discussion, consistent with our present notions, if proper account is taken of the angular momentum and parity properties of the nuclear levels involved.[1]

The nuclei involved are N^{14}, C^{14}, B^{11} (all in their ground states), and N^{15} (in various excited states). The spins of the nuclei are: N^{14}, $I = 1$; C^{14}, $I = 0$; B^{11}, $I = \frac{3}{2}$; and their ground-state parities are: N^{14}, probably even (assumed ^3D, from the magnetic moment and to explain the long half-life for the C^{14} beta-decay); C^{14}, even; B^{11}, probably odd (from the magnetic moment). Assuming these parity assignments, the parity of the level of N^{15}, involved in the resonance, completely determines the l value of the captured neutron, even l values being associated with the states of even parity, and odd l values with odd states. From the laws of conservation of parity and angular momentum, the lowest possible l value of the emitted proton or alpha-particle is uniquely determined according to the following scheme (J is the spin of the N^{15} state involved):

l_n \ J	$\frac{1}{2}$	$\frac{3}{2}$	$\frac{5}{2}$	$\frac{7}{2}$	
0	0	2	..	..	l_p
	1	1	..	..	l_α
1	1	1	3	..	l_p
	2	0	2	..	l_α
2	0	2	2	4	l_p
	1	1	1	3	l_α

[1] The author is indebted to Professor J. M. Blatt, who first called to his attention this possibility for explaining the N^{14} resonance separation. A similar discussion has been presented by Johnson and Barschall (J5).

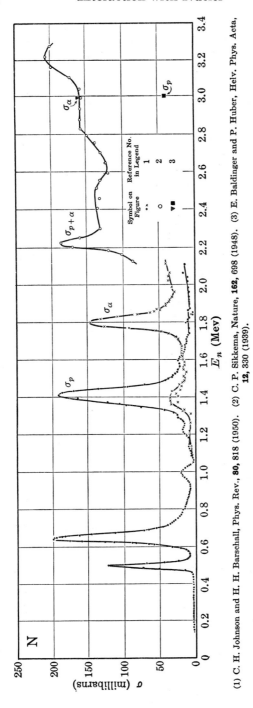

Fig. 23.   Cross sections for the $N^{14}(n,p)$ and (n,α) reactions for intermediate and fast neutrons.   The measurements up to 2.1 Mev are due to Johnson and Barschall (J5); the figure is from Adair (A2).   The total cross section in the range 0.15 to 1.45 Mev has been measured, with very good resolution, by Johnson, Petree, and Adair (J7).

(1) C. H. Johnson and H. H. Barschall, Phys. Rev., **80**, 818 (1950).   (2) C. P. Sikkema, Nature, **162**, 698 (1948).   (3) E. Baldinger and P. Huber, Helv. Phys. Acta, **12**, 330 (1939).

It is evident that for low-neutron energies and, correspondingly, low energies of the emitted proton and (especially) alpha-particle (so that small l values are favored for both incoming and outgoing particle) the resonances divide into two groups: those for which $J = \frac{1}{2}$, favoring proton emission; levels with $J \geq \frac{3}{2}$, which favor alpha-emission.

The same sort of arguments can be carried through for different assumptions concerning the parities of the nuclei. In particular, the assumption of odd parity for the N^{14} ground state (other states same as above) leads to a reversal in the division between proton-favored and alpha-favored levels; i.e., the absorption of a thermal neutron ($l_n = 0$) is followed by the emission of an $l = 1$ proton, etc. Unfortunately, the available data do not permit a choice between the two possibilities for the parity of N^{14} (J5, J7).

(c) *Fast Neutrons.* As the energy available to the charged particle becomes greater, the Gamow barrier penetration factor approaches 1, and charged particle emission is less inhibited. Thus, reactions which, although exoergic or only slightly endoergic, have very small cross sections for slow and intermediate neutrons become appreciable in the fast-neutron region. The $N^{14}(n,\alpha)$ reaction, discussed above, is one such case. Another example is $Ne^{20}(n,\alpha)O^{17}$ (J6).

There are a number of endoergic charged particle reactions whose thresholds, $E_t = -Q(A + 1)/A$, fall in the fast-neutron energy range. The cross sections for these reactions have a characteristic energy dependence, rising rapidly (from $\sigma = 0$ at the threshold) to a more-or-less constant value for energies greater than the "height" of the Gamow barrier. Figure 24 shows the measured (n,p) cross sections of two reactions (on P^{31} and S^{32}) whose thresholds fall at ~ 1 Mev.

The energy dependence of such "threshold reactions" is, at least for energies below the barrier heights, primarily determined by the probability for penetration of the Coulomb barrier by the emerging charged particle. The barrier penetration factor is a monotonically increasing function of the available energy $(E - E_t)$ and, for a given value of E, strongly dependent on the angular momentum of the charged particle; the smaller the angular momentum, the greater the penetration factor. The energy dependence of the penetration factor has been discussed by a number of authors (B24, B34, B40), and by Morrison in Part VI. In general, if the reaction can proceed with the emission of charged particles of zero angular momentum, it will prefer to do so, and the energy dependence near threshold will be determined by G_0, the Gamow factor for $l = 0$ particles. In this case the barrier height is

$$B_0 = \frac{zZe^2}{R} \tag{80}$$

where z and Z are the atomic numbers of the outgoing particle and product nucleus, respectively, and the nuclear radius is given by (B34):

$$R = 1.47A^{\frac{1}{3}} \times 10^{-13} \text{ cm} \qquad \text{for protons}$$

and

$$R = (1.30A^{\frac{1}{3}} + 1.2) \times 10^{-13} \text{ cm} \qquad \text{for alpha-particles} \qquad (80a)$$

Table 12 lists the properties of a number of useful (n,p) and (n,α) threshold reactions computed on the assumption of $l = 0$ outgoing particles.

TABLE 12

PROPERTIES OF FAST-NEUTRON THRESHOLD REACTIONS

Based on computations by Feld, Scalettar, and Szilard, (F8), and Kiehn, (K11)

Reaction	Product Nucleus Half-Life	E_t (Mev)	E (Mev) for $G_0 = 0.1$	E (Mev) for $G_0 = 0.5$	$E_t + B_0$ (Mev)
$P^{31}(n,p)Si^{31}$	2.7 h	0.97	2.8	3.8	5.3
$S^{32}(n,p)P^{32}$	14.3 d	0.96	3.0	4.1	5.6
$Al^{27}(n,p)Mg^{27}$	10 m	1.96	3.5	4.5	5.9
$Si^{28}(n,p)Al^{28}$	2.3 m	2.7	4.4	5.4	6.9
$Fe^{56}(n,p)Mn^{56}$	2.6 h	3.0	6.3	7.6	9.4
$P^{31}(n,\alpha)Al^{28}$	2.3 m	0.91	6.6	8.3	9.8
$Al^{27}(n,\alpha)Na^{24}$	14.9 h	2.44	7.5	9.1	10.9

The actual energy dependence of a given charged particle reaction is determined, in addition to the barrier penetration factor (in Γ_a), by the cross section for the formation of the compound nucleus, σ_c. Among the important aspects of the dependence of σ_c on E, the presence of resonances—especially in the light and medium nuclei, with which we are concerned—will be reflected in the reaction cross section; some of the resonances in σ_c may appear weakly or not at all in the reaction cross section because of the angular momentum and parity properties of the levels involved.

Although the Gamow penetration factor for the outgoing charged particle becomes relatively constant (it slowly approaches one but is prevented from being strictly constant or equal to one by the increasing importance of higher angular momenta and their associated angular momentum barriers) after the available energy exceeds the barrier height, B_0, the reaction cross section will not remain constant as the neutron energy is indefinitely increased. In the very fast- and ultrafast-

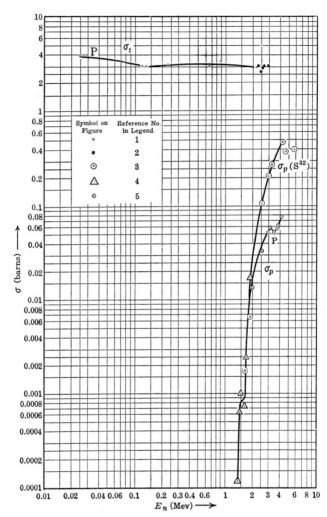

(1) R. Fields *et al.*, Phys. Rev., **71**, 508 (1947). (2) H. Aoki, Proc. Phys.-Math. Soc. Japan, **21**, 232 (1939). (3) E. D. Klema and A. O. Hanson, Phys. Rev., **73**, 106 (1948). (4) R. F. Taschek (unpublished). (5) E. Bretscher *et al.* (unpublished).

Fig. 24. The (n,p) cross sections of P^{31} and S^{32} in the fast-neutron region. Measurements between 1.4 and $\sim$6 Mev, with poor energy resolution; these curves illustrate the "threshold" behavior of endoergic charged particle reactions. Curves from Goldsmith, Ibser, and Feld (G20).

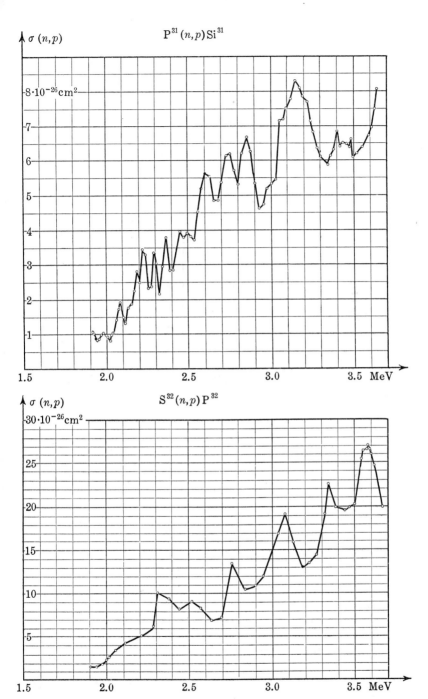

Fig. 24 (Continued). Good resolution measurements between ∼2 and 3.5 Mev, showing the effect of resonances in the compound nucleus. Curve for P³¹ due to Ricamo (R9); S³² curve due to Lüscher, Ricamo, Scherrer, and Zünti (L25).

neutron energy regions additional reactions, involving multiple neutron as well as charged particle emission, become energetically possible,
and the cross section for any given charged particle reaction will, in
the ensuing competition, decrease with increasing neutron energy.

4. Fission. For nuclei of $A \gtrsim 130$ the binding energy per nucleon decreases gradually with increasing A (Section 2B1). Consequently, most
of the heaviest nuclei are energetically unstable against division into two
fragments, i.e., $M(A) > M(A - a) + M(a)$, provided that one of the
fragments is a relatively tightly bound particle such as an alpha-particle
or O^{16} nucleus. However, as is well known, spontaneous nuclear disintegrations are only (with two exceptions) observed in the heaviest, the
naturally radioactive, elements. (Many nuclei, lighter than lead, which
disintegrate by alpha-particle emission, have been produced artificially;
but their lifetimes are much too short for them to be found in nature,
even if they had been present in the original distribution of the elements.)

It is, of course, the Gamow barrier against charged particle emission
which impedes the spontaneous disintegration of the heavy elements,
with the effect that alpha-emission is a relatively long-lived process and
the emission of heavier fragments proceeds at an unobservably slow rate.

There is, however, one mode of disintegration which involves the
release of such a large amount of energy that the disintegration can, for
the heaviest nuclei, proceed over the top of the barrier. This process is
fission, or the division of the nucleus into two approximately equal
fragments.

Consider a heavy nucleus, say $Z = 92$, $A = 240$. The binding energy
per nucleon is ≈ 7.5 Mev. Division into two fragments, e.g., $Z_1 = Z_2$
$= 46$ and $A_1 = A_2 = 120$, produces two nuclei which are approximately
at the peak of the binding energy curve with, however, a considerable
neutron excess, so that their average binding energy per nucleon is somewhat less than that of the stable nuclei in this region, say ≈ 8.3 Mev.
The energy release is then $\sim 240 \times 0.8 \approx 200$ Mev. The barrier height
against separation of the fragments is

$$B_0 = \frac{Z_1 Z_2 e^2}{R_1 + R_2} \cong \frac{Z_1 Z_2}{A_1^{1/3} + A_2^{1/3}} (2mc^2) \approx 200 \text{ Mev} \qquad (80')$$

[We have used the approximation $R = (e^2/2mc^2)A^{1/3}$.] However, because of the large charge of the fragments, the barrier is very "wide,"
and the lifetime against fission is a very strong function of the difference between the barrier height and the available energy, being exceedingly long for barriers only a few ($\sim$5–10) Mev higher than the
reaction energy, and exceedingly short for energies above the barrier.

The greater the atomic number of the nucleus, the smaller is the margin of barrier height over reaction energy. This increase of instability with atomic number places an upper limit on the possible Z of the heaviest nuclei which can be found among the naturally occurring elements; nuclei with $Z \gtrsim 100$ would be unstable against spontaneous fission (B46).[1]

For the heaviest of the naturally occurring nuclei, then, stability against fission depends on the slight deficiency in the available energy as compared to the barrier height. The addition of only a relatively small energy can serve to push the reaction over the barrier. The absorption of a neutron is one means of supplying energy, since capture is accompanied by release of the neutron's binding energy. If the binding energy is sufficiently great, as in the addition of a neutron to some odd-neutron nuclei, fission can be induced by the capture of a thermal neutron. Among the nuclei which undergo fission after thermal neutron capture are U^{233}, U^{235}, Pu^{239} (S42), Am^{241} (C35), and Am^{242} (H30).

Since the energy release is so great, the fission widths, Γ_f, for such nuclei should be essentially independent of the neutron energy. Thus, in the absence of close resonances, the thermal neutron fission cross section should follow a $1/v$ law. However, for such heavy nuclei the compound nucleus level spacing is expected to be relatively small. For U^{235}, $\sigma_{th}(n,\text{fiss.}) = 545$ barns (U2); additional data are given in Section 4D2.

In most of the heaviest nuclei, however, the energy release accompanying neutron capture is insufficient to cause fission. For such nuclei, fission can be induced only if the neutron also carries with it a certain amount of kinetic energy, so that $E + \epsilon + Q \geq B_0$. The fission cross sections of these nuclei exhibit comparatively sharp thresholds. Many of the thresholds are in the fast-neutron region, and the corresponding nuclei make excellent "threshold detectors." Some of these nuclei, and their fission thresholds, are collected in Table 13. Curves of $\sigma_{\text{fiss.}}$ vs. E for U^{238} and Np^{237} are shown in Fig. 25.

TABLE 13

APPROXIMATE VALUES OF FAST FISSION THRESHOLDS

Nucleus	Threshold (Mev)	Nucleus	Threshold (Mev)
Bi^{209}	60	U^{238}	1.1
Th^{232}	1.3	Np^{237}	0.4
Pa^{232}	0.5		

[1] The experimental data on spontaneous fission are summarized by Segrè [Phys. Rev., **86**, 21 (1952)].

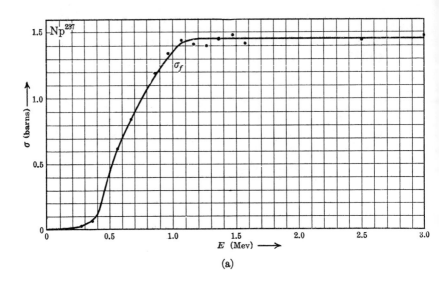

(a)

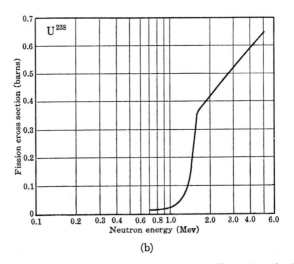

(b)

Fig. 25. Fast fission cross sections *vs.* neutron energy, illustrating the "threshold" nature of the fission reaction. (a) Np²³⁷. From E. D. Klema, Phys. Rev., **72,** 88 (1947). (b) Natural uranium; threshold due to U²³⁸ fission (U2).

In the very fast- and ultrafast-neutron regions, fission can be induced in nuclei of smaller atomic number. Thus, nuclei down to platinum have been shown to undergo fission on bombardment by 84-Mev neutrons (K7).

The fission process has a number of unique features. In addition to the relatively tremendous amount of energy released per fission ($Q \approx 200$ Mev), the process is also accompanied by the emission of neutrons since the fragments, which are comparatively neutron-rich, are emitted with sufficient excitation energy to evaporate one or more neutrons. It is this feature which has made possible the achievement of a nuclear "chain reaction."

Thermal neutron fission is actually asymmetrical, i.e., the two fragments have a tendency to be unequal in charge and weight, with the peaks in the fragment distribution occurring in the regions of $A \sim 100$ and $A \sim 140$. This tendency toward asymmetry is probably associated with the greater stability of nuclei containing the neutron magic numbers 50 and 82 (G7). For fission induced by ultrafast neutrons, on the other hand, the fragment distribution appears to be more nearly symmetrical. The change from asymmetry to symmetry with increasing bombarding energy is not inconsistent with an explanation in terms of the stability of magic number nuclei: a very highly excited nucleus will, before undergoing fission, evaporate a considerable number of neutrons; it will, therefore, not contain the ~132 neutrons necessary to produce nuclei close to two different magic numbers but will, rather, tend to split in such a way as to leave both fragments with as close as possible to 50 neutrons, i.e., symmetrically.

5. The $(n,2n)$ Reaction. The preceding discussion has covered all the exoergic reactions, and a few of the endoergic possibilities (inelastic scattering, charged particle emission), which can be induced by slow and intermediate neutrons. As the neutron energy is increased, through the fast, very fast, and ultrafast regions, a number of other threshold reactions become possible. One of the most important of these is the $(n,2n)$ reaction, whose Q value is the binding energy of a neutron in the target nucleus. The product nucleus is an isotope of the target; in many cases it is radioactive, frequently decaying by positron emission.

Neutron binding energies vary throughout the periodic table from 1.67 Mev in Be^9 to ~20 Mev in C^{12}. Table 14 is a compilation of $(n,2n)$ thresholds. Most of the thresholds have been obtained from observations on (γ,n) reactions which, starting from the same target and leading to the same product nucleus, have the same Q values as the corresponding $(n,2n)$ reactions.

TABLE 14

Thresholds for (γ,n) and $(n,2n)$ Reactions; Neutron Binding Energies

Target Element	A	(γ,n) Threshold † (Mev)	$(n,2n)$ Threshold † (Mev)	Product Nucleus Half-Life ‡		References
$_1$H	2	2.226 ± 0.003	3.34	stable		M34
	3	6.25 ± 0.01	8.33	stable		K16
$_3$Li	6	5.35 ± 0.20	6.2			S26
	7	7.15 ± 0.07 §	8.2	stable		S26
$_4$Be	9	1.666 ± 0.002	1.85	5×10^{-14} s	α	M34
$_5$B	10	8.55 ± 0.25	9.4			S26
	11	11.50 ± 0.25	12.6	stable		S26
$_6$C	12	18.7 ± 0.1 §	20.3	21 m	β^+	B6, M13
$_7$N	14	10.65 ± 0.2		10 m	β^+	M13
		10.54 ± 0.1 §	11.3			O1
$_8$O	16	16.3 ± 0.4	17.3	2 m	β^+	B6
$_9$F	19	10.40 ± 0.3 §	10.9	1.9 h	β^+	O1
$_{11}$Na	23	12.05 ± 0.2	12.6	2.6 y	β^+	S26
$_{12}$Mg	24	16.4 ± 0.2	17.1	12 s	β^+	M13, S26
	25	7.25 ± 0.2	7.5	stable		S26
	26	11.15 ± 0.2	11.6	stable		S26
$_{13}$Al	27	12.75 ± 0.2	13.2	7 s	β^+	S26, M13
$_{14}$Si	28	16.8 ± 0.4	17.4	5 s	β^+	M13
	29	8.45 ± 0.2	8.7	stable		S26
$_{15}$P	31	12.20 ± 0.2	12.6	25 m	β^+	M13, S26
$_{16}$S	32	14.8 ± 0.4	15.3	3.2 s	β^+	M13
	34	10.85 ± 0.2	11.2	stable		S26
$_{17}$Cl	?	9.95 ± 0.2	10.2			S26
$_{19}$K	39	13.2 ± 0.2	13.5	7.7 m	β^+	M13
$_{20}$Ca	40	15.9 ± 0.4	16.3	1 s		M13
$_{22}$Ti	46	13.3 ± 0.2	13.6	3.1 h	β^+	O2
	48?	11.6 ± 0.3	11.8	stable		S26
	49	8.7 ± 0.3	8.9	stable		S26
$_{23}$V	51	11.15 ± 0.2	11.4	stable		S26
$_{24}$Cr	50	13.4 ± 0.2	13.7	42 m	β^+	O2
	52	11.80 ± 0.25	12.0	25 d	K	S26
	53	7.75 ± 0.2	7.9	stable		S26

TABLE 14 (*Continued*)

THRESHOLDS FOR (γ,n) AND $(n,2n)$ REACTIONS; NEUTRON BINDING ENERGIES

Target Element	A	(γ,n) Threshold † (Mev)	$(n,2n)$ Threshold † (Mev)	Product Nucleus Half-Life ‡		References
$_{25}$Mn	55	10.1 ± 0.2	10.3	310 d	K	H35, S26
$_{26}$Fe	54	13.8 ± 0.2	14.1	8.9 m	β^+	M13
	56	11.15 ± 0.25	11.3	2.9 y		S26
	57	7.75 ± 0.2	7.9	stable		S26
$_{27}$Co	59	10.25 ± 0.2	10.5	72 d, 9.2 h	K, β^+, IT	S26
$_{28}$Ni	58	11.7 ± 0.2	11.9	36 h	β^+	O1
	61?	7.5 ± 0.3	7.6	stable		S26
$_{29}$Cu	63	10.9 ± 0.2	11.1	10 m	β^+	M13, S26
		11.2	11.4 ± 0.3			F40
	65	10.0 ± 0.2	10.2	12.8 h	β^+, β^-, K	M13, S26
$_{30}$Zn	64	11.7 ± 0.2	11.9	30 m	β^+	H35, S26
	66	11.15 ± 0.2	11.3	250 d	K, β^+	S26
	67	7.00 ± 0.2	7.1	stable		S26
	68	10.15 ± 0.2	10.3	stable		S26
	70	9.20 ± 0.2	9.3	52 m	β^-	H35
$_{31}$Ga	69	10.10 ± 0.2	10.2	68 m	β^+, K	S26
	71	9.05 ± 0.2	9.2			S26
$_{33}$As	75	10.2 ± 0.2	10.4	17 d	β^+, β^-, K	O1, S26
$_{34}$Se	82	9.8 ± 0.5	9.9	18 m	β^-	B6
		>9.8		57 m	IT	B6
	?	7.30 ± 0.2	7.4			S26
	?	9.35 ± 0.2	9.5			S26
$_{35}$Br	79	10.65 ± 0.2	10.9	6.3 m	β^+	M13, S26
	81	10.1 ± 0.2	10.3	18.5 m	β^-, β^+	M13, S26
$_{38}$Sr	86	9.50 ± 0.2	9.6	65 d	K	S26
	87	8.40 ± 0.2	8.5	stable		S26
	88	11.15 ± 0.2	11.2	stable		S26
$_{40}$Zr	90	12.48 ± 0.15	12.6	4.5 m	K or IT	← H35
		12.0 ± 0.2	12.1	78 h	β^+	O1
	91	7.2 ± 0.4	7.3	stable		H35
$_{41}$Nb	93	8.70 ± 0.2	8.8	10 d	β^-	S26
$_{42}$Mo	92	13.28 ± 0.15	13.4	16 m, 17 s	β^+	H35
	97	7.1 ± 0.3	7.2	stable		H35
	?	6.75 ± 0.25	6.8			S26
	?	7.95 ± 0.25	8.1			S26
$_{44}$Ru	?	7.05 ± 0.2	7.1			S26
	?	9.50 ± 0.2	9.6			S26

TABLE 14 (*Continued*)

Thresholds for (γ,n) and $(n,2n)$ Reactions; Neutron Binding Energies

Target Element	A	(γ,n) Threshold † (Mev)	$(n,2n)$ Threshold † (Mev)	Product Nucleus Half-Life ‡		References
$_{45}$Rh	103	9.35 ± 0.2	9.4	210 d	β^-, β^+	S26
$_{46}$Pd	?	7.05 ± 0.2	7.1			S26
	?	9.35 ± 0.2	9.4			S26
$_{47}$Ag	107	>9.5		24.5 m	β^+	B6
	109	9.05 ± 0.2	9.1	2.3 m	β^-	S26, B6
$_{48}$Cd	113	6.5 ± 0.15	6.6	stable		H35, S26
$_{49}$In	115	9.05 ± 0.2	9.1	50 d IT; 72 s	β^-, K, β^+	S26
$_{50}$Sn	118	9.10 ± 0.2	9.2	stable		S26
	119	6.55 ± 0.15	6.6	stable		H35, S26
	124	8.50 ± 0.15	8.6	40 m	β^-	H35
$_{51}$Sb	121	9.25 ± 0.2	9.3	17 m	β^+	M13
	?	8.95 ± 0.25	9.0		°	S26
	123	~9.3	~9.4	2.8 d	β^-	J4
$_{52}$Te	?	6.50 ± 0.2	6.6			S26
	?	8.55 ± 0.2	8.6			S26
$_{53}$I	127	9.3 ± 0.15	9.4	13 d	β^-	O1, M13, S26
$_{55}$Cs	133	9.05 ± 0.2	9.1	7.1 d	K	S26
$_{56}$Ba	?	6.80 ± 0.2	6.8			S26
	?	8.55 ± 0.25	8.6			S26
$_{57}$La	139	8.80 ± 0.2	8.9	stable; 18 h	K, IT	S26
$_{58}$Ce	140	9.05 ± 0.2	9.1	140 d	K	S26
	142	7.15 ± 0.2	7.2	33 d	β^-	S26
$_{59}$Pr	141	9.40 ± 0.10	9.5	3.5 m	β^+	H35
$_{60}$Nd	150	7.40 ± 0.2	7.4	2 h	β^-	H35
$_{73}$Ta	181	7.6 ± 0.2	7.6	8.2 h	β^-, K	M13, S26, J4
$_{74}$W	?	6.25 ± 0.3	6.3			S26
	?	7.15 ± 0.3	7.2			S26
$_{75}$Re	187	7.3 ± 0.3	7.3	93 h	β^-, K	S26
$_{77}$Ir	193	7.80 ± 0.2	7.8	70 d	β^-	S26
$_{78}$Pt	194	9.50 ± 0.2	9.5	4 d	K	S26
	195	6.1 ± 0.1	6.1	stable		P5, S26
	196	8.20 ± 0.2	8.2	stable		S26
$_{79}$Au	197	8.05 ± 0.10	8.1	5.6 d	β^-	P5, H35, S26

TABLE 14 (*Continued*)

THRESHOLDS FOR (γ,n) AND $(n,2n)$ REACTIONS; NEUTRON BINDING ENERGIES

Target Element	A	(γ,n) Threshold † (Mev)	$(n,2n)$ Threshold † (Mev)	Product Nucleus Half-Life ‡		References
$_{80}$Hg	201	6.25 ± 0.2	6.3	stable		H35
	?	6.6 ± 0.2	6.6			P5
$_{81}$Tl	203	8.80 ± 0.2	8.8	12 d	K	S26
	205	7.5 ± 0.15	7.5	3y	β^-	H35, S26, P5
$_{82}$Pb	206	8.25 ± 0.10	8.3			P1, P6
	207	6.88 ± 0.10	6.9	stable		P1, S26, P5
	208	7.40 ± 0.10	7.4	stable		P1, S26
$_{83}$Bi	209	7.4 ± 0.1	7.4			M13, P5, S26
$_{90}$Th	232	6.35 ± 0.04	6.4	26 h	β^-	H76, P5
$_{92}$U	238	5.97 ± 0.10	6.0	6.8 d	β^-	H76, P5

† The $(n,2n)$ thresholds are computed from the measured (γ,n) thresholds (or vice versa) according to the relationship $E_t(n,2n) = [(A + 1)/A]E_t(\gamma,n)$.

‡ The half-lives and radioactivities are from the compilation of Way, Fano, Scott, and Thew (W10).

§ Thresholds computed from nuclear mass data and used to calibrate the gamma-ray energy scale. The most recent data on the thresholds for light elements are summarized by F. Ajzenberg and T. Lauritsen, Revs. Modern Phys., **24**, 321 (1952).

In light nuclei, the $(n,2n)$ reaction competes with charged particle emission as well as with neutron scattering. In heavy nuclei, charged particle reactions are so strongly inhibited by the Coulomb barrier that the only important competing reaction—at least, for energies not too far above the $(n,2n)$ threshold—is scattering, mainly inelastic at these energies. Assuming that this situation prevails, the value of the cross section, $\sigma(n,2n)$, can be computed, given the energy distribution of the inelastically scattered neutrons, $d\sigma(\varepsilon,E)$,

$$\sigma(n,2n) = \int_0^{\varepsilon = E - E_t} d\sigma(\varepsilon,E) \tag{81}$$

That is, if the first neutron is emitted with sufficiently low energy ($\varepsilon < E - E_t$), the residual nucleus will still have enough excitation to emit a second neutron and, since neutron emission is the most probable mode of decay for heavy nuclei at high excitation energies, it will almost always do so.

At the excitation energies involved, and especially for the low-energy part of the spectrum, the distribution of inelastically scattered neutrons is given, to a good approximation, by the Maxwellian distribution (Eq. 69). Thus,

$$\sigma(n,2n) = \sigma_c \int_0^{E-E_t} \left(\frac{\varepsilon}{T^2}\right) e^{-\varepsilon/T}\, d\varepsilon$$

$$= \sigma_c[1 - (1+y)e^{-y}] \tag{82}$$

where $y = (E - E_t)/T$. For energies close to the threshold, i.e., $y \ll 1$,

$$\sigma(n,2n) \approx \frac{\sigma_c y^2}{2} = \frac{\sigma_c}{2T^2}(E - E_t)^2 \tag{82a}$$

The $(E - E_t)^2$ dependence of the $(n,2n)$ cross section near threshold has been verified by Fowler and Slye (F40) for the $Cu^{63}(n,2n)$ reaction.

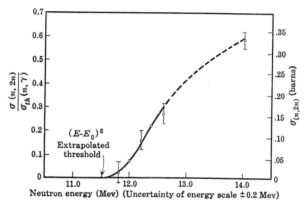

Fig. 26.   Cross section for the reaction $Cu^{63}(n,2n)Cu^{62}$ in the vicinity of the threshold, due to Fowler and Slye (F40). The left-hand scale gives the ratio of the $Cu^{63}(n,2n)$ cross section to the $Cu^{65}(n,\gamma)$ thermal neutron cross section. The absolute cross section scale, on the right, is based on $(0.56 \pm 20\%)$ barns for the thermal neutron cross section of Cu^{65} in normal copper; it should be increased by ~16 percent (private communication from Fowler).

Their cross-section measurements for neutron energies between $E = E_t = (11.4 \pm 0.3)$ Mev and ~14 Mev are shown in Fig. 26. This reaction is frequently used as a threshold detector of neutrons of energy $E > 11.5$ Mev.

The $C^{12}(n,2n)$ reaction has also been used as a threshold detector for very fast neutrons. The cross section from threshold $E_t \cong 21$ Mev to ~25 Mev increases rapidly with neutron energy in roughly the expected manner (S27).

The expression for $\sigma(n,2n)$, Eq. (82), has been derived on the assumption that the statistical theory, which leads to a Maxwell distribution of the emerging neutrons, is valid in the region of excitation under consideration. The cross sections near threshold bear out this assumption. The statistical theory has been verified over a much wider range of excitation energies by the measurements of Bradt and Tendam (B58) on the relative cross sections for the (α,n) and $(\alpha,2n)$ reactions on silver and rhodium with 15–20 Mev alpha-particles, and by the observations of Temmer (T7) and Kelly and Segrè (K8) on the excitation functions for the (α,n), $(\alpha,2n)$, and $(\alpha,3n)$ reactions on indium and bismuth with alpha-particles up to 40 Mev energy.

However, application of the statistical theory to $(n,2n)$ reactions induced by very fast (and, especially, ultrafast) neutrons is subject to the limitation, pointed out by Weisskopf (W17), that neutrons of such high energy have a large probability of penetrating through the nuclear surface and hence may emerge from the nucleus before they have fully shared their energy with the rest of the nuclear constituents. The energy distribution of the emerging (first) neutron will, under these circumstances, contain many more fast neutrons than predicted by the evaporation theory. This situation does not obtain for alpha-particle bombardment, since the Coulomb barrier impedes the emergence of the alpha-particle and helps to achieve the sharing of energy in a true compound nucleus.

In any event, if, after the emission of the first neutron, the residual (target) nucleus is still sufficiently excited to emit a neutron, it will do so. The energy distribution of the second neutrons is determined by the level spacing of the *product* (final) nucleus at the excitation energy remaining *after emission* of the second neutron. For incident neutron energies not very far above the $(n,2n)$ threshold, the energy available to the second neutron cannot be very large, and the spectrum of second neutrons cannot be assumed to follow the Maxwell distribution. In essence, the same considerations, which we have applied in the discussion of the energy distribution of inelastically scattered neutrons, will apply in this case.

6. Multiple-Particle Emission; Spallation Reactions and Stars. The interaction of very fast and ultrafast neutrons with nuclei can be considered to take place in two relatively distinct stages:

(1) The initial interaction of the incident neutron with one or several of the nuclear constituents. In this stage the nucleons can be treated as relatively independent particles (S21), and the recoiling nucleons (as well as the incident neutron) have a non-negligible probability of leaving the nucleus, carrying off a relatively large fraction of the incident energy.

(2) Those nucleons which do not directly escape from the nucleus will rapidly share their energy among the nuclear constituents. In general, the resulting excited nucleus will have sufficient energy to evaporate more than one particle.

The theory of the interaction of neutrons of $E \sim 100$ Mev with heavy nuclei has been developed by Goldberger (G11). He has computed the energy and angular distributions of the emerging nucleons in the first stage of the interaction, as well as the distribution of excitation energies in the residual nuclei; his computations take into account the velocity distribution of the nucleons in the target nucleus (which he treats as a Fermi gas confined to the nuclear volume).

The process of ejection of nuclear constituents through direct interaction with the incident particle is sometimes referred to as spallation.[1] The second or evaporation part of the reaction is usually referred to as star production, from the characteristic records that such reactions leave in nuclear emulsions which are sensitive only to relatively low-energy charged particles.

One method of studying high-energy nuclear interactions is through the yields of the various products, usually radioactive (K19). However, aside from the obvious limitation of this method (that only radioactive products can be detected), it has the disadvantage that the two stages of the reaction cannot be separated.

A more satisfactory method for studying such reactions is by observing the emerging particles, either in a cloud chamber or in a sensitive nuclear emulsion. In such investigations it is possible to separate the two stages of the reaction by the difference in the energy and angular distributions of the resulting charged particles. The products of the first stage have high energy and forward collimation (G11). Those of the second stage have relatively low energy and are distributed uniformly with respect to the direction of the incident particle (L12). The applicability of the Goldberger model to high-energy nuclear reactions has been strikingly verified by the work of Bernardini, Booth, and Lindenbaum (B19).

An interesting result of such investigations is the observation of a considerable number of high-energy deuterons, emitted in the forward direction (H2, B74, Y3, M37). These appear to result from a "pick-up" process in which the incident neutron is joined by a nuclear proton, which happens to be moving in the same direction and with the proper velocity, to form a deuteron (C13, H51, C34).

---

[1] Spall: A chip or fragment, esp. of stone. *Webster's Collegiate Dictionary*, fifth edition, G. and C. Merriam Co., 1948.

The interaction of ultrafast neutrons with nuclei has been studied in cosmic-ray investigations. Neutrons with energies exceeding 10^9 ev are present in the cosmic radiation. Many of these investigations have employed nuclear emulsions in which cosmic-ray stars are a common phenomenon. Le Couteur (L12) has shown that the energy distribution of the evaporation products in stars can be understood in terms of the statistical model; the energy of the emitted protons and alpha-particles is given by a modified Maxwell distribution, the modification arising from the inhibition of emission of low-energy charged particles by the Gamow barrier.

Owing to the decrease with energy of the primary (n,p) and (n,n) cross sections, nuclei are relatively transparent to ultrafast neutrons of energy $\lesssim 300$ Mev. However, at neutron energies greater than the threshold for meson production ($\sim$285 Mev for neutrons on protons or neutrons at rest) the reaction cross section is expected to rise again. The available evidence indicates that nuclei are essentially opaque (reaction cross section $\approx \pi R^2$) for neutrons of energy $\gtrsim 10^9$ ev. The products of the interaction of such neutrons with nuclei are, in the first stage, a number (increasing with neutron energy) of mesons (probably mostly pions) traveling in the forward direction, and fast nucleons ($E \sim 100 - 1000$ Mev) also in the forward direction; the residual nucleus, in the second stage, usually has sufficient energy to evaporate a large fraction of its particles (F10).

SECTION 3.   SOURCES AND DETECTORS: NEUTRON SPECTROSCOPY

A. Introduction

To investigate experimentally the properties of the neutron and its various interactions, it is necessary to have a neutron source and a neutron detector. If, in addition, it is desired to confine the investigation to neutrons of a specific energy, then either the source must emit mono-energetic neutrons or the detector must be sensitive only to neutrons of a single energy. The problems of neutron spectroscopy, and the discussions of this section, involve the choice of the proper sources or detectors or both in the various neutron energy ranges.

The resolution of a given experimental arrangement is a measure of the energy spread of the neutrons selected by the source and detector. As in other fields, good energy resolution must frequently be paid for by decreased intensity, if it can be achieved at all. On the other hand, poor resolution is by no means always an unmitigated ill. For example, for a comparison of intermediate- and fast-neutron cross sections with the predictions of the continuum theory of Feshbach and Weisskopf, it is necessary to average over many levels of the compound nucleus; such an average is most easily and accurately achieved by using a source whose energy spread is sufficient to cover many levels of the compound nucleus.

The term "resolution" is usually employed in a descriptive, qualitative connotation, mostly in conjunction with an adjective, such as "good" or "poor." The quantitative measure of energy resolution is the *resolution function*, $R(E) = S(E)D(E)$, the product of the source strength and the detector efficiency. For many measurements, especially cross-section determinations in which there is considerable variation with energy (e.g., resonances), a knowledge of $R(E)$ is indispensable for the interpretation of the experimental results. A considerable fraction of the literature on neutron cross sections is essentially uninterpretable, not so much because the experiments were performed with poor resolution as because they were performed with sources of unknown energy distribution or detectors with unknown efficiency curves.

However, although this criticism is sometimes applicable to recent work, it is certainly not fair to apply it to most of the early investigations. To the pioneers in neutron physics, in the pre-World War II era, the number of sources and detectors available was severely limited. Although many of their cross-section measurements may not have been good in the present-day sense, or even quantitatively interpretable, their exploratory investigations were invaluable, for only through the accumulated knowledge of such explorations were present-day techniques made possible. In many instances what the early masters lacked in technique was more than compensated by the ingenuity of their experiments and the penetration and insight of their interpretation.

The first available neutron sources were, naturally, those involved in the discovery of the neutron: (α,n) reactions on many elements, especially beryllium, using naturally radioactive alpha-emitters. Some of this early work has been described in the introductions to Sections 1 and 2.

The discovery of the photodisintegration of the deuteron by Chadwick and Goldhaber (C8), and of beryllium by Szilard and Chalmers (S63) uncovered another source of neutrons, the (γ,n) reaction on these elements by gamma-rays from various natural radioactivities. These sources differ from the (α,n) sources in that they provide lower-energy neutrons, usually in the intermediate-energy range, since (γ,n) reactions are endoergic. On the other hand, such sources are usually considerably weaker than (α,n) sources. However, with the production of strong artificially radioactive sources, at first through the use of particle accelerators and more recently by neutron irradiation in nuclear reactors, a large variety of gamma-ray sources have become available for photoneutron production. Furthermore, the development of high-energy electron accelerators for the production of intense x-ray beams has added another means of intense photoneutron production, although these sources are not monoergetic like those produced by a nuclear gamma-ray.

The first extensive investigation of photoneutron production in elements other than beryllium and deuterium was made by Bothe and Gentner (B52). They utilized the $\sim$17 Mev gamma-rays produced in the $Li^7(p,\gamma)$ reaction, using artificially accelerated protons of 0.4 Mev energy. Since then, a large number of investigations of (γ,n) reactions have been carried out with these and other gamma-ray sources, and with x-ray beams from electron accelerators. The results of many of these are summarized in Table 14 (Section 2) and in the references therein indicated. Of all the nuclei investigated, only beryllium and deuterium have photoneutron thresholds of energy less than 6 Mev.

The development of high-energy heavy-particle accelerators led to the discovery of a large number of new and useful neutron-producing reactions. In addition to providing monoenergetic alpha-particles of energy higher than those available from the natural radioactivities, with which it was possible to investigate further the (α,n) reactions on beryllium, boron, and other elements, it was found possible to utilize other accelerated nuclei, such as the proton and the deuteron, for neutron production.

It was soon discovered that (d,n) reactions have large yields at the deuteron energies available from accelerators. Crane, Lauritsen, and Soltan (C30) discovered the (d,n) reactions on lithium and beryllium. Soon afterward, Lawrence and Livingston (L8) extended the investigation of (d,n) reactions to a number of other elements. At about the same time (all this in 1933 and 1934) Oliphant, Harteck and Rutherford (O3) discovered the $d + d$ reaction; this reaction has been of great importance, since it provides a strong source of monoenergetic neutrons with comparatively low-energy deuterons, enabling the use of relatively low-voltage particle accelerators for neutron sources. Other (d,n) reactions have comparable or higher yields at deuteron energies of a few Mev, but the resulting neutrons are heteroenergetic (with the exception of the $d + t$ reaction).

Another reaction type of great importance to neutron spectroscopy is the (p,n) reaction. Crane and Lauritsen (C31) discovered the $Li(p,n)$ reaction, which has since been extensively used for a monoenergetic neutron source. However, this reaction does not really yield monoenergetic neutrons, since it also gives rise to a second neutron group, due to an excited state of Be^7, 435 kev above the ground state. Fortunately, the second group has a comparatively low yield ($\lesssim 10$ percent) for protons up to ~ 4 Mev. A number of other (p,n) reactions have been studied and used from time to time for neutron sources, but none so extensively as the $Li^7(p,n)$ reaction.

All the above-mentioned neutron sources yield energies in the intermediate, fast, and very fast ranges. Until the advent of ultrahigh-energy accelerators, the only source of neutrons in the ultrafast-energy range was from the cosmic radiation. The presence of high-energy neutrons as a component of cosmic rays was established by the experiments of Rumbaugh and Locher (R25) and of Fünfer (F51), and has been used by many investigators to study the nuclear interactions induced by ultrafast neutrons. Although particle accelerators are at present capable of producing neutrons of energy up to ~ 400 Mev, and higher-energy accelerators (a few Bev) are now being constructed, cosmic radiation still remains the only source in immediate prospect for neutrons of energies of, say, > 10 Bev.

At the other extreme, the slow-neutron region has been most extensively investigated. Sources of slow neutrons almost invariably have their origin in fast neutrons, slowed down in paraffin or some other material containing light elements. Since such sources yield a broad distribution of neutron energies, it is necessary to employ some form of neutron monochromator for studies requiring monoenergetic neutrons. A number of monochromators have been, and are being, developed, and their effective range has been slowly pushed up toward the intermediate-energy region, so that there now remains only a small gap between the monoenergetic neutrons available from charged particle reactions and from slow-neutron monochromators.[1] The availability of very great neutron intensities from nuclear reactors has provided a great impetus to the development of more effective neutron monochromators of greater range and flexibility.

The development of neutron detectors has rapidly followed the extension of knowledge of neutron reactions; practically every new discovery has led to a new means of neutron detection. Thus, the observation of proton recoils by Curie and Joliot (C37), made even before the identification of the neutron as a new particle, led to the technique of observing neutrons in ionization chambers, electroscopes, and cloud chambers by lining these instruments with paraffin. The discovery of charged particle reactions in lithium, boron, and nitrogen enabled the detection of

---

[1] Actually, the gap is being closed from the intermediate-energy end as well. Thus, Hibdon, Langsdorf, and Holland [Phys. Rev., **85**, 595 (1952)] have succeeded in studying the 2–25 kev range with an energy resolution of 2 kev, using the $Li(p,n)$ reaction.

neutrons through the incorporation of these substances in ionization chambers, proportional counters, and cloud chambers. These and other reactions, as well as proton recoils, can also be observed in nuclear emulsions.

The discovery of neutron-induced radioactivity provided still another means of neutron detection which could be used to investigate specific energies or energy ranges—thermal neutrons through $1/v$ capture cross sections, specific slow-neutron energies through various resonances, fast neutrons by means of threshold reactions. As neutron reactions have been further understood, and as various techniques of charged particle counting have been improved and extended, the variety of neutron detectors has increased until now it is possible to find a suitable neutron detector at almost any energy.

This is not to say that detector problems are negligible in neutron studies; as is so often the case, ease of detection is in direct proportion to the available intensity, so that the source and detector problems of neutron spectroscopy go hand in hand. Especially in the fast-, very fast-, and ultrafast-neutron energy ranges, detectors are of relatively low efficiency, and available sources are never quite strong enough, so that neutron spectroscopy in these energy regions still presents difficult problems.

Nevertheless, it seems fair to summarize by saying that the available techniques of neutron spectroscopy allow an almost complete coverage of the range of energies from 0 to $\sim$300 Mev with relatively few significant gaps, and that, with foreseeable extensions of available techniques, the existing gaps should soon be closed.

B. Neutron Sources

1. Radioactive (α,n) Sources. The discovery of the neutron involved the reaction

$$_4\mathrm{Be}^9 + {}_2\mathrm{He}^4 \rightarrow {}_6\mathrm{C}^{12} + {}_0n^1$$

induced by bombarding beryllium with α-particles emitted by the naturally radioactive elements. Although many other neutron-producing reactions have since been discovered, the above reaction is still the basis for some of the most extensively used neutron sources.

According to available mass values (T16, B2), this reaction is exoergic, with a Q value of 5.65 Mev. Thus, starting with the polonium alpha-particles (energy 5.30 Mev), the emergent neutrons should have a spread of energies between 10.8 Mev (outgoing neutron in the same direction as the incoming alpha) and 6.7 Mev (outgoing neutron in the opposite direction from the incoming alpha).

However, the neutrons observed in the bombardment of beryllium with polonium alpha-particles have a considerably greater energy spread, ranging from the above maximum to energies well below 1 Mev. The observed energy spread arises from two causes: (1) In the above reaction, the C^{12} nucleus may sometimes be left in an excited state, resulting in less available energy for the outgoing neutron. This possibility will, for monoenergetic incident alpha-particles, result in the appearance of groups in the spectrum of the outgoing neutrons, each group corresponding to an excited state of the C^{12} nucleus. Evidence for the existence and energy values of the C^{12} levels is summarized by Hornyak, Lauritsen, Morrison, and Fowler (H67). (2) In most (α,n) sources, the thickness of the beryllium target is large compared to the range of the impinging alpha-particles. (The range of a polonium alpha-particle is 3.66 cm in standard air.) Since the cross section for the neutron-producing reaction is small compared to the cross section for energy loss by collisions with atomic electrons, very few nuclear processes occur while the alpha-particle has its full, initial energy. Thus, even if all the reactions led to the ground state of C^{12}, the outgoing neutrons in the forward direction would have an energy spread ranging from the maximum (10.8 Mev) down to 5.2 Mev (corresponding to zero incident alpha-particle energy).

The energy spectrum of Po-α-Be neutrons is further complicated as a result of the variation of the reaction cross section with the incident alpha-particle energy. Thus, the necessity for the alpha-particle to penetrate through the potential barrier of the beryllium nucleus decreases the neutron yield for low-energy alpha-particles; the height of the potential barrier is $\sim$3.7 Mev. Furthermore, the level structure of the compound nucleus, C^{13}, leads to resonances in the cross section (H67).

As a result of the effects discussed above, the neutron spectrum from a (thick target) Po-α-Be source is complex, and cannot be predicted in detail. A number of attempts have been made (A27) to measure the neutron spectrum from such a source using proton recoils, in nuclear emulsions, as a neutron detector. The result of a recent measurement, due to Whitmore and Baker (W20), is shown in Fig. 27.

Among the alpha-emitting radioactive elements, polonium is comparatively difficult to obtain in quantities sufficient to produce strong neutron sources. The elements radium and radon are, however, commercially available in sufficient quantity so that they are most frequently used for neutron sources. Radium has the advantage of a very long half-life ($\sim$1600 years, as compared to 3.825 days for radon and 138 days for polonium), which makes it particularly suitable for long-lived sources.

On the other hand, polonium and, even more so, radon require a considerably smaller mass of beryllium in the source mixture to approximate a thick target (since the mass per unit radioactive strength of a radioactive element is proportional to its half-life). In particular, radon requires quite small quantities of beryllium for high neutron yields, and presents no difficulty in mixing, since it is a noble gas and diffuses uniformly through powdered beryllium; thus, Rn-α-Be sources

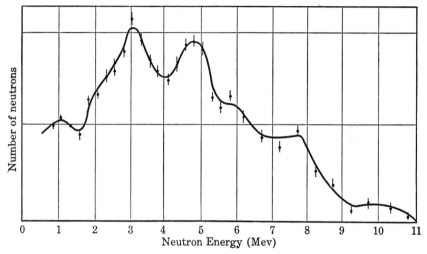

Fig. 27.   Energy distribution of neutrons from a Po-α-Be source (W20).

can be made quite small. However, owing to the inconvenience of working with a gas of such short half-life, radon is now seldom used for neutron sources.

Po-α-Be sources have the added advantage that in the decay of polonium there is a comparatively negligible gamma-ray emission, which makes the handling of such sources relatively simple. The decay products of radium, on the other hand, emit a prodigious quantity of gamma-radiation, and suitable precautions for protection against these radiations must be observed in the handling of these sources. Nevertheless, owing to the conveniences of availability and long life, Ra-α-Be neutron sources are very widely used.

Another disadvantage of polonium as compared to radium is that it is more difficult to manipulate, despite the absence of gamma-radiation. One method of preparation of a Po-α-Be source, described by Spinks and Graham (S49), consists in sandwiching a platinum foil, on which the polonium is deposited, inside a cylinder of beryllium. Such a source has a smaller yield per curie ($\sim\frac{1}{3}$) than an intimate mixture, and the neutron emission is not isotropic.

During World War II considerable experience was obtained in the preparation of radium-beryllium mixtures.[1] The preparation and handling of such sources has been described by Anderson and Feld (A26) and, in greater detail, by Anderson (A27). Most of these consist of an intimate, physical mixture of radium bromide and beryllium metal powder, pressed into pellets of density $\sim$1.75 g/cm^3. In addition to their small size (thereby more closely approximating a point source), pressed sources are more likely to remain constant in time because of the greater physical stability of the mixture.

The neutron spectrum from Ra-α-Be sources is even more complex than that of Po-α-Be, owing to the variety of alpha-particles emitted by radium and its decay products, as shown in Table 15. The presence of polonium alpha-particles in a Ra-α-Be source is governed by the decay of radium D, with a 22-year half-life. Hence, in relatively young (a few years old) sources, this last alpha-particle is not appreciably present.

TABLE 15

ALPHA-PARTICLE ENERGIES FROM RADIUM AND ITS DECAY PRODUCTS

Alpha-Emitter	Half-Life	Energy (Mev)
Ra	1620 y	$\begin{cases} 4.795 \ (93.5\%) \\ 4.611 \ (6.5\%) \end{cases}$
Rn	3.825 d	5.486
RaA	3.05 m	5.998
RaC'	1.5×10^{-4} s	7.680
RaF(Po)	138.3 d	5.300

The rest of the alpha-particles are fully present after a few weeks. All the following discussion (spectrum, yield) is concerned with such young sources. Since both the spectrum and yield of Po-α-Be sources are comparatively well known, it is easy to take into account the changes in the source due to the accumulation of polonium.

The Ra-α-Be neutron spectrum has not been nearly so extensively investigated as Po-α-Be, mainly because of the difficulties of neutron measurement in the accompanying high gamma-ray background. Its properties may be roughly summarized as follows (A27): The fast-neutron spectrum extends to a maximum energy of $\sim$13 Mev, with a broad peak at $\sim$4 Mev. There appears to be a substantial group of intermediate-energy neutrons, but there is considerable uncertainty as

---

[1] A large number of these sources were prepared in the laboratory of the Radium Chemical Company, 570 Lexington Ave., New York City.

to their amount and energy. Various estimates of the yield of intermediate neutrons range from ~10–30 percent of the total yield. These have been ascribed to the reaction

$$\text{He}^4 + \text{Be}^9 \rightarrow 3\text{He}^4 + n^1$$

(in which a number of intermediate steps have been omitted). The low-energy group may also arise, in some part, from a (γ,n) reaction on beryllium. In any event, the low-energy group does not seem to be present in Po-α-Be sources, owing either to the absence of higher-energy alpha-particles (those from RaC' are assumed mainly responsible for the 3α reaction) or of gamma-rays, or both.

Other light elements beside beryllium can be used to produce neutrons through (α,n) reactions. Thus, a pressed Ra-α-B source has been prepared, and its spectrum and yield studied (A27). Both B^{10} and B^{11} undergo exoergic (α,n) reactions ($Q = 1.18$ and 0.28 Mev, respectively), the latter being responsible for most of the neutron yield. The spectrum is comparatively simpler than that of a Ra-α-Be source, rising rapidly to a maximum at ~3 Mev, and then falling rapidly to zero at ~6 Mev. There does not appear to be any appreciable intermediate-energy component.

The reaction $F^{19}(\alpha,n)$ is believed (from mass values) to be slightly exoergic, by $\lesssim 0.5$ Mev. Bretscher, Cook, Martin, and Wilkinson (B62) have prepared a source composed of the relatively stable complex, $RaBeF_4$, which they suggest for a standard neutron source, since the characteristics of the complex are not expected to change appreciably with time.

The yields of the various sources discussed above have been studied by a number of methods (A27). In general, for a given mixture of

TABLE 16

Yields of Radioactive (α,n) Sources for Intimate Mixtures of an Alpha-Emitter and a Neutron-Producing Material

Source	Y_0 (10^6 neutrons/curie·sec)
Ra-α-Be	17
Rn-α-Be	15
Ra-α-B	6.8
Po-α-Be	3
RaBeF$_4$	2.53 †

† Since the mixture is fixed, the value given is that of an actual source composed of the complex. This yield could be improved by adding beryllium, but this would nullify the purpose of such a source, namely, the elimination of possible changes due to alteration of the physical composition.

some alpha-emitting compound (α-mat) and neutron-producing material (X), the yield is given by the relationship

$$Y = Y_0 \frac{M(X)}{M(X) + M(\alpha\text{-mat})} \tag{83}$$

Values of Y_0 (yield for an ∞ ratio of X to α-mat) are given in Table 16.

(α,n) yields from various materials have been extensively investigated, and are summarized by Anderson (A27). A number of these investigations have employed thin sources and targets (S61, W3, H9), while others have measured thick target yields. Most of the investigators employed polonium alpha-particles, varying their energy by changing the pressure of gas between source and detector. The thin target (α,n) cross section for beryllium (due to Halpern, H9) is shown in Fig. 28a. Figure 28b shows the results of Segrè and Wiegand on the thick target yields of beryllium, boron, and fluorine. Thick target yields, for (artificially accelerated) 9-Mev alpha-particles, have been measured by Ridenour and Henderson (R11), and for 30-Mev alpha-

TABLE 17

NEUTRON YIELDS FOR POLONIUM ALPHA-PARTICLES ON THICK TARGETS

Element	Yield per 10^6 Alphas				
	Roberts (A27)	Segrè and Wiegand (A27)	Walker (W3)	Halpern (H9)	Szalay (S61)
Li	2.6	4.7			
Be	80	73		50	
B	24	19	19		
C	0.11				
N	0.01				
O	0.07				
F	12	10			
Na	1.5				
Mg	1.4			0.5	
Al	0.74			0.25	0.22
Si	0.16				
Cl	0.11				
A	0.38				

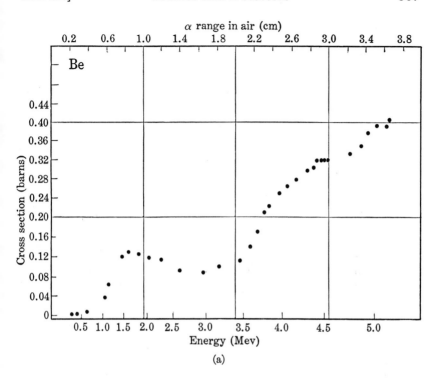

α range in air (cm)

(a)

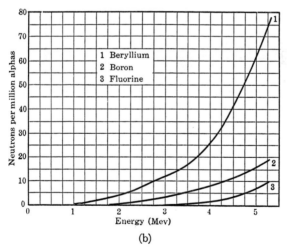

(b)

Fig. 28. (α,n) yields *vs.* neutron energy for a number of elements. (a) Thin target (α,n) cross section of beryllium, due to Halpern (H9). (b) Thick target (α,n) excitation functions of beryllium, boron, and fluorine, due to Segrè and Wiegand (A27).

particles by Allen, Nechaj, Sun, and Jennings (A8), who also measured the angular distributions of the neutrons. The results of a number of investigations of thick target yields from various elements for polonium alpha-particles are summarized in Table 17, in which the data of Roberts and of Segrè and Wiegand are taken from Anderson's summary (A27). The results of the last three investigators are obtained by integration of their thin target yield curves.

2. Photoneutron Sources. Photons can cause neutron emission from nuclei, provided that their energy is greater than the neutron binding energy. In so far as the (γ,n) reaction is concerned, the periodic table is conveniently divided into two groups: (1) deuterium and beryllium, and (2) all the rest. The former have (γ,n) thresholds of (2.226 ± 0.003) and (1.666 ± 0.002) Mev, respectively. The latter have thresholds in excess of 6 Mev. Since no radioactive nuclei which emit gamma-rays of such high energy are known, radioactive (γ,n) sources employ only beryllium or deuterium. The (prompt) gamma-rays from various nuclear reactions or the x-rays obtainable from high-energy electron accelerators can be used to obtain neutrons from other nuclei as well.

(a) *Radioactive (γ,n) Sources with Deuterium and Beryllium.* The bombardment of deuterium or beryllium by monoenergetic gamma-rays results, for a given angle θ between the emitted neutron and incident gamma-ray, in monoenergetic neutrons, according to the relationship (W8)

$$E_n = \left(\frac{A-1}{A}\right)\left[E_\gamma - Q - \frac{E_\gamma^2}{1862(A-1)}\right] + \delta \cos \theta \qquad (84a)$$

$$\delta \cong E_\gamma \left[\frac{2(A-1)(E_\gamma - Q)}{931A^3}\right]^{1/2} \qquad (84b)$$

E_n is the neutron energy; E_γ, the gamma-ray energy; Q, the neutron binding energy, all in Mev. A is the mass number of the target nucleus.

In almost all practical photoneutron sources, for reasons of intensity, the gamma-ray source is surrounded by beryllium or deuterium, so that the neutrons have an inherent energy spread corresponding to an isotropic distribution in the angle θ,

$$\Delta E_n = 2\delta \qquad (84c)$$

For 100-kev neutrons, $\Delta E_n/E_n \approx 4$ percent for beryllium, and ≈ 25 percent for deuterium. The relative spread decreases with increasing neutron energy.

The above is, however, not the main cause of energy spread. For most sources, a larger uncertainty in the neutron energy arises from the fact that considerable quantities of beryllium or deuterium must be used to obtain usable neutron intensities. Since both beryllium and deuterium are quite light, and since the neutrons have a non-negligible probability of undergoing a scattering before emerging from the source, an appreciable energy spread may thereby be introduced. In addition, neutron scattering in the source has the effect of reducing the mean energy of the emerging neutrons. Furthermore, the gamma-rays can lose energy by Compton scattering and then produce neutrons, an effect which introduces a further uncertainty in the neutron energy. Since the Compton cross section is $\sim 10^3$ times that for photodisintegration, a source containing an infinite quantity of beryllium or deuterium will produce only ~ 1 neutron per 1000 gamma-rays.

TABLE 18

PHOTONEUTRON SOURCES

Source	$T_{1/2}$	E_γ (Mev)	E_n (Mev)	Standard Yield † (10^4 neutrons/ sec · curie) (1 gram at 1 cm)
$Na^{24} + Be$	14.8 h	2.76	0.83	13
$Na^{24} + D_2O$		2.76	0.22	27
$Mn^{56} + Be$	2.59 h	1.81, 2.13, 2.7	0.15, 0.30	2.9
$Mn^{56} + D_2O$		2.7	0.22	0.31
$Ga^{72} + Be$	14.1 h	1.87, 2.21, 2.51	(0.78) ‡	5
$Ga^{72} + D_2O$		2.51	0.13	6
$Y^{88} + Be$	87 d	1.9, 2.8	0.158 ± 0.005 §	10
$Y^{88} + D$		2.8	(0.31)	0.3
$In^{116} + Be$	54 m	1.8, 2.1	0.30	0.82
$Sb^{124} + Be$	60 d	1.7	0.024 ± 0.003 §	19
$La^{140} + Be$	40 d	2.50	0.62	0.3
$La^{140} + D_2O$		2.50	0.151 ± 0.008 §	0.8
$MsTh + Be$	6.7 y	1.80, 2.62	0.827 ± 0.030 §	3.5
$MsTh + D_2O$		2.62 (ThC'')	0.197 ± 0.010 §	9.5
$Ra + Be$	1620 y	1.69, 1.75, *1.82*, 2.09, 2.20, *2.42*	a mess	3.0
$Ra + D_2O$		2.42	0.12	0.1

† The standard yield is taken to be that of 1 gram of beryllium or heavy water at 1 cm from 1 curie of the substance indicated.

‡ Values in parentheses are estimates.

§ Due to Hanson (H33).

These factors, as well as other aspects of the production and use of photoneutron sources, are discussed in considerable detail by Wattenberg (W8,W7). Table 18 summarizes the properties of available radioactive (γ,n) sources.

The characteristics of the cross section for the $D(\gamma,n)$ reaction have been discussed in Section 1. Considerably less is known concerning the $Be(\gamma,n)$ cross section. The available evidence, both experimental (R26)

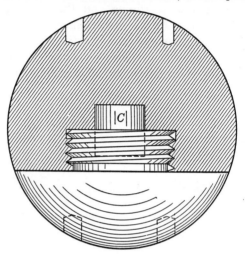

Fig. 29. Design of the primary photoneutron source standard at the National Bureau of Standards (C42). The beryllium sphere is 4 cm in diameter and holds, at the center (C), a 1-gram capsule of radium.

and theoretical (G32), indicates that the cross section passes through at least one maximum and one minimum as the gamma-ray energy is increased from threshold to 2.76 Mev.

Prior to the extensive availability of strong artificially produced gamma-ray sources, Ra-γ-Be sources were extensively used to provide intermediate-energy neutrons. Following a suggestion of Gamertsfelder and Goldhaber (G2), such a source has been prepared by Curtiss and Carson (C42) at the National Bureau of Standards, to serve as a permanent neutron standard. Since a Ra-γ-Be source does not require mixing of the radium and beryllium (with the attendant possibilities for physical change), its neutron output should not vary with time. In the standard source, a pressed radium bromide pellet is placed at the center of a carefully machined sphere of beryllium metal; the design of the standard source is shown in Fig. 29.

The absolute yield of such a source could be obtained, without the necessity of any neutron measurement, by a method developed by

Paneth and Glückauf (P2, G8). They measure the total accumulation of helium [1] after a known time of irradiation of the beryllium.

An interesting application of the photodisintegration process is as a gamma-ray detector which is completely insensitive to gamma-rays of energy below the photodisintegration threshold (P8a). Myers and Wattenberg (M42) have used this device to detect the presence of a small component of "cross-over" gamma-rays when two or more gamma-rays, both of which are below the photodisintegration threshold of beryllium or deuterium, are emitted in cascade.

(b) *Photoneutrons from High-Energy Gamma-Rays and X-Rays.* Photoneutron reactions with high-energy gamma-rays have been investigated in a large number of elements. Following the work of Bothe and Gentner (B52), the ~17-Mev Li(p,γ) gamma-rays have been used to study the (γ,n) cross sections of many elements, by Wäffler and Hirzel (W1) and by McDaniel, Walker, and Stearns (M12). However, the most extensive investigations have employed x-ray beams from electron accelerators, mainly betatrons.

The x-rays are produced by causing the accelerated electrons to strike a target, usually of some heavy element. The resulting radiation is allowed to fall on the material under investigation. (γ,n) reactions are detected either through direct observation of the neutrons, or by detection of the radiations from the product (usually β^+-radioactive) nuclei.

The shape of the x-ray spectrum from an electron accelerator depends on the target thickness. For relatively thin targets, the distribution of x-ray quanta follows a bremsstrahlung spectrum, at least for energies not too far below the maximum (electron) energy,

$$dN(E_\gamma) = \frac{kdE_\gamma}{E_\gamma} \tag{85}$$

The measurement of (γ,n) cross sections with such x-ray beams involves the complication of dealing with a heteroenergetic source. However, if the electron energy can be varied, (γ,n) yields can be measured as a function of the maximum x-ray energy. The results of three such studies, due to Diven and Almy (D15), are shown in Fig. 30a. Such curves can be interpreted in terms of the (γ,n) cross section *vs.* E_γ, provided that the x-ray spectrum is known and the x-ray intensity (the value of k in Eq. 85) is calibrated.

---

[1] The reaction is $Be^9(\gamma,n)Be^8$; $Be^8 \rightarrow 2He^4$.

Some curves of $\sigma(\gamma,n)$ vs. E_γ are shown in Fig. 30b. The striking feature of such cross-section curves, first noted by Baldwin and Klaiber (B7), is the strong resonance shape. This shape has been observed for all the nuclei studied, although the positions of the maxima and the

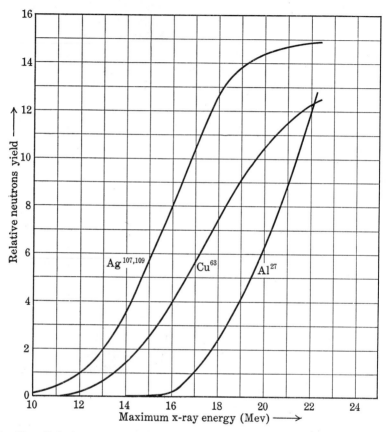

Fig. 30a.   Relative neutron yields *vs.* maximum x-ray energy for three nuclei, due to Diven and Almy (D15). The ordinates are in arbitrary units.

resonance widths vary from nucleus to nucleus (D15, M13). Particularly accurate work, determining the resonance constants for many nuclei, has been done by the Saskatchewan Group (J4, K4).

An explanation of these resonances has been advanced by Goldhaber and Teller (G16). They have postulated the possibility of dipole vibrations in which the protons (as a whole) oscillate with respect to the neutrons in the nucleus. The general features of the process of dipole radiation capture have been derived by Levinger and Bethe (L16).

Neutron yields, due to the (γ,n) reaction, have been measured for many elements and at many x-ray energies, up to 330 Mev (P31, T8). Neutron sources of considerable strength can be obtained, through (γ,n) reactions, from electron accelerators. Thus, by using the electrons from a 3.2-Mev linear accelerator to produce gamma-rays in a lead target, and by irradiating a heavy water (or beryllium) target with these gamma-rays, Cockroft, Duckworth, and Merrison (C16) obtained

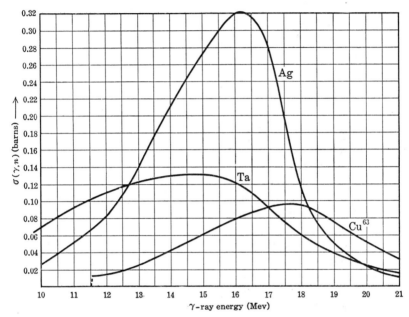

Fig. 30b. (γ,n) cross sections vs. γ-ray energy for copper, silver, and tantalum (D15,M13).

average neutron yields of $\sim 10^9$ neutrons/sec and peak yields of $\sim 2 \times 10^{12}$ neutrons/sec (in ~ 2 μsec bursts). Calculations based on the curves of Fig. 30 indicate that an electron beam of 1 μamp (average) and 20 Mev energy, impinging directly on a thick target of a medium or heavy element, should yield $\sim 10^{10}$ neutrons/sec.

The spectrum of neutron energies resulting from x-ray-induced (γ,n) reactions is relatively broad, corresponding to "evaporation" from an excited compound nucleus; the theory of the evaporation process, and of its Z-dependence, has been discussed by Heidmann and Bethe (H52). The Maxwellian form of the neutron energy distribution has been verified by Byerly and Stephens (B80). However, there is expected to be a high-energy "tail" of neutrons ejected by direct gamma-ray action, with a non-spherical angular distribution (C29).

3. Accelerated Charged Particle Sources. Radioactive alpha-particle and gamma-ray neutron sources are of rather limited usefulness, especially for the production of intense beams of monoenergetic neutrons. The availability of Van de Graaff and cyclotron accelerators, capable of delivering strong monoenergetic currents of various nuclear projectiles, makes possible the production of strong neutron sources by a variety of nuclear reactions. These projectiles include protons (p), deuterons (d), tritons (t), alpha-particles (α), and heavier nuclei. In this section we shall consider only reactions induced by the first three. [(α,n) reactions have been discussed in connection with radioactive neutron sources.]

We shall mainly emphasize, in this section, reactions which can lead to monoenergetic neutrons. This possibility exists whenever the energy of the first excited state of the product nucleus is too great to be excited by the projectiles used. Depending on the nucleus involved, the first excited state may lie anywhere from a few hundred kev to many Mev above the ground state. In some cases, sources may be effectively monoenergetic even when the first excited state is energetically available, owing to a relatively low yield of excited product nuclei.

With the available reactions which yield monoenergetic neutrons, it appears possible to cover the neutron energy range from a few kev to 20 Mev. To cover the rest of the very fast- and the ultrafast-neutron ranges, it is necessary to resort to heteroenergetic sources, and to depend on the detector for any sorting out of the neutron energies. Prior to the availability of tritium, and the use of the t-d reaction, heteroenergetic (d,n) reactions were the only ones available for obtaining very fast neutrons. Such sources will also be considered in this discussion.

Given the requisite reaction, a strong current of monoenergetic projectiles, and a thin target, the neutrons emerging at a given angle with respect to the projectile direction have a definite energy. The relationship between the neutron energy E_n, the angle θ, the projectile energy E_i, the reaction Q value, and the masses of the particles involved has been frequently described.[1] The properties of monoenergetic neutron sources are collected in a review article by Hanson, Taschek, and Williams (H34), upon which this summary leans heavily. The energy-angle relationships in a given reaction are conveniently represented in the form of a nomograph, developed by McKibben (M15),[2] of which some examples will be shown in the following.

[1] See, for example, Part VI.

[2] Such nomographs for the most extensively used reactions can be purchased as document MDDC 223 from the Document Division of the AEC, Oak Ridge, Tennessee. They have been reprinted in the article of Hanson, Taschek, and Williams (H34).

A McKibben nomograph (Figs. 31, 33, 37, 40) consists of two sets of semicircles (solid and broken) and two sets of radial lines. The solid semicircles, centered at the origin of the (lower) neutron energy scale, represent various values of the neutron energy in the laboratory coordinate system. The solid radial lines, from the same origin, represent angles of emission of the neutrons in the laboratory system. The broken semicircles (which are *not* concentric) represent various energies of bombarding particle (p or d); the bombarding energy is given by the intersection of a broken semicircle with the upper of the two horizontal axes. The broken radial lines represent loci of equal values of the angle of neutron emission in the center-of-mass coordinate system.

Thus, given a value of the bombarding particle energy, the energies of the emitted neutrons are given by the intersections of the appropriate broken semicircle and the solid semicircles; to each neutron energy (intersection) there corresponds a definite laboratory angle (solid line) and a definite center-of-mass angle (broken line).

(a) *Intermediate and Fast Neutrons from (p,n) Reactions.* These reactions are endoergic. Hence, by bombarding thin targets with protons of energy only slightly above threshold it is possible to obtain monoenergetic neutrons of relatively low energy. The minimum energy obtainable from such sources is limited by the fact that, at proton energies only slightly above threshold, there are two neutron energies corresponding to each angle of emergence. (Neutrons emitted at forward and backward angles in the center-of-mass system all lie within a cone of apex angle $<180°$ in the laboratory system.) However, as soon as the apex angle of the cone of neutron emergence becomes $180°$, the energy-angle relationship is unique. In this respect, the heavier the target nucleus, the lower the energy at which the neutrons for a given angle are monoenergetic. However, the necessity for penetration, by the proton, of the Coulomb barrier limits the possible target nuclei to low Z ($\lesssim 25$).

Some properties of known (p,n) reactions are summarized in Table 19. Most of these data are from the work of Richards and co-workers at the University of Wisconsin, and have been collected by Richards, Smith, and Browne (R10), who give references to the original investigations. The minimum neutron energy at threshold (fifth column) arises from the center-of-mass motion of the system.

$$E_{n,\min} = \frac{E_t}{(A + 1)^2} \tag{86}$$

where A is the mass number of the target nucleus. The sixth column gives the minimum energy of monoenergetic neutrons in the forward

TABLE 19

PROPERTIES OF (p,n) REACTIONS FOR $Z \leq 25$ (MOSTLY FROM R10)

Target	Product	Observed E_t (Mev)	$-Q$ (Mev)	$E_{n,min}$ (kev)	$E'_{n,min}$ at 0° (kev)	Lowest Level (Mev)
$_1H^2$	$_2{}_1H^1$	3.339 ± 0.015	2.225	371	1979	
$_1H^3$	$_2He^3$	1.019 ± 0.001	0.764	63.7	286.5	>2.5
$_3Li^7$	$_4Be^7$	1.882 ± 0.002	1.646	29.4	120.1	0.435
$_4Be^9$	$_5B^9$	2.059 ± 0.002	1.852	20.6	83.4	>1.5
$_5B^{11}$	$_6C^{11}$	3.015 ± 0.003	2.762	20.9	84.5	2.02
$_6C^{12}$	$_6N^{12}$	$20.0 \quad \pm 0.1$	18.5	118	477	
$_6C^{13}$	$_6N^{13}$	3.236 ± 0.003	3.003	16.5	66.4	2.383
$_6C^{14}$	$_6N^{14}$	0.664 ± 0.009	0.620	2.9	11.8	2.3
$_8O^{18}$	$_8F^{18}$	2.590 ± 0.004	2.453	7.2	28.8	
$_9F^{19}$	$_{10}Ne^{19}$	$4.18 \quad \pm 0.25$	3.97	10.5	42	
$_{11}Na^{23}$	$_{12}Mg^{23}$	$4.78 \quad \pm 0.3$	4.58	8.3	33	
$_{17}Cl^{37}$	$_{18}A^{37}$	1.640 ± 0.004	1.598	1.1	4.6	1.4
$_{18}A^{40}$	$_{19}K^{40}$	$\leq 2.4(?)$	2.3(?)	1.6	5.7	0.81
$_{19}K^{41}$	$_{20}Ca^{41}$	$1.25 \quad \pm 0.02$	1.22	0.7	2.8	1.95
$_{21}Sc^{45}$	$_{22}Ti^{45}$	~ 2.85	2.79	1.35	5.4	
$_{23}V^{51}$	$_{24}Cr^{51}$	1.562 ± 0.006	1.532	0.58	2.3	0.775 †
$_{25}Mn^{55}$	$_{26}Fe^{55}$	$1.18 \quad \pm 0.01$	1.16	0.38	1.5	
		1.020 ± 0.010	1.00	0.33	1.3	0.42 ‡

† (S52).   ‡ (S54, M10).

direction, $E'_{n,min}$, which corresponds to the forward cone just filling the forward hemisphere. The properties of the most important of these neutron sources follow:

$$H^3(p,n)He^3$$

McKibben's nomograph for this reaction is shown in Fig. 31. Since tritium has only recently become extensively available, this reaction has not been very widely used for a neutron source; only the Wisconsin group has reported extensive (cross section) measurements with this source (B41, M31). Most of the information concerning yields, angular distributions, etc., vs. proton energies up to 2.5 Mev is due to the Los Alamos group (J2, H34). The cross section is shown in Fig. 32. The rapid increase may be due to a resonance of He^4 corresponding to incident protons of >2.5 Mev energy. The angular distribution of the emerging neutrons is quite complex (J2). A large yield of 20-Mev

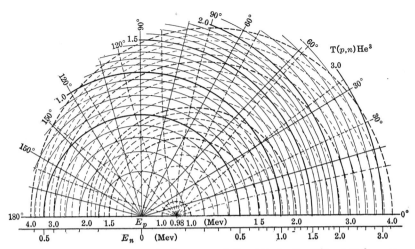

Fig. 31. McKibben nomograph of energy relationships in the $H^3(p,n)$ He^3 reaction (H34). Directions for its use are given on p. 375.

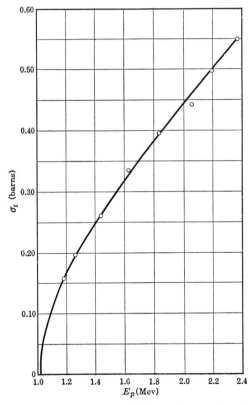

Fig. 32. Total cross section of the $H^3(p,n)He^3$ reaction as a function of the incident proton energy (J2).

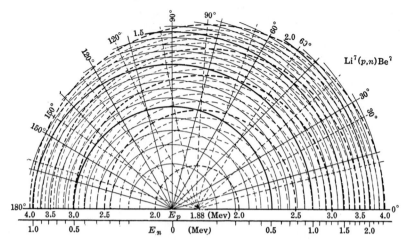

Fig. 33.   McKibben nomograph for the $Li^7(p,n)Be^7$ reaction (H34).   Directions for
its use are given on p. 375.

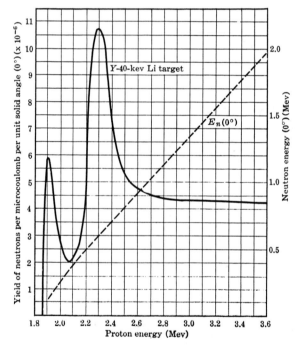

Fig. 34.   Yield of the $Li^7(p,n)Be^7$ reaction in the forward direction (H34).

gamma-radiation, arising from the $H^3(p,\gamma)He^4$ reaction, accompanies the (p,n) reaction, and may interfere with some forms of neutron detection (A30).

$$Li^7(p,n)Be^7$$

This reaction has provided the most extensively used source of intermediate-energy neutrons. Its nomograph is shown in Fig. 33. The

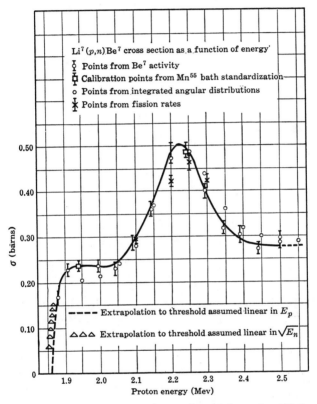

Fig. 35.   Total cross section for the $Li^7(p,n)Be^7$ reaction (H34).

yield in the forward direction is shown in Fig. 34. The first peak is due to the concentration of neutrons in the forward cone for proton energies close to threshold. The second peak, at $E_p \approx 2.3$ Mev, is real, and corresponds to a resonance of the compound nucleus Be^8. The angular distribution is peaked in the forward direction, especially in the vicinity of the resonance, and requires terms up to $\cos^2 \theta$ (P_2) for its description (T1). The total cross section *vs.* proton energy is shown in Fig. 35.

Until relatively recently, it was thought that the neutrons from this reaction were truly monoenergetic (H8). However, the reaction is now known to yield a low-energy group of neutrons corresponding to an excited state of Be^7 at 435 kev. The results of various investigators on the relative yield of the low-energy group are summarized in Table 20.

TABLE 20

RELATIVE YIELD OF NEUTRONS ARISING FROM EXCITATION OF THE 435-KEV STATE OF Be^7 IN THE $Li^7(p,n)Be^{7*}$ REACTION

Proton Energy (Mev)	Angle of Observation	Intensity Relative to Ground-State Group (%)	References
2.378 $(E_t{}^*)$	0°	~3	W33
2.705	0°	8 ± 2	H20
2.75	30°	9 ± 1.5	J5
2.89	30°	10.5 ± 1	J5
3.120	0°	8 ± 2	H20
3.31	0°	17 ± 10	J8
3.49	0°	10 ± 3	F42
3.66	30°	12 ± 1	J5
3.91	0°	9 ± 4	J8
	60°	16 ± 6	J8

Additional Be^7 levels have been reported below 1 Mev (G30), but these have not been confirmed in other investigations (K6).

Other Possibilities

Other possible (p,n) reactions are discussed by Hanson, Taschek, and Williams (H34) and by Richards, Smith, and Browne (R10). The $Be^9(p,n)B^9$ reaction is quite similar to that on Li^7, but does not give a low-energy group up to neutron energies of ~1.5 Mev (J9). However, its yield is lower, and thin beryllium targets are considerably more difficult to prepare.

The (p,n) reactions on scandium, vanadium, and manganese are being considered for producing monoenergetic neutrons in the ~1-kev energy range. Their yields have been studied by a number of investigators (H34, R10, B4, M10, S52, S54).

(b) *Fast and Very Fast Neutrons from* (d,n) *Reactions.* These reactions are, with the exception of $C^{12}(d,n)N^{13}$, exoergic. They are useful in producing fast neutrons in the range 1–20 Mev. The Q values for the most useful (d,n) reactions are shown in Table 21. The last two yield heteroenergetic neutrons, but have been extensively used because of their high yields.

TABLE 21

PROPERTIES OF SOME (d,n) REACTIONS

Reaction	Q Value (Mev)		E_{n0} for $E_d = 0$ (Mev)
$H^2(d,n)He^3$	3.265 ± 0.018	(T16)	2.45
$H^3(d,n)He^4$	17.6	(H34)	14.1
$C^{12}(d,n)N^{13}$	-0.281 ± 0.003	(T16)	($E_t = 0.328$)
$N^{14}(d,n)O^{15}$	5.1	(H34)	4.8
$Li^7(d,n)Be^8$	15.0	(T16)	13.3
$Be^9(d,n)B^{10}$	3.79	(T16)	3.44

The last column gives the energy E_{n0} of neutrons which would result from the absorption of zero energy deuterons; this energy is independent

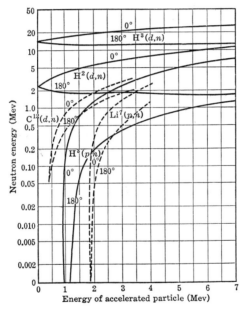

Fig. 36.   Energies of neutrons, emitted at 0° and 180°, for the most important monoenergetic (d,n) and (p,n) reactions (H34).

of the angle of emergence of the neutron.   For deuterons with a given kinetic energy, the neutron energy is uniquely determined by its angle of emergence, provided that the reaction goes to the ground state of the product nucleus.   The neutron energies vary on both sides of E_{n0}, being greater for emission in the forward direction and less for backward emission.   The energies of neutrons emitted at 0° and 180° are shown in Fig. 36, as a function of the bombarding energy, for the first three reactions in the table. Also included are curves for the two (p,n) reactions discussed above.

$$H^2(d,n)He^3$$

The d-d reaction has been extensively used, and its characteristics widely investigated (H34). It has high yields for low bombarding energies, which makes it particularly useful as a neutron source with low-voltage (<1 Mev) particle accelerators. The neutrons are mono-energetic up to bombarding energies of 10 Mev. Figure 37 is the Mc-Kibben nomograph for this reaction.

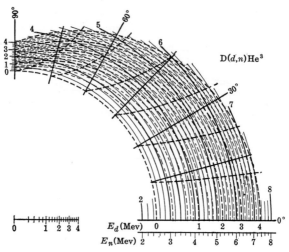

Fig. 37.   McKibben nomograph for the d-d reaction (H34). Directions for its use are given on p. 375.

The angular distribution of d-d neutrons has been extensively studied, both experimentally and theoretically. At energies of a few hundred kev, the distribution in the c.m. system is symmetrical about 90°, being ~60 percent lower at 90° than at 0° and 180° (H34, M16). For higher energies the distribution becomes much more anisotropic. Hunter and Richards (H78) have investigated the angular distribution for deuterons of from 0.5 to 3.7 Mev. They find that it can be represented by an expression of the form

$$N(\theta) = A_0 P_0(\theta) + A_2 P_2(\theta) + A_4 P_4(\theta) + A_6 P_6(\theta) + \cdots \quad (87)$$

in which the $P_n(\theta)$'s are the Legendre polynomials, and all the coefficients vary with energy, as shown in Fig. 38a. The theory of the angular distribution has been discussed by Konopinski and Teller (K21) and by Beiduk, Pruett, and Konopinski (B14). The total cross section *vs.* deuteron energy is shown in Fig. 38b.

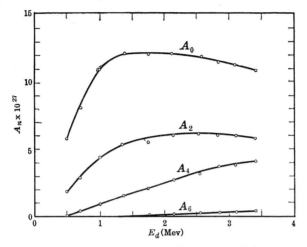

Fig. 38a. Variation with deuteron energy, E_d, of the coefficients of the Legendre polynomial fit to the angular distribution of the neutrons from the *d-d* reaction in the center-of-mass coordinate system (H78).

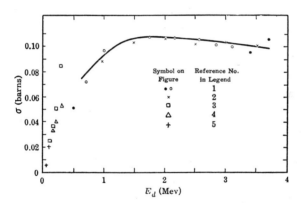

Symbol on Figure	Reference No. in Legend
● ○	1
×	2
□	3
△	4
+	5

(1) Hunter and Richards (H78). (2) Blair, Freier, Lampi, Sleator, and Williams, Phys. Rev., **74,** 1599 (1948). (3) Manley, Coon, and Graves, Phys. Rev., **70,** 101(A) (1946). (4) Graves, Graves, Coon, and Manley, Phys. Rev., **70,** 101(A) (1946). (5) Bretscher, French, and Seidl, Phys. Rev., **73,** 815 (1948).

Fig. 38b. Total cross section for the $H^2(d,n)He^3$ reaction (H78).

The *d-d* reaction is frequently used to provide strong neutron sources by bombarding thick targets of heavy ice with deuterons. The thick target yield curve (H34) is given in Fig. 39.

The companion reaction $H^2(d,p)H^3$ has a comparable cross section (M16, H34). The protons are frequently used to "monitor" the neutron yield. At high bombarding deuteron energies the He^3 recoils from the

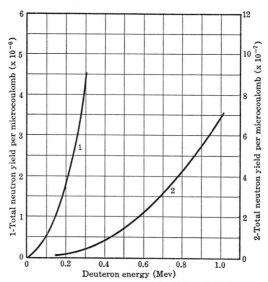

Fig. 39.   Thick heavy ice target $H^2(d,n)He^3$ neutron yields (H34).

(d,n) reaction can be used as a monitor, and also, by observing He^3 neutron coincidences, to eliminate background effects due to (d,n) reactions on target impurities.

$H^3(d,n)He^4$

This, the t-d reaction, is the most strongly exoergic of the reactions capable of yielding monoenergetic neutrons; it can provide neutrons of from 12 to 20 Mev by using deuterons of up to 3 Mev (Fig. 36). The McKibben nomograph for the reaction is shown in Fig. 40. This reaction is especially useful with low-voltage deuteron accelerators, since it has very large yields for deuterons of a few hundred kev energy, owing to a resonance in the cross section at $\sim$100 kev. The low-energy cross-section data (up to $\sim$1 Mev deuterons) can be fitted by the expression (H34)

$$\sigma = \frac{58}{E} \frac{\exp\left(-1.72/E^{1/2}\right)}{1 + (E - 0.096)^2/(0.174)^2} \text{ barns} \qquad (88)$$

where E is the deuteron energy in Mev. From 1 to 2.5 Mev the cross section remains essentially flat at $\sim$0.15 barn. The cross section is 0.05 barn at 10.5 Mev (B72).

The angular distribution in the *t-d* reaction, for incident deuterons up to 2.5 Mev, has been measured by Taschek, Hemmendinger, and Jarvis (T2) by observing the distribution of recoil alpha-particles. Their re-

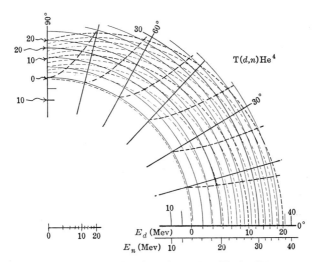

Fig. 40. McKibben nomograph for the *t-d* reaction (H34). Directions for its use are given on p. 375.

sults are shown in Fig. 41. Detection of the recoil alphas provides an effective means for monitoring the neutron yield from this source. The angular distribution for $E_d = 10.5$ Mev has been measured by Brolley, Fowler, and Stovall (B72).

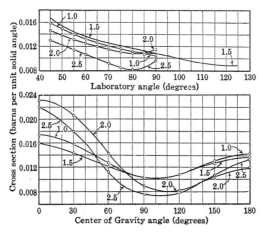

Fig. 41. Angular distribution of recoil alpha-particles from the $H^3(d,n)He^4$ reaction for various deuteron energies (in Mev) (T2, H33).

Because of the strong low-energy resonance, the t-d reaction is expected to have large thick target yields. Thus, for a thick gas target and 600-kev d's the yield is 5×10^8 neutrons per microcoulomb; for tritons adsorbed in a thick zirconium target, the yield at $E_d = 200$ kev is about 10^8 neutrons per microcoulomb (H34).

One interesting application of the t-d reaction is in the possibility of converting intense sources of thermal neutrons (such as those available from piles) into strong fast-neutron sources. Thus, if thermal neutrons are allowed to fall on a mixture of lithium and deuterium, fast tritons ($E = 2.65$ Mev) will be produced by the $Li^6(n,\alpha)H^3$ reaction. These tritons then react with the deuterons to produce 14-Mev neutrons by the t-d reaction. A recent investigation by Almqvist (A11) has shown that such sources also produce neutrons by reactions of tritons on the lithium nuclei; the latter reactions have a considerably greater yield than the t-d reaction in the mixtures used. Since the neutrons from lithium result from a variety of reactions on both lithium isotopes, with Q values ranging from 16 to 8.9 Mev, the neutrons from such sources have a complex spectrum. The neutron yields for a number of compounds are shown in Table 22. From these data the author derives

TABLE 22

NEUTRON YIELDS FROM THERMAL NEUTRON IRRADIATION OF LITHIUM AND
LITHIUM-DEUTERIUM COMPOUNDS (A11)

Substance	Neutrons per 10^5 Tritons	
	From Li	From D
LiF	26.8	
Li_2CO_3	17.2	
$LiOH \cdot H_2O$	15.2	
LiOD	20.3	3.4
$LiOD \cdot D_2O + D_2O$	9.3	12.1

average cross sections of 1.5 and 0.41 barns for 2.65-Mev tritons on thick targets of lithium and deuterium, respectively. Crews (C32) has measured the yield and angular distribution of neutrons from thin lithium targets for triton energies between 0.25 and 2.10 Mev; he derives $\bar{\sigma} \approx 0.76$ barn for $E_t = 2.0$ Mev on a thick Li target.

$C^{12}(d,n)N^{13}$

This, among the (d,n) reactions of interest, is the only endoergic reaction. It is mainly useful because of its low threshold (Table 21;

Fig. 36), which makes it a convenient low-voltage accelerator source for neutrons of from a few hundred kev to $\sim$1.5 Mev. Since the first excited state of N^{13}, observed in this reaction, is at $\sim$2.3 Mev (G29), the neutrons are monoenergetic to $\sim$2 Mev. The reaction yield is relatively low and shows a complex angular distribution and energy dependence (H34).

The companion reaction $C^{12}(d,p)C^{13}$ has a similar yield curve at low deuteron energies, and is useful for monitoring the neutron yield. A complicating feature is the presence, with normal carbon targets, of the reaction $C^{13}(d,n)N^{14}$, with a Q value of 5.2 Mev, which gives a fast-neutron group of intensity $\sim$1 per cent of the C^{12} neutrons.

$$N^{14}(d,n)O^{15}$$

This reaction, very seldom used, gives monoenergetic neutrons for deuterons of up to $\sim$1 Mev energy. At 1 Mev the cross section relative to that of the d-d reaction has been measured by Gibson and Livesey (G4), and is shown in Table 23.

TABLE 23

RATIO OF d-d TO N^{14}-d CROSS SECTIONS FOR 1-MEV DEUTERONS (G4)

Angle	Ratio (d-d/N^{14}-d)
0°	4.4
30°	4.4
90°	1.5
150°	2.1

$$Li^7(d,n)Be^8$$

Because of its large Q value and large yield, this source has been extensively used, especially with cyclotrons. However, the large number of levels, in both the compound and product nuclei, gives rise to a complicated neutron spectrum with a wide energy spread (H34). The thick target yield for a bombarding energy of 600 kev is 17×10^6 neutrons per microcoulomb. Above $E_d = 1$ Mev the thick target yields are greater than for the d-d reaction.

$$Be^9(d,n)B^{10}$$

This reaction also gives rise to a complex neutron spectrum of lower maximum energy than that from Li^7 (A4). The thick target yields at low deuteron energies are shown in Table 24. Above ~1 Mev the thick target yields are between those of the d-d and the $Li^7(d,n)$ reactions.

TABLE 24

THICK TARGET YIELDS FOR THE $Be^9(d,n)B^{10}$ REACTION

E_d (kev)	10^6 Neutrons/Microcoulomb
400	4
600	21
800	106

Other Possibilities

Many other (d,n) reactions have been employed as neutron sources. Among these the $F^{19}(d,n)Ne^{20}$, $Q = 10.7$ Mev, has received some attention, but its characteristics are not more favorable than the other reactions which yield heteroenergetic sources, and its yield is lower. While such sources have frequently been used in the past to produce very fast neutrons, they have been mainly superseded by the t-d reaction.

The (d,n) yields of a variety of elements, for deuteron energies of ~10 Mev and greater, have been studied by a number of investigators. Thick target yields for 10-Mev deuterons (due to Smith and Kruger, S41) are shown in Table 25, together with the yields at 15 Mev (due to Allen, Nechaj, Sun, and Jennings, A8). The latter results are sur-

TABLE 25

NEUTRON YIELDS FROM 10- AND 15-MEV DEUTERONS ON THICK TARGETS

Target	Z	Yield (10^8 neutrons/ microcoulomb)		Target	Z	Yield (10^8 neutrons/ microcoulomb)	
		10 Mev	15 Mev			10 Mev	15 Mev
Be	4	320	190	Nb	41		15
B	5	190		Mo	42	42	15
C	6	120		Ag	47		14
Al	13	87	64	Cd	48		12
P	15	105		Sb	51	35	
Ti	22		65	Ta	73	7.4	3.3
Cr	24		29	W	74	7.0	
Mn	25	76	52	Pt	78	6.0	
Co	27		26	Au	79	4.7	2.1
Ni	28	33		Pb	82		2.1
Cu	29	55	29	Bi	83		1.3

prisingly lower than those at 10 Mev, although the trend with atomic number is the same for both series of measurements. The discrepancy probably arises, at least in part, from the fact that the 10-Mev measurements counted neutrons of all energies while the 15-Mev results apply only to those neutrons capable of exciting the $S^{32}(n,p)$ reaction.

The angular distributions of (d,n) neutrons have been investigated by Roberts and Abelson (R14), by Falk, Creutz, and Seitz (F1), by Allen et al. (A8, S58) (all at $E_d = 15$ Mev), by Ammiraju (A22) ($E_d = 18$ Mev), by Schecter (S4) ($E_d = 20$ Mev), and by others. These distributions show a strong peaking in the forward direction. [Some, e.g., Be, when only the highest-energy neutrons are detected, show structure in the angular distribution (S58).]

The observed characteristics of the (d,n) reaction for high-energy deuterons can be explained in terms of the "stripping" theory of Serber (S20) and Peaslee (P8), according to which most of the neutrons are produced by a process in which the neutron never enters a compound nucleus; the deuteron is polarized in the field of the nucleus and then split, the proton being captured (and occasionally scattered) by the target nucleus. Recently, Butler (B78, B79) has made a significant contribution to the "stripping" theory by considering in greater detail the angular distribution of neutrons from such reactions when the product nucleus is left in a definite quantum state. His calculations predict structure (i.e., maxima and minima) in the angular distribution which can be interpreted in terms of the angular momentum and parity properties of the initial and final states.

(c) *Ultrafast Neutrons from Accelerated Deuterons and Protons.* When charged particles from ultrahigh-energy accelerators strike a target, neutrons are produced through a variety of reactions. Those reactions which involve the capture of the bombarding particle into a compound nucleus give rise to neutrons by the process of evaporation. Such neutrons have the broad energy distribution characteristic of the statistical theory, with the maximum in the fast- or very fast-energy region and a more-or-less symmetrical angular distribution. However, when deuterons (and, to a lesser extent, protons) are used as the bombarding particles, there is observed, superimposed on the evaporated neutrons, a strong forward peak of ultrafast neutrons with a relatively narrow energy distribution. In the case of deuteron bombardment, the neutrons arise mainly from the stripping process, mentioned briefly in the preceding section. Serber (S20) has given a simple picture of this process, as follows:

The deuteron is a relatively loosely bound structure in which neutron and proton spend a large fraction of the time far apart. Hence, it is not improbable that, as a deuteron traverses the target, the proton will strike one of the target nuclei while the neutron remains outside the nucleus. In such a collision the proton will be stopped while the neutron will go on, carrying off approximately half of the original deuteron energy.

However, the neutron has internal motion, relative to the center of mass of the deuteron. Hence, as the neutron leaves the proton behind, this relative motion is superimposed on the forward motion of the deuteron, giving rise to an energy spread centered around the average value of half the deuteron energy. Another result of the relative motion is that the emergent "stripped" neutrons have a spread in directions, around the original deuteron direction.

The magnitudes of the energy and angular spreads of the neutron beam can be estimated as follows: The forward momentum of the neutron, due to the kinetic energy, E_d, of the deuteron, is

$$p_0 = (ME_d)^{1/2} \qquad (89a)$$

The internal momentum of the neutron is, roughly,

$$p_1 \cong (M\epsilon_d)^{1/2} \qquad (89b)$$

where ϵ_d is the deuteron binding energy. The stripped neutrons have energies within the limits given by

$$E \cong \frac{(p_0 \pm p_1)^2}{2M} \cong \frac{1}{2}E_d \pm (\epsilon_d E_d)^{1/2} \qquad (90)$$

A more accurate calculation (S20) gives, for the full width at half maximum,

$$\Delta E = 1.5(\epsilon_d E_d)^{1/2} \qquad (90a)$$

The angular spread in the neutron beam is determined by the relative values of the forward and transverse neutron momenta:

$$\Delta\theta \approx \frac{2p_1}{p_0} = 2\left(\frac{\epsilon_d}{E_d}\right)^{1/2} \text{ radians} \qquad (91)$$

The more accurate calculation (S20) gives

$$\Delta\theta = 1.6\left(\frac{\epsilon_d}{E_d}\right)^{1/2} \qquad (91a)$$

as the full angular width at half maximum. The above considerations, with respect to the angular spread, apply only to targets of light nuclei, in which the coulomb deflection of the deuterons is negligible. For the heaviest nuclei the coulomb deflections lead to about twice as large a spread as Eq. (91a).

The energy and angular distributions of the stripped neutrons are superimposed on the background of neutrons produced as a result of evaporations. However, this background is expected to be small, especially since it is spread, approximately uniformly, over all directions. In addition, some neutrons are produced by the disintegration of deuterons in the coulomb field of the target nuclei; this effect is relatively small for light nuclei and becomes comparable to the stripping production for the heaviest target materials (D1, K20).

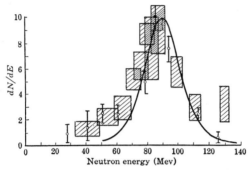

Fig. 42. Energy distribution of neutrons obtained by stripping 190-Mev deuterons in a 1.27-cm thick beryllium target, due to Hadley *et al.* (H1). The curve is from the theory of Serber (S20).

The observations of Helmholz, McMillan, and Sewell (H53) on angular distributions of the neutrons produced by bombarding various nuclei with 190-Mev deuterons and of Hadley, Kelly, Leith, Segrè, Wiegand, and York (H1) on the energy distribution of the neutrons from a beryllium target bombarded by 190-Mev deuterons are in good agreement with Serber's theory, and demonstrate the possibility of using the stripping process to obtain relatively monoenergetic ultrafast neutron beams from ultrahigh-energy particle accelerators. The energy distribution due to the latter investigators is shown in Fig. 42.

When ultrafast protons are used as the bombarding particles, the emerging neutrons are neither so sharply collimated nor so nearly monoenergetic. However, observations by Miller, Sewell, and Wright (M32) (330-Mev protons on beryllium, aluminum, copper, and uranium) and by DeJuren (D11) (340-Mev protons on beryllium) have demonstrated that there is an appreciable component of ultrafast neutrons emitted at forward angles. The results of the first-mentioned investigators, on the full angular widths at half maximum for neutrons of $E > 20$ Mev, are: beryllium, 54°; aluminum, 59°; copper, 59°; uranium, 58°.

Such forward-collimated, ultrafast neutrons result primarily from one or a few p-n collisions in the nucleus; at these energies the scattering of neutrons by protons is predominantly forward (charge exchange), and the scattered neutron has an appreciable probability of emerging from the nucleus without undergoing any further scattering.

Relative neutron yields for targets of various Z have been measured by Knox (K20) with both high-energy deuterons and protons as the bombarding particles. For 190-Mev deuteron bombardment the relative yields agree well with stripping plus disintegration by the Coulomb field. In the case of 340-Mev proton bombardment, the yield varies approximately as $(A - Z)^{\frac{2}{3}}$.

The energy distribution of the neutrons from beryllium and carbon targets bombarded with $\sim$100-Mev protons has been investigated by Bodansky and Ramsey (B42, B43). For a beryllium target they observe a sharp peak at $E_n \approx 93$ Mev, with a width at half maximum of $\sim$30 Mev. Below $\sim$70 Mev, the neutron energy distribution becomes essentially flat, with a yield of $\sim$40 percent of the peak value. The neutron yield from a carbon target shows a slight peak at $\sim$70 Mev ($\sim$25 percent above the roughly constant yield below $E_n = 60$ Mev) and falls off rapidly above 70 Mev. Similar studies on neutrons from beryllium, carbon, aluminum, and uranium bombarded with 170-Mev protons have been made by Taylor, Pickavance, Cassels, and Randle (T3).

4. Neutrons from U^{235} Fission. One of the most important present-day neutron sources is the fission reaction. Fission of the heaviest elements is accompanied by the emission of fast neutrons. The neutron spectrum resulting from thermal neutron fission of U^{235} is closely approximated by the expression (U2)

$$\frac{dN}{dE} = e^{-E} \sinh (2E)^{\frac{1}{2}} \tag{92}$$

where E is the neutron energy in Mev. This expression, suggested by Watt, agrees with the observed fission spectrum to within ± 15 percent up to $E = 17$ Mev.[1] Equation (92) is plotted in Fig. 43.

As seen in the figure, the fission spectrum has a rather broad energy distribution, with an average energy of $\sim$1.5 Mev. However, this is by no means the spectrum of neutrons normally observed either inside or emerging from piles, since neutrons in piles suffer considerable moderation by elastic scattering on light nuclei or by inelastic scattering on heavy nuclei. Nevertheless, strong sources of unmoderated fission neu-

[1] See T. W. Bonner, R. A. Ferrell, and M. C. Rinehart, Phys. Rev., **87**, 1032 (1952); D. L. Hill, Phys. Rev., **87**, 1034 (1952); B. E. Watt, Phys. Rev., **87**, 1037 (1952).

trons can be obtained by irradiating a uranium target with an intense thermal neutron beam (as from a pile). Such a source was used in the measurements by Hughes *et al.* (H72) of capture cross sections for fast neutrons, discussed in Section 2.

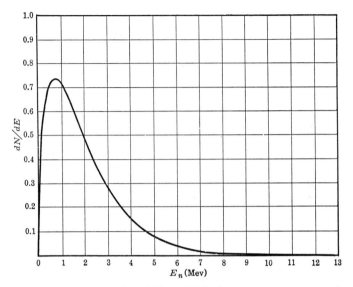

Fig. 43. Approximate shape (to within $\pm 15\%$) of the neutron spectrum from the fission of U^{235} by thermal neutrons (U2).

5. Neutrons in the Cosmic Radiation. Because the neutron is unstable, it is not expected to be one of the components of the primary cosmic radiation. Nevertheless, neutrons constitute an appreciable fraction of the "hard" or "penetrating" component of cosmic rays. These neutrons arise from nuclear disintegrations (stars) in the atmosphere and are responsible, in turn, for a large fraction of the observed nuclear disintegrations, especially at low altitudes (R21, S38, K22).

The observations on neutrons in the cosmic radiation are of two general types:

(1) The detection of very fast and ultrafast neutrons by observation of their interaction with nuclei, especially star production. Of such experiments, the most unambiguous are those in which stars are observed in sensitive nuclear emulsions, where the particle responsible for the disintegration can be seen or, in the case of neutrons, deduced from the absence of any charged particle of sufficient energy. Results of such experiments are reported and summarized by Bernardini, Cortini, and Manfredini (B18).

(2) The detection of slow neutrons in paraffin-surrounded and cadmium-covered BF_3 counters (Y4, S50). Many such experiments have been performed by many investigators; one of the most recent and most extensive, due to Yuan (Y4), has been carried to an altitude of $\sim$100,000 ft (pressure $\sim$1 cm Hg). The thermal neutron intensity shows an exponential increase (mean free path $\approx$ 156 g/cm^2) up to about 20 cm of Hg, a maximum at $\sim$8.5 cm of Hg, and a rapid falling off at higher altitudes.

The interpretation of experiments of the second type requires consideration of the processes by which the neutrons, produced mainly as fast neutrons in nuclear disintegrations, lose energy by scattering and, at the same time, diffuse through the atmosphere. (The general discussion of such problems is reserved for Section 4.) The theory of the slowing down of neutrons in the atmosphere has been given by Bethe, Korff, and Placzek (B26); the diffusion problem is discussed by Flügge (F35). Their calculations have recently been revised (in the light of more accurate data on nuclear cross sections) by Davis (D5) and by Lattimore (L6).

6. Sources of Slow Neutrons. By far the greatest number of neutron investigations have involved the use of slow neutrons. Sources of slow neutrons are invariably derived from intermediate- or higher-energy neutrons by allowing the neutrons to diffuse through a "moderating" material. [The lower limit of monoenergetic neutrons from threshold charged particle reactions, mostly (p,n), is being slowly pushed toward the slow-neutron region.]

Neutrons lose energy through inelastic collisions with medium or heavy nuclei and through elastic collisions with light nuclei; the first process is most effective for fast neutrons and the second for intermediate and slow neutrons. Consider a source of fast neutrons embedded in a large mass of material, preferably one containing light nuclei. The neutrons diffuse through the material, losing energy as they suffer scatterings. If the capture cross section is small compared to the scattering cross section (as it is in the intermediate- and fast-neutron ranges for most materials, especially light elements), the neutrons continue to lose energy until their energy is comparable to the energy of thermal agitation of the nuclei in the moderating material. After this, a neutron is as likely to gain as to lose energy in a scattering, and the slowing down stops. The neutrons are then said to be in "thermal equilibrium" with the moderating medium.

The energy distribution of neutrons in thermal equilibrium is in many respects similar to that of the molecules of a gas at the temperature of the medium. It is closely approximated by the Maxwell distribution function,

$$\frac{dn}{dv} = Av^2 e^{-Mv^2/2kT} \tag{93}$$

where M is the neutron mass, k is Boltzmann's constant, and T is the absolute temperature of the moderating medium; the factor A is generally a function of the position in the medium. The Maxwell distribution gives as the most probable velocity

$$v' = \left(\frac{2kT}{M}\right)^{1/2} \tag{94}$$

which is 2.2×10^5 cm/sec for $T = 300°K$; the average velocity is

$$\bar{v} = \frac{2}{\pi^{1/2}} v' = 1.128 v' \tag{95}$$

Strictly speaking, in an infinite homogeneous moderating medium the thermal neutrons will have a Maxwell energy distribution only under special circumstances, of which two are: (1) the nuclei in the moderating medium scatter but do not absorb neutrons; (2) the neutrons are emitted into the medium with the Maxwell energy distribution and the absorption cross section obeys the $1/v$ law. In this case, since the rate of neutron absorption, $\sim n v \sigma(v)$, is proportional to n, the original distribution shape will maintain itself.

Most thermal neutron sources deviate somewhat from the Maxwell distribution. If the medium strongly absorbs neutrons in the thermal energy range, the neutrons will never attain very low velocities, and the average velocity will be greater than that given by Eq. (95). If the size of the slowing-down medium is not sufficiently great, the neutrons will escape before attaining thermal equilibrium. In this situation, the average energy will again be greater than in Eq. (95). In any event, there is always present in the medium, at distances relatively close to the source, a component of neutrons in the process of being slowed down. These have an energy distribution characterized by equal fluxes ($\phi = nv$) of neutrons in equal logarithmic energy intervals, i.e.,

$$d\phi = \frac{B\,dE}{E} \tag{96}$$

where B depends both on the position in the medium and on the neutron energy. Such neutrons (called epithermal) are observed as a tail on the Maxwell distribution.

The theory of slowing down and diffusion of neutrons will be discussed in Section 4. Some results, useful in the planning and interpretation of experiments involving slow-neutron sources, are summarized below.

The most frequently used moderating media are water or paraffin, and graphite. The former have the advantage of containing a large proportion of hydrogen, the most effective nuclei for slowing down intermediate energy neutron; hence, for a given source strength, higher thermal neutron densities can be obtained with smaller quantities of moderating material than for any other slowing-down medium. On the other hand, carbon has a considerably smaller capture cross section than hydrogen, so that it is possible to obtain purer thermal neutron sources by making observations at greater distances from the fast-neutron source. Other materials which have proved useful as slowing-down media include heavy water, beryllium, and beryllium oxide (BeO); these are intermediate between water and graphite in slowing-down effectiveness, but are considerably more difficult to obtain in sufficient quantity.

Since the early work of Fermi and co-workers (F17, A20) on the moderating properties of water there have been many investigations of slow-neutron distributions in water for many fast-neutron sources. The results of one such study, due to Anderson, Koontz, and Roberts, are shown in Fig. 44, a plot of activity $\times r^2$ (proportional to $r^2\overline{nv}$) vs. distance from the source. The characteristic features of such curves are the peak at a relatively small distance and the exponential decrease at large distances from the source.

The results of such studies are frequently summarized in terms of the value of the second moment of the distribution,

$$\overline{r^2} = \frac{\displaystyle\int_0^\infty Ar^4\,dr}{\displaystyle\int_0^\infty Ar^2\,dr} \qquad (97)$$

where A is the measured activity of the detector used. The measurements of Anderson, Koontz, and Roberts (Fig. 44) give $\overline{r^2} = 278$ and 353 cm^2 for the indium resonance (1.44 ev) and thermal neutron detector, respectively. (These are in fair agreement with the results of other investigators.) The characteristic lengths of the exponential decrease at large distances,

$$r^2 A(r) \sim e^{-r/\lambda} \qquad (98)$$

were found to be $\lambda = 9.43$ and 10.00 cm for the indium resonance and thermal detectors, respectively.

The slowing down of neutrons in graphite has also been studied with various sources. The results of measurements by Feld and Fermi are shown in Fig. 45 as curves of thermal and indium resonance detector

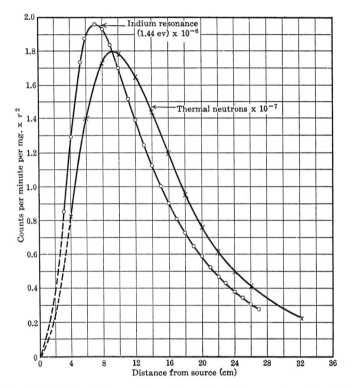

Fig. 44.   Distribution of slow neutrons from a Ra-α-Be source in water. The ordinate is the activity $\times r^2$ of a thin indium foil. The curve labeled "indium resonance" represents the activity of a cadmium-covered foil; the curve labeled "thermal neutrons" represents the activity of a bare foil minus 1.07 times the activity of the cadmium-covered foil. The source had a strength of 13.2×10^6 neutrons/sec. The indium foils had an area of 3×6.4 cm^2 and a thickness of 1.69 g/cm^2. The cadmium covers were 0.96 g/cm^2 thick. Data due to Anderson, Koontz, and Roberts (unpublished). The ordinate scale can be converted to a scale of thermal neutron flux $(\overline{nv}) \times r^2$ by multiplying by 1.6×10^6.

activation *vs.* distance from the source, for a Ra-α-Be source (Fig. 45a) and a Ra-γ-Be source (Fig. 45b). Since these measurements were made in a graphite column of non-negligible lateral dimensions, the geometry is not strictly comparable to that for a point source in an effectively infinite medium (Fig. 44). However, the geometric effects can be taken into account in interpreting such experiments (see Section 4).

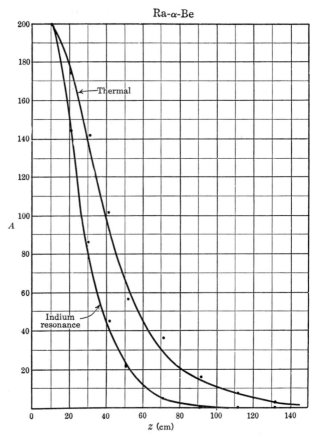

Fig. 45a. Thermal neutron flux and indium resonance neutron flux for a Ra-α-Be source in graphite, density 1.6 g/cm³, due to Feld and Fermi (unpublished). All the data are normalized to the same value at $z = 10.2$ cm. The neutrons were slowed down in a rectangular graphite column, 4 ft by 4 ft square by 7 ft high. The source was placed on the long axis 2 ft from the bottom face of the column. The abscissa z is distance, along the column axis, between source and indium detector. The actual ratio of thermal to indium resonance activity at $z = 10.2$ cm for the detector used was 3.72.

For a monoenergetic source in a graphite column, the distribution of indium resonance neutrons is expected to be Gaussian:

$$(nv)_{\text{In res}} = \alpha e^{-(z/z_0)^2} \tag{99}$$

The distribution of indium resonance neutrons for the Ra-α-Be and Ra-γ-Be sources could be expressed as a superposition of 3 and 2 Gaussian functions, respectively, with the proportions and ranges given in Table 26.

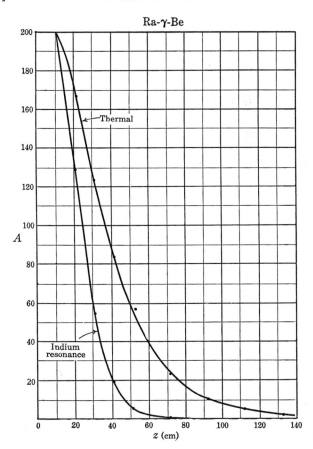

Fig. 45b. Thermal neutron flux and indium resonance neutron flux for a Ra-γ-Be source in a graphite column (see legend of Fig. 45a), due to Feld and Fermi (unpublished). The actual ratio of thermal to indium resonance activity at $z = 10.2$ cm for the detector used was 2.57. The ratio of the strength of the Ra-α-Be source (see Fig. 45a) to the Ra-γ-Be source was 0.231. The corresponding ratio of thermal neutron activities at 10.2 cm was 0.355.

The distribution of thermal neutrons is a somewhat more complicated function of distance from the source. However, at distances greater than ∼60 cm, for the Ra-α-Be source, and ∼30 cm, for the Ra-γ-Be source, the thermal neutron density becomes exponential:

$$(\overline{nv})_{th} = \beta e^{-z/\lambda} \tag{99a}$$

with the same value of $\lambda = 24.2$ cm applying to both sources. It is the difference between the exponential (Eq. 99a) and Gaussian (Eq. 99) functions which results, in graphite, in the rapid increase of the ratio of

TABLE 26

Analysis of Indium Resonance Neutron Distributions along the Axis of a Graphite Column for Ra-α-Be and Ra-γ-Be Sources in Terms of Gaussian Functions (Eq. 99 and Fig. 45)

Ra-α-Be		Ra-γ-Be	
α_i (%)	z_0 (cm)	α_i (%)	z_0 (cm)
15.0	22.8	38.7	22
69.3	36.9	61.3	29
15.7	57.1		
mean †	39.2	mean †	26.5

† The mean is computed as the square root of the weighted mean square.

thermal to epithermal neutron flux with increasing distance from the source.

While slow-neutron sources of the types described above have been and continue to be extensively used, the most potent available slow-neutron sources are those associated with chain reactors (piles). The spectrum of neutrons inside a slow-neutron reactor contains an appreciable component of fast, intermediate, and epithermal neutrons.[1] However, by use of a "thermal column," it is possible to obtain high fluxes of practically pure thermal neutrons. The usual thermal column is simply a large block of graphite placed directly adjacent to the pile. Neutrons which enter the column are slowed down as they diffuse to the outside, the ratio of epithermal to thermal neutrons falling off rapidly with the distance into the column. Figure 46 shows the activity of bare and cadmium-covered indium foils at various positions in the thermal column adjacent to the Argonne heavy-water-moderated pile.

Thermal neutron fluxes, available from various sources, are summarized in Table 27.

For many purposes, the thermal neutrons diffusing in a mass of moderating material can be utilized directly, *in situ*. Thus, for example, in irradiating a sample for the purpose of observing the resulting radioactivity, the maximum slow-neutron flux and consequently the maximum activation are attained when the sample is embedded in the moderator as close as possible to the source.

For some investigations, on the other hand, it is desirable to have a beam of thermal neutrons, e.g., for the measurement of cross sections by a transmission experiment. One method of obtaining a beam of thermal neutrons is to collimate (with a cadmium or boron slit system) a portion of the neutrons which are diffusing out through the bounding surface of

[1] For the spectrum of neutrons leaving a pile, see Fig. 54.

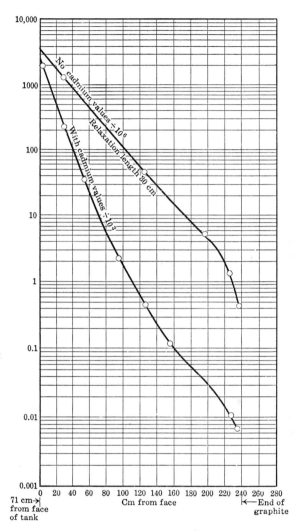

Fig. 46. Activities of bare and cadmium-covered indium foils in the thermal column of the Argonne heavy water pile. The thermal column is of graphite, 5 ft square and 240 cm long. Its front face is separated from the reactor by 71 cm of graphite. The average thermal neutron flux $(\overline{nv})$ can be obtained by multiplying the ordinates corresponding to the bare indium foils by 0.10. The number of neutrons per cubic centimeter passing through the indium resonance energy per second (slowing-down density) can be obtained by multiplying the ordinates corresponding to the cadmium-covered indium foils by 0.0019. Measurements due to Seren (unpublished).

TABLE 27

SOME AVAILABLE THERMAL NEUTRON FLUXES

(a) Laboratory Sources

Source	Strength (n/sec)	Position	Thermal $\overline{nv}$ (n/cm^2·sec)
1 curie of Ra-α-Be in infinite H_2O	13.2×10^6	4 cm from the source	8.5×10^4
		10 cm from the source	2.9×10^4
		20 cm from the source	0.31×10^4
		50 cm from the source	0.0025×10^4
1 curie of Ra-α-Be in graphite column, 4 ft x 4 ft x 7 ft; source 2 ft from base, on axis	14×10^6	at source	0.7×10^4
		10 cm from the source, on the axis	0.65×10^4
		50 cm from the source, on the axis	0.25×10^4
		100 cm from the source, on the axis	0.04×10^4
2 curies of Ra-γ-Be (608 grams Be) in graphite column, as above	3.2×10^6	at source	0.3×10^4
		10 cm from the source, on the axis	0.2×10^4
		50 cm from the source, on the axis	0.07×10^4
		100 cm from the source, on the axis	0.008×10^4

(b) The Center of a Nuclear Reactor [1]

Pile Type	Location	Power Level (kw)	Flux (n/cm^2·sec)
Heterogeneous Graphite—U	Oak Ridge, Tenn., U.S.A.[2]	$\sim10^3$	2×10^{12}
	Harwell, England (GLEEP)[3] (BEPO)[4]	— 4×10^3	10^8 10^{12}
	Brookhaven, L.I., U.S.A.[5]	2.8×10^4	4×10^{12}
Homogeneous H_2O—U^{235}	Los Alamos, N. Mex., U.S.A. (HYPO)[6]	6	3×10^{11}
Heterogeneous D_2O—U	Argonne, Ill., U.S.A. (CP3)[1]	300	10^{12}
	Chalk River, Canada (NRX)[7]	$>10^4$	5.8×10^{13}
	Châtillon, France (Zoé)[8]	~10	3×10^{10}
	Oslo, Norway[9]	~100	3×10^{11}

TABLE 27 (*Continued*)

SOME AVAILABLE THERMAL NEUTRON FLUXES

(c) *Pile Thermal Columns*

Pile	Position	Flux (n/cm²·sec)
Argonne (CP3) [10]	inner face	3×10^8
Chalk River (NRX) [11]	1 meter from inner face	10^9
Châtillon (Zoé) [8]	outer face	2×10^4

(d) *Holes in the Shield*

Pile	Flux (n/cm²·sec)
Oak Ridge [10]	10^7
Chalk River (NRX) [12]	4×10^7
Châtillon (Zoé) [8]	10^6

[1] D. J. Hughes, Nucleonics, **6** [2], 5(1950); H. S. Isbin, Nucleonics, **10** [3], 10 (1952).

[2] A. H. Snell, Nucleonics, **8** [3], 3 (1951).

[3] F. C. W. Colmer and D. J. Littler, Nucleonics, **8** [1], 3 (1951).

[4] Nucleonics, **8** [6], 36 (1951).

[5] Physics Today, Jan. 1951, p. 6.

[6] Nucleonics, **7** [6], 2 (1950).

[7] Nucleonics, **6** [3], 77 (1950); F. W. Gilbert, Nucleonics, **10** [1], 6 (1952).

[8] L. Kowarski, Helv. Phys. Acta, **23**, Supp. 3, 70 (1950).

[9] Bulletin of the Atomic Scientists, **7**, 380 (1951).

[10] Preliminary reports (unpublished) for NRC Subcommittee on Neutron Standards, by Bernstein and others.

[11] E. Almquist, Can. J. Research, **A28**, 433 (1950).

[12] D. G. Hurst, A. J. Pressesky, and P. R. Tunnicliffe, Rev. Sci. Instr., **21**, 705 (1950).

the moderating medium. However, the beam intensities, which can be attained by this means (especially with easily available sources), are very low, since relatively large masses of moderating material are required to thermalize the source neutrons, and the neutron densities, at the surface of the moderator, are consequently low; in addition, the emerging neutrons have a relatively broad angular spread, so that most of them are absorbed by the collimating slits.

The common method of attaining strong thermal neutron beams is to use a "howitzer," which is a relatively large mass of moderator (usually paraffin) with a hole reaching down to a region of high thermal neutron flux, close to the source. The hole is usually lined with cadmium or boron or both, thereby providing the necessary collimation for the beam. By proper design, it is thus possible to obtain relatively strong, well-collimated thermal neutron beams, even when only radioactive (α,n) sources are available (J13).

C. Neutron Detectors

1. Induced Radioactivity. Neutrons are capable of inducing a variety of nuclear reactions, many of which result in radioactive product nuclei. Thus, neutrons can frequently be detected by the resulting radioactivity of the exposed substance.

Radioactivity is detectable in many ways: Geiger counters for beta-rays of energy sufficient to penetrate the counter walls or, with lesser efficiency, for gamma-rays; electrometers or ionization chambers for alpha-, beta-, or gamma-radiation; scintillation counters, electron multipliers, etc. The feasibility of detecting the radioactivity resulting from neutron exposure depends on the lifetime of the induced radioactivity; it cannot be appreciably shorter than the time which must (for experimental reasons) elapse between exposure to neutrons and measurement of the resulting radioactivity; on the other hand, the lifetime must not be so long that the radioactive decay rate is negligible. These considerations normally have the effect of limiting the lifetimes of possible radioactivities to between $\sim 10^{-1}$ sec and $\sim 10^{4}$ years.

Consider a detector which absorbs neutrons at the rate of R_0 per second, and whose consequent radioactivity decays with a mean life of τ sec. The number of radioactive nuclei, N^*, is governed by the differential equation

$$\frac{dN^*}{dt} = R_0 - \frac{N^*}{\tau} \tag{100}$$

The activity of the detector (disintegrations per second), t sec after a (constant) exposure of duration t_e, is

$$R(t,t_e) = R_0(1 - e^{-t_e/\tau})e^{-t/\tau} \tag{100a}$$

The observed activity (usually counting rate),

$$R'(t,t_e) = \varepsilon R(t,t_e) \tag{101}$$

contains the factor ε, the efficiency of the detecting system; ε depends on the properties of the radiations involved, on the geometry of the absorber and detector, and on the efficiency of the radiation detector.

The activity which would be observed immediately after an infinite irradiation,

$$R_0' = R'(t=0, t_e=\infty) = \frac{R'(t,t_e)}{(1 - e^{-t_e/\tau})e^{-t/\tau}} = \varepsilon R_0 \tag{101a}$$

is usually referred to as the "saturated activity." Its value is independent of the schedule of neutron exposure and radioactivity measurement.

R_0' is usually measured by integrating the activity over a finite energy interval, say from $t = t_1$ to $t = t_2$. The integrated activity is

$$C(t_1,t_2,t_e) = \int_{t_1}^{t_2} R'(t,t_e)\, dt = \tau[R'(t_1,t_e) - R'(t_2,t_e)] \qquad (102)$$

and the saturated activity is

$$R_0' = \frac{C(t_1,t_2,t_e)}{\tau(1 - e^{-t_e/\tau})(e^{-t_1/\tau} - e^{-t_2/\tau})} \qquad (102a)$$

The saturated activity is a measure of the neutron flux impinging on the absorber. If ε is known, the radioactivity measurements yield R_0, which can be directly interpreted in terms of the neutron flux $\phi = nv$. We consider two types of measurement:

(1) The absorber is embedded in an isotropic neutron flux whose spectrum is given by $\phi(E)$, the density of neutrons per unit energy interval, at the energy E, multiplied by the neutron velocity corresponding to E. If, furthermore, the absorber is weak,[1] the rate of neutron absorption is

$$R_0 = NV \int \phi(E)\sigma_a(E)\, dE \qquad (103)$$

where N is the density of absorbing nuclei and V the volume of absorbing material. (NV is the total number of absorbing nuclei.)

In general, both $\phi(E)$ and $\sigma(E)$ are relatively complicated functions of E, and a measurement of R_0 serves only to determine the integral. However, there are some interesting special cases: Suppose that the neutron density has a Maxwell distribution

$$\phi(v) = vM(v) = Av^3 e^{-(v/v')^2} \qquad (93a)$$

and the cross section follows the $1/v$ law,

$$\sigma_a(v) = \frac{\sigma_a'v'}{v} \qquad (94a)$$

Then

$$R_0 = NV\sigma_a'v'A \int_0^\infty v^2 e^{-(v/v')^2}\, dv$$

$$= \frac{NVA(v')^4\sigma_a'\pi^{\frac{1}{2}}}{4} \qquad (103a)$$

---

[1] By which we mean that its presence does not disturb the neutron density.

The total flux is

$$\Phi = \int_0^\infty M(v) \, dv = \frac{A(v')^4}{2} \tag{93b}$$

whence

$$R_0 = \frac{NV\Phi\sigma_a'\pi^{\frac12}}{2} = \frac{NV\Phi\sigma_a'}{1.128} \tag{103b}$$

Thus, for a Maxwell neutron distribution and a $1/v$ detector, the mean detector cross section is

$$\overline{\sigma_a} = \frac{\sigma_a'v'}{\bar{v}} = \frac{\pi^{\frac12}}{2}\sigma_a' = \frac{\sigma_a'}{1.128} \tag{95a}$$

where σ_a' is the absorption cross section corresponding to the neutron energy $E' = kT$.

Suppose, on the other hand, that the absorber has a single sharp resonance at the energy E_r. (The effect of thermal neutron absorption can be eliminated by surrounding the detector with cadmium.) The cross section can be represented by a delta-function:

$$\sigma_a(E) = \rho\delta(E,E_r) \tag{104}$$

where

$$\rho = \int \sigma_a(E) \, dE = \frac{\pi}{2}\sigma_0\Gamma \tag{104a}$$

for a resonance, of peak cross section σ_0 and width Γ, which follows the Breit-Wigner formula. Provided that $\phi(E)$ does not vary appreciably over the resonance,

$$R_0 = NV\rho\phi(E_r) \tag{103c}$$

When, as is frequently the case in the resonance region,

$$\phi(E) = \frac{B}{E} \tag{96}$$

Eq. (103c) gives

$$R_0 = \frac{NV\rho B}{E_r} \tag{103c'}$$

If more than one resonance is involved,

$$R_0 = NVB\sum_i \frac{\rho_i}{E_{ri}} \tag{103c''}$$

The expression

$$\sum_i \frac{\rho_i}{E_{ri}} = \int_{\sim\frac12\,\mathrm{ev}}^{\sim 1\,\mathrm{Mev}} \frac{\sigma_a(E) \, dE}{E} \tag{104b}$$

is called the "resonance integral."

Usually, the insertion of an absorber into the neutron flux causes a perturbation of the flux measured, so that the activity of the detector is not an exact measure of the true flux in the absence of the absorber. This perturbation arises from two causes: a reduction of the neutron density inside the detector which is due to the absorption of neutrons by the outside layers; and a depression of the flux directly outside the detector due to the finite neutron absorption. Such effects have been considered by Bothe (B53), who has derived a correction factor f for the reduction of the specific activity of a sphere of radius R,

$$\frac{1}{f} = 1 + \frac{\alpha}{2}\left[\frac{3RL}{2\lambda_{tr}(R + L)} - 1\right] \qquad \text{for } R \gg \lambda_{tr} \qquad (105a)$$

$$\frac{1}{f} = 1 + \frac{0.34\alpha R}{\lambda_{tr}} \qquad \text{for } R \ll \lambda_{tr} \qquad (105b)$$

In the above expressions, L is the diffusion length (see Section 4) of the neutrons in the medium outside the detector; λ_{tr} is their transport mean free path; α is the average probability that a neutron will be absorbed in a single traversal of the detector. For an isotropic flux

$$\alpha = 1 - e^{-\mu T}(1 - \mu T) + \mu^2 T^2 E_i(-\mu T) \qquad (105')$$

where $\mu = N\sigma_a$ is the absorption coefficient, in cm^{-1}, of the detector, and T is the average absorber thickness. ($T = R$ for a spherical absorber.) $E_i(-x)$ is the exponential integral.

Tittle (T12) has shown experimentally that the above expressions also apply without modification to an absorber in the form of a disk of radius R and thickness T.

(2) The second situation of interest involves neutron beams. Consider a neutron detector of area (perpendicular to the beam direction) A and thickness T. The absorption rate is

$$R_0 = A\int \phi(E)(1 - e^{-\mu T})\, dE \qquad (103')$$

An absorber for which $\mu T = NT\sigma_a(E) \gg 1$ is said to be "black" for neutrons of energy E. Since

$$R_0 \text{ (black)} = A\int \phi(E)\, dE \qquad (103'a)$$

such an absorber gives a direct measure of the total neutron flux. At the other extreme, a "transparent" detector is one for which $\mu T \ll 1$, in which case

$$R_0 \text{ (transparent)} = ATN \int \phi(E)\sigma_a(E) \, dE \qquad (103'b)$$

Owing to the large variation with energy of slow-neutron cross sections, most absorbers are transparent at some energies, black at some, and translucent at others.

2. The Szilard-Chalmers Reaction. In many nuclear reactions, e.g., (n,p), (n,α), (n,f), the product nuclei differ in their chemical properties from the target nuclei, and can therefore be separated from the target with relative ease. For such detectors the radioactivity from large masses of absorber can be reduced to moderately small samples for counting, and the absolute detection efficiency can be made relatively high. However, many of the important neutron reactions—(n,γ), (n,n'), $(n,2n)$—lead to isotopes of the target element. For such detectors the specific activity of the absorber may be too small to permit accurate measurement of relatively weak neutron fluxes.

To overcome these difficulties Szilard and Chalmers (S62) in 1934 devised a technique for separating radioactive nuclei, induced by the (n,γ) reaction, from their isotopic environment. This technique takes advantage of the fact that the emission of gamma-radiation after slow-neutron capture causes a recoil of the product nucleus; the recoil energy is usually sufficient to disrupt the molecular bond and, thereby, to change the chemical state of the product nucleus as compared to a normal nucleus in the medium. The radioactive nuclei can then, in favorable circumstances, be separated chemically from the normal nuclei, with efficiencies as high as 100 percent.

For the emission of a single gamma-ray of energy E_γ (in Mev) from a nucleus of mass number A, the nuclear recoil energy E (in ev) is

$$E = \frac{536E_\gamma^2}{A} \qquad (106)$$

For typical values, $E_\gamma = 7.5$ Mev and $A = 100$, the recoil energy is $E = 300$ ev, which is considerably in excess of that usually necessary to disrupt chemical bonds, say ~5 ev. Even if two or more gamma-rays are emitted after slow-neutron capture, all but a few percent of the recoiling nuclei will usually have $E > 5$ ev.

In their original experiment Szilard and Chalmers irradiated ethyl iodide with neutrons from a Ra-α-Be source (most of the absorptions are due to slow neutrons) and extracted the radioactive I^{128} (25-min half-life) by shaking with an aqueous reducing solution containing a trace of free iodine as a carrier. Similar techniques have been applied to other halogens, and methods have been worked out for separating the product nuclei, due to the (n,γ) reaction, of many other elements. Specific Szilard-Chalmers processes for different substances are described and discussed in excellent summaries (with references) of the technique by McKay (M14), by Broda (B68), and by Barnes, Burgus, and Miskel (W2).

The Szilard-Chalmers reaction has frequently been used to obtain radioactive samples of high specific activity, especially when only relatively weak neutron sources were available. Thus, von Halban, Kowarski, and Magat (H6) employed a solution of bromine to measure the intensity of neutrons in the cosmic radiation. The strength of relatively weak fast-neutron sources is frequently measured by stopping the neutrons in a water solution of potassium permanganate, and removing the radioactive Mn^{56} (2.6-h half-life) as MnO_2 by filtration through fine paper or sintered glass (E6); the efficiency of this Szilard-Chalmers reaction is greatest for a neutral or slightly acid solution. Broda and Rieder (B67) have shown that the same reaction can be used to detect fast neutrons.

3. Ionization Chambers and Proportional Counters. Many neutron reactions involve the prompt emission of a charged particle. Such reactions can be detected, through the ionization caused by the emitted particle, in an ionization chamber or a proportional counter. In addition to whatever other distinctive properties such detectors may possess, they have the advantage over induced radioactivity that they can be used to observe neutrons *in situ* during the irradiation, and will reflect short-time fluctuations in the neutron density; a radioactive detector, on the other hand, is inherently a time-integrating device.

Owing to the relatively short range of the heavy charged particles resulting from neutron reactions, the target nuclei must, in general, be inside the chamber. They can be introduced into the chamber either as a constituent of the gas with which the chamber is filled (and in which the detected ionization takes place) or as a coating on the inside walls.

In ionization chambers the ionization of the gas is measured (without amplification in the chamber) either as a current or, in the case of pulsed ionization chambers, as individual pulses associated with single nuclear disintegrations. Proportional counters differ only in that the ionization is amplified in the gas of the chamber. In both cases, the observed charge or pulse height is proportional to the energy dissipated in the chamber (although the constant of proportionality may vary somewhat with the position in the chamber at which the event occurs).

The construction and use of ionization chambers and proportional counters has been discussed in Part I of Volume I. The following is intended as a brief summary of the main considerations involved in the use of such devices to measure neutron fluxes: When a neutron-detecting ionization chamber or proportional counter is placed in a neutron flux $\phi(E)$, the observed intensity, I (ionization rate or counting rate), is determined by the same factors as the saturated activity R_0' of a radio-active detector (Section 3C1) with the important difference that the detection efficiency is, in general, a function of the neutron energy. Thus, we have (neglecting the variation of efficiency with position in the chamber): for a chamber in an isotropic neutron flux,

$$I = NV \int \mathcal{E}(E)\phi(E)\sigma(E)f(E)\,dE \qquad (103'')$$

where the symbols are as previously defined and $f(E)$ is given by Eqs. (105a), (105b), (105'); for a chamber in a neutron beam,

$$I = A \int \mathcal{E}(E)\phi(E)(1 - e^{-\mu T})\,dE \qquad (103''')$$

The efficiency function, $\mathcal{E}(E)$, depends on the particular reaction used, on the chamber geometry, on the method of introduction of the reacting nuclei, and on the particular detection method used. The following discussion applies only to neutron reactions in which all the energy is carried away by charged particles. Reactions involving the emission of neutrons as well as charged particles (of which the most important is neutron scattering, especially by protons) will be taken up in a separate section. We consider a number of the most widely used detection schemes:

(1a) I = ionization current; the reacting nuclei are in the chamber gas:

$$\mathcal{E}(E) = K \times (E + Q) \times G(E) \qquad (107)$$

where E is the neutron energy and Q is the reaction Q value. (*Note*: For $Q < 0$, $\mathcal{E} = 0$ for $E < -[(A + 1)/A]Q$.) $G(E)$ is a geometric factor which depends on the chamber shape, on the gas pressure, and on the range-energy relationship for the emitted charged particles in the chamber gas. It represents the average (over the chamber) fraction of the reaction energy which is dissipated in the chamber gas; $G(E) \to 1$ as the range of the emitted particles becomes small compared to the chamber dimensions. The calibration constant K can be determined by measuring the ionization produced by a known flux of known energy; alternatively, K can be determined by observing the ionization resulting from the insertion into the chamber of a calibrated source of polonium alpha-particles.

(1b) I = ionization current; the reacting nuclei are introduced as a coating on the chamber walls. If the coating is thin compared to the range of the emitted charged particles, the situation is similar to that for a gas-filled chamber, except that only $\sim\frac{1}{2}$ the reaction energy is dissipated in the chamber gas. As the coating thickness is increased, the emerging charged particles will lose energy in traversing the coating. For a thick coating ($T >$ range of the emitted charged particles) only those reactions taking place within a layer of thickness equal to the range of the emitted charged particles can be effective in producing ionization in the chamber gas. The efficiency function of an ionization chamber with a given coating can, in general, be computed. In addition to its dependence on the specific properties of the reaction, the efficiency may also depend on the angular distribution of the neutron flux being detected.

The form of $\mathcal{E}(E)$ is quite different for the counting of individual pulses. In general, the associated electronic equipment is designed so that only pulses of magnitude greater than a predetermined value are counted. (This type of discrimination makes it possible to use pulse counters even when the neutron flux is accompanied by a considerable background of gamma-radiation.) A pulse detector in which all pulses greater than a given size are counted is called an "integral" detector. It is also possible to arrange the electronics so that only those pulses are counted whose sizes lie between two definite (usually variable) limits; such arrangements are called "differential" detectors.

(2) I = counting rate; integral detection. If the reacting nuclei are in the chamber gas, $\mathcal{E}(E)$ is, as a first approximation, given by a step function, having the value zero for neutron energies less than E_t, and one for $E > E_t$; E_t is the neutron energy for which the ionization of the reaction products is just sufficient to produce a pulse of the required size. However, in a chamber of finite size the step function must be modified by a geometric factor $G(E)$, to take into account the possibility that some products of an otherwise detectable reaction may dissipate part of their energy in the chamber walls and give rise to pulses smaller than the detectable minimum.

When the target nuclei are coated on the chamber walls the same considerations apply as in scheme (1b).

(3) I = counting rate; differential detection, with the reactions occurring in the gas of the chamber. Ideally (for a chamber of infinite dimen-

sions) $\mathcal{E}(E)$ is given by the difference between two step functions with thresholds E_{t1} and E_{t2}. In practice, the effect of the finite size of the chamber is to make $\mathcal{E}$ smaller than 1 between these limits and to add to $\mathcal{E}(E)$ a tail extending beyond E_{t2}.

When the reacting nuclei are introduced as a wall coating, differential detection is useful only if the coating thickness is small compared to the range of the reaction products.

(a) *Detection by the* $B^{10}(n,\alpha)$ *Reaction.* Because of its large cross section, the $B^{10}(n,\alpha)$ reaction is extensively used in slow-neutron detectors. The reaction is highly exoergic, $Q = 2.78$ Mev. However, most slow-neutron captures lead to the 0.48-Mev excited state of Li^7 (which decays to the ground state by gamma-ray emission); the ionization energy released in such captures is 2.30 Mev. Bichsel, Hälg, Huber, and Stebler (B29) and Petree, Johnson, and Miller (P14) have measured the ratio of captures leading to the ground and to the 0.48-Mev excited states for neutron energies from thermal to 3.9 Mev. The ratio follows a smooth curve, from ~ 0.07 for thermal neutrons to a maximum of somewhat greater than 2 at 1.9 Mev, and then falls to ~ 1 above 2.5 Mev.

The (n,α) cross section of normal boron element follows the $1/v$ law up to energies of at least 1 kev, with $\sigma'(v' = 2.2 \times 10^5$ cm/sec$) = 710$ barns. Its behavior in the intermediate range is not so well established, but its general features have been determined; there is a resonance at 1.9 Mev (G20, A2, P14).

The isotope B^{10} has a natural abundance of 18.83 percent. Its isotopic (n,α) cross section is greater than that for natural boron by the factor 5.31; i.e., $\sigma'(B^{10}) = 3770$ barns.[1] The availability of B^{10} enriched boron thus makes possible the construction of neutron detectors with high efficiency over a wide range of neutron energies.

Boron-containing ionization chambers and proportional counters have been operated under a variety of conditions, as current-measuring devices and disintegration counters, with the boron introduced as a gas or as a wall coating. Because of the large Q value, $\mathcal{E}(E)$ is essentially energy independent in the slow- and intermediate-neutron energy ranges. Furthermore, the large Q value makes it easy to discriminate between pulses resulting from neutron capture and background pulses arising from relatively strong gamma-ray intensities; hence, boron-containing chambers are normally operated as integral pulse counters.

BF_3 is usually used as the chamber-filling gas. It has relatively good ionization chamber and proportional counter characteristics, provided that the gas is free of impurities. Techniques for the construction, fill-

---

[1] See the footnote to Table 11, p. 339.

ing, and operation of BF_3 counters have been discussed by a number of authors (S15, B31, F39, B56).

For a chamber containing BF_3 at one atmosphere pressure, the slow-neutron absorption coefficient is

$$\mu \text{ (normal } BF_3) = 0.0191 \ (0.025/E)^{\frac{1}{2}} \text{ cm}^{-1}$$

$$\mu \ (B^{10}F_3) \qquad = 0.101 \quad (0.025/E)^{\frac{1}{2}} \text{ cm}^{-1}$$

(E is in ev.) Thus, a typical counter (of average thickness ~ 25 cm) would vary in effectiveness from black to transparent over the thermal neutron range. However, most BF_3 counters—even $B^{10}F_3$—are transparent for epithermal neutrons. For a slow-neutron-induced disintegration in such a chamber, the range of (93% of) the alpha-particles is ~ 0.8 cm. (The Li^7 fragment, which carries off $\frac{4}{11}$ of the energy, has a much smaller range.) Thus, for chambers of reasonable dimensions, the wall effect correction $G(E)$ is relatively small, and $\mathcal{E}(E) \approx 1$.

Chambers in which the boron is introduced as a wall coating are less extensively used for slow-neutron detection. The thickness of the coating must be kept very small, both because of the small range of the reaction products and because of the strong neutron absorption of boron (if the neutrons must penetrate the coating from the outside). Hence, such chambers are usually quite transparent to neutrons. It is possible to decrease the transparency, without decreasing the efficiency, by designing the chamber to contain a multiplicity of thin boron layers (L24).

(b) *The Long Counter.* The sensitivity of BF_3 counters decreases rapidly with neutron energy, becoming prohibitively small, for most counters, in the intermediate-energy range. In order to increase the sensitivity to intermediate and fast neutrons, experimenters have frequently immersed the counter in a moderating medium, usually water or paraffin. However, because of the strong dependence of the sensitivity of such arrangements on the source energy and on the geometry, the results of this method of neutron flux measurement are usually very difficult to interpret, especially when the source has a heterogeneous energy distribution.

Hanson and McKibben (H32) have devised an arrangement which is uniformly sensitive to neutrons from ~ 10 kev to ~ 3 Mev. This arrangement, the "long counter," consists of a cylindrical BF_3 counter (diameter $\sim \frac{1}{2}$ in., length ~ 10 in.) placed along the axis of a paraffin cylinder ~ 8 in. in diameter. Two of their successful long counter designs are shown in Fig. 47.

The long counter is used in observations on neutron beams which enter the circular face (right-hand side in Fig. 47a) of the arrangement

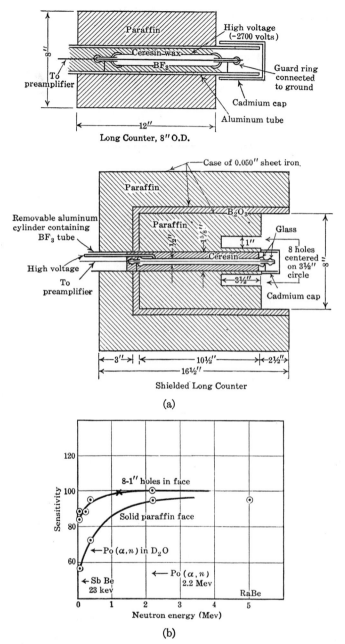

Fig. 47. (a) Two long counters, designed by Hanson and McKibben (H32), with uniform sensitivity (to within ~10 percent) from 10 kev to 3 Mev. The second, or shielded, counter is designed to operate in a region of relatively high scattered neutron background. (b) Sensitivity vs. neutron energy of the shielded long counter with and without holes in the front face of the paraffin.

and diffuse parallel to the axis. The second arrangement shown is designed for situations in which there is an appreciable background of scattered neutrons impinging on the paraffin from all directions. The uniform energy sensitivity is based on the approximate cancellation of two effects: (1) low-energy neutrons do not penetrate far into the paraffin, and have an appreciable probability of being turned around and escaping out of the front face; (2) high-energy neutrons penetrate much farther before being slowed down, but have an appreciable probability of escaping through the sides. The success of the arrangements of Hanson and McKibben is based on a proper choice of the diameter of the paraffin cylinder. In the second design, holes can be bored into the front face to decrease the loss of low-energy neutrons (Fig. 47b).

For the shielded counter shown in Fig. 47a, the sensitivity does not vary by more than $\sim$10 percent between 10 kev and 3 Mev, as shown in Fig. 47b. At lower energies the sensitivity decreases to $\sim$70 percent for thermal neutrons; at higher energies the sensitivity again falls off (it is $\sim$85–95 percent for Ra-α-Be neutrons). The absolute sensitivity of the counters is such that they give $\sim$1 count per 10^5 neutrons emitted isotropically from a source 1 meter from the face.

(c) *Fission Chambers.* Fission of the heaviest nuclei by neutrons provides an ideal source of ionizing particles for pulse detectors. Since the fission fragment energies are $\sim$100 Mev and their ranges are very small, the pulse due to a fission fragment is easy to distinguish from the background due to other ionizing radiation (e.g., pulses due to alpha-particles, spontaneously emitted from most fissionable nuclei). Thus, fission chambers are almost always operated as integral pulse-counting ionization chambers.

The fissionable nuclei may be introduced into the chamber as a gas (e.g., UF_6) or as a wall coating. Owing to the general unavailability of gases containing the heaviest elements or the inconvenience in handling these gases, or both, the latter method is usually used; uranium, for example, is easily obtainable in a solid oxide or nitrate form. In either event, the efficiency function, $\varepsilon(E)$, is essentially independent of neutron energy, since the Q value of the (n,f) reaction is so great. (We neglect the possibility that the coating may be so thick as to prevent the neutrons from penetrating into the chamber.)

Fission chambers containing thermally fissionable nuclei (U^{233}, U^{235}, Pu^{239}) are efficient thermal neutron detectors. Chambers containing natural uranium, or uranium enriched in the U^{238} isotope, can be used as fast-neutron detectors, with an effective threshold of $\sim$1.5 Mev; thorium, protactinium, and neptunium can also be used in the same fashion (see Section 2C4).

Bismuth undergoes fission by ultrafast neutrons; it has a threshold of $\sim$50 Mev and a cross section, for $\sim$84 Mev neutrons, of $\sim$0.05 barn (K7, W26). Ionization chambers coated with bismuth have been used as specific ultrafast-neutron detectors (W26).

(d) *Proton Recoil Detectors.* Perhaps the most common method of detecting and measuring fast-neutron fluxes involves the observation of proton recoils from neutron-proton scattering. Use of this reaction has the advantage that the cross section is comparatively large (14 barns at $E = 0.1$ Mev; 4 barns at $E = 1$ Mev; 1 barn at $E = 10$ Mev; see Fig. 2). The main disadvantage of the proton recoil method is that for a given incident neutron energy, E_n, the proton recoil energies, E, are uniformly distributed between 0 and E_n; the recoil energy as a function of the angle θ in the laboratory coordinate system (θ is confined to the interval 0–90°) is

$$E = E_n \cos^2 \theta \qquad (108)$$

Let us assume a monoenergetic neutron flux $\phi(E_n)$ incident on a transparent chamber containing NV atoms of hydrogen. Neglecting, for the moment, the effects of the finite dimensions of the chamber, the number of pulses corresponding to the proton energy E is

$$P(E_n,E)\, dE = \frac{NV\phi(E_n)\sigma(E_n)\, dE}{E_n} \qquad (109)$$

for $E < E_n$; $P(E_n,E) = 0$ for $E > E_n$.

The chamber may be operated as an integral counter, in which all pulses are counted whose energy exceeds the bias energy E_t. In this case, the counting rate is

$$I(E_n,E_t) = \int_{E_t}^{E_n} P(E_n,E)\, dE = NV\phi(E_n)\left[\frac{\sigma(E_n)}{E_n}\right](E_n - E_t) \quad (110)$$

Proton pulses of energy less than $\sim$0.1 Mev are usually too small to be distinguished from the background. In the region 0.1–10 Mev, the neutron-proton scattering cross section follows, to a good approximation, a $1/v$ law; i.e., $\sigma(E_n) \cong (E_t/E_n)^{1/2}\sigma(E_t)$. In this energy range

$$I(E_n,E_t) \cong NV\phi(E_n)\sigma(E_t)\left(\frac{E_t}{E_n}\right)^{3/2}\left[\frac{E_n}{E_t} - 1\right]$$

$$= NV\phi(E_n)\sigma(E_t)S\left(\frac{E_n}{E_t}\right) \qquad (110a)$$

The sensitivity of such an integral pulse counter is plotted as the solid curve in Fig. 48. $S(E_n/E_t)$ has the property, in this energy range, of being relatively independent of the neutron energy; its value is within 30 percent of the maximum for $1.5E_t < E_n < 11.5E_t$.

For neutrons of $E_n > 10$ Mev, the neutron-proton cross section can be approximated by $\sigma(E_n) = (E_t/E_n)\sigma(E_t)$, whence

$$S\left(\frac{E_n}{E_t}\right) = \left(\frac{E_t}{E_n}\right)^2 \left[\left(\frac{E_n}{E_t}\right) - 1\right] \qquad (110a')$$

This sensitivity function is plotted as the broken curve in Fig. 48. In

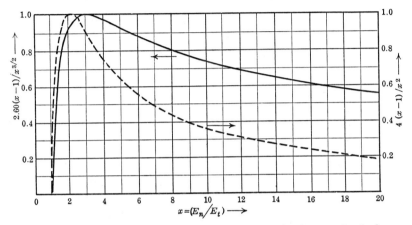

Fig. 48. The sensitivity function $S(E_n/E_t)$ of an integral pulse-counting hydrogen-filled chamber (neglecting wall effects) vs. $x = E_n/E_t$. The solid curve is for $\sigma(E_n)$ $= (E_t/E_n)^{1/2}\sigma(E_t)$, a good approximation to the neutron-proton scattering cross section for the range 0.1 Mev $< E_n < 10$ Mev. The broken curve is for $\sigma(E_n)$ $= (E_t/E_n)\sigma(E_t)$, which applies for $E_n > 10$ Mev. The curves are normalized to a value of 1 at the maximum.

this energy range the integral counting rate is much more strongly dependent on E_n. However, for neutron energies above $\sim$20 Mev, the angular distribution in neutron-proton scattering is no longer spherically symmetrical in the center-of-mass coordinate system, and the formulas developed above must be correspondingly modified.

Hydrogen-filled chambers are frequently operated as ionization chambers. For such operation the chamber sensitivity to neutrons of energy E_n is

$$I'(E_n) = \int_0^{E_n} P(E_n,E)E \, dE = \frac{NV\phi(E_n)\sigma(E_n)E_n}{2} \qquad (111)$$

for neutrons of energy up to $\sim$20 Mev, and neglecting wall effects. However, ionization chambers are particularly sensitive to backgrounds of all kinds. Since most neutron fluxes are accompanied by an appreciable gamma-ray intensity, the background presents a serious problem. One device for eliminating such background effects is to employ two chambers of identical geometry, one filled with the hydrogen-containing gas and the second filled with argon. The external electronic amplifications are adjusted in a pure gamma-ray beam so that both chambers give the same current. The difference in the currents, when the chambers are placed in a neutron flux, can be attributed to the proton recoils from neutron scattering.

The effect of the finite dimensions of the chamber is to decrease the sensitivity by a factor which depends on the neutron energy and which can be computed for most chambers. The geometric factor, $G(E_n)$, is a monotonically decreasing function of E_n. Unfortunately, the recoil proton ranges are in general comparable to the chamber dimensions, so that $G(E_n)$ usually represents a sizable correction. For a given chamber geometry the correction becomes less important as the gas pressure is increased. Thus, the development of techniques for the operation of ionization chambers and counters at high pressure (W35) is of considerable importance for the future of fast-neutron spectroscopy. Alternatively, since organic phosphors (solid and liquid) have a high hydrogen content, it is possible to employ such materials for fast-neutron counting by observing the scintillations resulting from the recoil protons (J3, O6);[1] the recoil proton range is usually small compared to the dimensions of the phosphor. Unfortunately, the pulses from such counters do not appear to be strictly proportional to the recoil proton energy.

The above discussion applies to monoenergetic neutron sources. If the neutron source is heteroenergetic, the pulse height distribution is a superposition of pulses due to all the neutrons:

$$P(E)\ dE = \int_E^\infty P(E_n,E)\ dE_n\ dE = NV\ dE \int_E^\infty \frac{\phi(E_n)\sigma(E_n)\ dE_n}{E_n} \quad (109')$$

The function $\phi(E_n)\sigma(E_n)/E_n$ can be obtained by differentiation of the curve of $P(E)$ vs. E. However, in order to determine $\phi(E_n)$ vs. E_n to a reasonable accuracy, the curve of $P(E)$ vs. E must be determined to a much greater—frequently unattainable—accuracy. The use of integral counting to obtain $\phi(E_n)$ vs. E_n is even less satisfactory in that it requires exceptionally high precision.

When the incident neutrons are in a beam (unique direction of motion) it is possible to choose, for counting, only those proton recoils whose directions are the same as that of the incident neutrons. In such a de-

---

[1] An ingenious application of this principle has been devised by W. F. Hornyak, Rev. Sci. Instr., **23**, 264 (1952).

vice it is necessary to collimate the protons. However, the collimation need not be too sharp; a proton recoil at, say, 20° from the incident neutron direction has an energy $E = 0.88E_n$ (Eq. 108). Assuming a collimating system which accepts protons within the relatively small angle θ_0, and neglecting the small variation of pulse heights within the cone of acceptance,

$$P(E) = NV\phi(E)\sigma(E)f(\theta_0) \tag{109''}$$

where

$$f(\theta_0) = \frac{\Delta E}{E} = 1 - \cos^2 \theta_0 \cong \frac{\theta_0^2}{2} \tag{108a}$$

(θ_0 may be a function of the proton recoil energy E.) The smaller the angle θ_0, the smaller is the value of $f(\theta)$, but the sharper the energy resolution of the device. Thus, in common with almost all problems in spectroscopy—neutrons or otherwise—the practically attainable resolution is primarily determined by the strength of the source.

Many arrangements can be conceived for collimating the observed protons. One possibility is to detect the protons in a long cylindrical chamber, the incident neutrons traveling along the chamber axis, and to divide the chamber into two or more independent regions, requiring coincidences between adjoining regions. In some cases, the last section is operated in anti-coincidence with the preceding sections, thereby defining the range of the detected protons. Another possibility is to separate the sections by barriers, with holes in them for the proton collimation. The hydrogen may be introduced into the chamber as a gas or, more usually, as a thin radiator at the incident face of the cylinder.

A thin radiator is, by definition, one in which a proton, originating in the back of the radiator, loses only a small fraction of its energy before emerging into the counter. The figures in Table 28 give the approxi-

TABLE 28

Some Typical Proton Recoil Ranges

E_p (Mev)	Range (cm std. air)	Range (mg/cm² paraffin)	Range (mm paraffin)
1	2.3	3.2	0.036
2	7.1	9.7	0.11
5	34	47	0.52
10	115	160	1.8
15	238	330	3.7

mate ranges of fast protons in standard air and in paraffin, a typical radiator material. It may be seen that, for neutrons of energy ~1 Mev or less, "thin" radiators must be very thin indeed. As the radiator thickness becomes comparable to the proton range, the energy resolution of the detector rapidly deteriorates. For thick radiators (thickness > maximum proton recoil range) the situation again arises wherein a monoenergetic neutron produces pulses of all energies up to its own. However, the pulse height distribution is much more complicated than that from neutrons scattered in the chamber gas. For neutrons of energy E_n incident normally on a thick radiator, with the chamber counting all pulses above the bias energy E_t, the sensitivity function is approximately (B9)

$$S(E_n, E_t) \cong k\sigma(E_n)E_n^{-\frac{3}{2}}(E_n^{\frac{3}{2}} - E_t^{\frac{3}{2}})^2 \qquad (110a'')$$

in which the range-energy relationship has been approximated by $R(E_p) \propto E_p^{\frac{3}{2}}$. This function has zero slope at $E_n = E_t$, and is a monotonically increasing function of E_n; hence, such a chamber is most sensitive to the highest-energy neutrons in the beam.

(e) *Other Possibilities.* In principle, any neutron reaction can be used as the basis for a neutron detector. Thus, the radiative capture process can be observed by detection of the prompt capture gamma-rays; inelastic scattering can be detected by observation of the accompanying gamma-radiation. With the recent development of scintillation counter techniques, the efficiency of gamma-ray detection is comparable with that for the detection of charged particles.

One application of these techniques to neutron counting is of special interest in that it can be used to provide an efficient detector of intermediate-energy neutrons (D16). This technique takes advantage of the fact that, for slow and intermediate neutrons, the $B^{10}(n,\alpha)$ reaction goes mainly to the 0.48-Mev excited state of Li^7, from whose decay the gamma-ray can be detected by a scintillation counter. Since, in such a detector, solid boron can be used, the size being limited only by the penetrability of the 0.48-Mev gamma-ray, high efficiencies are easily obtainable.

As previously pointed out, charged particle reactions are easily observable if they take place in a scintillating material. Thus, Hofstadter *et al.* have detected thermal neutrons, with high efficiency, by the scintillations produced, in a LiI(Tl) crystal, as a result of the $Li^6(n,\alpha)$ reaction (H64). Such reactions can also be observed by allowing the charged particle to impinge, from the outside, on a scintillator. The zinc sulfide screen, so important in the pioneer work on natural radioactivity, has been used in this connection (M38).

Other charged particle reactions, both exoergic and endoergic, can be used for ionization chamber and proportional counter materials. Among these, the $N^{14}(n,p)$ reaction, $Q = 0.626$ Mev, has possibilities as an intermediate-neutron detector, since its relatively low Q value permits identification of the energy of the neutron responsible for the reaction through a pulse height measurement (F7). Unfortunately, the presence of resonances in this reaction, for neutron energies above $\sim$500 kev, limits its usefulness to intermediate-energy-neutron spectroscopy. Other reactions with similar characteristics are $He^3(n,p)$ and $Cl^{35}(n,p)$.

Finally, recoils from elastic scattering by light nuclei other than H^1 can be used for neutron detection. In this regard, He^4 recoils have the advantage of shorter range (thereby decreasing the wall effect correction) and less energy spread for a given incident neutron energy.

4. Photographic Emulsion and Cloud Chamber Detectors. Photographic emulsions and cloud chambers have been among the most useful tools for the observation of nuclear reactions. Both of these devices have the property that the path traversed by a charged particle appears as a visible track. From the length of the track (range) and the density of ionization (grain or droplet density), it is possible to determine the energy and velocity, respectively, of the ionizing particle. A curve of ionization density *vs.* residual range for a track uniquely determines the energy, mass, and magnitude of charge of the particle. Measurement of the multiple Coulomb scattering in the photographic emulsion or in the gas or plates in a cloud chamber provides a measure of the particle energy. The curvature of the track in a known magnetic field yields the particle's momentum, as well as the sign of its charge. Since track curvature results both from small-angle Coulomb scattering and from applied magnetic fields, the use of magnetic fields is usually confined to cloud chambers, or to regions between two photographic emulsions, since the Coulomb scattering is smaller and the range is greater in a gas than in the emulsion; however, for sufficiently strong fields and particles of high energy, curvature due to magnetic fields has been observed on tracks in emulsions (D14).

In essence, photographic emulsions and cloud chambers yield the same sort of information; indeed, the photographic emulsion can be said to be identical with a cloud chamber operated at very high pressure. However, owing to the differences in their mode of operation, emulsions and cloud chambers should be regarded as complementary instruments, the choice between the two being primarily determined by the nature of the problem under investigation. Cloud chambers have the advantage that it is easier to choose and change the filling gas. On the other hand, emulsions are continuously sensitive, and are therefore much more useful in experiments involving weak sources. Furthermore, the sensitivity of emulsions is variable over a very wide range—emulsions are available which are insensitive to tracks of ionization density less than that of a fission fragment; at the other extreme, it is possible to obtain emulsions which show tracks of electrons at the minimum of the ionization rate curve. Another advantage of emulsions is their small size and light weight.

The main disadvantage in the use of photographic emulsions arises from the short range, in them, of charged particles. (A 1-Mev proton has a range of $\sim$15 μ, a 1-Mev alpha-particle of $\sim$3.5 μ.) As a result, it is necessary to detect and measure tracks with a microscope, and the accumulation of large amounts of data becomes a relatively tedious affair compared to experiments involving electronic detection. However, the wide flexibility and the possibility of unambiguous identification of reactions frequently more than compensate for this disadvantage.

The earliest experiments with photographic emulsion detection of charged particles employed x-ray and "halftone" plates. Thus, Taylor and Goldhaber (T4), as early as 1935, used boron-impregnated Ilford R emulsions, irradiated by slow neutrons, to prove that the B(n,α) reaction involves the emission of a single alpha-particle. However, the emulsions available at that time could only detect low-energy charged particles; their lack of sensitivity and uniformity greatly discouraged their use in nuclear physics. Since World War II, tremendous progress has been made in the development of more sensitive emulsions and of techniques for their use, in large measure through the instigation and inspiration of Occhialini, Powell, and their collaborators. Emulsions called "nuclear emulsions," with various degrees of sensitivity, and with various thicknesses, from 25 to 600 μ, are now available. (Thicker emulsions can be obtained by special arrangement with the manufacturers.) The use of nuclear emulsions has been extensively described by Powell and Occhialini (P25), by Yagoda (Y2), and in a recent summary by Rotblat (R22). Rotblat also gives the most recent data on the composition and properties of the various available emulsions (his Tables I, II, and III) and on processing techniques.

There is an extensive literature on cloud chambers. A recent monograph by Wilson (W34) summarizes the techniques of cloud chamber operation. Further details on these subjects are given in Volume I, Part I.

(a) *Detection of Slow Neutrons.* Nuclear emulsions contain an appreciable amount of nitrogen (0.073, 0.080, 0.11 g/cm^3, respectively, in Ilford, Kodak, and Eastman Kodak emulsions). The N$^{14}(n,p)$ reaction has a Q value of 0.626 Mev, with a cross section $\sigma' = 1.76$ barns for thermal neutrons. The protons resulting from thermal neutron capture (range $\sim$7 μ) can be observed and counted in the emulsion, thereby providing a measure of the thermal neutron flux (C33).

The sensitivity of nuclear emulsions to slow neutrons can be greatly enhanced by adding small amounts (plates are available with $\sim$1% by weight) of lithium or boron to the emulsions. The (n,α) reactions in such loaded emulsions can be used for measuring even small slow-neutron fluxes with relatively high accuracy (S25, T10, B35, R22).

It is also possible to impregnate emulsions with uranium acetate or citrate, and to observe tracks due to fission by slow neutrons (M43). Owing to the high background of alpha-particle tracks from the uranium, such plates must ordinarily be exposed and processed within a short time after preparation. However, emulsions are available whose sensitivity to alpha-particles has been greatly decreased, so that only the fission fragment tracks are observable (Ilford D1, Eastman Kodak NTC).

It is also possible to measure slow-neutron fluxes by observing the blackening of x-ray and electron sensitive emulsions resulting from slow-neutron-induced radioactivity (B35).

The reactions mentioned above can also be observed in cloud chambers, although it is considerably more difficult to obtain a suitable gas containing lithium, boron, or uranium; instead, these elements are usually introduced into the chamber as thin coatings on plates.

(b) *The Observation of Proton Recoils.* Nuclear emulsions contain an appreciable hydrogen content ($\sim$0.04–0.05 g/cm^3 in dry emulsions; considerably more in a moist atmosphere). Thus, irradiation with fast neutrons will give rise to proton recoil tracks.

Because of the variation of the proton recoil energy with angle, according to Eq. (108), measurement of the energy of a proton recoil will yield the neutron energy only if the relative directions of neutron and proton are known. In other words, to use proton recoils for neutron energy and flux measurements, it is necessary for the incident neutrons to have a well-defined direction. (The previous discussion of proton recoil ionization chambers and proportional counters is fully applicable to this section.) Thus, in measuring a fast-neutron flux distribution by observing the proton recoil range spectrum, it is necessary to set up strict criteria for the acceptance of tracks. Such criteria usually involve the choice of a limiting angle, θ_0 of Eqs. (109'') and (108a). In observing tracks which "dip" in the emulsion, it must be kept in mind that emulsions shrink by a factor $\sim$2 in being processed.

It is relatively easy to make corrections for the background due to other (n,p) reactions in the emulsion—say on N^{14}—or due to scattered neutrons which strike the emulsion from all directions. Since the recoil protons from neutrons in the beam are confined to the forward hemisphere and the background protons are usually distributed with approximate spherical symmetry, measurement of the proton recoil spectrum in the backward hemisphere can provide the necessary data for this correction.

For neutrons of energy greater than $\sim$10 Mev, an appreciable fraction of the recoil protons leave the emulsion before coming to the end of their ranges; the range of a 10-Mev proton is $\sim$600 μ of emulsion. Thus, as the neutron energy is increased, an appreciable correction must be applied for the loss of tracks. This correction can be decreased by using

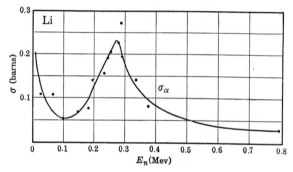

Fig. 49. Li$^6(n,\alpha)$H^3 cross section for normal lithium (7.4%Li^6, 92.6%Li^7) due to J. M. Blair *et al.* (unpublished) (G20, A2).

thicker emulsions. For very fast and especially ultrafast neutrons, it is more accurate to measure the proton energy by the track's grain density, or by the small-angle scattering.

In the intermediate-energy range, the proton recoil method is limited by the short range of the recoil protons, which renders inaccurate the measurement of range and of angle. Most experimenters regard 1 Mev as a practical lower limit of the neutron energies to which the technique is applicable. Recently, Nereson and Reines (N1) have shown that, by careful application of the technique, accurate neutron flux measurements can be made down to $E_n \cong 0.5$ Mev, and possibly pushed (with poor resolution and large corrections) to 0.3 Mev.

The use of hydrogen-containing cloud chambers for neutron detection is subject to the same considerations as have been outlined above.

(c) *Other Reactions—Especially* Li$^6(n,\alpha)$H^3. For the detection of fast neutrons by a charged particle reaction in nuclear emulsions, it is necessary that the cross section for the reaction in the emulsion be at least comparable with that of neutron-proton scattering, and that the reaction products be distinguishable from the recoil protons. In the energy range $\sim$0.1–10 Mev, the Li$^6(n,\alpha)$ reaction, $Q = 4.79$ Mev, has the desired properties.   The (n,α) cross section of normal lithium (7.4% Li^6) is shown in Fig. 49 for neutron energies up to 0.8 Mev.

In order to overcome the large proton recoil background, it is necessary to employ emulsions impregnated with enriched Li^6.   Such emulsions have been used by Keepin and Roberts (K5) (Eastman Kodak

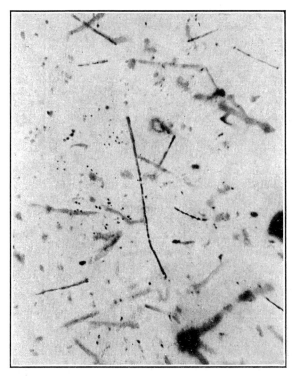

Fig. 50.   Photomicrograph of a $Li^6(n,\alpha)He^3$ disintegration in a Li^6 loaded NTA emulsion.   The lower track is due to the alpha-particle.   The background tracks are mainly due to proton recoils.   Courtesy J. H. Roberts (private communication).

NTA, with 0.04 $g/cm^3 Li^6$ loading), who have successfully demonstrated the usefulness of this method of fast-neutron detection and flux measurement.

In the measurements of Keepin and Roberts, the range of the alpha-particle and of the triton are measured, as well as the angle between them.   They have found that the best energy resolution, ± 0.1 Mev for neutrons from 0 to a few Mev, is obtained by selecting only those events for which the angle between the particles is between 175° and 180°.   It is necessary to use special processing techniques to permit discrimination between the alpha-particle and triton tracks.   A photomicrograph of a typical event is shown in Fig. 50.

The above-mentioned resolution of ± 0.1 Mev has been achieved for collimated neutron sources. With isotropic neutron fluxes, for which this method is possible where the proton recoil method cannot be used, such good energy resolution has not been attained (R12).

For neutrons of energy greater than ~ 5 Mev, the very large background of protons of comparable range renders the use of the $Li^6(n,\alpha)$ reaction relatively inaccurate. However, for $E_n > 10$ Mev, the $B^{10}(n,2\alpha)H^3$ reaction has been successfully used for neutron detection with boron-impregnated emulsions (L5).

D. Slow-Neutron Spectroscopy

Probably more work has been done, and more information obtained, on the properties of neutrons between 0 and 10 ev energy than on all the rest of the neutron energy spectrum. This was certainly true before and during World War II, and continues, to a somewhat lesser extent, to be true today. This emphasis has not been entirely due to the greater ease of producing and detecting slow neutrons. The existence and the properties of distinct, narrow, slow-neutron resonances provide a confirmation and a test of the ideas of Bohr and his followers on the properties of the compound nucleus, and on the possibility of a statistical treatment of nuclei. Furthermore, the wave properties of the neutron and the fact that slow-neutron wavelengths are of the order of interatomic distances in molecules, liquids, and solids hold forth the intriguing prospect of using slow neutrons as a tool for the study of the structure of matter. While a number of such studies were carried out in pre-World War II days, this aspect of slow-neutron physics is only now, owing to the availability of the strong sources from piles, bearing fruit; these studies will be the subject of Section 5.

The history of the development of techniques for slow-neutron investigations was summarized in Section 2A. In this section these techniques are discussed in detail. Although many types of experiments can be designed to measure the variation of some effect or other with neutron energy, the quantity most frequently measured is the cross section. The cross section is usually measured by a transmission experiment.

A "good geometry" transmission experiment measures the total cross section, $\sigma = \sum_i \sigma_i$, the sum of the cross sections for all processes which remove neutrons from a beam; these include scattering as well as absorption processes. The quantity measured in a transmission experiment is the attenuation

$$\frac{I}{I_0} = e^{-N\sigma T} \tag{112}$$

the ratio of neutron intensities at the detector with and without an absorber (NT = number of absorber atoms per square centimeter of absorber [1]) in the beam. Such a measurement does not require any knowledge of the value of the neutron flux.

In order to obtain maximum accuracy in a minimum of counting time, especially if the available beam intensities are not very great, it is necessary to make a proper choice of the absorber thickness. The optimum thickness, which depends on the details of the experimental arrangement and on the background, is, over a wide range of experimental conditions, for $N\sigma T \approx 1\text{--}2$ (R17, R9).

Since scattering is always one of the components of the total cross section, it is necessary, in a good geometry experiment, to correct the measured transmission for those scattering processes in which the deflected neutron strikes the detector.[2] The smallness of the correction is the measure of the goodness of the geometry. In order to make this correction, it is necessary to know the magnitude and the angular distribution of the scattering cross section.

Under certain circumstances, a "poor geometry" transmission experiment can yield independent and useful information. Consider a beam of neutrons and an absorber, both large in cross-sectional area compared to the detector. Let the detector be placed directly behind the absorber. The attenuation, I/I_0, due to the absorber is, in this case, $e^{-N\sigma' T}$, where $\sigma' = \sigma - \frac{1}{2}\sigma_{sc}$ (provided that the scattering is symmetrical with respect to 90°) since half of the scattered neutrons leave the absorber through the back face. In all these considerations we assume that the neutrons have a negligible probability of making more than one nuclear encounter in the absorber; otherwise, the problem approaches one of diffusion, to be considered in Section 4.

A still more extreme case of poor geometry is that of a point source completely surrounded by a (spherical) absorber. In this case, if the detector is sufficiently far from the source—so that the distribution of scattered neutrons also resembles that of a point source—the measured cross section is $\sigma_a = \sigma - \sigma_{sc}$. Thus, the results of good and poor geometry transmission experiments enable the determination of both σ_{sc} and $\sigma_a = \sigma - \sigma_{sc}$. Experiments in which the geometry is intermediate between good and poor are rather more difficult to interpret (S65).

---

[1] If the absorber contains more than one type of nucleus, the exponent of Eq. (112) is replaced by $N\sigma T = T \sum_k N_k \sigma_k$.

[2] With respect to this correction, inelastic scattering must be regarded as an absorption process if the detector is insensitive to the inelastically scattered neutrons, and as a scattering process if the detector is sensitive to them.

Transmission experiments are, of course, not the only means of measuring neutron cross sections. All the techniques whereby specific reactions can be used for measuring neutron fluxes (discussed in Section 3C) can be reversed, and cross sections determined if the neutron flux is known. Mention must also be made of the techniques developed by Dempster and co-workers (L4) and by Inghram, Hess, and Hayden (I1, H50, H55) for the detection of (strong) neutron absorption and measurement of cross sections by mass-spectrographic observations of the changes in isotopic abundances resulting from neutron bombardment. The reader's attention is especially called to a beautiful photograph published by Dempster [Phys. Rev., **71**, 829 (1947)] showing the decrease in abundance of the Cd^{113} isotope when normal cadmium is subjected to intense neutron irradiation. Finally, a transmission measurement can be changed into a direct measurement of σ_{sc} by moving the detector out of the neutron beam; however, such a measurement requires either an exact knowledge of the geometry and the neutron flux, or calibration with a scatterer of known cross section, say carbon (H38, H40).

1. Slow-Neutron Monochromators. Devices for singling out neutrons of a specific (usually variable) energy are known as monochromators or velocity selectors. A number of such devices, based on various principles, have been designed and constructed. They all employ, as the slow-neutron source, neutrons emerging from a mass of slowing-down material (paraffin, heavy water, graphite) whose energy distribution is approximately Maxwellian, with an epithermal tail ($1/E$ flux distribution) extending into the intermediate-energy range. As neutron detector, a boron-containing proportional counter is usually employed. For maximum sensitivity over the widest possible range, the counter is filled with enriched $B^{10}F_3$.

Although the type of monochromator employed depends primarily on the nature of the primary neutron source, there are two basic factors which determine the usefulness of a given device: (1) the energy range over which it can be operated, and (2) the resolution at a given energy, which is a measure of the energy spread at the energy under consideration. In order to define the resolution, it is necessary to specify the shape of the resolution function. The resolution function can usually be approximated by an isosceles triangle. Unless otherwise specified, a triangular resolution function will be assumed, the monochromator energy being defined as the energy at the apex, and the "resolution" as the energy spread at the base. The characteristics of some of the best existing monochromators are summarized in Table 29. The figures in the third column for the "time of flight" velocity selectors give the ratio of the time resolution of the instrument (in microseconds) to the flight path (in meters); this ratio sets the basic limitation both on the usable energy range and on the resolution of the velocity selector. The last five columns give the energy resolutions which are normally attained in operation.

TABLE 29

CHARACTERISTICS OF SOME SLOW-NEUTRON MONOCHROMATORS

Device	Usable Range (ev)	Resolution (μsec/m)	Resolution (ev)					
			0.025	0.1	1	10	100	1,000
Argonne thermal chopper (B65)	0.002–0.2	(50)	0.005	0.05	...	...	..	...
Argonne fast chopper (S18, S19)	0.001– 5,000	0.6	0.001	0.05	0.1	1.7	40	1,000
Columbia modulated cyclotron (R4)	0.001–10,000	1	0.001	0.05	0.07	1.2	30	1,000
Harwell electron accelerator (M26)	0.001–20,000	0.5	0.001	0.05	0.1	1.3	20	500
Crystal spectrometer (S56)	0.02 –100	...	0.0015	0.01	0.2	5	..	...

(a) *Mechanical Velocity Selectors or Choppers.* The first slow-neutron monochromator, built by Dunning, Pegram, Fink, Mitchell, and Segrè (D20), was based on the principle used by Fizeau in his classic measurements of the velocity of light. In this device two cadmium disks were mounted, one at each end, on a shaft. Both disks had a series of uniformly spaced radial slits; the disks could be displaced by an arbitrary angle with respect to each other. With the disks so misaligned, thermal neutrons, moving along the direction of the shaft, which passed through the first set of slits were absorbed in the second disk, provided that the shaft remained stationary. However, with the shaft rotating, those neutrons which passed through the slits of the first disk, whose time of flight between disks was equal to the time required for the second disk to move through the angle of misalignment, could also pass through the second slits and be detected. Thus, by varying the velocity of rotation or the angular displacement, it was possible to select neutrons of a predetermined velocity. Although the resolution of this device was poor (S13a), the velocity selector was useful in demonstrating the $1/v$ nature of a number of thermal neutron cross sections. Improvements and further measurements on this velocity selector were carried out by Fink (F29).

Taking advantage of the greater thermal neutron fluxes available from the first pile, Fermi, Marshall, and Marshall (F22) constructed a thermal neutron velocity selector based on the same principle, but with a number of significant modifications. In this device a beam of neutrons, from the thermal column, falls on a cylinder whose axis is perpendicular to the beam direction. The cylinder is made up of alternate, lengthwise, thin layers of aluminum (effectively transparent to thermal neutrons) and cadmium, as shown in Fig. 51. Neutrons can pass through the cylinder only when the layers are parallel, within ±3°, to the beam direction. Thus, when the disk is rotated (at speeds up to 15,000 rpm) about its axis, neutrons are transmitted in short bursts.

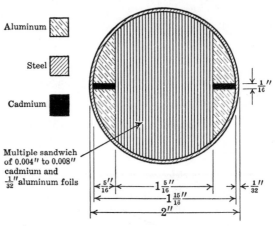

Fig. 51. Cross section, perpendicular to the axis of rotation, of the mechanical "chopper" used in the thermal neutron velocity selector of Fermi, Marshall, and Marshall (F22, B65).

The neutrons which get through the shutter are detected in a bank of BF$_3$ proportional counters, 1.46 meters away. The neutron time of flight between shutter and detector is determined electronically, by allowing the neutron detector to be sensitive only for short periods, delayed by an arbitrary time interval t with respect to the shutter-open times. The synchronization between the shutter position and the detector-on time is achieved by attaching to the cylinder axis a mirror which reflects a beam of light into a photocell when the shutter has a given orientation. By varying the position of the photocell, the delay time t can be chosen at will. Only those neutrons will be recorded whose time of flight between the shutter and the detector is equal to t. If the burst time duration and detector-on times are both equal to Δt, and both have square shapes, the velocity resolution function is a triangle with apex at the velocity $v = L/t$ and base width $\Delta v = 2v\,\Delta t/t = 2v^2\,\Delta t/L$, where $L = $ the length of the flight path.

This velocity selector was subsequently improved by Brill and Lichtenberger (B65), who used it to measure the cross sections of a number of elements in the thermal neutron region. The numbers given in the first line of Table 29 apply to the improved model.

Velocity selectors which employ cadmium in the neutron shutter cannot be used for energies above the cadmium cut-off. This limitation

Fig. 52a.   The fast chopper of Selove, at the Argonne Laboratory (S18, S19).   Photograph shows the stator, rotor, and photocell (box) for timing.

does not apply to the "fast chopper" constructed by Selove at the Argonne laboratory (S18, S19), which employs, as a neutron shutter, a long cylinder of steel with thin slits cut into the cylinder parallel to the axis, which is also the direction of the neutron beam. In line with this cylinder, which can be rotated about its axis, there is a stationary cylinder with identical slits. Neutrons can pass through both sets of slits only when the two sets are aligned; when the slit systems are misaligned, the thickness of steel is sufficient to remove neutrons of all energies from the beam. This device is shown in Figs. 52a and 52b.

The neutron detection and timing system is, in principle, the same as that of the thermal chopper. In operation, the flight path $L = 10$ meters and the burst length $\Delta t \approx 6\ \mu$ sec. The characteristics of this velocity selector are given in the second line of Table 29. The possibility of using such a relatively high resolution device is dependent upon

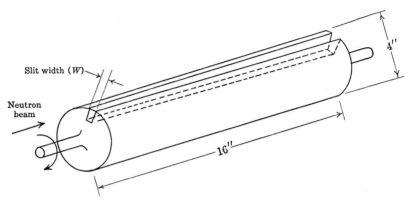

Fig. 52b.　Details of the rotor construction of the chopper in Fig. 52a.

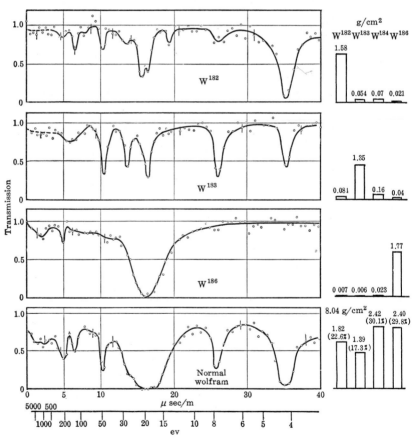

Fig. 52c.　Transmission curves for separated wolfram (W) isotopes, made with the fast chopper of Fig. 52a.

the availability of very strong epithermal neutron fluxes from the Argonne heavy water pile. An additional advantage of this velocity selector is the very small area of the slits, which makes possible transmission measurements on relatively small amounts of material. The transmission curves for separated wolfram isotopes (S19), measured with samples of ∼0.1 gram, are shown in Fig. 52c.

(b) *Modulated Source Velocity Selectors.* Mechanical velocity selectors are designed for use with continuous (in time) neutron sources, the function of the chopper being to transform a continuous beam into a series of bursts. The necessity for the chopper would be eliminated if the neutrons were originally produced in bursts. This can be accomplished with charged particle accelerators by causing the beam to impinge intermittently on the target, either by producing the beam intermittently (modulation of the ion source or the acceleration mechanism) or by deflecting a continuous beam into the target at stated intervals. Once the neutron bursts are produced, the time-of-flight selection is achieved by modulation of the detector in the manner previously described.

The first modulated source velocity selectors were built by Alvarez (A12), who produced an intermittent beam from a cyclotron by modulating the accelerating voltage on the "Dees"; by Milatz and ter Horst (M30), who modulated the focusing potential of a linear accelerator used as a d-d source; and by Fertel, Moon, Thomson, and Wynn-Williams (F26), who modulated the ion source of the Cockcroft-Walton accelerator, used as a d-d source. These were soon followed by the velocity selectors of Haworth, Manley, and Luebke (H48) (modulation of a linear accelerator beam) and of Baker and Bacher (B3) (modulation of the arc source of a cyclotron).

The early modulated source velocity selectors, although they represented great progress over the first mechanical velocity selector, were not capable of very good energy resolution. However, a great deal of effort has been expended in the improvement of such instruments. The progress is mainly the result of work at Cornell University by Bacher, Baker, and McDaniel (B1, M11), and at Columbia University by Rainwater, Havens, Wu, and Dunning (R3, H45, R4). The figures in line 3 of Table 29 and the specific data quoted in this discussion are for the 1950 version of the Columbia velocity selector.

The limitations on the resolution of modulated source velocity selectors arise mainly from two causes: (1) the usual problem of intensity and (2) the fact that accelerator sources yield fast neutrons, which must be slowed down before they start to traverse the flight path. The cyclotron beam (8–10 Mev deuterons, peak currents of a few hundred microamperes) strikes a beryllium target; the resulting neutrons are slowed down in a paraffin slab adjacent to the target. While the available source strength, as well as the possible detector efficiency, is more or less prescribed, much work has been done toward the more efficient utilization of available intensities. The greatest gains have come from the development of circuits for the simultaneous counting of a large number ($\sim$100) of velocity groups. Important progress has also been made in shielding, to reduce the scattered neutron background and thereby enlarge the available energy range.

In addition to the time spread introduced by the widths of the source pulse and the detector-on interval, an inherent energy spread (as well as a delay) is introduced by the time required for the slowing down and diffusion of thermal neutrons. This spread is $\sim$30 μsec for thermal neutrons, when the paraffin moderating slab is $\sim$2–3 cm thick, and increases (roughly linearly) with increasing slab thickness. The slowing-down time for epithermal neutrons is small compared to other sources of time delay.

Another source of loss of resolution, common to all monochromators using BF_3 counters for detection, is introduced by the variable delay between neutron capture in the detector and the resulting pulse. In addition, the finite length of the detector introduces an uncertainty in the length of the flight path of the neutrons.

The inherent time delay between the arc modulation and the detection, at the source, of an epithermal neutron is $\sim$10 μsec for the improved Columbia velocity selector. The corresponding time resolution, Δt, is also $\sim$10 μsec.

The most promising recent development in modulated source velocity selectors is the production of intense, pulsed electron beams from microwave electron accelerators (C16). Such devices, especially if they yield electrons of $\gtrsim$20 Mev energy, are capable of producing neutron bursts of much greater intensity than can be achieved with a cyclotron. By increasing the neutron flight path, it should be possible to extend the usable energy range into the intermediate-energy region. The Harwell velocity selector (fourth line of Table 29) has demonstrated the potentialities of this source (M26).

(c) *Crystal Spectrometers.* A slow neutron of energy E has the associated wavelength $\lambda = h/(2ME)^{1/2}$. When a heteroenergetic beam of slow neutrons impinges on a crystal at an angle θ with the crystal planes, those neutrons will be preferentially reflected (angle of reflection $= \theta$) whose wavelengths satisfy the Bragg condition,

$$m\lambda = 2d \sin \theta \tag{113}$$

where m, an integer, is the order of the reflection, and d is the distance between crystal planes.

The possibility of obtaining monoenergetic neutron sources by Bragg reflection was first demonstrated by Zinn (Z3), who used the strong neutron flux from the Argonne heavy water pile. Zinn's spectrometer is shown in Fig. 53a. Similar results were obtained by Borst, Ulrich, Osborne, and Hasbrouck (B49). Crystal spectrometers with improved intensity and resolution have since been constructed and used in many slow-neutron investigations, by Sturm (S56); by Sawyer, Wollan, Bernstein, and Peterson (S3), who used a curved crystal, as shown in Fig. 53b; by Wollan and Shull (W41); and by Chamberlain (C11), whose spectrometer was specially designed to obtain high intensities for liquid scattering measurements. The spectrometer of Hurst, Pressesky, and Tunnicliffe (H79), designed for use with the high fluxes available from the Chalk River heavy water pile, is an all-purpose monochromator with excellent resolution up to ~ 1 ev.

All these spectrometers require high intensities, available only from piles. The spectrum of neutrons emerging from a hole in the shield of the Argonne heavy water pile, as measured by Sturm (S56), is shown in Fig. 54. The rapid falling-off of the Maxwell distribution on both sides of the maximum is one of the major limitations on the available energy range of crystal spectrometers.

The figures quoted in Table 29 are for a conventional single-crystal spectrometer. It follows from Eq. (113) that the resolution of a crystal spectrometer is given by

$$\frac{-\Delta E}{E} = 2 \cot \theta \, \Delta \theta \qquad (114)$$

where the angular divergence, $\Delta \theta$, results from the angular spread in the neutron beam and from crystal imperfections; $\Delta \theta$ can be obtained from the crystal "rocking curve." The figures in Table 29 correspond to $\Delta \theta \approx 40'$ (S56); Sawyer $et\ al.$ (S3), by using a curved crystal, were able to reduce $\Delta \theta$ to $7.5'$, thereby improving the resolution by a factor of ~ 5. Hurst $et\ al.$ (H79) achieve similar resolution with their conventional spectrometer. Further improvements in resolution could be obtained by using a double-crystal spectrometer, but such an instrument requires much greater neutron intensities.

Improvement in resolution can also be obtained by choosing a crystal with the smallest possible spacing between planes, d. Such a choice will also raise the upper limit of the available energy range. Another possible way of increasing the range is to use second-order reflection from a crystal with very weak intensity of reflection in the first order.

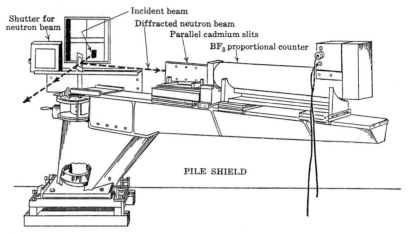

Fig. 53a.   Crystal spectrometer used by Zinn (Z3) in the first demonstration of the possibility of using Bragg reflection for obtaining monoenergetic neutrons.

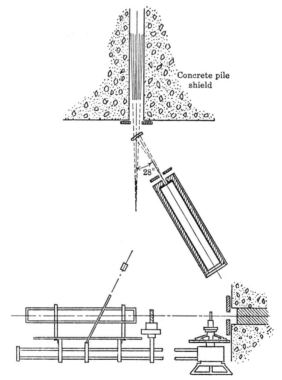

Fig. 53b.   Curved crystal spectrometer of Sawyer, Wollan, Bernstein, and Peterson (S3).   Above, horizontal section; below, vertical section.

However, in addition to the limitation of very small Bragg angles, high-energy measurements suffer from the rapid falling-off of the source intensity.

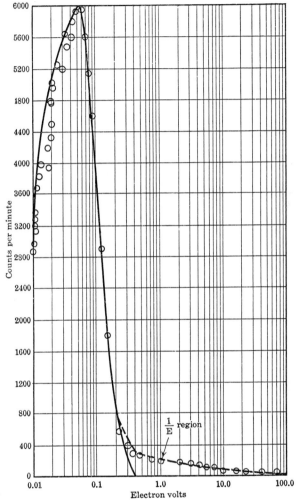

Fig. 54. Neutron spectrum from a hole in the shield of the Argonne heavy water pile, as measured by Sturm (S56), who used a crystal spectrometer. The spectrum is roughly Maxwellian, $T = 400°$K (solid curve), with a $1/E$ tail.

The lower limit on the useful energy range results indirectly from the falling-off of the Maxwell distribution at very low energies; at the large angle of first-order reflection for $E \lesssim 0.04$ ev, there will be present appreciable higher-energy components due to reflection of the more abundant higher-energy neutrons in higher orders. The lower limit can be reduced somewhat (to ~0.01–0.02 ev) by using crystals (such as the 111 planes of lithium fluoride) which have relatively low intensity of reflection in the second and third orders. A further decrease in the low-energy limit, to ~0.005 ev, has been achieved, by Allen, Stanford, Stephenson, and Bernstein (A10), by employing "cold" neutrons, totally reflected at glancing angles from suitable mirrors. However, the low-energy end of the useful energy range is absolutely bounded at $\lambda_c = 2d$.

(d) *Cold Neutrons.* It follows from the Bragg condition, Eq. (113), that for neutrons of wavelength greater than $\lambda_c = 2d$ there is no possible

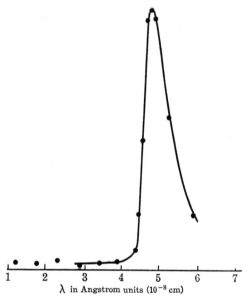

Fig. 55.   Distribution of cold neutrons from a beryllium oxide filter, analyzed by Bragg reflection from the 001 planes of celestite (F21).

angle of coherent scattering except $\theta = 0$. Thus, neutrons of $\lambda > \lambda_c$ ($E < E_c = h^2/2M\lambda_c^2$) will pass through a perfect crystal without deflection and, if the crystal is composed of non-absorbing nuclei, without attenuation. This phenomenon is the basis for the production of cold neutrons by the method of filtration, first suggested by Wick (W24) and demonstrated by Anderson, Fermi, and Marshall (A24).

Consider an intense beam of thermal neutrons from the pile impinging on the base of a long, thin column of graphite, which is a polycrystalline material whose crystals are randomly oriented. In their passage through the column, the neutrons will encounter many crystals with all possible orientations; those neutrons of $\lambda < \lambda_c$ will suffer Bragg reflections, change their direction, and eventually leave the column. Although the neutrons of $\lambda > \lambda_c$ will suffer some attenuation (due to incoherent scattering resulting from crystal imperfections and thermal agitation and to absorption), the beam emerging from the far end of the filter will consist, predominantly, of neutrons of $E < E_c$. Such sources are referred to as cold-neutron sources. For polycrystalline graphite, $\lambda_c = 2d = 6.69$ A; $E_c = 0.002$ ev.

For a substance to be usable as a filter, it is necessary that its capture cross section for the cold neutrons be small. (The reader is reminded of the $1/v$ law.) Another possible filter is polycrystalline beryllium oxide, used by Fermi and Marshall (F21) to produce cold-neutron beams. For the beryllium oxide crystal, $\lambda_c = 4.4$ A; $E_c = 0.004$ ev. The distribution of cold neutrons from a beryllium oxide filter (40 cm x 10 cm x 10 cm) is shown in Fig. 55. It rises abruptly at $\lambda \cong 4.5$ A, has a peak at ~ 5 A, and falls off rapidly for longer wavelengths. The sharp descent is due to the rapid decrease of the Maxwell distribution with decreasing neutron energy. Table 30 lists the values of cut-off wavelengths, λ_c, and energies, E_c, for a number of polycrystalline materials.

Cold neutrons can also be produced by total reflection from suitable mirrors (F21) (Section 5C1).

TABLE 30

CUT-OFF WAVELENGTHS, λ_c, AND ENERGIES, E_c, FOR A NUMBER OF POLYCRYSTALLINE MATERIALS SUITABLE FOR THE PRODUCTION OF COLD NEUTRONS

Filter	λ_c (A)	E_c (ev)	Filter	λ_c (A)	E_c (ev)
Be	3.95	0.0052	Fe	4.04	0.0050
BeO	4.4	0.0042	Ni	4.06	0.0050
C	6.69	0.00183	Cu	4.16	0.0047
Al	4.67	0.00375	Pb	5.7	0.0025
Mn	12.6	0.00052	Bi	8.00	0.00128

2. Measurement of Thermal Neutron Cross Sections. The data on thermal neutron cross sections—the average value in a thermal neutron flux distribution—are voluminous. Provided that the energy dependence of the cross section (e.g., $1/v$ absorption) and that of the thermal neutron flux are known, the value of $\bar\sigma$ is equivalent to a complete curve of σ vs. E in the thermal range. However, for many nuclei the energy dependence of the neutron cross sections is not known a priori—e.g., σ_c in the case of a resonance close to or in the thermal range or σ_{sc} for crystalline materials, which varies in a complicated way. For such nuclei the average value of the thermal neutron cross section is not sufficient to describe completely the behavior throughout the thermal neutron range.

It need hardly be pointed out that measurement with a monochromator of the complete curve of σ vs. E for slow neutrons provides sufficient information for practically all purposes. Although such measurements give the total cross section, they can almost always be interpreted unambiguously in terms of a (constant) scattering cross section and a capture cross section, usually $1/v$ in the thermal range; crystal effects in the thermal region will also be observed, provided that the capture is not overwhelmingly large.

Nevertheless, for many purposes the thermal neutron cross section is of interest in its own right. The most important example is the case of absorption leading to radioactivity; it is frequently desirable to predict, through use of a single constant, the activation resulting from the immersion of a given absorber in a given thermal neutron flux. Conversely, the activation of an absorber of known thermal neutron cross section is a measure of the magnitude of the thermal neutron flux.

While thermal neutron flux distributions in moderating media can usually be closely approximated by the Maxwell distribution function (Eq. 93), the temperature, to which the distribution corresponds ($kT = E'$), is seldom that of the medium. In hydrogenous media of finite size, in piles, or in a thermal column close to a pile, the neutron temperature is usually higher than that of the medium; the neutron temperature at large depths in a thermal column may be lower. The temperature can be determined by measurement of the average capture cross section of a known $1/v$ absorber, say boron (F22).

Conversely, thermal neutron cross sections can be deduced, without knowledge of the magnitude of the flux or of the temperature of the neutron distribution, by comparison with a known $1/v$ absorber. Most thermal neutron activation cross sections have been measured in this fashion; e.g., the extensive measurements of activation cross sections in the Argonne piles by Seren, Friedlander, and Turkel (S24).

(a) *The Cadmium Difference Method.* Thermal neutron sources usually contain an epithermal component which, in view of the existence of strong resonances, may contribute an appreciable fraction of the observed absorption or activation. The effect of resonances above $\sim$0.5 ev, can be eliminated by taking the difference between the absorption of a bare detector and one surrounded by a cadmium shield.

The peculiar usefulness of cadmium as a thermal neutron filter arises from a capture resonance in the thermal neutron region ($E_r = 0.176$ ev, $\sigma_0 = 7200$ barns, $\Gamma = 0.115$ ev; see Fig. 20a, page 327). Because of the $1/v$ increase with decreasing neutron energy, the cross section on the low-energy side of the resonance never falls below 2000 barns. On the high-energy side, on the other hand, the cross section descends abruptly; above ~4 ev the cross section (5 barns) is due entirely to scattering, there being no additional resonances observed up to ~100 ev. A thickness of 1 g/cm^2(~1 mm) of cadmium metal will transmit less than 1 percent of all the incident neutrons of energy below 0.3 ev, and ~⅓ of the neutrons of energy 0.45 ev.

Only a negligible portion of the Maxwell distribution (for reasonable neutron temperatures) extends into the epicadmium region. On the other hand, if the absorber has a resonance fairly close to the thermal region, the low-energy tail of the resonance may extend to below the cadmium cut-off; in this case, the absorption of a cadmium-covered detector will be less than the true resonance absorption, and it is necessary to apply a correction (increase) to the cadmium-covered detector reading before subtracting it from the bare detector value, in order to obtain the true thermal neutron absorption. The magnitude of this correction will depend on the thickness of the cadmium shield.

Indium is frequently used for a thermal neutron detector because of the magnitude of its cross section ($\bar{\sigma} \cong 190$ barns), the ease of handling indium metal foils, and the convenient half-life of the resulting radioactivity (54 min). The lowest indium resonance is at 1.44 ev ($\sigma_0 \cong 35,000$ barns, $\Gamma \cong 0.08$ ev; see Fig. 7c, page 281). The correction to the activity of cadmium-covered indium foils to obtain the true resonance activation has been investigated experimentally by Kunstadter (K26), who gives the following correction formula:

$$\text{True activity} = \text{observed activity} \times e^{0.138T} \qquad (115)$$

where T is the thickness of cadmium metal in millimeters.[1]

(b) *The Pile "Danger Coefficient" Method.* A useful and accurate method of measuring thermal neutron absorption cross sections has been reported by Anderson, Fermi, Wattenberg, Weil, and Zinn (A25). This method involves the use of a thermal pile (see Section 4), and depends on the fact that introduction of absorbing material into the pile causes a decrease in the pile reactivity. If the pile is operating at a constant neutron flux level, the insertion of the absorber will result in a gradual decrease in the flux; the effect of the absorber can be compensated by displacing the pile control rods by an amount sufficient to maintain the pile at a constant power level.

If the compensating motion of the control rod is calibrated against a series of absorbers of known cross section, the required motion of the

---

[1] Below ~0.5 mm of cadmium, the shield is no longer black to thermal neutrons, and the above considerations break down.

control rod for an unknown absorber provides a measure of the unknown absorption cross section. This method was first devised in order to ascertain the harmful effects (with respect to pile reactivity) of various contemplated pile construction materials; hence the term danger coefficient.

One of the characteristics of this method is that it measures the *absorption* cross section, in contrast to the total (absorption plus scattering) and the activation (absorption leading to a measurable radioactivity) cross sections. The pile reactivity is relatively insensitive to the scattering properties of the absorber, even if the absorption cross section is comparatively small. Since the products of the particular absorbing reaction (provided they are not neutrons) are of no concern to the pile, this method provides one of the few means of observing absorptions which lead to a stable product nucleus, or to a product nucleus whose radioactivity is difficult to observe; for example, although activation measurements (S24) seemed, at first, to yield an apparent absorption cross section of $0.0\overset{?}{2}$ barn for niobium, which has the single isotope $_{41}Nb^{93}$, the danger coefficient method gives a value of 1.4 barns (A25). The discrepancy was resolved when a previously unrecognized isomer of Nb^{94} was discovered.

A modification of the danger coefficient method suggested by Wigner greatly increases its sensitivity. This is the method of the "pile oscillator," in which the absorber is intermittently introduced into the pile, resulting in an oscillation of the flux (power) level of the pile. The magnitude of the resulting pile oscillation is a measure of the absorption cross section of the sample. The effect of scattering by the sample is to introduce an out-of-phase component into the pile oscillation; accordingly, the effects of scattering and absorption can be separated experimentally, and the absorption of samples for which the absorption cross section is only a small fraction of the scattering cross section (e.g., bismuth) can be measured.

The theory of the pile oscillator has been developed by Weinberg and Schweinler (W12). Extensive pile oscillator measurements of thermal neutron absorption cross sections have been made at the Argonne Laboratory by Harris, Muehlhause, Rasmussen, Schroeder, and Thomas (H42), who used an oscillator constructed by Langsdorf (L3), and at the Oak Ridge National Laboratory by Pomerance (P22, P23) with the oscillator of Hoover, Jordan, Moak, Pardue, Pomerance, Strong, and Wollan (H65). A pile oscillator has also been developed and used with the French heavy water reactor by Raievski and Yvon (R2).

In using a thermal pile for a danger coefficient measurement of a thermal neutron absorption cross section, it is necessary to correct for the absorption of an appreciable epithermal neutron component. This correction can be determined by the cadmium difference method.

The danger coefficient method can also be applied to the measurement of epithermal absorption cross sections (cadmium-covered foils) (L3). It can be used with intermediate- and fast-neutron piles. In these cases the absorption is an average over the relatively broad neutron flux distribution in the pile. However, in these applications it is much more difficult to correct for the effects of the scattering properties of the sample.

3. Measurement of the Characteristics of Slow-Neutron Resonances.
One of the most important problems of slow-neutron spectroscopy is the precise determination of the constants associated with resonances. In the following discussion, we consider only capture resonances, neglecting scattering and associated interference effects; i.e., we assume $\Gamma \approx \Gamma_\gamma \gg \Gamma_n$. (Similar considerations can be applied, with minor modifications, to scattering resonances.) In this case, the Breit-Wigner formula is most conveniently written

$$\sigma(E) = \frac{(E_r/E)^{\frac{1}{2}}\sigma_0}{[1 + 4(E - E_r)^2/\Gamma^2]} \tag{116}$$

A resonance is completely described in terms of three parameters: E_r, the resonance energy; σ_0, the peak cross section; Γ, the full width at half maximum.

Equation (116) is not symmetrical about the energy E_r, owing to the factor $(E_r/E)^{\frac{1}{2}}$. The variation of this factor is important for resonances occurring in or near the thermal region. However, for resonances for which $\Gamma \ll E_r$, the deviation of the factor $(E_r/E)^{\frac{1}{2}}$ from 1 is negligible over the region of significant values of $\sigma(E)$; this situation prevails for practically all the observed resonances for which $E_r \gtrsim 1$ ev.

(a) *Monochromator Measurements.* In principle, a measurement of $\sigma(E)$ vs. E provides all possible resonance data. In practice, the finite resolution of the monochromator has a profound influence on the observed shape of the resonance, and on the possibility of deducing the resonance parameters. In the following considerations of the effects of finite resolution we assume a rectangular resolution function, of width R, mainly for ease of computation. The computations can be performed for triangular, or any other shape, resolution functions by numerical iteration if necessary; furthermore, a resolution function of arbitrary shape can usually be approximated with reasonable accuracy by the superposition of a number of rectangles.

Since monochromators measure $\sigma(E)$ by transmission experiments, the absorber thickness is important to these considerations. We define (1) a thin absorber as one which is at least translucent over the entire resonance, i.e., $NT\sigma_0 \lesssim 3$; (2) a thick absorber is black in the region of the resonance, $NT\sigma_0 \gtrsim 10$. It should be remarked that the choice between using a thin or a thick absorber is not entirely a question of the available techniques of absorber preparation. The monochromator resolution is the determining factor: for $R \gg \Gamma$ it is impossible to obtain sufficient absorption, and consequently to make any measurement at all, by using a thin absorber. On the other hand, for $R \lesssim \Gamma$ the use of thin absorbers is, as we shall see, possible and desirable.

The available monochromator resolutions have been summarized in Table 29. Since resonance widths are, for heavy nuclei, $\sim$0.1 ev, good resolution ($R < \Gamma$) is possible only below $\sim$1 ev; in the region 1–10 ev, the available resolutions are fair; above $\sim$10 ev, resolutions are poor. The situation with respect to scattering resonances in medium nuclei is somewhat better; however, very few such resonances fall in the slow-neutron region. The considerations of this section can also be applied to measurements in the intermediate and fast regions, where many scattering resonances have been observed.

(1) Thin Absorber Measurements. For a sufficiently thin absorber, the transmission is determined by the average, over the resolution function, of the cross section. Neglecting the variation of $(E_r/E)^{\frac{1}{2}}$,

$$\bar{\sigma}(E) = \frac{1}{R} \int_{E-R/2}^{E+R/2} \sigma(E) \, dE$$

$$= \frac{\sigma_0 \Gamma}{2R} \left\{ \tan^{-1} \left[\frac{2(E - E_r)}{\Gamma} + \frac{R}{\Gamma} \right] - \tan^{-1} \left[\frac{2(E - E_r)}{\Gamma} - \frac{R}{\Gamma} \right] \right\}$$

$$(116a)$$

Curves of $\bar{\sigma}/\sigma_0$ are plotted in Fig. 56 as a function of $2(E - E_r)/\Gamma$, for a number of values of R/Γ. For $R/\Gamma < 1$, the main effect of the finite resolution is to depress the peak without greatly broadening the resonance (although the observed width at half-maximum is somewhat increased). Thus, for good resolution experiments, it is relatively easy to make the appropriate corrections to the transmission curves, and to determine the resonance parameters. (The work of McDaniel, M11, on the 1.44 ev resonance of indium, see Fig. 7d, illustrates the method.)

However, for $R/\Gamma > 1$ the observed width is essentially the resolution. It is impossible, from such a measurement, to determine separately the resonance width or the peak cross section; a poor resolution thin absorber experiment can only yield the product $\sigma_0\Gamma$, through

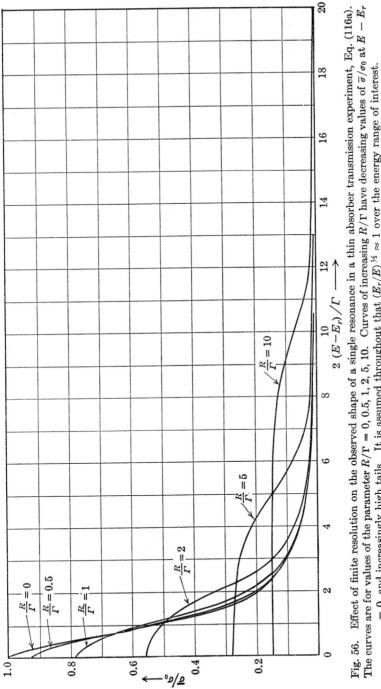

Fig. 56. Effect of finite resolution on the observed shape of a single resonance in a thin absorber transmission experiment, Eq. (116a). The curves are for values of the parameter $R/\Gamma = 0$, 0.5, 1, 2, 5, 10. Curves of increasing R/Γ have decreasing values of $\bar{\sigma}/\sigma_0$ at $E - E_r = 0$, and increasingly high tails. It is assumed throughout that $(E_r/E)^{1/2} \approx 1$ over the energy range of interest.

either the observed peak cross section or the area under the observed resonance:

(a) The apparent (observed) peak cross section [1] is

$$\bar{\sigma}(E_r) = \sigma_0 \frac{\Gamma}{R} \tan^{-1} \frac{R}{\Gamma}$$

$$\cong \sigma_0 \left[1 - \frac{1}{3} \left(\frac{R}{\Gamma} \right)^2 \right] \qquad \text{for } \frac{R}{\Gamma} \ll 1$$

$$\cong \sigma_0 \frac{\Gamma}{R} \left(\frac{\pi}{2} - \frac{\Gamma}{R} \right) \qquad \text{for } \frac{R}{\Gamma} \gg 1 \qquad (116a')$$

The reduction of the peak cross section (by the factor 1.571 Γ/R) makes it virtually impossible to use a thin absorber when $R/\Gamma \gtrsim 10$.

(b) It may be seen, by visual inspection of Fig. 56, that the decrease in the peak cross section is accompanied by a raising of the tail of the observed resonance, so that the area underneath the resonance curve appears relatively insensitive to the resolution. Actually (from Eqs. 116 and 116a) [2]

$$\int \bar{\sigma}(E) \, dE = \int \sigma(E) \, dE = \frac{\pi}{2} \sigma_0 \Gamma \qquad (116b)$$

independent of R!

Another possible effect of poor resolution is the failure to resolve close resonances. This difficulty is illustrated in Fig. 57, in which $\bar{\sigma}/\sigma_0$ has been plotted, for two identical resonances separated by the energy D, for a number of values of R/Γ. The classic example of the phenomenon of close resonances is the case of iodine, which appeared, from early experiments, to have a single, anomalously broad resonance at $\sim$40 ev. Careful investigation by Jones (J12) established the existence of a number of sharp resonances between 20 and 50 ev. Many of the relatively broad peaks in cross-section curves (G20, A2) observed above $\sim$10 ev

---

[1] Another resolution shape, for which the average can be performed analytically, is the Gaussian function of half-width R. In this case,

$$\bar{\sigma}(E_r) = \sigma_0 [1.665(\Gamma/R) e^{0.693\Gamma^2/R^2} \, \text{erfc} \, (0.833\Gamma/R)]$$

$$\cong 1.476\sigma_0 \Gamma/R \qquad \text{for } R/\Gamma \gg 1 \qquad (116a'')$$

in which erfc $(x) \equiv (\pi/4)^{1/2} - \int_0^x e^{-t^2} \, dt$.

[2] The integrals are conventionally and most easily performed between the limits $-\infty$ and ∞. Since the entire contribution is for values relatively close to E_r, this extension of the limits of integration introduces a negligible error.

in monochromator measurements on heavy nuclei are probably due to the failure to resolve such groups of resonances.

(2) Thick Absorber Measurements.   If a thick absorber is employed in a good resolution experiment, the transmission is ~ 0 over the main portion of the resonance; only the wings of the resonance can be studied in any detail.   However, as we have seen above, thick absorbers are necessary in a poor resolution experiment to obtain transmissions which differ significantly from 1.

The interpretation of the transmission curve for a thick absorber in a poor resolution monochromator experiment can be achieved by numerical and graphical techniques, as described by Havens and Rainwater (H45).   The result of such interpretation—either by detailed fitting of the transmission curve or by integration of the absorption over energy —yields a value of the combination $\sigma_0 \Gamma^2$.   The interpretation requires a knowledge of the value of the resolution width, R, and of the shape of the resolution function; the results are, however, not very sensitive to the exact form of the resolution function.

The fact that the combination $\sigma_0 \Gamma^2$ determines the results of a poor resolution thick absorber transmission measurement can be seen by the following argument: The mean transmission at the energy E is

$$\overline{I/I_0(E)} = \left(\int R(E',E) e^{-NT\sigma_0/[1+4(E'-E_r)^2/\Gamma^2]} \, dE' \right)/R(E) \quad (117)$$

where $R(E',E)$ is the resolution function; the resolution width is defined as

$$R(E) = \int R(E',E) \, dE' \quad (117')$$

Assuming $NT\sigma_0 > 10$, the integrand vanishes unless $4(E' - E_r)^2/\Gamma^2 \gg 1$; hence, the integral may be replaced by

$$\overline{I/I_0(E)} \cong \left(\int R(E',E) e^{-NT\sigma_0 \Gamma^2/4(E'-E_r)} \, dE' \right)/R(E)$$

$$= F(E,E_r,\sigma_0 \Gamma^2) \quad (117a)$$

The area under the absorption curve is

$$\int (1 - \overline{I/I_0}) \, dE = F'(E_r,\sigma_0 \Gamma^2) \quad (117b)$$

Since almost all monochromator measurements for $E \gtrsim 50$ ev employ poor resolution and thick absorbers, a resonance in this region must be comparatively strong in order to be observed at all.   There is no doubt that such measurements fail to detect a fair fraction of the resonances.

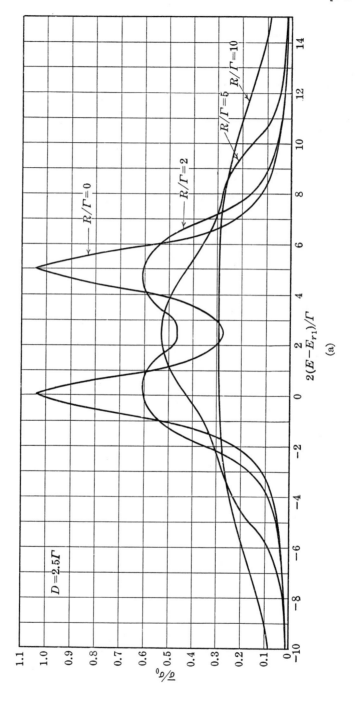

$D = 2.5\Gamma$

$R/\Gamma = 0$

$R/\Gamma = 2$

$R/\Gamma = 5$ $R/\Gamma = 10$

σ/σ_0

$2(E - E_{r1})/\Gamma$

(a)

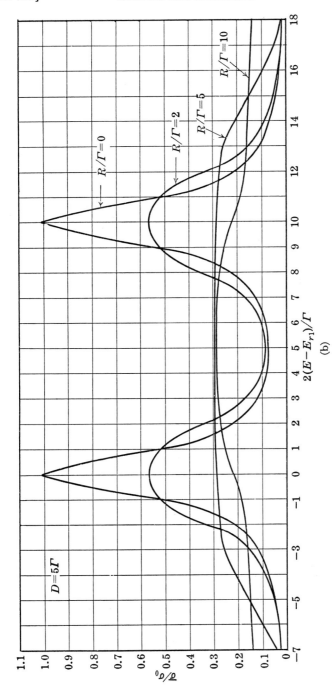

Fig. 57.   Effect of finite resolution on the observed shape of a pair of identical resonances, in a thin absorber transmission experiment. The curves are for two values of the separation of the resonances, $D = 2.5\Gamma$ and 5Γ, and for $R/\Gamma = 0, 2, 5, 10$.

Many of the observed peaks (G20, A2) are probably due to resonance groups, as in the case of iodine.

Finally, it should be noted that considerable progress has been made in the direct application of slow-neutron monochromators to the study of the details of resonance scattering, by Tittman, Sheer, Rainwater, and Havens (T15). The interpretation of measurements on the scattered neutrons is quite complicated, but it follows, roughly, the techniques outlined above.

(b) *Self- and Mutual-Indication Techniques.* In the pre-velocity selector era of slow-neutron physics, a number of techniques were developed for studying resonances from which it was possible to deduce the resonance parameters, with surprising accuracy in some cases. While some of these techniques have been rendered obsolete by more recent developments, others still find useful application in resonance investigations. Unfortunately, in the first rush to exploit the new-found wealth of velocity selectors and pile intensities, some of these old methods have been disparaged, neglected, or forgotten. Their revival should contribute useful information to the growing fund of resonance data. These techniques are admirably summarized in the famous "Bethe Bible" (B24).

One of these is the method of self-indication, in which the resonance under investigation is used as its own detector (F16). For a thin resonance detector in a slow-neutron beam, the saturated activity is (from Eqs. 103'b, 104, 104a, 103c)

$$R_0 = NTA\phi(E_r)\left(\frac{\pi}{2}\right)\sigma_0\Gamma \tag{103d}$$

Thus, knowledge of $\sigma_0\Gamma$ will directly yield the flux $\phi(E_r)$, and vice versa.[1]

If now a thin absorber of the same material (thickness T') is placed in the beam, the saturated activity of the detector will be reduced, becoming

$$R' = NTA\int[\phi(E) - NT''\phi(E)\sigma(E)]\sigma(E)\,dE$$

$$= R_0[1 - NT'\int\sigma^2\,dE/\int\sigma\,dE]$$

$$= R_0[1 - NT''\sigma_0/2] \tag{118}$$

---

[1] We assume, here and in the following, that $\sigma = \sigma(n,\gamma)$; i.e., $\Gamma \approx \Gamma_\gamma \gg \Gamma_n$. This holds, of course, only for capture resonances in heavy nuclei. The necessary modifications, if this is not the case, can be obtained by arguments similar to those employed in this section.

Thus, the effective cross section for a thin resonance absorber in a self-indication experiment is $\sigma_0/2$.

Thus, it is, in principle, possible to measure σ_0 without a monochromator. There are, however, a number of difficulties inherent in the use of this technique. In the first place, since σ_0 can be very large ($\sim 10^4$–10^5 barns for resonances at a few ev energy in heavy nuclei), the preparation of thin absorbers may present serious technical problems. The common solution is to use absorbers of decreasing thickness, and to extrapolate the resulting values of σ_0 to zero absorber thickness.

Another difficulty arises from the possible activation of the detector by neutrons of energies outside the resonance. Thermal neutrons are easily excluded by cadmium. Other resonances are more difficult to eliminate, especially if they should happen to be of comparable strength ($\sigma_0\Gamma$) to the one in question. Fortunately, this is seldom the case; the lowest resonance usually dominates the rest so that, especially if absorber and detector are truly thin, the observed effects can be attributed to a single resonance. It should be noted that the availability of a monochromator of even poor resolution would eliminate the effects of other resonances in a self-indication experiment. However, only the crystal spectrometer can be used in this connection, since other velocity selectors do not remove neutrons from the beam.

When the resonance is used as its own detector, the resonance energy can be determined by measuring the cross section of boron for the detected neutrons. Since the cross section of boron follows the $1/v$ law, and its absolute value is known, this method can yield an accurate value of E_r. However, the $1/v$ dependence of the total (transmission) boron cross section holds only as long as the absorption cross section is much greater than the (constant) scattering cross section. This limits the use of normal boron to energies below ~ 100 ev; for absorbers enriched in B^{10}, the range is considerably extended.

An interesting example of the use of these techniques for the study of a single resonance (rhodium, $E_r = 1.2$ ev) is the work of Manley, Goldsmith, and Schwinger (M3). These authors also used the shape of the curve of transmission vs. (self-indicated) absorber thickness to obtain a measure of the resonance width, Γ. However, as the absorber thickness is increased, the effects of other resonances are of greater importance.

A natural extension of the technique of self-indication can be made for the case of two resonances (in different materials) which partially overlap; one can be used as absorber and the second as detector, thereby obtaining a measure of the area of overlap of the levels; this is the method of mutual indication. By measuring all four absorption coefficients (two

self, two mutual) it is possible to obtain the relative widths and resonance energies for the two levels (B24, A20, F16, H66).

The techniques described above, with a number of ingenious modifications, have been extensively investigated and exploited by a group at the
University of Groningen, Holland (C27, C28). The technique of
mutual indication has recently been applied by Hibdon and Muehlhause
(H57) to the detection of resonances in a number of substances; they
used the scattering resonances of cobalt and manganese as indicators.

(c) *Interpretation of Resonance Data; the Doppler Effect.* The foregoing discussion may be summarized as follows: There are available a
number of techniques for the measurement of the constants which characterize a single resonance (Eq. 116). Monochromator measurements
determine E_r and, for good resolution and thin absorbers, σ_0 and Γ.
Poor resolution monochromator measurements yield $\sigma_0\Gamma$ for thin absorbers, or $\sigma_0\Gamma^2$ for thick absorbers. Self-indication measurements
yield σ_0 and $\sigma_0\Gamma$ (if the neutron flux can be measured independently), as
well as E_r and, possibly, Γ. Mutual-indication measurements, in conjunction with another resonance of known characteristics, can give E_r
and Γ.

There is still another method for obtaining information concerning a
resonance, provided that it is permissible to extend the single resonance
formula into the thermal region; this is possible if the resonance in question is the strongest of all the resonances of the nucleus in question, and
also has the lowest energy. For the thermal energy region, if $E_{th} = E$
$\ll E_r$, the one-resonance (n,γ) cross section is

$$\sigma_{th}(n,\gamma) \cong \frac{\sigma_0\Gamma^2}{4E_r^{3/2}E^{1/2}} \tag{119}$$

which is the usual $1/v$ law. Thus, the value of the thermal neutron
capture cross section determines the constant $\sigma_0\Gamma^2$, if E_r is known. We
recall that, for a $1/v$ absorber in a Maxwellian neutron distribution of
temperature T,

$$\bar{\sigma}_{th} = \frac{\sigma(E = kT)}{1.128} \tag{95a}$$

whence

$$\sigma_0\Gamma^2 \cong 1.128\bar{\sigma}_{th}\cdot 4E_r^{3/2}(kT)^{1/2} \tag{119a}$$

If this method is used to derive $\sigma_0\Gamma^2$ from the thermal neutron capture
cross section of In^{115} (Table 10, page 328) the value obtained, ~185
barns-ev^2, agrees, to within ~10 percent, with that computed from the
constants of the 1.44-ev resonance as measured by McDaniel (M11).

The connection between σ_{th} and the first resonance depends on the possibility of neglecting the effect of all higher resonance. The resonance energy factor in Eq. (119) favors this possibility. The value of σ_0,

$$\sigma_0 = \frac{4\pi\lambda_r{}^2 f\Gamma_{nr}}{\Gamma} \qquad (120)$$

is also a decreasing function, $\propto E_r{}^{-\frac{1}{2}}$, of the resonance energy, provided that the resonances are all of the same type; i.e., $\Gamma_{nri} \cong CE_{ri}{}^{\frac{1}{2}}$ and Γ_i = constant.

Equation (120) also shows that the neutron width, $f\Gamma_{nr}$, can be obtained from a measurement of σ_0 and Γ (actually, from $\sigma_0\Gamma$).

In the preceding discussion, Γ has been associated with the true width of the resonance. Actually these are not identical, owing to the Doppler effect of the thermal motion of the absorber nuclei. The Doppler effect is equivalent to introducing an inherent finite resolution into any measurement, since an incident neutron of energy E will have a spread of energies relative to the absorbing nuclei. The "resolution function" which describes the Doppler effect is

$$R_D(E',E) = e^{-(E'-E)^2/\Delta^2} \qquad (121)$$

where

$$\Delta = 2\left(\frac{EkT}{A}\right)^{\frac{1}{2}} \qquad (121a)$$

and A is the mass number of the absorbing nucleus. The Doppler width, Δ, is by no means negligible. For $E = 1$ ev, $kT = \frac{1}{40}$ ev, $A = 100$, Eq. (121a) gives $\Delta = 0.032$ ev; Δ increases like $E^{\frac{1}{2}}$. The effective cross section of a given absorber is

$$\sigma_{eff}(E) = \left(\int \sigma(E')R_D(E',E)\,dE'\right)/R_D(E) \qquad (121b)$$

with

$$R_D(E) = \int R_D(E',E)\,dE' = \pi^{\frac{1}{2}}\Delta(E) \qquad (121c)$$

Any additional effects due to the finite resolution of the measuring device are superimposed on the Doppler broadening.

The result of this Gaussian resolution function is to reduce the peak cross section and broaden the resonance in the manner previously described.[1] The details of the Doppler broadening were derived and discussed by Bethe and Placzek (B25, B24), who give formulas and curves for the interpretation of the measured constants (also in self-indication experiments) in terms of the true constants of the resonance.

[1] See footnote 1 on page 446.

(d) *Effects of Many Resonances; the Resonance Integral.* Some medium and most heavy nuclei have many resonances in the slow-neutron region. The absorption, scattering, and activation of these nuclei in a slow-neutron flux will be due to the combined effect of all the resonances.

Consider a thin detector of a given type of nuclear reaction, with cross section $\sigma_i(E)$. In the unusual $1/E$ slow-neutron flux, with the thermal neutrons eliminated by cadmium, the total number of processes of type i will be (Eqs. 96, 103c″, 104b)

$$R_i = NV \int_{\sim 0.5 \, \text{ev}} \phi(E)\sigma_i(E) \, dE = NVB \int_{\sim 0.5 \, \text{ev}} \sigma_i(E) \left(\frac{dE}{E}\right) \quad (122)$$

If $\sigma_i(E)$ is characterized by a number of resonances, their effect is summarized by the resonance integral

$$\Sigma_i = \int_{\sim 0.5 \, \text{ev}} \sigma_i(E) \left(\frac{dE}{E}\right) \cong \left(\frac{\pi}{2}\right) \sum_j \frac{\sigma_{0j}\Gamma_j}{E_{rj}} \quad (123)$$

Recalling that, for a process of type i,

$$\sigma_{0j} = \frac{4\pi \lambdabar_{rj}^2 f_j \Gamma_{nrj} \Gamma_{ij}}{\Gamma_j^2} \quad (120')$$

we have

$$\Sigma_i = 2\pi^2 \sum_j \frac{\lambdabar_{rj}^2 f_j \Gamma_{nrj} \Gamma_{ij}}{\Gamma_j E_{rj}} \quad (123a)$$

Resonance integrals can be evaluated, given a $1/E$ epicadmium flux, in a straightforward fashion. The activation of an (n,γ) detector gives Σ_a for the resonances leading to the observed activity. Pile danger coefficient measurements can yield Σ_a for all capture processes, including those which lead to undetectable product nuclei. Measurements of the total scattering cross section yield Σ_s, provided that a reliable means can be found for subtracting the effect of the relatively constant potential scattering.

Harris, Muehlhause, and Thomas (H40) have reported measurements of Σ_a and Σ_s for a number of nuclei. They measured Σ_a by observing the activation of thin detectors in the $1/E$ flux next to the Argonne heavy water reactor. Absolute values were obtained by comparison with the thermal neutron activation of the same detector, using the known thermal neutron cross sections and correcting for the effect of $1/v$ absorption above the cadmium cut-off. The ratio of thermal to epicadmium flux was determined from the known values of $\overline{\sigma_{a_{th}}} = 93$

barns and $\Sigma_a = 1296$ barns (due almost entirely to the resonance at ~ 5 ev) of gold.

Values of Σ_s were measured by the scattering of thin samples placed at the center of an annular BF_3 counter. Absolute values were obtained by comparison with the scattering of a carbon target, for which the average epicadmium cross section (4.60 barns) was independently determined. Corrections were computed for the (constant) potential scattering, when known. In other cases, the potential scattering contribution was measured by using a neutron beam which had been filtered through a thick absorber of the same material as the scatterer (a sort of self-indication in reverse). Unfortunately, the scattering chamber efficiency depended on the energy of the scattered neutrons, so that the interpretation of the results required a knowledge (or assumption) of the energies of the most important—i.e., first few—scattering resonances.

The results of these measurements were interpreted in terms of average values of Γ_n/Γ for the nuclei in question (see Section 2). From the energy dependence of the factors in Eq. (123a) it is seen that the particular average, deduced from $\Sigma_s/(\Sigma_a + \Sigma_s)$, is strongly weighted in favor of the lowest-lying resonances.

E. The Calibration of Neutron Sources

Along with the large variety of available neutron sources with different spectra and yields, there have been devised a number of methods for measuring source spectra, some of which have been described in the preceding, and for measuring source yields—the subject of the following discussion. Some of these methods are quite specific to the reaction under investigation. Thus, for charged particle reactions on light nuclei, the recoil (product) nucleus can frequently be detected and counted by conventional means, thereby providing a measure of the neutron yield. An example is the measurement of the yield of the reaction $H^3(d,n)He^4$ by counting the recoil alpha-particles (T2).

Alternatively, if the product nucleus is radioactive, the yield of a reaction can be obtained from the resulting radioactivity of the target. This technique requires, however, a determination of the absolute value of a radioactive decay rate; such measurements are, in general, difficult to perform with good accuracy. This method is applicable to some of the threshold (p,n) reactions.

An important variation on this theme is the method of Paneth and Glückauf (P2, G8) for obtaining the yield of the $Be^9(\gamma,n)Be^8 \rightarrow 2\alpha$ source by measuring the total helium accumulation in the beryllium. This method could serve as the basis for the calibration of the standard neutron source (C42).

Another general technique for the measurement of source strengths is the observation of the excitation of a reaction of known cross section by the source neutrons. This method requires the use of a detector of known efficiency and, clearly, is applicable only when the neutrons are either monoenergetic or have a relatively simple, known spectrum. The most useful reactions for this application are neutron-proton scattering, for fast neutrons, and the $B^{10}(n,\alpha)$ reaction, for intermediate and slow neutrons.

Most of the useful laboratory sources—radioactive (α,n), photoneutron, and many accelerated charged particle reactions—have complex spectra and are, in general, not susceptible to the above-mentioned techniques. The calibration of such sources is usually achieved by the method of "space integration." There are almost as many variations on this technique as there have been applications thereof. However, the salient features can be described as follows:

Consider a source of fast or intermediate neutrons in an infinite slowing-down medium.[1] Let the source strength be Q (neutrons/sec), the density of the medium be N (nuclei/cm³), and the absorption cross section of the medium be $\sigma_a(E)$. At equilibrium, we have

$$Q = 4\pi \int_0^\infty r^2 \, dr \int_0^{E_{max}} N\phi(r,E)\sigma_a(E) \, dE$$

$$= 4\pi N \int_0^\infty \Phi(r)\overline{\sigma_a(r)}r^2 \, dr \qquad (124)$$

where r is the distance from the source. The problem of absolute source calibration reduces to the experimental determination of the function $\Phi(r)\overline{\sigma_a(r)}$.

Now, the slowing-down media most commonly used (e.g., water, paraffin, graphite) have the property that $\sigma_a(E)$ obeys the $1/v$ law; there are no known absorption resonances up to at least a few Mev. Furthermore, the thermal neutron absorption cross sections are small so that the absorption during slowing down is negligible; practically all the absorption takes place after the neutrons have reached thermal equilibrium. Thus, it is possible to measure $\Phi(r)\overline{\sigma_a(r)}$ by using any thermal neutron detector whose absorption also follows the $1/v$ law and for which the ratio $\sigma_a(\text{medium})/\sigma_a(\text{detector})$ is known. (Since both medium

---

[1] The practical definition of infinite is: large enough so that not more than a small fraction of the neutrons escape through the outer boundary; actually, if the geometry is sufficiently well defined so that it is possible to compute the probability of escape, this requirement can be relaxed.

and detector absorb according to the $1/v$ law, the ratio of their absorption cross sections is independent of the position in the medium.)

As an example consider a small, thin BF_3 counter of known efficiency (i.e., known $N'V'$). The counting rate of this detector at the position r in the medium is

$$R'(r) = N'V'\Phi(r)\overline{\sigma_a'(r)} \tag{103b'}$$

Combining (124) and (103b'), we have

$$Q = \left(\frac{4\pi N}{N'V'}\right)\left(\frac{\sigma_a}{\sigma_a'}\right)\int_0^\infty R'(r)r^2\,dr \tag{124a}$$

It is frequently more convenient to use a radioactive (n,γ) detector for the flux measurement. (Manganese and indium foils, using the cadmium-difference technique, are convenient $1/v$ thermal neutron detectors.) In this case, a calibration of the detector efficiency is necessary in order to convert measurements of saturated activity to neutron absorption rates. Such calibrations can be made if the efficiency of the radioactivity counter is known for the particular foils used. Greater accuracy of calibration can usually be achieved by comparing the saturated activity of the foils used with the counting rate of a thin BF_3 counter, of known efficiency, in the same thermal neutron flux; this method was developed by Frisch, Halban, and Koch (F48).

An interesting technique of foil calibration [1] was carried out by Seidl and Harris (S16). In this method the absorption rate of a thin boron absorber, exposed in a thermal neutron flux, is determined by measuring the accumulation of He due to the $B^{10}(n,\alpha)$ reaction. The saturated activity of the foil used in the integration is measured in the same flux. This method does not depend on knowing the efficiency of a BF_3 counter. It does, however, require the availability of very strong thermal neutron fluxes, i.e., a pile.

A useful and ingenious modification of the above techniques has been described by O'Neal and Scharff-Goldhaber (O4). Their calibration method has the advantages that it requires no knowledge of the values of absorption cross sections and the space integration is performed physically. The measurement is made in three stages:

(1) The source is placed at the center of a large tank of water in which is dissolved a quantity of a $1/v$ detector (they used manganese sulfate). After saturation is achieved, the source is removed, the solution thoroughly stirred, and the activity measured by immersing a Geiger

---

[1] Proposed by L. W. Alvarez.

counter in the solution, at the center. Let the counting rate be R_1:

$$R_1 = \alpha \int_0^\infty \Phi_1(r)\overline{\sigma_a(r)}r^2\,dr \qquad (125a)$$

[This method of "physical integration" is described by Anderson, Fermi, and Szilard (A23.)]

(2) Now mix uniformly into the same solution a known amount $(N'V')$ of $1/v$ absorber (they used finely divided manganese powder) which can be removed from the solution after irradiation. Irradiate to saturation, remove the absorber, and repeat the activity measurement on the solution:

$$R_2 = \alpha \int_0^\infty \Phi_2(r)\overline{\sigma_a(r)}r^2\,dr \qquad (125b)$$

Let $R = R_2/R_1$.

(3) It is finally necessary to obtain an absolute measurement of the total saturated activity (rate of neutron absorption) of the absorber:

$$I = 4\pi N' \int_0^\infty \Phi_2(r)\overline{\sigma_a'(r)}r^2\,dr \qquad (125c)$$

This step requires the absolute calibration of the radioactivity-measuring device and of the absorber sample used.

Now, since

$$Q = 4\pi\{N_{\mathrm{H_2O}} \int_0^\infty \Phi_1(r)\overline{\sigma_{\mathrm{H_2O}}(r)}r^2\,dr$$

$$+ N_{\mathrm{MnSO_4}} \int_0^\infty \Phi_1(r)\overline{\sigma_{\mathrm{MnSO_4}}(r)}r^2\,dr\}$$

$$= I + 4\pi\{N_{\mathrm{H_2O}} \int_0^\infty \Phi_2(r)\overline{\sigma_{\mathrm{H_2O}}(r)}r^2\,dr$$

$$+ N_{\mathrm{MnSO_4}} \int_0^\infty \Phi_2(r)\overline{\sigma_{\mathrm{MnSO_4}}(r)}r^2\,dr\} \qquad (125d)$$

and assuming that all absorption is $1/v$, which means

$$\Phi_2(r)\overline{\sigma_a(r)} = \left(\frac{\sigma_a}{\sigma_a'}\right)\Phi_2(r)\overline{\sigma_a'(r)} \qquad (125e)$$

in all possible combinations, it follows that

$$Q = \frac{I}{1-R} \qquad (125)$$

A minor modification and inversion of the same technique, first used by Segrè (S14), has been used for the most accurate comparisons of the absorption cross sections of hydrogen and boron by Whitehouse and Graham (W19) and others. Consider first a source in a tank of pure water:

$$Q = 4\pi N_{H_2O} \int \Phi_0 \overline{\sigma_{H_2O}} r^2 \, dr \qquad (126a)$$

Now dissolve in the tank some boron of density N_B; then

$$Q = 4\pi \{ N_{H_2O}' \int \Phi_1 \overline{\sigma_{H_2O}} r^2 \, dr + N_B \int \Phi_1 \overline{\sigma_B} r^2 \, dr \} \qquad (126b)$$

The activation integral is measured, in each case, with the same $1/v$ detector:

$$I_0 = \alpha \int \Phi_0 \overline{\sigma_a} r^2 \, dr$$

$$I_1 = \alpha \int \Phi_1 \overline{\sigma_a} r^2 \, dr \qquad (126c)$$

Since all the absorbers follow the $1/v$ law, we can apply Eq. (125e), whence

$$\left(\frac{I_0}{I_1} \right) = \left(\frac{N_{H_2O}'}{N_{H_2O}} \right) + \left(\frac{N_B}{N_{H_2O}} \right) \left(\frac{\sigma_B}{\sigma_{H_2O}} \right) \qquad (126)$$

The difficult step in any of the many methods of source calibration is the absolute determination, at one point, of the rate of absorption of a given absorber. Indeed, the various modifications simply shift this determination from one stage to another. This difficulty need only be solved once, however, for, after the yield of one source is known, the yield of any other source can be compared with the standard.

The methods of comparison are exactly those described above, with the exception that the detector does not require calibration. Thus, the ratio of the space absorption integrals (Eq. 125c) for two sources in the same medium, using the same detectors, is the ratio of the source yields. Actually, if the two sources are of the same type—i.e., same dimensions and the same energy spectrum—it is merely necessary to compare the detector activations at one point in the slowing-down medium.

In practice, the use of a resonance detector (e.g., cadmium-shielded indium) for obtaining the space activation integral is frequently more convenient, since the curves of resonance activation vs. r fall off more rapidly than for thermal neutrons. Since the activation of a resonance detector is proportional to the rate at which neutrons are passing through the resonance energy (see Section 4) and since, for the usual moderating media, there is no resonance absorption, the space integral for a resonance detector is also proportional to the source strength. This technique derives directly from the early experiments of Amaldi and Fermi (A20).

An entirely different method of source comparison and calibration can be used if a pile is available. Consider a pile which is exactly critical, i.e., there is one neutron produced for every neutron lost. If a source is placed in this pile, the neutron density will increase linearly with time, since there is no net loss of neutrons in an exactly critical pile. The rate of rise of the total number of neutrons in the pile, N, is

$$\frac{dN}{dt} = Q \qquad (127)$$

In practice, it is necessary to calibrate the pile and neutron detector, and to correct for the absorption by the source. This method is discussed by Bretscher (B63).

Alternatively, if the pile is slightly subcritical, and there is a source in the pile, the equilibrium neutron density will be determined by the condition that the rate of neutron loss equals the source strength. Since the rate of neutron loss from a subcritical pile is proportional to the neutron density in the pile, the equilibrium density will be proportional to the source strength, and it can be used (with proper calibration) as a measure of Q. The theory of this method has been discussed by Placzek and Volkoff (P18) and by Friedman (F44).

SECTION 4. THE INTERACTION OF NEUTRONS WITH MATTER IN BULK

A. Introduction

The preceding sections were devoted to the discussion of the interactions of neutrons with nuclei and of the instruments and techniques for the study of neutron phenomena. In this section we consider the successive interaction of neutrons with nuclei in large masses of material. For our present purposes the neutrons can be considered to behave incoherently, their interaction with the medium depending only on the densities and cross sections of the constituent nuclei. Coherent interaction phenomena, which depend on the structure of the medium, will be discussed in Section 5.

The subjects of this chapter are: (1) the diffusion of monoenergetic neutrons; (2) the slowing down of neutrons; and (3) slowing down and diffusion in multiplicative media. The treatment is "elementary"; by this we mean that simplifying assumptions are made in order to permit the handling of problems by well-known mathematical techniques. The emphasis throughout is on methods of computation which can be used, with comparative ease, in planning and interpreting experiments. These methods, although not exact, are sufficiently transparent so as to be useful for obtaining physical understanding of and insight into the phenomena under investigation.

The basis principles underlying the mathematic treatments in this section were laid down by Fermi (F17), soon after the discovery of the "Fermi effect"—the increase of neutron-induced radioactivity resulting from the interposing of hydrogenous material between source and detector (F14). In general, the diffusion of neutrons in a medium is governed by the Boltzmann equation: Let $f(E,\mathbf{r},\theta,\varphi,t)$ be the number of neutrons per cubic centimeter per steradian per unit energy interval with the energy E and direction of motion characterized by θ and φ at the position $\mathbf{r}$ and time t. Let N be the average nuclear density and σ, σ_s, and σ_a (all functions of E) be the average total, scattering, and absorption cross sections, respectively, at $\mathbf{r}$. The Boltzmann equation (which is the equation of continuity, or conservation of neutrons) is

$$\frac{\partial f}{\partial t} + \mathbf{v} \cdot \mathrm{grad}\, f = -N\sigma v f + \int_0^\infty dE' \int_0^{2\pi} d\varphi' \int_0^\pi N\sigma_s' v' f(E',\mathbf{r},\theta',\varphi',t) \cdot$$

$$p(E'\rightarrow E,\ \theta'\rightarrow\theta,\ \varphi'\rightarrow\varphi)\sin\theta'\, d\theta' + S(E,\mathbf{r},\theta,\varphi,t) \qquad (128)$$

In the above, the first term on the left side represents the rate at which neutrons are accumulating in a unit volume at the position in question; the second term is the net neutron current out of the unit volume. The first term on the right is the rate of removal of neutrons due to all interactions; the second term is the rate at which neutrons are being scattered into the energy and angle intervals in question. In this term the correlation function p is defined so that

$$\int_0^\infty dE \int_0^{2\pi} d\varphi \int_0^\pi p(E'\rightarrow E,\ \theta'\rightarrow\theta,\ \varphi'\rightarrow\varphi)\sin\theta\, d\theta = 1 \qquad (128a)$$

It is evident, on physical grounds, that p depends only on the initial and final energies and on the angle between the initial and final directions. The third term on the right represents the neutron source. Most commonly, we deal with an isotropic point source at, say, the position $\mathbf{r}_0$, in which case

$$S(E,\mathbf{r},\theta,\varphi,t) = \frac{s(E)\delta(\mathbf{r} - \mathbf{r}_0)}{4\pi} \qquad (128b)$$

where $\delta(\mathbf{r} - \mathbf{r}_0)$ is the Dirac delta function, and

$$\int_0^\infty s(E)\, dE = Q \tag{128b'}$$

In a multiplicative medium in which the absorption of a neutron gives rise to the isotropic emission of, say, k neutrons with the energy distribution $k(E)$ [i.e., $\int_0^\infty k(E)\, dE = k$],

$$S(E,\mathbf{r},\theta,\varphi,t) = \frac{k(E)}{4\pi} \int_0^\infty dE' \int_0^{2\pi} d\varphi' \int_0^\pi N\sigma_a' v' f(E',\mathbf{r},\theta',\varphi',t) \sin \theta'\, d\theta' \tag{128c}$$

The most common simplifications of the Boltzmann equation involve the introduction of the neutron density (neutrons/cm^3·unit of energy)

$$n(E,\mathbf{r},t) = \int_0^{2\pi} d\varphi \int_0^\pi f(E,\mathbf{r},\theta,\varphi,t) \sin \theta\, d\theta \tag{129a}$$

and the neutron flux

$$\phi(E,\mathbf{r},t) = \int_0^{2\pi} d\varphi \int_0^\pi v f(E,\mathbf{r},\theta,\varphi,t) \sin \theta\, d\theta$$

$$\Phi(\mathbf{r},t) = \int_0^\infty \phi(E,\mathbf{r},t)\, dE \tag{129b}$$

The elementary diffusion and slowing-down equations, to be discussed in this section, deal with these quantities.

The solution of the Boltzmann equation in its most general form (Eq. 128) is a formidable problem, especially for finite media. Considerable progress has been made in this field by investigators too numerous to permit complete enumeration by even the most conscientious of historians. Early extension of the theoretical work of Fermi was carried out by, among others, Wick (W23), Condon and Breit (C23), Goudsmit (G26), and Lamba (L1). Important advances toward the rigorous solution of the Boltzmann equation were made by Halpern, Luneburg, and Clark (H12, H13). The problem of slowing down by medium and heavy nuclei was treated by Placzek (P16), by Adler (A3), and, recently, by Bethe, Tonks, and Hurwitz (B27). Verde and Wick have devised useful methods for the approximate solution of the Boltzmann equation (V2, W25). A useful treatment of slowing down in hydrogenous materials has been presented by Flügge (F34).

During World War II, a number of teams of theoretical physicists, working in various laboratories in various countries, on the various "uranium projects," made important contributions to the solution of problems of neutron diffusion, slowing down, and multiplication; groups were led by Wigner (in Chicago), Nordheim (at Oak Ridge), Bethe (at Los Alamos), and Placzek (in Montreal). The progress in slowing-down theory is summarized by Marshak (M5). Much of the work of the English and Canadian groups has been reported in the *Canadian Journal of Research* (now *Canadian Journal of Physics*). A number of summaries have appeared in *Nucleonics*. The specific problems encountered in the atomic energy establishments in a number of countries still provide considerable impetus toward the solution of the fundamental problems of neutron diffusion.

The methods of elementary diffusion theory have been discussed by a number of authors. An excellent survey is contained in the notes for a course on Nuclear Physics given by Enrico Fermi (O5). Reference should also be made to a number of excellent articles in *The Science and Engineering of Nuclear Power* (F44, P20, S46, W13, and others), to *Elementary Pile Theory* by Soodak and Campbell (S47), and to Glasstone and Edlund, *Elements of Nuclear Reactor Theory* (G6a).

Another attack on the problems of neutron diffusion which has received considerable attention in the last few years takes advantage of the statistical (or random) nature of the fundamental neutron interaction processes. In this approach, commonly referred to as the "Monte Carlo" method, the progress of a single neutron is followed in detail from birth to death; the direction of emission, distance of travel, fate in a collision, change of direction in a scattering, etc., are all determined by resort to chance through the use of a table of random numbers. (The cast of a die would serve the purpose, if it could provide a wide enough range of alternatives.) The weighting of the various reactions is, of course, determined by the known properties of the neutron cross sections. By mapping the fate of a sufficient number of neutrons, each following its independently determined random flight, it is possible to derive the statistically average neutron behavior. The Monte Carlo technique is summarized by Kahn (K1).

B. Diffusion of Monoenergetic Neutrons

Under certain physically realizable circumstances, it is valid to make the following assumptions: (1) all the neutrons have a single (or average) energy, and neither gain nor lose energy (on the average) in collisions with nuclei; (2) all neutron sources produce neutrons of the same (average) energy; (3) the neutron absorption cross section is small compared to the scattering (or transport) cross section of the medium; (4) neutron distributions are considered only at distances from sources and boundaries which are large compared to the transport mean free path in the medium. Integration of Eq. (128) then yields an equation of continuity:

$$-\operatorname{div} \mathbf{j} + \frac{(k-1)}{\tau_a} n + q = \frac{\partial n}{\partial t} \qquad (130)$$

where $\tau_a = (N\sigma_a v)^{-1}$ is the mean life of a neutron against capture (sec), q the source density (neutrons/cm$^3 \cdot$sec), n the neutron density (neutrons/cm^3), k the number of neutrons produced per neutron capture, and $\mathbf{j}$ the current density (neutrons/cm$^2 \cdot$sec):

$$\mathbf{j} = -D \operatorname{grad} n = -\left(\frac{\lambda_{tr}v}{3}\right) \operatorname{grad} n \qquad (130a)$$

Combination of Eqs. (130) and (130a) gives

$$\nabla^2 n + \left[\frac{(k-1)}{L^2}\right] n = \left(\frac{\tau_a}{L^2}\right)\left(-q + \frac{\partial n}{\partial t}\right) \qquad (130')$$

with

$$L^2 = \frac{\lambda_{tr}\tau_a v}{3} = \frac{1}{3N^2\sigma_{tr}\sigma_a} = \frac{\lambda_{tr}\lambda_a}{3} \qquad (130'a)$$

The length L is known as the "diffusion length." Equation (130') is usually referred to as the "one-velocity elementary diffusion equation."

The elementary approximation can be improved, so as to be applicable to moderately absorbing media. For this case, Wigner (unpublished) has shown that Eq. (130') remains approximately valid with, however,

$$L^2 = \frac{\lambda_{tr}\lambda_a}{3(1 - 2\lambda_{tr}/5\lambda_a)} \qquad (130'a')$$

1. Stationary Distributions in Infinite Media. The effects of neutron multiplication will be considered in the discussion of the chain reaction. For the present, we consider uniform media (L and τ_a independent of $\mathbf{r}$) in which $k = 0$. Owing to the absorption, a stationary neutron density (different from zero) can be maintained only if there are sources somewhere in the medium. The stationary state ($\partial n/\partial t \equiv 0$) diffusion equation is, under these conditions,

$$\nabla^2 n - \frac{n}{L^2} = -\frac{\tau_a q}{L^2} \qquad (131)$$

We consider first the trivial problem of a uniformly distributed source, $q =$ constant $\neq 0$. In this case, if the medium is infinite, the solution is $n =$ constant. Since $\nabla^2 n = 0$, we have $n/L^2 = \tau_a q/L^2$, or $n/\tau_a = q$.

This merely tells us that, for a uniform source in an infinite medium, the equilibrium rate of neutron absorption is everywhere equal to the rate of neutron production.

(a) *One-Dimensional Case.* We consider next a plane source, of strength α neutrons per second per unit area, spread uniformly over the yz plane at $x = 0$. In this case, because of the symmetry, $n = n(x)$. At all $x \neq 0$, the source strength is zero, and the diffusion equation becomes

$$\frac{d^2 n}{dx^2} - \frac{n}{L^2} = 0 \tag{131a}$$

The solution to this equation, which vanishes at $x = \pm\infty$, is

$$n = Ce^{-|x|/L} \tag{131b}$$

The meaning of L, the diffusion length, is now clear; it is the distance over which the neutron density drops by a factor e. (For obvious reasons, L is also sometimes referred to as the "relaxation length.")

To evaluate the constant C, we recall that the net current across unit area is given by

$$j_x = -\frac{\lambda_{tr} v}{3} \frac{\partial n}{\partial x} \tag{130a'}$$

Considering a unit area in the yz plane at $0 < x_0 \ll L$,

$$j_{x_0} = \frac{\lambda_{tr} v}{3} \frac{C}{L} = \frac{1}{2}\alpha \tag{131c}$$

$$C = \frac{3}{2} \frac{L\alpha}{\lambda_{tr} v} = \frac{\alpha}{2}\left(\frac{3\tau_a}{\lambda_{tr} v}\right)^{\frac{1}{2}}$$

The same result can be obtained by setting the rate of neutron production equal to the rate of neutron absorption:

$$\int_{-\infty}^{\infty} \frac{n}{\tau_a}\, dx = \alpha \tag{131d}$$

In the above evaluation of C we seem, at first glance, to have overstepped one of the bounds of elementary diffusion theory (that the solutions are only valid at distances from the source greater than λ_{tr}), having assumed that $n = C$ at $x = 0$. However, this violation is not serious, provided that the capture cross section σ_a is very much smaller than the transport cross section σ_{tr}. In this case, $\lambda_{tr} \ll L \ll \lambda_a$, and it is valid to apply the continuity equation at a distance $\lambda_{tr} \ll x_0 \ll L$; the absorption of the source neutrons in the interval 0 to x_0 is negligible.

(b) *Point-Source Solution.* Consider a point source, of strength Q (neutrons/sec), in an infinite medium. If the neutron emission from the source is isotropic in space, $n = n(r)$, and, for $r > 0$ (the source is at $r = 0$), the diffusion equation is

$$\frac{1}{r}\frac{d^2(rn)}{dr^2} - \frac{n}{L^2} = 0 \tag{131a'}$$

The solution is

$$n = \frac{C}{r}e^{-r/L} \tag{131b'}$$

Setting the rate of neutron absorption equal to the source strength,

$$\int_0^\infty \frac{n}{\tau_a} 4\pi r^2 \, dr = Q \tag{131d'}$$

leads to

$$C = \frac{3Q}{4\pi\lambda_{tr}v} \tag{131c'}$$

The same result could, of course, be obtained by letting

$$Q = 4\pi r_0^2 j_{r_0} \tag{131c''}$$

with $\lambda_{tr} \ll r_0 \ll L$, and neglecting the neutron absorption within the (small) sphere of radius r_0.

It is of interest to note that the effect of the diffusion process is, in this case, to cause the neutron flux density to fall off as r^{-1}, at distances $\lambda_{tr} \ll r \ll L$ from the source; if the source were in a vacuum, the neutron flux density would, from the inverse square law, be

$$nv = \frac{Q}{4\pi r^2} \tag{131b''}$$

2. Stationary Distributions in Finite Media. (a) *Boundary Conditions at a Material-Air Interface.*

When the medium is finite, it is necessary to solve the diffusion equation subject to boundary conditions. Let us consider, first, a uniform mass of material of finite size, bounded by vacuum (air). Inside the material, the neutrons diffuse away from the source; because of scattering in the medium, some of the neutrons reverse their direction and return toward the source. Considering a small element of volume, located within the material, neutrons pass through the volume element in all directions; the net flux is, however, away from the source.

At the material-air boundary, the situation is different; those neutrons which leave the medium suffer no more scatterings. Hence, at the interface, there will be no flow of neutrons into the medium (toward the source). The neutron density will fall precipitously toward zero as the boundary is approached from inside the medium. A first approximation to the boundary condition is to set the neutron density equal to zero at the interface.

It is comparatively easy to improve upon this approximation. The problem is one of determining the neutron distribution in the vicinity of the interface. As a convenient model, we consider a completely non-absorbing ($\sigma_a = 0$, $\tau_a = \infty$) half space, with a uniform plane source on

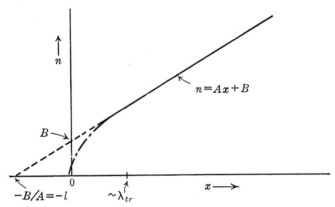

Fig. 58. Schematic representation of the neutron density in the vicinity of the medium-air boundary ($x = 0$). The solid line is the solution of the elementary diffusion equation; the broken line is its extrapolation. The dash-dotted line represents the actual neutron density in the region $x \lesssim \lambda_{tr}$.

the yz plane at $x = +\infty$; the region $0 < x < +\infty$ is filled with the non-absorbing, scattering medium. For this region, the diffusion equation is $d^2n/dx^2 = 0$, having the solution

$$n = Ax + B \qquad (132)$$

as depicted by the solid line in Fig. 58.

Since elementary diffusion theory tells us nothing about the actual behavior of the neutron density within a distance of $\sim\lambda_{tr}$ from the boundary (schematically represented by the dash-dotted line in Fig. 58), it is convenient to represent the solution in this region, for the purpose of analysis, by the continuation of the straight line.

The intercept (B) and slope (A) of the straight line solution must now be determined. For this purpose we have two conditions: (1) the net current across the boundary is

$$j(x=0) = -\frac{\lambda_{tr}v}{3}\frac{\partial n}{\partial x}(x=0) = -\frac{\lambda_{tr}v}{3}A \qquad (132a)$$

and (2) the flux at the boundary is all to the left, i.e., there are no neutrons returning to the medium from the vacuum. In order to apply
this second condition, it is necessary to go into some detail concerning
the angular distribution of the directions of motion of the neutrons in
the medium. Clearly, the distribution of directions cannot be isotropic,
since this would lead to zero current, and therefore to a uniform neutron
density. As a first approximation to the required distribution, we
assume

$$f(x,\theta) = f_0(x) + f_1(x)\cos\theta \qquad (132b)$$

where θ is the angle between the direction of the neutron's motion and
the x axis. This is equivalent to expanding f in terms of the spherical
harmonics, and neglecting all but the first two terms. The connections
between f_0, f_1, n, and j are obtained from the following identities:

$$n(x) \equiv \int_0^\pi f(x,\theta)\sin\theta\, d\theta = 2f_0(x) \qquad (129a')$$

$$j(x) \equiv \int_0^\pi vf(x,\theta)\cos\theta\sin\theta\, d\theta = \tfrac{2}{3}vf_1(x) \qquad (129b')$$

Thus,

$$f_0 = \frac{1}{2}(Ax + B) \qquad f_1 = -\frac{\lambda_{tr}A}{2} \qquad (132b')$$

Now, to apply the second condition, it is necessary to compute the out-
ward flux at $x = 0$,

$$j_{\text{out}}(x=0) \equiv \int_{\pi/2}^\pi vf(0,\theta)\cos\theta\sin\theta\, d\theta = v\left[-\frac{f_0(0)}{2} + \frac{f_1(0)}{3}\right]$$

$$= -v\left(\frac{B}{4} + \frac{\lambda_{tr}A}{6}\right) \qquad (132c)$$

Equating (132a) to (132c), $j(x=0) = j_{\text{out}}(x=0)$, we obtain

$$l = \frac{B}{A} = \frac{2}{3}\lambda_{tr} \qquad (133a)$$

An exact calculation (e.g., considering the rest of the expansion in Eq.
132b) gives

$$l = 0.7104\lambda_{tr} \qquad (133b)$$

The quantity l is known as the *extrapolation length*. Its use in describing the neutron distribution inside a finite, weakly absorbing medium,

bounded by air, may be described by the following statement: the neutron distribution can be computed as though the elementary diffusion equation held at all points inside the medium, including the boundary, with the boundary condition that the neutron density falls to zero at a distance $l = 0.71\lambda_{tr}$ from the physical edge of the medium.

Since the above derivation was based on the assumption that neutrons leaving the medium cannot return, the resulting boundary condition is clearly applicable to problems in which the diffusing medium is surrounded by a perfectly absorbing (black) layer. Thus, if we are concerned with the diffusion of thermal neutrons, the same considerations apply when the medium is surrounded by cadmium or boron. From the experimental point of view, it is in fact advantageous to surround the medium with one of these substances, rather than with air, since a black boundary will not allow neutrons to escape and, having escaped, to return (via room scattering) to the medium.

Returning to the problem at hand—the semi-infinite, non-absorbing medium—the neutron density is

$$n = Ax + B = A(x + 0.71\lambda_{tr}) \qquad (132')$$

For a source strength of α neutrons/sec·cm^2,

$$\alpha = -j(x) = \frac{\lambda_{tr}v}{3} A \qquad (132a')$$

and

$$n = \frac{3\alpha}{\lambda_{tr}v} (x + 0.71\lambda_{tr}) \qquad (132'')$$

(b) *One-Dimensional Case.*   Having established the necessary boundary condition, it is now possible to discuss media in which $\sigma_a \neq 0$. We consider the following problem: A uniform, weakly absorbing medium, extending from $-\infty < x < X' > 0$, contains a plane source of α neutrons/sec/cm^2 on the yz plane at $x = 0$; the region $x > X'$ is air. The diffusion equation for $x \neq 0$,

$$\frac{d^2n}{dx^2} - \frac{n}{L^2} = 0 \qquad (131a)$$

has the familiar solution in the negative half-plane

$$n(x < 0) = Ce^{x/L} \qquad (131b)$$

since n must vanish at $x = -\infty$. For $x > 0$, we must apply the boundary condition

$$n = 0 \quad \text{at} \quad x = X = X' + 0.71\lambda_{tr}$$

To satisfy this condition, it is necessary to use a combination of the two possible solutions of the differential equation (131a):

$$n(x > 0) = A^{x/L} + Be^{-x/L} \qquad (134)$$

with

$$n(x = X) = Ae^{X/L} + Be^{-X/L} = 0 \qquad (134a)$$

Thus

$$A = -Be^{-2X/L} \qquad (134b)$$

and

$$n(x > 0) = 2Be^{-X/L} \sinh \frac{X - x}{L} \qquad (134')$$

Finally, joining the solutions from the left and right at $x = 0$,

$$n(0) = C = 2Be^{-X/L} \sinh \frac{X}{L} \qquad (134c)$$

the neutron densities may be written

$$n(x < 0) = Ce^{x/L}$$

$$n(x > 0) = C \left(\sinh \frac{X}{L} \right)^{-1} \sinh \frac{X - x}{L} \qquad (134'')$$

The constant C is evaluated by adding the currents to the left and right, at small distances from the source:

$$\alpha = -j(x \gtrless 0) + j(x \gtrless 0) = \frac{\lambda_{tr} v}{3L} \left[1 + \frac{\cosh (X/L)}{\sinh (X/L)} \right] C \qquad (134d)$$

For $X \gg L$, the solution approaches that previously obtained for an infinite medium.

(c) *Conditions at the boundary between two media.* The situation is, of course, different when the boundary under consideration separates two media which have different neutron-scattering and -absorbing properties. In this case, neutrons leaving the first medium can diffuse back; the flow of neutrons at the boundary has components in both directions. Provided that there are no neutron sources on the boundary, the continuity equation requires at the boundary

$$n_1 = n_2 \qquad (135a)$$

and

$$j_1 = j_2 \quad \text{or} \quad \lambda_{tr1} \frac{\partial n_1}{\partial s} = \lambda_{tr2} \frac{\partial n_2}{\partial s} \qquad (135b)$$

The subscripts 1 and 2 refer to the two media, and the gradients are computed along the direction normal to the interface.

(d) *Solution for spherical symmetry.* As an example of the application of these boundary conditions, we consider a uniform sphere of radius R, characterized by the constants λ_{tr1} and L_1, containing at its center a source of Q neutrons/sec; the sphere is embedded in an infinite, homogeneous medium characterized by the constants λ_{tr2} and L_2. The stationary-state diffusion equation for spherical symmetry is

$$\frac{d^2(rn)}{dr^2} - \frac{(rn)}{L^2} = 0 \tag{131a$'$}$$

The solutions in the inside and outside media are, respectively,

$$n_1(r<R) = \frac{A}{r} e^{r/L_1} + \frac{B}{r} e^{-r/L_1} \tag{136a}$$

and

$$n_2(r>R) = \frac{C}{r} e^{-r/L_2} \tag{136b}$$

The constants A, B, and C are evaluated by applying the boundary conditions at $r = R$, giving

$$Ae^{R/L_1} + Be^{-R/L_1} = Ce^{-R/L_2} \tag{135a$'$}$$

$$Ae^{R/L_1}\left(1 - \frac{R}{L_1}\right) + Be^{-R/L_1}\left(1 + \frac{R}{L_1}\right) = \frac{\lambda_{tr2}}{\lambda_{tr1}} Ce^{-R/L_2}\left(1 + \frac{R}{L_2}\right) \tag{135b$'$}$$

and by applying the continuity equation close to the source, at $\lambda_{tr1} \ll r_0 \ll L_1$:

$$Q = -\frac{\lambda_{tr1}v}{3}\frac{\partial n_1}{\partial r}\Big|_{r_0} \cdot 4\pi r_0{}^2 \cong \frac{4\pi\lambda_{tr1}v}{3}(A + B) \tag{131c$'''$}$$

3. The Albedo Concept and Its Use. For diffusion problems involving two media, it is frequently convenient to lump all the boundary conditions into a single property, known as the *albedo*.[1] The albedo concept was first introduced by Fermi (F17). Its use, in problems involving the diffusion of thermal neutrons in hydrogenous materials, is discussed by Bethe (B24). The application of the albedo concept to the solution of problems in elementary diffusion theory is described in an excellent summary by Placzek (P20).

---

[1] Albedo (= whiteness in Latin) is used by astrophysicists for the ratio of reflected to incident light at the surface of a planet.

The albedo is simply the neutron reflection coefficient at a boundary. Let a and b denote two media with different neutron diffusion properties. The albedo, γ, at the interface between a and b is defined as

$$\gamma(a \rightarrow b) \equiv \frac{j_\perp(b \rightarrow a)}{j_\perp(a \rightarrow b)} \tag{137}$$

The albedo concept is useful because, from a knowledge of $\gamma(a \rightarrow b)$ and of the properties of medium a alone, it is possible to obtain the neutron distribution in medium a. This simplification is, however, somewhat illusory, since a calculation of the albedo involves, of necessity, the properties, nuclear and geometric, of medium b, as well as the application of the boundary conditions at the interface. Nevertheless, if the albedo is known, either experimentally or through previous calculation, the use of the albedo concept introduces a major simplification.

We again adopt, as a first approximation to the neutron flux distribution,

$$f(x,\theta) = f_0(x) + f_1(x) \cos \theta \tag{132b}$$

and obtain, by application of Eqs. (132c), (129a'), and (129b'),

$$j_\perp(b \rightarrow a) = \frac{nv}{4} - \frac{j}{2}$$

$$j_\perp(a \rightarrow b) = \frac{nv}{4} + \frac{j}{2} \tag{132d}$$

where both n and $j = -(\lambda_{tr}v/3)(\partial n/\partial s)$ are evaluated at the interface for the neutron density function in medium a. Using the general definition of the extrapolation length,

$$l \equiv -\frac{n}{\partial n/\partial s} \tag{133}$$

the albedo may be written

$$\gamma(a \rightarrow b) = \frac{(l - \frac{2}{3}\lambda_{tr})}{(l + \frac{2}{3}\lambda_{tr})} = 1 - \frac{\frac{4}{3}\lambda_{tr}}{(l + \frac{2}{3}\lambda_{tr})} \tag{137a}$$

This expression leads immediately to the previous result (Eq. 133a) for the extrapolation length when medium b is vacuum, by setting $\gamma = 0$.

(a) *Application to One-Dimensional Problems.* As an illustration of the use of the albedo in elementary diffusion problems, we consider again the neutron distribution in a uniform medium, extending from $x = -\infty$ to $x = X' > 0$, with a plane source at $x = 0$. The material filling the rest of space $(x > X')$ is specified only by the albedo, γ, at the boundary. From Eq. (137a) the extrapolation length is

$$l = \frac{2}{3} \lambda_{tr} \frac{(1 + \gamma)}{(1 - \gamma)} \qquad (137b)$$

In this (one-dimensional) case,

$$l = -\frac{n}{dn/dx} \quad \text{or} \quad \frac{dn}{dx} = -\frac{n}{l} \qquad (133c)$$

at the boundary. The solution of the diffusion equation, in the region $0 < x < X'$, is given by Eq. (134). At the boundary,

$$\frac{dn}{dx} = \frac{1}{L}(Ae^{X'/L} - Be^{-X'/L}) = -\frac{1}{l}(Ae^{X'/L} + Be^{-X'/L}) \qquad (133c')$$

Hence,

$$A = -\frac{(1 - l/L)}{(1 + l/L)} Be^{-2X'/L} \qquad (134b')$$

gives the required connection between the constants. For $l/L \ll 1$, we have $(1 - l/L) \simeq e^{-l/L}$ and $(1 + l/L) \simeq e^{l/L}$, giving

$$A \cong -Be^{-2(X'+l)/L} \qquad (134b'')$$

The assumption $l/L \ll 1$ is justified for weakly absorbing media $(\lambda_{tr} \ll \lambda_a)$.

(b) *Miscellaneous Considerations.* It is sometimes possible to calculate the albedo from first principles. Thus, for a neutron beam incident at an angle θ with the normal to the plane surface of a semi-infinite medium, Fermi (F17) has derived the albedo,

$$\gamma(\theta) = \frac{\sqrt{R} - 1}{\sqrt{R} + \sqrt{3} \cos \theta} \qquad (138)$$

where $R = \sigma_{sc}/\sigma_a$ for the medium on which the neutrons are impinging. It is seen that as $\sigma_a \rightarrow 0$ $(R \rightarrow \infty)$, $\gamma \rightarrow 1$; i.e., for a semi-infinite, non-absorbing medium, any neutron impinging on the surface will eventually return to the surface.

Fermi has also described a neat method of measuring the average value of γ for thermal neutrons. Consider a large mass of the material in question. A thin $(N\sigma T \ll 1)$ detector is placed in the medium at a position where the neutron density is relatively uniform; its saturated activity is found to be I_0. The same detector, with one side now shielded by cadmium, is placed at the same position; its new saturated activity is I_1. The ratio I_1/I_0 is related to the albedo, γ, as follows:

In the second situation, a neutron striking the detector from the un-shielded side will either activate the detector or be absorbed by the cadmium on the far side. The neutron has only one chance to activate the detector, and that only if it impinges on the no-cadmium side. In the first situation, on the other hand, neutrons pass through the detector from both sides. Since the detector is thin, the probability of passing unabsorbed through the detector is close to 1. A neutron which traverses the detector has the probability γ of returning once, the probability γ^2 of returning twice, etc. Thus, on the average, the total number of passages through the detector, for a single incident neutron, is

$$1 + \gamma + \gamma^2 + \gamma^3 + \cdots = \frac{1}{(1 - \gamma)} \qquad (139a)$$

Since (1) the neutrons have the same (small) probability of absorption per traversal in both situations and (2) the neutrons impinge on both sides of the unshielded detector and on only one side of the shielded detector,

$$\frac{I_1}{I_0} = \frac{(1 - \gamma)}{2} \qquad (139)$$

For example, for thermal neutrons in paraffin, $I_1/I_0 \approx 1/11$, which yields $\gamma \approx 0.82$.

4. Thermal Neutron Diffusion Lengths. From the preceding, we see that the neutron density is determined by two types of considerations: (1) the geometry of the source and medium; and (2) the neutron-scattering and -absorption properties of the medium. The solutions of the diffusion equation, for different geometries, have been summarized and tabulated by Wallace (W4). The nuclear properties of the medium are described in terms of a single constant, the diffusion length,

$$L \cong \left(\frac{\lambda_{tr}\lambda_a}{3}\right)^{\frac{1}{2}} \qquad (130'a)$$

The diffusion length is connected, in a simple way, with the average distance traversed by a neutron from its emission to its capture. For a point source in an infinite medium, the neutron density is

$$n = \frac{C}{r} e^{-r/L} \qquad (131b')$$

and the mean square distance from the source, to which the neutrons diffuse, is [1]

$$\overline{r^2} = \frac{4\pi \int_0^\infty r^2 n r^2 \, dr}{4\pi \int_0^\infty n r^2 \, dr} = 6L^2 \tag{140}$$

This relationship can also be derived from elementary considerations pertaining to the "random walk" problem (C12). Let $R = \sigma_{sc}/\sigma_a = \lambda_a/\lambda_{sc}$, the average number of scatterings per neutron capture. Then, from purely statistical considerations,

$$\overline{r^2} = 2R\lambda_{sc}\lambda_{tr} = 2\lambda_a\lambda_{tr} = 6L^2 \tag{140a}$$

Thermal neutron diffusion lengths have been determined in a variety of media. Such determinations have used pile thermal columns for sources, or they have involved observations on the thermal neutron densities resulting from fast neutron sources (see Section 4C). From the value of L, and given the value of λ_a, it is possible to derive λ_{tr}. The transport mean free path can also be obtained from a measurement of the extrapolation length l at a black boundary. Some values of L and λ_{tr} for thermal neutrons in commonly used media are shown in Table 31.

TABLE 31

THERMAL NEUTRON DIFFUSION LENGTHS AND TRANSPORT MEAN FREE PATHS

Medium	Density (g/cm^3)	L (cm)	λ_{tr} (cm)	References
H_2O	1.0	2.76 ± 0.03	0.425 ± 0.02	T13
Paraffin (CH_2)	0.895	2.42 ± 0.04	0.395 ± 0.02	T13
D_2O	1.1	171 ± 20	2.4 ± 0.1	S2, A37
Be	1.8	31	2.0	O5
C	1.6	51 ± 3	2.4 ± 0.1	H54, A37

[1] For the one-dimensional case of a plane source in an infinite medium, for which the neutron density is given by Eq. (131b),

$$\overline{x^2} = \frac{\int_0^\infty x^2 n \, dx}{\int_0^\infty n \, dx} = 2L^2 \tag{140'}$$

C. The Slowing-Down Process

The previous considerations apply when the average neutron energy remains constant through all the processes involved in the diffusion. In most problems of practical interest, however, the source emits intermediate or fast neutrons, which lose energy while diffusing. Since the energy distribution of the diffusing neutrons is of practical interest, techniques are required for the solution of the Boltzmann equation with variable neutron energy.

Neutrons can lose energy through inelastic and elastic scattering. The former is the most important for fast neutrons in media consisting of medium or heavy nuclei; the latter process predominates in media containing light nuclei, and is effective down to thermal energies. Because of the great difference between the mechanisms of inelastic and elastic scattering, the methods of treating the slowing down of fast neutrons are essentially different for light and for medium and heavy nuclei. Problems involving light nuclei are usually treated by the methods of "age theory." Inelastic scattering is inherently a much more complex process than elastic scattering, and the methods for describing slowing down by medium and heavy nuclei are correspondingly more complex and less accurate; we shall describe only one of these, "multi-group theory."

1. Multi-Group Diffusion Theory for Medium and Heavy Nuclei. We consider the following hypothetical problem: a homogeneous, isotropic medium, having N nuclei/cm³, contains sources of two types of neutrons, q_1 and q_2. The neutrons in either group can be scattered and absorbed. In addition, there is a process by which neutrons of group 1 are transferred into group 2, and a process by which neutrons of group 2 are transferred into group 1; these processes have cross sections $\sigma_{1,2}$ and $\sigma_{2,1}$, respectively. The diffusion of neutrons in each group is described by a one-velocity diffusion equation,

$$\frac{\lambda_{tr1}v_1}{3}\nabla^2 n_1 - N\sigma_{a1}v_1 n_1 + q_1 + N\sigma_{2,1}v_2 n_2 = \frac{\partial n_1}{\partial t}$$

$$\frac{\lambda_{tr2}v_2}{3}\nabla^2 n_2 - N\sigma_{a2}v_2 n_2 + q_2 + N\sigma_{1,2}v_1 n_1 = \frac{\partial n_2}{\partial t}$$

(141)

The absorption cross sections, σ_{a1} and σ_{a2}, include the cross sections for transfer ($\sigma_{1,2}$ and $\sigma_{2,1}$) as well as for any true absorption processes. Equations (141) differ from the ordinary elementary one-velocity diffusion equations (130) only in that each contains an additional source term connecting it to the other group. The solutions of these coupled differential equations are subject to the same types of geometric and boundary conditions as have been previously described for the one-group case.

The use of the two-group method for treating the slowing down of fast neutrons by medium or heavy nuclei is based on the assumption that a single inelastic scattering of a fast neutron is sufficient to reduce its energy to below the threshold for inelastic scattering. Under this condition, we can separate the neutrons into a "fast" and a "slow" group. It is assumed that these groups are relatively homogeneous in energy, and that the slowing down in either group, by elastic scattering, is negligible. Thus, "fast" neutrons are "absorbed" both by inelastic scattering and true capture, $\sigma_{a1} = \sigma_{af} + \sigma_{in}$, $\sigma_{1,2} = \sigma_{in}$; "slow" neutrons disappear only through true capture, $\sigma_{a2} = \sigma_{as}$, $\sigma_{2,1} = 0$.

As an example of the two-group method, let us consider a point source of "fast" neutrons in an infinite medium. Equations (141) become (for $r > 0$)

$$\frac{d^2(rn_f)}{dr^2} - \frac{rn_f}{L_f{}^2} = 0$$

$$\frac{d^2(rn_s)}{dr^2} - \frac{rn_s}{L_s{}^2} + \frac{rn_f}{L_{f,s}{}^2} = 0 \tag{141a}$$

where

$$L_f{}^2 = \frac{1}{3N^2\sigma_{trf}(\sigma_{af} + \sigma_{in})}$$

$$L_s{}^2 = \frac{1}{3N^2\sigma_{trs}\sigma_{as}} \tag{130'a''}$$

$$L_{f,s}{}^2 = \frac{v_s}{v_f 3N^2\sigma_{trs}\sigma_{in}}$$

These have the solutions

$$rn_f = Ce^{-r/L_f}$$

$$rn_s = Ae^{-r/L_s} + Be^{-r/L_f} \tag{141b}$$

with

$$B = \frac{L_f{}^2 L_s{}^2}{L_{f,s}{}^2(L_f{}^2 - L_s{}^2)} C \tag{141c}$$

The evaluation of the two remaining constants is achieved through the application of conservation conditions. (1) The source emits Q "fast" neutrons per second,

$$-4\pi r_0{}^2 \frac{\lambda_{trf} v_f}{3} \frac{dn_f}{dr}\bigg|_{r_0 \approx 0} = Q \tag{141d}$$

(2) All the emitted neutrons eventually suffer a true absorption,

$$4\pi N[\sigma_{af}v_f\int_0^\infty n_f r^2\,dr + \sigma_{as}v_s\int_0^\infty n_s r^2\,dr] = Q \qquad (141e)$$

The two-group approximation is not a very good one for most problems, mainly because inelastically scattered neutrons are by no means monoenergetic, and many of them may have sufficient energy to suffer further inelastic scattering. It is, of course, possible to subdivide the neutrons into three, four, or more groups, thereby improving the approximation. However, as the number of groups is increased, the mathematics very rapidly becomes excessively unwieldy. Less cumbersome and more accurate techniques for treating the slowing down of neutrons by medium and heavy nuclei have been developed by Placzek (P16) and by Bethe, Tonks, and Hurwitz (B27).

2. Slowing Down by Elastic Scattering. We consider the elastic collision of a neutron of energy E_0 with a stationary nucleus of mass number A. The energy of the scattered neutron is

$$E = \frac{A^2 + 1 + 2A\cos\theta}{(A+1)^2} E_0 \qquad (142)$$

where θ is the angle through which the neutron is scattered, measured in the center-of-mass coordinate system. If φ is the (observed) angle of scattering in the laboratory system,

$$\cos\varphi = \frac{A\cos\theta + 1}{(A^2 + 1 + 2A\cos\theta)^{\frac{1}{2}}} \qquad (143)$$

The extremes in the energy of the scattered neutrons are

$$E_{\max} = E_0 \qquad\qquad \text{for } \theta = 0$$

$$E_{\min} = \left(\frac{A-1}{A+1}\right)^2 E_0 \qquad \text{for } \theta = \pi \qquad (142a)$$

In order to obtain the energy distribution of the elastically scattered neutrons, it is necessary to know their angular distribution. Scattering by light nuclei, in the energy range of interest, is primarily S scattering; the distribution of scattered neutrons is isotropic in the center-of-mass coordinate system, the relative number depending only on the fractional solid angle,

$$dN(\theta) = \tfrac{1}{2}\sin\theta\,d\theta \qquad (144)$$

The differential energy distribution is, from Eqs. (142) and (144),

$$dE = - \frac{4A}{(1 + A)^2} E_0 \, dN(\theta) \tag{145}$$

or

$$\frac{dN(E)}{dE} = \frac{(1 + A)^2}{4A} \frac{1}{E_0} \tag{145'}$$

which is independent of E. The elastically scattered neutrons are *uniformly* distributed between E_{min} and E_{max}.

Equations (142) to (145') show that the *fractional* energy loss, either for scattering through a given angle or on the average, is independent of the initial neutron energy. Thus, if we plot the successive energies of a scattered neutron on a logarithmic energy scale, the intervals between points will, on the average, be equal. It is therefore most convenient to adopt, as the energy variable in the theory of slowing down of neutrons by elastic scattering, the logarithm of the energy, $\varepsilon \equiv \ln E$, rather than the energy itself.

In treating the slowing down of fast neutrons we are usually concerned with situations in which many collisions are required to reduce the neutron energy from its initial value to the energy at which it is detected. Under these circumstances it is sufficient to assume that the effects of all collisions are the same; i.e., that the energy loss per collision is given by its average value. On the logarithmic scale, this average is

$$\xi = \overline{\varepsilon_0 - \varepsilon} = \overline{\ln (E_0/E)} = \int_{E_{min}}^{E_{max}} \ln \frac{E_0}{E} \, dN(E)$$

$$= 1 - \frac{(A - 1)^2}{2A} \ln \left(\frac{A + 1}{A - 1} \right) \tag{146}$$

$$\xi \cong \frac{2}{(A + \frac{2}{3})} \qquad \text{for } A > 1 \tag{146a}$$

Some typical values of ξ are shown in Table 32. Thus, to reduce a 1-Mev neutron to thermal energies ($\frac{1}{40}$ ev) by scattering in hydrogen ($\xi = 1$) requires, on the average, $\ln (4 \times 10^7) = 17.5$ collisions; the same energy reduction by scattering in carbon requires $17.5/0.158 = 111$ collisions.

The mean square distance, from a point source (energy E_0), "diffused," while being slowed down, by neutrons of energy E, can be computed by the statistical methods of the "random flight." Assuming that σ_{sc} is energy independent, and provided that the neutron suffers

TABLE 32

VALUES OF THE AVERAGE LOGARITHMIC ENERGY LOSS PER COLLISION, ξ †

Element	H	D	He	Be	C	N	O	Fe	Pb
A	1	2	4	9	12	14	16	56	207
ξ	1	0.7254	0.4251	0.2066	0.1578	0.1363	0.1200	0.0353	0.0096
$2/(A + \frac{2}{3})$	..	0.750	0.429	0.207	0.158	0.136	0.120	0.0353	0.0096
$2/A$	..	1.00	0.500	0.222	0.167	0.143	0.125	0.0357	0.0097

† Also included in the table are approximate values, obtained from Eq. (146a) (line 3) and from the frequently used, but less accurate, $\xi \approx 2/A$.

many collisions while slowing down, $\overline{r^2}$ is given by Eq. (140a), with $R = [\ln (E_0/E)]/\xi$. Recalling that

$$\lambda_{tr} = \frac{\lambda_{sc}}{(1 - \overline{\cos \varphi})} \tag{147}$$

and, from Eqs. (143) and (144),

$$\overline{\cos \varphi} = \int_0^\pi \cos \varphi \, dN(\theta) = \frac{2}{3A} \tag{147'}$$

we obtain

$$\overline{r^2} = \frac{2 \ln (E_0/E)}{\xi} \frac{\lambda_{sc}^2}{(1 - 2/3A)} \tag{148}$$

If the scattering cross section depends on the neutron energy, Eq. (148) becomes

$$\overline{r^2} = \frac{2}{\xi(1 - 2/3A)} \int_E^{E_0} \lambda_{sc}^2(E') \frac{dE'}{E'} \tag{148'}$$

It is convenient to define a new parameter, analogous to the L^2 of one-velocity diffusion,

$$\tau(E_0,E) = \frac{\overline{r^2}}{6} \tag{149}$$

$\tau(E_0,E)$ is usually referred to as the Fermi "age."

(a) *The Age Equation.* Elementary diffusion theory can be applied to the description of the neutron distribution during the slowing-down process (in a manner first demonstrated by Fermi). For this purpose it is necessary to introduce, in addition to the space variables x, y, z, a fourth variable, corresponding to the neutron energy.   The natural variable to use for this purpose is $\varepsilon \equiv \ln E$.   The neutron density distribution in space and in energy is described by the function $n(x,y,z,\varepsilon)$, representing the number of neutrons per unit volume and unit logarithmic energy interval.

We consider first the stationary-state (time-independent) situation in a region of the medium far (as compared to λ_{tr}) from sources or boundaries: The net number of neutrons of energy ε, per unit ε, which diffuse into unit volume per unit time, is $D\nabla^2 n$, where, as before, $D = \lambda_{tr}(E)v/3$. There is another source of neutrons of energy ε which is due to the slowing down of higher energy neutrons: Neutrons of energy ε make v/λ_{sc} collisions per unit time.   Since they lose, on the average, the logarithmic energy ξ per collision, the rate at which neutrons leave the energy ε is

$$\frac{n(\varepsilon)\xi v(\varepsilon)}{\lambda_{sc}(\varepsilon)} \equiv q(\varepsilon) \tag{150}$$

Similarly, at the energy $\varepsilon + d\varepsilon$, the rate at which neutrons are being scattered into the energy interval $d\varepsilon$ is

$$q(\varepsilon + d\varepsilon) = q(\varepsilon) + \frac{\partial q(\varepsilon)}{\partial \varepsilon} d\varepsilon$$

Hence, for unit $d\varepsilon$ the rate of increase in the neutron density due to "slowing in" is $\partial q(\varepsilon)/\partial \varepsilon$, and the stationary-state diffusion equation, assuming no true absorption, is

$$D\nabla^2 n + \frac{\partial q}{\partial \varepsilon} = 0 \tag{151}$$

The new variable, $q(x,y,z,\varepsilon)$, called the "slowing-down density," represents the rate at which the neutrons (in unit volume at x,y,z, and unit logarithmic energy, at ε) pass through the energy ε.   It is most convenient to express the differential equation for slowing down in terms of q and τ, by using the relationships

$$\frac{\partial q}{\partial \varepsilon} = \left(\frac{\partial q}{\partial \tau}\right)\left(\frac{d\tau}{d\varepsilon}\right)$$

$$\tau = \frac{1}{3\xi(1 - 2/3A)} \int_{\varepsilon}^{\varepsilon_0} \lambda_{sc}{}^2(\varepsilon)\, d\varepsilon \tag{152}$$

$$\frac{d\tau}{d\varepsilon} = -\frac{\lambda_{sc}{}^2(\varepsilon)}{3\xi(1 - 2/3A)} = -\frac{\lambda_{tr}(\varepsilon)\lambda_{sc}(\varepsilon)}{3\xi}$$

Substituting, we obtain

$$\nabla^2 q = \frac{\partial q}{\partial \tau} \qquad (151')$$

The slowing-down diffusion equation, in this form, is known as the *age equation*, in analogy to the well-known heat conduction equation; the variable τ plays the same role in the slowing-down equation as does the time in the heat conduction equation. The analogy is, of course, not a complete one, since the slowing-down equation describes a stationary-state situation, while the heat conduction equation applies to transient phenomena. Furthermore, τ has the dimensions of the square of a length (thus, the occasional reference to it as the "slowing-down area"), rather than of time, so that τ is more strictly analogous to the variable $\kappa t/c\rho$ in heat conduction.

In this last sense $\tau(\varepsilon_0, \varepsilon)$ is related to the time required for the slowing down of neutrons, of initial energy ε_0, to the energy ε: Consider a neutron at the energy ε'. The average rate of energy loss, on the logarithmic scale, is

$$\frac{d\varepsilon'}{dt} = -\frac{\xi v(\varepsilon')}{\lambda_{sc}(\varepsilon')} \qquad (150a)$$

Hence the time required for slowing down to the energy ε is

$$t(\varepsilon_0 \rightarrow \varepsilon) = \frac{1}{\xi} \int_{\varepsilon}^{\varepsilon_0} \frac{\lambda_{sc}(\varepsilon')}{v(\varepsilon')} d\varepsilon' = \frac{2}{\xi} \int_{v_f}^{v_0} \lambda_{sc}(v) \frac{dv}{v^2} \qquad (150b)$$

since

$$d\varepsilon = \frac{dE}{E} = \frac{2\,dv}{v}$$

For $v_f \ll v_0$, the major contribution to the above integral comes from near the lower limit, in the region of which $\lambda_{sc}(v)$ is usually constant. Thus

$$t(v_0 \rightarrow v_f) \cong \frac{2\lambda_{sc}(v_f)}{\xi v_f} \qquad (150b')$$

For constant λ_{sc},

$$\tau(\varepsilon_0, \varepsilon_f) = \frac{\lambda_{sc}^2 \ln (E_0/E_f)}{3\xi(1 - 2/3A)} \qquad (148a)$$

whereupon

$$t(\varepsilon_0 \rightarrow \varepsilon_f) \cong \frac{6(1 - 2/3A)}{\lambda_{sc} v_f \ln (E_0/E_f)} \tau(\varepsilon_0, \varepsilon_f) \qquad (150b'')$$

The age equation (151') provides a complete description of the neutron distribution in space and in energy. If we consider an isotropic point source emitting Q neutrons per second of energy ε_0, in an infinite, homogeneous slowing-down medium, the solution of the age equation is

$$q(r,\tau) = \frac{Q}{(4\pi\tau)^{3/2}} e^{-r^2/4\tau} \tag{153}$$

The density function for neutrons of a given energy (ε) and correspond-ing age (τ) is

$$n(r,\varepsilon) = \frac{\lambda_{sc}(\varepsilon)}{\xi v(\varepsilon)} q(r,\tau) \tag{150'}$$

a Gaussian function of r, for which

$$\overline{r^2} = \frac{4\pi \int_0^\infty n(r,\varepsilon) r^4\, dr}{4\pi \int_0^\infty n(r,\varepsilon) r^2\, dr} = 6\tau(\varepsilon_0,\varepsilon) \tag{149'}$$

as expected.   The integral

$$4\pi \int_0^\infty q(r,\tau) r^2\, dr = Q \tag{153'}$$

is independent of the neutron energy and expresses the condition that, since we have assumed that there is no true absorption during the slowing-down process, the rate at which neutrons pass through any energy must, in the stationary state, be equal to the rate at which they are emitted from the source.

(b) *Solution of the One-Dimensional Age Equation in a Finite Medium.* We have already obtained the solution of the age equation for a point source in an infinite medium, Eq. (153). Correspondingly, for a plane source (at $x = 0$) of strength α (neutrons/sec·cm²), the solution is

$$q(x,\tau) = \frac{\alpha}{(4\pi\tau)^{1/2}} e^{-x^2/4\tau} \tag{154}$$

If, however, the medium is bounded by vacuum or by a perfect absorber at, say, $x = \pm X'$ (and infinite in the y and z directions) the boundary condition is $n(\pm X,\tau) = q(\pm X,\tau) = 0$ at $X = X' + 0.71\lambda_{tr}$.[1] A solu-tion of the one-dimensional age equation, with the above boundary condition, is

$$q_m(x,\tau) = A_m e^{-m^2\pi^2\tau/4X^2} \cos\frac{m\pi x}{2X} \tag{155}$$

where m is any odd *integer*.   The general solution is

$$q(x,\tau) = \sum_{m\ \text{odd}} q_m(x,\tau) \tag{155'}$$

[1] We assume here and in the following that the extrapolation length is independent of neutron energy; i.e., we use an average value of λ_{tr} for the determination of X.

The constants A_m are determined from the source distribution, $q(x,0)$, by the usual methods of Fourier analysis. For a plane source at $x = 0$,

$$A_m = \frac{\alpha}{X} \qquad (155a)$$

whence

$$q(x,\tau) = \frac{\alpha}{X} \sum_{m \text{ odd}} e^{-m^2\pi^2\tau/4X^2} \cos \frac{m\pi x}{2X} \qquad (155a')$$

The exponential factors in the above summation decrease rapidly with increasing m. For neutron energies not too far below the source energy or for very wide media ($\tau \ll X^2$) the exponential factors will be close to 1 for many terms, and all of these must be included in the summation. However, for relatively narrow media or low-energy neutrons, for which $\tau > X^2$, the terms with $m > 1$ may be neglected as compared to the first term, and

$$q(x, \tau > X^2) \cong \frac{\alpha}{X} e^{-\pi^2\tau/4X^2} \cos \frac{\pi x}{2X} \qquad (155b)$$

(c) *Thermal Neutron Distribution in the One-Dimensional Case.* After the source neutrons have been slowed down to thermal energies, they continue to diffuse at constant energy until either they are absorbed or they leak out through the boundary. The equilibrium thermal neutron diffusion equation is

$$\nabla^2 n_{th} - \frac{n_{th}}{L^2} + \frac{3q_{th}}{(\lambda_{tr}v)_{th}} = 0 \qquad (131')$$

in which the third term represents the source of thermal neutrons due to slowing down, $q_{th} = q(r, \tau_{th})$, and is obtained by the solution of the age equation.

In the one-dimensional problem considered above, with the condition $\tau_{th} > X^2$, the source is given by Eq. (155b). The solution of the thermal neutron diffusion equation, which satisfies the boundary condition $n_{th} = 0$ at $x = \pm X$, is

$$n_{th} = C \sinh \frac{(X - |x|)}{L} + A \cos \frac{\pi x}{2X} \qquad (155c)$$

with

$$A = \frac{(3\alpha/\lambda_{tr}v_{th}X)e^{-\pi^2\tau_{th}/4X^2}}{\pi^2/4X^2 + 1/L^2} \qquad (155d)$$

The evaluation of the second constant C is achieved by application of the condition that the net rate of loss of thermal neutrons, by absorp-

tion or leakage across the boundary, is equal to the rate at which they
are produced;

$$\int_{-X'}^{X'} \frac{n_{th}v_{th}}{\lambda_{a_{th}}}\,dx - \frac{2(\lambda_{tr}v)_{th}}{3}\frac{dn_{th}}{dx}\bigg|_{X'} = \int_{-X'}^{X'} q_{th}\,dx \qquad (155e)$$

(d) *The Three-Dimensional Case with Rectangular Symmetry.* Although the one-dimensional problem is illustrative of the simultaneous

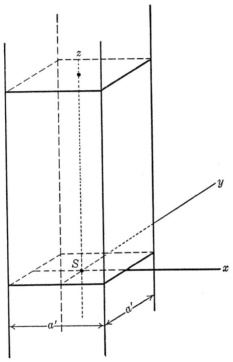

Fig. 59. Square parallelepiped with source on the axis, at the origin of the xyz
coordinate system.

solution of the slowing-down and thermal neutron diffusion equations
in a finite medium, it is of limited practical usefulness. Usually, the
fast neutrons originate from a point source, and the medium is finite in
all directions or, at best, effectively infinite (dimension of medium
$\gg \tau_{th}$) in only one direction. As an example of the type of problem
frequently encountered in experimental investigations, we consider a
square parallelepiped of slowing-down material, as illustrated in Fig. 59.
The source is on the axis, at the origin of the rectangular coordinate system. The medium is assumed infinite in the z direction, and to extend
to $x,y = \pm a'/2$. The source emits Q neutrons/sec.

The solution of the age equation (151'), with the boundary condition $q = 0$ at x or $y = \pm a/2 = \pm(a' + 1.42\lambda_{tr})/2$ and at $z = \pm\infty$, is most easily obtained by consulting a standard text on heat conduction:

$$q = \frac{2Q}{a^2(\pi\tau)^{\frac{1}{2}}} e^{-z^2/4\tau} \sum_{k,m \text{ odd}} e^{-(k^2+m^2)\pi^2\tau/a^2} \cos\frac{k\pi x}{a} \cos\frac{m\pi y}{a} \quad (156)$$

The rectangular geometry depicted in Fig. 59, with the above solution for the slowing-down density, has frequently been used for studying the properties of fast-neutron sources, with graphite as the moderating medium. By employing resonance detectors to measure $q(z, \epsilon_{res})$ it is possible to determine $\tau(\epsilon_0, \epsilon_{res})$ for the source and medium under investigation. The results of one such investigation, using a Ra-α-Be and a Ra-γ-Be source, have been summarized in Table 26 on page 400 ($z_0^2 = 4\tau$).

By substituting the solution for q_{th}, from Eq. (156), into the thermal neutron diffusion equation (131'), it should be possible to derive the thermal neutron density. While the exact analytical solution for n_{th} is quite complicated in this case, the asymptotic solution, valid for $z^2 > 4\tau$, is readily obtained. At such large distances from the source, q_{th} falls off exponentially with z^2 while, as will be seen, n_{th} falls off exponentially with z. Thus, at sufficiently large distances from the source, q_{th} can be neglected in Eq. (131'). The solution of

$$\nabla^2 n_{th} - \frac{n_{th}}{L^2} = 0 \quad (131'')$$

with the boundary conditions $n_{th} = 0$ at $x, y = \pm a/2$ and $z = \pm\infty$ is

$$n_{th}(z^2 > 4\tau) \cong \sum_{k,m \text{ odd}} C_{k,m} e^{-|z|/b_{k,m}} \cos\frac{k\pi x}{a} \cos\frac{m\pi y}{a} \quad (157)$$

with

$$\frac{1}{b_{k,m}^2} = \frac{(k^2 + m^2)\pi^2}{a^2} + \frac{1}{L^2} \quad (157a)$$

Owing to the inverse dependence of $b_{k,m}$ on increasing k and m, the higher terms in the summation are of rapidly decreasing importance. Thus, sufficiently high up in the column,[1]

$$n_{th}(z^2 \gg 4\tau) \approx C_{1,1} e^{-|z|/b_{1,1}} \cos\frac{\pi x}{a} \cos\frac{\pi y}{a} \quad (157b)$$

---

[1] The possibility of using the above approximations depends on having $L \gtrsim \tau_{th}$; otherwise, the thermal neutron density would be too small to be observed at distances from the source at which the approximations are valid. This condition is eased, somewhat, by the fact that it is possible to obtain highly efficient thermal

The thermal neutron densities along the axis of a graphite column, a' = 4 ft, for a Ra-α-Be and a Ra-γ-Be source, are shown in Fig. 60. It is seen that the densities assume an exponential dependence on z, for sufficiently large z, with the slope of the exponential independent of the

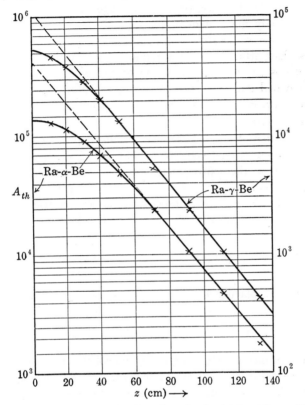

Fig. 60.   Thermal neutron densities along the axis of a 4 ft by 4 ft graphite column with the source on the axis. The data, due to Feld and Fermi (unpublished), are those plotted in Fig. 45; the methods of plotting differ, however.

source. Most of the values of L^2 quoted in Table 31 are obtained from the application of Eq. (157a), ($k = m = 1$) to such observations.

(e) *Slowing Down with Capture.*   In the usual treatment of slowing down problems by age theory, it is assumed that the capture cross sec-

neutron detectors, so that measurements can be made in regions of comparatively low thermal neutron density. Even so, for a substance like water the thermal neutron diffusion length is too small, and the solutions given above cannot be used. On the other hand, if the source contains only thermal neutrons (as, for instance, from the thermal column of a pile), Eq. (157) is valid for all z, and Eq. (157b) holds for $z > b_{1,1}$.

tion of the medium is negligible for neutrons above thermal energies. Although this is a valid assumption in most cases when the medium contains only light nuclei, problems are frequently encountered in which the medium contains an appreciable admixture of absorbing nuclei, e.g., heavy nuclei. In this case, the results of age theory can usually be employed with only slight modification.

If we define the quantity $p(\varepsilon_0, \varepsilon)$, equal to the fraction of all source neutrons which attain the energy ε in an infinite medium (p is called the "resonance escape probability"), the results of age theory (Eq. 151′) apply, provided that the quantity $q' = pq$ is substituted for q. Thus, the source term in the thermal neutron diffusion equation (131′) should be $3p_{th}q_{th}/(\lambda_{tr}v)_{th}$.

The evaluation of $p(\varepsilon_0, \varepsilon)$ proceeds as follows, provided that the slowing-down process is relatively continuous (i.e., $\xi \ll 1$): Starting with a single neutron at the source energy ε_0, the fraction which attains the energy ε' is $p(\varepsilon_0, \varepsilon')$. The probability of capture per collision is $\sigma_a/(\sigma_{sc} + \sigma_a) = \sigma_a/\sigma$; the average number of collisions, corresponding to the decrease in energy from ε' to $\varepsilon' - d\varepsilon'$, is $d\varepsilon'/\xi$. Hence

$$dp(\varepsilon_0, \varepsilon') = - \frac{\sigma_a(\varepsilon')}{\sigma(\varepsilon')} p(\varepsilon_0, \varepsilon') \frac{d\varepsilon'}{\xi} \tag{158}$$

Integrating, and placing $p(\varepsilon_0, \varepsilon_0) = 1$, we obtain

$$p(\varepsilon_0, \varepsilon) = e^{-\int_\varepsilon^{\varepsilon_0} (\sigma_a/\sigma) \, d\varepsilon'/\xi} = e^{-(1/\xi)\int_E^{E_0} (\sigma_a/\sigma) \, dE/E} \tag{158'}$$

Actually, in media containing heavy nuclei the absorption is mostly by resonance capture, with very large peak cross sections and relatively narrow widths, as compared to the average energy loss per collision. Thus, any given neutron has an appreciable chance of "jumping across" a resonance. However, if many collisions are made during the slowing down, and if many neutrons are involved, Eq. (158′) still yields the average probability of attaining the energy E.

3. Validity of the Age Equation; Slowing Down by Hydrogen. The use of age theory as discussed in the preceding is subject to certain limitations: (1) If the source emits neutrons of energy E_0, age theory can only be applied at energies such that $[\ln (E_0/E)]/\xi \gg 1$, since the age equation assumes continuous slowing down and, therefore, implies many collisions. In particular, $q(r, \tau = 0)$ for a point source is described by a δ-function in age theory, whereas in reality the source neutrons penetrate into the slowing-down medium before making their first collisions. (2) The last sentence implies that the spatial distributions, as given by the solutions of the age equation, do not apply close to the source; this is, of course, a limitation on all elementary diffusion theories. In the case of slowing down, the limitation applies most strongly to the higher-energy neutrons. (3) A further and serious deficiency of the age equation is that it yields the wrong asymptotic dependence of the neutron density on distance from the source for large $r \gg \tau^{\frac{1}{2}}$; this is not the case for the solutions of the one-velocity diffusion equation. The solution of the age equation, in an infinite medium, is a Gaussian function of the distance from the source. On the other hand, the collision probability, for the source neutrons, is an exponential function of the distance. While the Gaussian predominates at intermediate distances $(\lambda_{tr} < r \approx \tau)$, where it provides a relatively accurate description of the neutron density, the main contribution at very large distances comes from those neutrons which have penetrated to these distances without making many collisions.

The above-mentioned difficulties are all accentuated in the case of slowing down by collisions with hydrogen nuclei. In the first place, ξ has its largest possible value, namely 1, so that fewer collisions are required for the same energy loss. In the second place, the scattering cross section of hydrogen decreases rapidly with increasing neutron energy, so that the neutrons travel farthest between the first few collisions; this property has the effect of emphasizing the exponential nature of the asymptotic solution.

Various methods for taking into account the above-mentioned effects are summarized by Marshak (M5). Wick (W25) has derived useful expressions for the neutron density and energy distribution at *all* distances from the source in a medium for which λ_{tr} is independent of the neutron energy. Wick has also given asymptotic expressions for the neutron density and energy distribution in a medium for which λ_{tr} increases with increasing energy (as is the case for hydrogen). These results, although quite general, require numerical evaluation of complicated functions, and are therefore not easily applicable.

The general features of the slowing down of neutrons in hydrogenous media can be derived from relatively simple physical considerations, as follows: The cross section for scattering of neutrons by hydrogen (see Fig. 2, page 229) is relatively constant from $\sim$1 ev to $\sim$0.05 Mev; from $\sim$0.05 to $\sim$10 Mev, it falls rapidly, roughly like $1/v$; above $\sim$10 Mev, it decreases approximately as $1/E$. For neutron sources of $E_0 \lesssim 0.1$ Mev, age theory provides a reasonably accurate description of the slowing-down density. For fast neutrons, on the other hand, the first few mean free paths are long compared to the subsequent ones. After the first few collisions, the neutrons are slowed down and captured in a relatively short distance. This situation is schematically depicted in Fig. 61.

According to the above quite crude description, the slow-neutron distribution is essentially determined by the spatial distribution of the

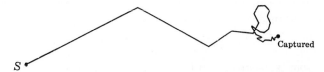

Fig. 61. Schematic representation of the slowing down and diffusion of an initially fast neutron, from birth to capture, in a hydrogenous medium.

first few collisions. At relatively large distances from the source, therefore, the slowing-down densities should be given by an expression of the form

$$q \approx \left(\frac{C}{r^2}\right) e^{-r/\lambda_{tr}'(E_0)} \tag{159}$$

where $\lambda_{tr}'(E_0)$ is of the order of, but somewhat larger than, $\lambda_{tr}(E_0)$.

The results of many investigations have shown that the asymptotic form of $r^2 q$ or $r^2 n_{th}$, for a point source of fast neutrons in a hydrogenous medium, is indeed exponential. The thermal neutron density for a Ra-

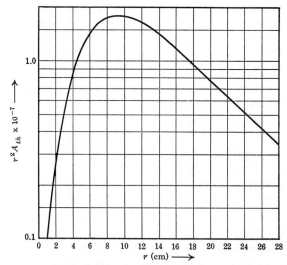

Fig. 62. Thermal neutron density from a Ra-α-Be source in water, due to Anderson, Koontz, and Roberts (unpublished). The curve for $r^2 n_{th}$ becomes exponential beyond $r \approx 15$ cm. The curve for $r^2 q$ (indium resonance), shown in Fig. 44, also becomes exponential at approximately the same distance from the source.

α-Be source in water is shown in Fig. 62.   It becomes exponential, with $\lambda_{tr}' \cong 10$ cm, at $r \approx 15$ cm.   Other sources have been similarly studied. Some observed values of λ_{tr}' for a paraffin moderator are given in Table 33.   The relaxation lengths are seen to be independent of the detector

TABLE 33

ASYMPTOTIC RELAXATION LENGTHS IN PARAFFIN FOR A NUMBER OF NEUTRON SOURCES †

Source	λ_{tr}' (cm)	
	Indium Resonance Detector	Thermal Neutron Detector
Ra-α-Be	9.3	9.3
Ra-α-B	6.6	6.7
Ra-γ-Be	1.8	3.2
Ra-γ-D	2.4	3.4

† Due to Bernstein and Feld (unpublished).

for the two fast-neutron sources; for the photoneutron sources, which emit neutrons of intermediate energy, the above considerations break down.

Other features of the slow-neutron densities from fast-neutron sources in hydrogenous media can be qualitatively understood in terms of the above arguments.   Some measured values of $\bar{r^2}$ in water and graphite are compared in Table 34, together with values of $\bar{r^2}_{th} = 6L^2$.   As can

TABLE 34

COMPARISON OF r^2 FOR VARIOUS ENERGY DETECTORS FOR A Ra-α-Be SOURCE IN WATER AND GRAPHITE

Detector	$\bar{r^2}$ in Water † (cm^2)	$\bar{r^2}$ in Graphite ‡ (cm^2)
Iodine resonance ($E \approx 40$ ev)	273	1,860
Indium resonance ($E \approx 1.4$ ev)	283	2,300
Thermal (dysprosium detector)	330	18,000
$\bar{r^2}_{th} = 6L^2 =$	45.7	15,100

† Munn and Pontecorvo (M41) and Tittle, Faul, Secrest, and Goodman (T11).
‡ Fermi (O5).

be seen, $\overline{r^2}$ in water is relatively independent of the energy of the neutrons detected; the same is far from true for a carbon moderator.

The above qualitative considerations can be put into a more quantitative form. For a point source, the effective source density is approximated by the density of first collisions:

$$q(r,E_0') = \left(\frac{Q}{4\pi\lambda_{tr}(E_0)r^2}\right) e^{-r/\lambda_{tr}(E_0)} \qquad (159')$$

with $E_0' = E_0/e$. The solution of the age equation (151') with this source can be obtained by numerical evaluation of the following expression, as demonstrated by Flügge (F34):

$$q(r,E) = \left(\frac{Q}{4\pi\lambda_{tr}(E_0)r^2}\right) xe^{-x^2}[F(a+x) - F(a-x)] \qquad (159a)$$

where

$$a = \left[\frac{\tau(E_0',E)}{\lambda_{tr}^2(E_0)}\right]^{1/2}$$

$$x = \frac{r}{2\tau^{1/2}(E_0',E)} \qquad (159a')$$

$$F(z) = \int_0^z e^{t^2}[1 - \Phi(t)]\, dt$$

$$\Phi(t) = \text{erf } t = \left(\frac{4}{\pi}\right)^{1/2} \int_0^t e^{-v^2}\, dy$$

Flügge has given numerical tables for $F(z)$ and $F(-z)$; these have been extended by Secrest (S13). The application of Eq. (159a) to the slowing down of fast neutrons by hydrogenous media has been studied experimentally by Tittle, Faul, Secrest, and Goodman (T11).

Another possibility has been suggested by Christy (unpublished). If the effective source (Eq. 159') is replaced by

$$q(r,E_0') = \left(\frac{Q}{4\pi\lambda_0^2 r}\right) e^{-r/\lambda_0} \qquad (159'')$$

the solution of the age equation can be obtained in terms of tabulated functions. The constant λ_0 is chosen so that the mean square distances of the two source distributions (Eqs. 159' and 159'') are equal:

$$\overline{r^2} = 2\lambda_{tr}^2(E_0) = 6\lambda_0^2 \qquad (159b)$$

D. The Nuclear Chain Reaction

The first self-sustaining nuclear chain reaction was achieved on December 2, 1942, in a squash court, underneath the west stands of the athletic field of the University of Chicago. On this occasion, a structure of graphite and uranium (appropriately called a "pile") was shown to be capable of attaining and maintaining relatively high neutron densities. This achievement was the culmination of investigations which started, in many laboratories, with the discovery of uranium fission by Hahn and Strassmann (H4) early in 1939; the work which led to the first pile was carried on mainly at Columbia University, Princeton University, and the University of Chicago, under the scientific leadership of Enrico Fermi, Leo Szilard, and Eugene P. Wigner. This work has been described in articles by Fermi (F19) and by Wigner (W28).

Concerning the individual and cooperative efforts which contributed to the successful operation of a nuclear chain reaction, much has been written. The early efforts of the French group are summarized in an article (submitted in 1939 and published in 1949) by Halban, Joliot, and Kowarski (H7) in which the fundamental ideas of the chain reaction are developed and in which the conditions for its achievement are explored. The first and third of these authors, having escaped from the German occupation with the French stock of heavy water, continued their experiments in England, together with a British group, under the general direction of Chadwick. The British group eventually moved to Canada, where the work finally resulted in the successful construction and operation of a $U-D_2O$ pile. The work of the British scientists is summarized in a report issued by the British Government (B66). The Canadian effort is summarized in an official Canadian document (C1). The work in this country is described in the Smyth report (S42), and a general historical survey is presented in a report to the United States Senate (U1).

Some of the properties of existing piles have been given in Table 27 (page 402). Further details, as well as some of the fundamental data required for pile design, will be given in a later part of this section.

The controlled nuclear chain reaction is made possible by the property of certain nuclei (U^{233}, U^{235}, Pu^{239}) of undergoing fission, with high probability, upon thermal neutron capture, and by the fact that, for these nuclei, the absorption of a neutron results, on the average, in the subsequent emission of more than one neutron. The main features of the fission process, which are important to an understanding of the chain reaction, are: (1) The number of neutrons per fission is sufficiently greater than 1 that some neutrons can be ultilized for purposes not involving the maintenance of the chain reaction. This circumstance makes possible the achievement of piles of finite, and reasonable, size. It also makes possible the utilization of the excess neutrons for the production of other fissionable nuclei (as in the plutonium-producing piles) or for the production of various radioactive nuclei, so useful in many fields of research. (2) The circumstance that a small fraction (<1 percent) of all the neutrons emitted when a fission takes place are given off after a short delay makes possible the control of the chain reaction. These "delayed" neutrons are emitted in the chain of radioactivity through which an unstable fission fragment attains stability. A delayed neutron can be emitted when a nucleus resulting from the β^--decay of one of the fission fragments has an excitation energy greater than the binding energy of a neutron in that nucleus; the period of delayed neutron emission is thus determined by the relatively long beta-decay periods preceding the neutron emission. (3) The fission process is accompanied by a relatively large energy release; ordinary radioactivity involves energies of a few Mev per reacting nucleus, while the energy release per fission is $\sim$200 Mev. Although this circumstance proves to be somewhat embarrassing in piles constructed for the primary purpose of attaining high neutron fluxes or for producing radioactive or other nuclei by neutron absorption (since the energy must somehow be disposed of), the large energy release introduces the possibility of a new and tremendously important power source.

In the following sections we describe the fundamentals of the nuclear chain reaction, and several approximate methods for computing the characteristics of chain-reacting systems. No attempt will be made to develop highly accurate theories, or to treat any particular system in detail. Nor will we include any discussion of the manifold interesting and complicated engineering problems associated with the construction of a pile or a nuclear power plant. In particular, attention will be confined to mixtures of fissionable and slowing-down (moderating) materials which mainly utilize thermal neutrons for the maintenance of the chain reaction.

1. Elementary Pile Theory. (a) *The Multiplication Constant.* The feature which describes the neutron-reproducing properties of a given mixture of fissionable and other nuclei is called the multiplication constant, k, and defined as the number of neutrons of a given energy which result, on the average, from a single neutron of the same energy in a single generation in an infinite medium. Clearly, $k > 1$ means that an unlimited reaction is possible; $k < 1$ means that a chain reaction cannot sustain itself.

The multiplication constant, k, can be computed provided that the neutron cross sections are known for all the elements in the mixture.

For a thermal neutron fission reactor, k can be decomposed into four separate factors:

$$k = f\eta\epsilon p \tag{160}$$

The first factor, f, is known as the thermal utilization. It represents the fraction of the thermal neutrons which are absorbed by the fissionable material proper. If the elements of the mixture are homogeneously distributed,

$$f = \frac{N_0\sigma_0}{N_0\sigma_0 + \sum_i N_i\sigma_i} \tag{160a}$$

where N_0 and σ_0 are the nuclear density and thermal neutron absorption cross section of the fissionable material, and N_i and σ_i are the densities and absorption cross sections of the other nuclei comprising the mixture. In the case of a lattice arrangement, f can be computed by application of the thermal neutron diffusion equation to the unit cell (W13).

The second factor, η, represents the number of neutrons emitted for each neutron captured by the fissionable material. It must be determined experimentally for a given fissionable material, and represents one of the nuclear constants associated with the material.

The third factor, ϵ, is known as the fast-neutron multiplication factor. $\epsilon - 1$ is the average number of additional fast neutrons produced by a single fast fission neutron, before it has been slowed down. $\epsilon - 1$ is appreciable only when the fissionable material is in the form of lumps (as in a lattice pile); in this arrangement, the fast neutrons resulting from thermal neutron fission pass through an appreciable thickness of fissionable material before they enter the moderator and are slowed down. As a fast neutron traverses the lump of fissionable material, there is a small, but finite, probability of inducing fission, thereby generating additional fast neutrons.

The fourth factor, p, is the resonance escape probability. It represents the fraction of all the fast neutrons which are slowed down to thermal neutron energies without being absorbed. (It is assumed that absorption in the resonance region is by a non-fission process, and does not produce additional neutrons.) On the assumption of a continuous slowing-down process in a homogeneous mixture, p is given by Eq. (158′).

Thus, if we start out with a single thermal neutron, f neutrons are captured by the fissionable nuclei, producing $f\eta$ fast neutrons; by the process of fast-neutron fission, this number is increased to $f\eta\epsilon$; as a result of resonance capture during the slowing-down process, the number of neutrons attaining thermal energies is $k = f\eta\epsilon p$.

When natural uranium is used as the fissionable material, it is advantageous to separate the uranium from the moderator. U^{238} exhibits strong resonance absorption; the light elements, used as moderating materials, have negligible absorption cross sections in the resonance region. It is therefore desirable to separate the region of strong resonance absorption, the uranium, from the region where the slowing down takes place, by introducing the uranium into the moderator in the form of lumps.[1]

While the maximization of p calls for large lumps of uranium, the need to keep f large opposes this tendency. Maximum f is obtained, for a given ratio of uranium to moderator, in homogeneous mixtures. When the uranium is in the form of lumps, the neutron density falls off toward the center of the lump, and the average neutron density in the moderator is greater than that in the lump, favoring neutron absorption in the moderator. For uniform dispersal, on the other hand, the neutron density, as seen by a uranium nucleus, is the same as that seen by all other nuclei.

The result of these conflicting requirements is that there is an optimum lump size, for a given uranium to moderator ratio, at which k is a maximum.

(b) *The Critical Size.* Given a configuration of fissionable material and moderator in which k (by definition the multiplication in an infinite medium) is greater than 1, there is a definite, finite size at which a neutron distribution, once established, will maintain itself, neither increasing nor decreasing in time; this size is called the critical size. The critical size is determined by the condition that the rate at which neutrons diffuse out, at the boundaries, be equal to the difference between the rate at which neutrons are produced and the rate at which they are absorbed. Thus, for a given mixture, the critical size depends both on the value of $k - 1$ and on the geometrical configuration of the finite medium.

As a first approximation, we shall assume that the neutrons are thermal throughout their entire lifetime, i.e., that they are both created and absorbed as thermal neutrons. We shall assume throughout that the

---

[1] An additional reason for separating the uranium from the slowing-down material arises out of the fact that, for lumps of uranium, resonance capture is essentially a surface phenomenon. Those neutrons in the resonance region which enter the uranium lump at one of the uranium resonance energies will be captured in a relatively thin layer on the surface of the lump. Other resonance neutrons, not at a uranium resonance energy, will have negligible capture probability, and will emerge from the lump to continue the slowing-down process. Thus, in order to maximize p, it is necessary for the lumps to have a small surface to volume ratio; this factor favors large lumps.

pile is homogeneous, neglecting the lattice structure except in its effect on the value of k. For a lattice arrangement, this assumption is justified as long as the critical size is large compared to the dimensions of the unit cell of the lattice. With these assumptions, the thermal neutron diffusion equation can be used to describe the neutron distribution:

$$D\nabla^2 n + \frac{(k-1)}{\tau_a}n + q = \frac{\partial n}{\partial t} \qquad (161)$$

The critical condition is characterized by the absence of neutron sources and the constancy of n with time:

$$q = \frac{\partial n}{\partial t} = 0 \qquad (161')$$

giving, for the equation which determines the critical size,

$$\nabla^2 n + \frac{(k-1)}{L^2}n = 0 \qquad (161'')$$

The nature of the solutions is determined by the boundary condition that $n = 0$ at a distance $0.71\lambda_{tr}$ beyond the edge of the medium. We consider three simple geometrical configurations; in each case the origin of the coordinate system is taken at the geometric center of the medium:

(1) Rectangular parallelepiped, of sides

$$a' = a - 1.42\lambda_{tr}$$

$$b' = b - 1.42\lambda_{tr}$$

$$c' = c - 1.42\lambda_{tr}$$

Taking the coordinate axes parallel to the sides,

$$n = C \cos\frac{\pi x}{a} \cos\frac{\pi y}{b} \cos\frac{\pi z}{c} \qquad (161a)$$

with

$$\pi^2\left(\frac{1}{a^2} + \frac{1}{b^2} + \frac{1}{c^2}\right) = \frac{k-1}{L^2} \qquad (161a')$$

Equations (161a) and (161a') give the critical neutron distribution and the dimensions of the critical pile.

(2) Right circular cylinder, with the axis along the z direction, of radius $R' = R - 0.71\lambda_{tr}$ and height $h' = h - 1.42\lambda_{tr}$. In this case,

$$n = CJ_0\left(\frac{2.4048}{R}\rho\right)\cos\frac{\pi z}{h} \qquad (161b)$$

with

$$\left(\frac{2.4048}{R}\right)^2 + \frac{\pi^2}{h^2} = \frac{k-1}{L^2} \tag{161b'}$$

where $\rho^2 = x^2 + y^2$ and $\zeta_0 = 2.4048$ is the first root of the zero-order Bessel function, $J_0(\zeta)$.

(3) Sphere of radius $R' = R - 0.71\lambda_{tr}$.

$$n = \frac{C}{(\pi r/R)} \sin \frac{\pi r}{R} \tag{161c}$$

$$\frac{\pi^2}{R^2} = \frac{k-1}{L^2} \tag{161c'}$$

The examples cited above illustrate the effect of the geometry on the critical dimensions of a pile. The nuclear characteristics are described by the quantity $(k-1)/L^2$. The general relationship

$$\frac{-\nabla^2 n}{n} \equiv B_0^2 = \frac{k-1}{L^2} \tag{162}$$

determines the critical dimensions. The quantity B_0^2 is frequently referred to as the Laplacian (a rather unfortunate adoption of a perfectly good and definite mathematical term) or as the "buckling."

With a view toward appraising the relative efficiency of different geometrical configurations of the same material, it is of interest to compare critical volumes. We cite three examples (neglecting the difference between the primed and unprimed dimensions):

(1) A critical cube ($a = b = c$):

$$V_c = \frac{161.5}{B_0^3} \tag{161a''}$$

(2) A critical square cylinder ($h = 2R$):

$$V_c = \frac{148.6}{B_0^3} \tag{161b''}$$

(3) A critical sphere:

$$V_c = \frac{129.9}{B_0^3} \tag{161c''}$$

$$V_c(1):V_c(2):V_c(3) = 1.244:1.144:1.000 \tag{161d}$$

The above description of the critical condition assumes that neutrons are born and die as thermal neutrons. Actually, the neutrons are born fast and must be slowed down before they are captured. An accurate determination of the critical dimensions therefore involves the simultaneous solution of the slowing down and the thermal neutron diffusion equations. In media to which age theory applies, the equations which determine the critical dimensions are

$$D_{th}\nabla^2 n_{th} + pq_{th} - \frac{n_{th}}{\tau_{ath}} = 0 \tag{163a}$$

$$\nabla^2 q_{th} = \frac{\partial q_{th}}{\partial(L_f{}^2)} \tag{163b}$$

together with the condition

$$\frac{n_{th}f\eta\epsilon}{\tau_{ath}} = q(E = E_0) \tag{163c}$$

[For convenience and to avoid confusion with the mean life for absorption, τ_a, we have adopted a new symbol for the Fermi age: $L_f{}^2 \equiv \tau(E_0,E_{th})$.]

The thermal neutron diffusion equation has the same solutions as given above for the case of no slowing down (Eq. 161″ and following). For the solution of the age equation, we can write

$$q_{th}(\mathbf{r},L_f{}^2) = n_{th}(\mathbf{r})q_{th}'(L_f{}^2) \tag{163b'}$$

Using the definition from Eq. (162), $B_0{}^2 \equiv -\nabla^2 n_{th}/n_{th}$, we obtain

$$q_{th}'(L_f{}^2) = \frac{f\eta\epsilon}{\tau_{ath}} e^{-B_0{}^2 L_f{}^2} \tag{163b''}$$

Substituting into Eq. (163a), the equation for the critical dimensions becomes (after introducing the appropriate definitions and combinations)

$$(1 + B_0{}^2 L^2) = ke^{-B_0{}^2 L_f{}^2} \tag{162'}$$

Equation (162′) reduces to Eq. (162) for $L_f{}^2 = 0$. Furthermore, under the (frequently applicable) assumption that the critical dimensions are large compared to the slowing-down and diffusion lengths ($B_0{}^2 L^2 \ll 1$ and $B_0{}^2 L_f{}^2 \ll 1$), Eq. (162′) becomes

$$B_0{}^2 \cong \frac{k-1}{L^2 + L_f{}^2} = \frac{k-1}{M^2} \tag{162''}$$

$M^2 \equiv L^2 + L_f{}^2$ is known as the migration area.

In hydrogenous media, the age equation approximation for slowing down no longer applies. In this case, we have seen that the slowing-down density in an infinite medium is more closely approximated by an exponential solution than by a Gaussian. This observation suggests that it may be more appropriate to use a diffusion equation to describe the slowing-down process, since the diffusion equation leads to exponential solutions. We are thus led to a two-group approximation, with the simultaneous diffusion equations

$$D_f \nabla^2 n_f + \frac{f \eta \epsilon}{\tau_{ath}} n_{th} - \frac{n_f}{\tau_{af}} = 0$$

$$D_{th} \nabla^2 n_{th} + \frac{p}{\tau_{af}} n_f - \frac{n_{th}}{\tau_{ath}} = 0$$

(163')

Since the solutions for n_{th} and n_f have the same space dependence, whence $-\nabla^2 n_{th}/n_{th} = -\nabla^2 n_f/n_f = B_0{}^2$, and since by definition $D_f \tau_{af} = L_f{}^2$, $D_{th} \tau_{ath} = L^2$, we obtain

$$(1 + B_0{}^2 L_f{}^2)(1 + B_0{}^2 L^2) = k$$

(162''')

Again, assuming pile dimensions large compared with L and L_f, the critical condition can be approximated by Eq. (162'').

In the elementary theory described above, it has been assumed that the pile is bounded by a perfectly absorbing medium (e.g., empty space). It is evident that a considerable saving in fissionable material can be effected by surrounding the pile with a medium capable of reflecting an appreciable fraction of the neutrons, which would otherwise leak out of the pile, back into the active region. The effect of such a "reflector" is to raise the average neutron density inside the active region (as compared to the bare pile situation), thereby increasing the ratio of neutron absorption to leakage; the critical size (of the active core) is correspondingly reduced.

The effect of reflectors can be treated, in the one-velocity approximation, by the methods developed in Sections 4B2 (*c* and *d*) and 4B3. The use of the albedo concept for the treatment of such problems has been discussed by Placzek (P20). A more accurate treatment, described by Soodak and Campbell (S47), considers the effects of thermal and fast neutrons separately, by use of the two-group diffusion approximation.

(c) *Pile Kinetics.* In the foregoing, the boundary conditions for a just-critical pile serve only to determine the shape of the neutron distribution; the magnitude is completely unspecified. Once the magnitude of the neutron density (the constant C in Eqs. 161a, 161b, and 161c) is chosen, it remains constant in time. In practice, however, the problem of achieving the required neutron density and of increasing or decreasing it at will is of considerable importance in pile operation. Control of the pile can be achieved by varying the value of k (by the insertion or removal of neutron-absorbing materials) or by varying the dimensions of the pile (which determine the rate of neutron leakage) from the critical dimensions.[1] In either event, it is necessary to consider the kinetics of pile operation.

The time which elapses between the fission absorption of a neutron and the emission of the fission neutrons is negligibly small (S45). Considerably more time is required for the slowing down of the fission neutrons, and much more time elapses while they diffuse as thermal neutrons before producing another fission. All these times are quite small, the emission time being $<10^{-8}$ sec, the slowing down time (in, say, a graphite moderated pile) being of the order of microseconds, and the thermal capture time being of the order of milliseconds. Were it not for the existence of the delayed neutrons, piles would be very difficult to control.

However, before proceeding to the consideration of the effect of the delayed neutrons on the time behavior of pile neutron densities, it is instructive to consider the time behavior of piles in which it is assumed that there are no delayed neutrons. In the following considerations, we neglect the comparatively small times required for prompt neutron emission and for slowing down, as compared to the thermal neutron diffusion time. For simplicity, we assume that the thermal neutron density is described by the equation

$$\nabla^2 n + \frac{(k-1)}{M^2} n = \frac{1}{D} \frac{\partial n}{\partial t} \tag{164}$$

Equation (164) provides a reasonable approximation to the thermal neutron distribution, provided that the migration length M is small compared to the pile dimensions, since it also takes into account the diffusion which accompanies the slowing down of the fission neutrons. It leads directly to Eq. (162'') for the critical size. However, as we shall see, some care must be exercised in using Eq. (164) to obtain the time dependence of the neutron density.

The general solution of Eq. (164) has the form

$$n(\mathbf{r},t) = n(\mathbf{r})e^{t/\tau} \tag{164a}$$

with the pile "relaxation" time, τ, given by

$$\frac{1}{\tau} = \frac{k - 1 - B^2 M^2}{M^2/D} \tag{164b}$$

where

$$B^2 \equiv -\frac{\nabla^2 n}{n} \tag{162a}$$

---

[1] The insertion of a very strong absorber (e.g., a control rod) may produce a sufficiently profound alteration in the neutron distribution to affect the leakage rate; indeed, this is the true basis for the effect of most control rods.

Depending on the initial conditions, $n(\mathbf{r}, t = 0)$ can have any form. The spatial part of the solution of the diffusion equation is then expressed as a Fourier series of the possible solutions of Eq. (164), each component having a different associated time constant. However, it follows from the dependence of τ on B^2 that only the fundamental solution need be considered, after a time of the order of a few times the τ associated with the fundamental. Neglecting higher harmonics, the neutron densities have the same spatial dependence as in the stationary state, e.g.,

$$B^2 = \frac{3\pi^2}{a^2} \quad \text{for a cube, etc.} \tag{161a'''}$$

The effect of the finite size is conveniently incorporated into the equations by defining a new quantity, the effective multiplication constant,

$$k_{eff} \equiv k - B^2 M^2 \tag{165}$$

For a pile of infinite dimension, $k_{eff} = k$. For $k_{eff} < 1$, $\tau < 0$ and the pile is subcritical; in supercritical piles ($\tau > 0$) $k_{eff} > 1$; in general,

$$\frac{1}{\tau} = \frac{k_{eff} - 1}{M^2/D} = \frac{k_{eff} - 1}{\tau_0} \tag{164b'}$$

The characteristic time, τ_0, is independent of the pile dimensions. Actually the expression $\tau_0 = M^2/D_{th}$ cannot be correct, since it assumes that both the slowing down and the thermal diffusion take place at thermal velocities. From purely physical consideration, it is evident that a more accurate expression is

$$\tau_0 = \tau_{ath} + t(\varepsilon_0 \rightarrow \varepsilon_{th}) \cong \tau_{ath} = \frac{L^2}{D_{th}} \tag{166}$$

in which τ_{ath} and $t(\varepsilon_0 \rightarrow \varepsilon_{th})$ represent, respectively, the thermal neutron diffusion time and the slowing-down time.

The characteristic times, associated with graphite moderated piles, are of the order of milliseconds, $\tau_0 \sim 10^{-3}$ sec. Assuming even a small, say ~ 0.1 percent, excess of k_{eff} over 1, the time constant for the exponential rise in neutron density, $\tau = \tau_0/(k_{eff} - 1) \approx 10^{-3}/10^{-3} = 1$ sec, is uncomfortably short. Fortunately, a small fraction of the fission neutrons are delayed by times of up to the order of minutes. These amount to ~ 0.7 percent of all the neutrons resulting from fission (H69).

In order to take advantage of the delayed neutrons to lengthen the pile time constant, it is necessary that $(k_{eff} - 1) < 0.007$. For, if $(k_{eff} - 1) > 0.007$, the delayed neutrons will have little effect in controlling the rate of rise of the neutron density, since the promptly emitted ("prompt") neutrons multiply at a faster rate than the delayed neutrons. However, if the dimensions of the pile are such that $0 < (k_{eff} - 1) < 0.007$, the prompt neutrons are, by themselves, not sufficient to cause the pile to be supercritical. The increase in neutron density is then dependent on the emission of the delayed neutrons, and the time constant of the pile is limited by the characteristic times, τ_d, associated with delayed neutron emission.

In considering the effects of delayed neutrons, it is useful to separate the pile multiplication constant into two parts,

$$k = k_p + k_d \tag{167}$$

If β (≈ 0.007) is the fraction of all the neutrons which are delayed in their emission,

$$k_d = \beta k$$

$$k_p = (1 - \beta)k \tag{167a}$$

Assuming, for simplicity and temporarily, that there is a single time constant, τ_d, governing the emission of all the delayed neutrons (τ_0 is the time constant for the prompt neutrons), the thermal neutron diffusion equation becomes

$$D\nabla^2 n + \frac{k_p - 1}{\tau_0} n + \frac{c}{\tau_d} = \frac{\partial n}{\partial t} \tag{164'}$$

in which c is the density of latent delayed neutron emitters (sometimes referred to as "pregnant" nuclei), for which

$$\frac{k_d}{\tau_0} n - \frac{c}{\tau_d} = \frac{\partial c}{\partial t} \tag{164''}$$

From the simultaneous solution of these equations, we obtain the neutron density as a function of time.

The equations are simplified by eliminating the space and time dependence as follows: Let

$$n = n_0 \, n(\mathbf{r}) \, e^{t/\tau}$$

$$c = c_0 \, n(\mathbf{r}) \, e^{t/\tau} \tag{164a'}$$

Then the simultaneous equations become

$$\frac{(k_{p\,eff} - 1)}{\tau_0} n_0 + \frac{c_0}{\tau_d} = \frac{n_0}{\tau}$$

$$\frac{k_d}{\tau_0} n_0 - \frac{c_0}{\tau_d} = \frac{c_0}{\tau} \tag{164'''}$$

where

$$k_{p\ eff} = k_p - B^2 M^2 = k_{eff} - k_d \qquad {}^1 \text{(165')}$$

The solution of the above equations by straightforward algebraic procedures results in

$$\frac{1}{\tau} = \frac{1}{2}\left\{ \frac{(k_{p\ eff}-1)}{\tau_0} - \frac{1}{\tau_d} \pm \left[\left\{ \frac{(k_{p\ eff}-1)}{\tau_0} - \frac{1}{\tau_d} \right\}^2 + \frac{4(k_{eff}-1)}{\tau_0 \tau_d} \right]^{\frac{1}{2}} \right\}$$

$$\text{(164b'')}$$

There are two solutions for τ, depending on whether the $+$ or $-$ sign is used. If $k_{eff} < 1$, both of these solutions lead to negative τ, or a subcritical pile. When $k_{eff} > 1$, only one of the solutions yields $\tau > 0$ (the $+$ solution); thus, if we are interested in the rate of increase of the neutron density after a reasonable time has elapsed, we need only consider this solution. We shall consider, in greater detail, two situations: (1) The pile is supercritical on the prompt neutrons alone ($k_{p\ eff} > 1$), with the lifetime for prompt multiplication much shorter than the delayed neutron lifetime. Formally, this condition can be stated as $\tau_0/(k_{p\ eff} - 1) \ll \tau_d$. In this case, the prompt neutrons govern the multiplication, and Eq. (164b'') reduces to

$$\tau_+ \cong \frac{\tau_0}{(k_{p\ eff}-1)} \qquad \text{(164b}_1\text{'')}$$

(2) The pile is subcritical on the prompt neutrons alone, but supercritical when the delayed neutrons are also taken into account. In this case, the multiplication requires the delayed neutron contribution and Eq. (164b'') is not easily simplified. However, under the assumption $\tau_d/(k_{eff} - 1) \gg \tau_0/(1 - k_{p\ eff})$, we obtain

$$\tau_+ \cong \frac{\tau_0}{k_{eff}-1} + \tau_d \left(\frac{1-k_{p\ eff}}{k_{eff}-1} \right) \qquad \text{(164b}_2\text{'')}$$

The assumption upon which Eq. (164b$_2$'') is based implies that the transient due to the prompt neutron multiplication is rapidly damped out.

The treatment of the real situation, in which there are a number of delayed neutron groups, each characterized by its emission fraction β_i ($\beta = \sum_i \beta_i$) and delay period, τ_i, follows by a straightforward generalization of the above considerations. Equation (164') is altered by the

---

¹ This relationship involves the assumption that the leakage probability for delayed neutrons is the same as for prompt neutrons.

substitution of $\sum_i c_i/\tau_i$ for c/τ_d; Eq. (164″) becomes j equations (for j delayed neutron emitters):

$$\frac{k\beta_i}{\tau_0} n - \frac{c_i}{\tau_i} = \frac{\partial c_i}{\partial t} \qquad (164''\text{a})$$

Assuming solutions of the form of Eqs. (164a′), we obtain the relationship

$$\frac{k_{eff} - 1}{k} = \frac{\tau_0}{k\tau} + \sum_i \frac{\beta_i \tau_i}{\tau + \tau_i} \qquad (168)$$

for the connection between the multiplication constant k, the pile geometry $k_{eff} \cong k - B^2M^2$, and the pile period τ. More accurate treatments (taking into account the slowing-down diffusion) are given by Soodak and Campbell (S47) and by Friedman (F44).[1]

In the foregoing considerations, transient phenomena have been neglected; nor have we considered the possibility that the pile constants may vary with time. Many problems of great interest in pile operation involve the insertion or removal of absorbers and the corresponding transient variations of the pile neutron density. Some techniques for the treatment of such problems, involving the use of Laplace transform methods, have been discussed by Soodak (S46). Another, rather ingenious, approach to the problem has been developed by Bell and Straus (B15), who have constructed a "pile simulator." This device is simply an electronic network for which the output is determined by a set of coupled differential equations, completely analogous to Eq. (164′) (appropriately modified to include all delayed neutrons) and Eq. (164″a). The variation of one of the pile constants is simulated by the appropriate variation of one of the components; the output gives the solution of the pile differential equations.

2. Some Pertinent Constants for Pile Calculations. In the preceding sections, methods have been developed for the calculation of pile properties: multiplication constant, critical size, period, etc. The application

---

[1] The calculation of the properties of nuclear chain-reacting systems has intrigued physicists ever since the announcement, by Halban, Joliot, and Kowarski (H5) in 1939, of the emission of fission neutrons, and especially after the report, by Roberts, Meyer, and Wang (R13) in the same year, of the delayed neutrons. Indeed, many more calculations have been made than published. (Theoretical chemists were concerned with the problems of chain reactions for many years before the discovery of fission.) Among the early calculations are those of Flügge (F33), Perrin (P12), Peierls (P9), and Zeldovitch and Khariton (Z2). More recently, a number of aspects of pile theory have been discussed by Salvetti (S1), by Gallone and Salvetti (G1), and by Stephens et al. (S55).

of these and similar methods has been described by a number of authors, e.g., in *The Science and Engineering of Nuclear Power*. For a specific computation, it is, of course, necessary to have a specific pile in mind.

The nuclear absorption, scattering, and moderating properties of various materials used in pile construction have been tabulated under the appropriate headings in previous parts of this work. In the following, we summarize the available data on the properties of uranium and plutonium. Most of these data—in particular, all the data necessary for the design of a thermal pile using natural uranium—have recently been publicized by the U. S. Atomic Energy Commission (U2).[1]

(a) *Thermal Neutron Cross Sections.* The thermal neutron (v_0 = 2200 m/sec) fission, radiative capture, and scattering cross sections of U^{235}, U^{238}, natural uranium, and Pu^{239} are summarized in Table 35.

TABLE 35

THERMAL NEUTRON CROSS SECTIONS † OF THE URANIUM ISOTOPES,
NATURAL URANIUM, AND Pu^{239} (U2)

	U^{235}	U^{238}	Natural U	Pu^{239}
$\sigma_{th}(n,f)$	549	0	3.92	664
$\sigma_{th}(n,\gamma)$	101	2.80	3.5	361
σ_{sc}	8.2	8.2	8.2	...

† All cross sections in barns.

(b) *Number of Neutrons per Thermal Fission of* U^{235} *and* Pu^{239}.

$$\nu(U^{235}) = 2.5 \pm 0.1$$

$$\nu(Pu^{239}) = 3.0 \pm 0.1$$

Using these values of ν and the data in Table 35, the constant η, the number of neutrons per thermal neutron absorption, is readily computed:

$$\eta(U^{235}) = \frac{549}{650} 2.5 = 2.11$$

$$\eta(\text{nat. U}) = \frac{3.92}{7.42} 2.5 = 1.32$$

$$\eta(Pu^{239}) = \frac{664}{1025} 3.0 = 1.94$$

[1] We quote these rather than the data previously published in the open literature, since these are based on more recent and, presumably, more reliable measurements.

(c) *Delayed Neutrons.*   The delayed neutron periods, τ_i, and their emission strengths, β_i ($\nu_i = \beta_i \nu$), for U^{235} fission, are summarized in Table 36 (from Soodak and Campbell, S47).   The delayed neutrons

TABLE 36

DELAYED NEUTRONS FROM U^{235} FISSION

Mean Life, τ_i (sec)	Percent of All Fission Neutrons ($10^2 \beta_i$)	Neutron Emitter (when identified)
0.07	0.029	. . .
0.62	0.085	. . .
2.19	0.24	. . .
6.51	0.21	. . .
31.7	0.17	Xe^{137}
80.2	0.026	Kr^{87}

$$\beta = 0.76 \times 10^{-2}$$

from Pu^{239} fission have substantially the same periods, but their partial yields, β_i, (and correspondingly the total yield, β) are reduced by a factor of ~ 2 from those of U^{235} (D7).[1]

(d) *The Energy Spectrum of Fission Neutrons.*   The fission spectrum is given (U2) by

$$\frac{dN}{dE} = e^{-E} \sinh (2E)^{\frac{1}{2}}$$

where E is in Mev.   This approximation is good to ± 15 percent up to $E = 17$ Mev.   The fission spectrum was shown in Fig. 43 (page 393).

(e) *Fission in U^{238}.*   The cross section for the "fast fission" of uranium was shown in Fig. 25 (page 348).   Using these data and the energy spectrum given above, it is possible (albeit tedious) to compute the fast-

[1] As previously pointed out, delayed neutron emission occurs whenever a beta-decay leaves the product nucleus in a state of excitation greater than the neutron binding energy (in the product nucleus).   The period of delayed neutron emission is, accordingly, the same as that of the preceding beta-decay or decays (if the neutron emitter is a link in a chain with more than one preceding member).   The neutron-emitting nucleus is given, for the two cases in which it has been identified, in Table 36.   It is noteworthy that both nuclei contain one more than a magic number of neutrons.   The first example of delayed neutron emission outside of fission was discovered by Knable, Lawrence, Leith, Moyer, and Thornton (K18); it is a 4.2-sec activity resulting from high-energy deuteron (and proton) bombardment of oxygen and some higher atomic number targets.   It was identified by Alvarez (A15) as resulting from the decay of N^{17} to an excited state of O^{17}, which immediately (in $\sim 10^{-21}$ sec) disintegrates into O^{16} plus a neutron.   Another delayed neutron emitter, Li^9 with an 0.168-sec halflife, has been found by Gardner, Knable, and Moyer (G3).   It was produced by high-energy deuteron and proton bombardment of beryllium and the elements immediately following it in the periodic table.

fission multiplication factor, ϵ, for a given size and shape of uranium lump. The AEC release (U2) quotes $\epsilon = 1.029$ for reactors of the "Gleep" and CP-2 variety (uranium square cylinders, diameter 2.25 in., weight about 6 lb, in a 8.25-in. cubic lattice in graphite), and $\epsilon = 1.031$ for reactors of the "Zeep" and CP-3 type (uranium rods, 1.1-in. diameter, in a 5.375-in. square lattice in heavy water).

(*f*) *Resonance Capture by* U^{238}. Anderson (A28) has measured the slow-neutron resonance capture properties of U^{238}. The lowest, and most important, resonance was found to have the following constants:

$$E_r \approx 11 \text{ ev} \qquad \Gamma \approx 0.20 \text{ ev}$$

$$\sigma_0 \approx 10,000 \text{ barns} \qquad \Gamma_{nr} \approx 0.0086 \text{ ev}$$

Anderson also obtained a value of the U^{238} resonance integral:

$$\int_{\text{Cd cut-off}} \sigma_a \frac{dE}{E} = 290 \text{ barns } (\pm 40\%)$$

The value of the resonance integral is used to compute the resonance escape probability p for a homogeneous mixture of uranium and non-absorbing moderator, by use of Eq. (158'). For uranium lumps in a moderating matrix, the computation of p involves the evaluation of the self-shielding effects. The above-mentioned AEC release (U2) quotes the following formula for the effective resonance integral for uranium lumps:

$$\text{"} \int \sigma_a \, dE/E \text{"} = 9.25 \, (1 + 2.67 \, S/M) \text{ barns}$$

where S is the surface area in square centimeters and M is the mass in grams.

There are, by now, a variety of nuclear reactors in operation. Their characteristics and properties have been described in a number of publications, to which references are given in Table 27 (page 402). Further details on the American reactor program are available in the literature (H3).

SECTION 5. COHERENT SCATTERING PHENOMENA WITH SLOW NEUTRONS

A. Introduction

Despite the early recognition by Elsasser and by Wick (E5, W24) of the possibility of coherent neutron scattering, the observation of neutron interference effects proved to be a formidable experimental problem.

The first indications of such effects (P29, M33) were far from spectacular. However, careful experimentation, mainly by groups at Columbia University and New York University (B28), established the existence of interference in neutron scattering and confirmed many theoretical expectations.

The difficulty of the early experiments stemmed from the inadequacy of the available slow-neutron sources. The conventional thermal neutron sources, e.g., Ra-α-Be in paraffin, provided relatively low intensities; furthermore, the broad energy spread in the neutrons from such sources tended to "wash out" the interference effects. The development of neutron velocity selectors (see Section 3) greatly broadened the range of possible investigations.

Among the important phenomena involving coherent neutron scattering which were demonstrated and investigated before World War II are: (1) the polarization of neutrons by passage through magnetized iron, the Bloch effect (B36); (2) the difference in the scattering of neutrons by ortho- and parahydrogen as predicted by Teller (T6). For a complete summary of these and other early studies, the reader is referred to a survey article by Van Vleck (V1).

Owing to the strength of available pile neutron sources, the situation with regard to the observation of neutron interference is now completely altered. Not only has it become possible to demonstrate and study a variety of such phenomena, using the results of these investigations to increase our knowledge of the interaction of neutrons with nuclei, but also neutron diffraction has been developed into a powerful tool for the study of the structure of matter. The variety and scope of possible investigations have been demonstrated by Fermi and Marshall (F21). The application to the study of matter has been reviewed by Wollan and Shull (W39).

In many important respects, neutron diffraction and x-ray diffraction phenomena are completely similar. (See Table 1 for the magnitudes of slow-neutron wavelengths.) This is strikingly illustrated in Fig. 63, a Laue photograph of the diffraction of *neutrons* by an NaCl crystal, taken by Wollan, Shull, and Marney (W40). Indeed, much of the theory of neutron diffraction can be obtained from standard x-ray texts, e.g., Compton and Allison (C22) and Zachariasen (Z1).

There is, however, a most important difference between slow-neutron and x-ray scattering: Neutrons are scattered by atomic nuclei, whereas x-ray scattering is due to the atomic electrons. This difference has a number of important consequences for the observed diffraction phenomena: (1) Neutron diffraction patterns are affected, with essentially equal efficiency, by both light and heavy elements, since slow-neutron scat-

(a)

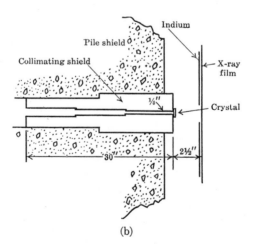

(b)

Fig. 63.   (a) Laue photograph showing neutron diffraction by a NaCl crystal; from Wollan, Shull, and Marney (W40).   (b) Schematic diagram of the Laue camera used to obtain the neutron diffraction pattern.

tering cross sections are of the same order of magnitude for almost all nuclei. In x-ray scattering, on the other hand, the cross section is proportional to the square of the number of atomic electrons, Z^2. Thus, in crystals containing both light and heavy elements, x-ray interference effects due to the light elements are usually masked by the presence of the heavy elements; this is not the case for neutron diffraction. (2) Slow-neutron absorption cross sections may be very large compared to scattering cross sections. In neutron diffraction by crystals containing strongly absorbing nuclei, the depth of penetration of the neutron beam is very much smaller than for x-ray diffraction. For such materials, surface impurities or irregularities may play a major role in determining the nature of the observed interference phenomena. (3) Because neutron scattering is a nuclear phenomenon, different isotopes of the same element behave, essentially, like different types of atoms. In addition, because of the strong spin dependence of nuclear forces, the scattering properties of a given nucleus may depend on the orientation of its spin with respect to that of the neutron. In x-ray scattering, on the other hand, isotopes of a given element behave in an identical fashion and, aside from minor effects of the electronic spin, x-ray scattering is independent of the atom's orientation. (4) In x-ray scattering, the "phase shift" of the scattered radiation is practically always negative. (A negative phase shift corresponds, as we shall see, to an index of refraction less than 1.) For neutrons, on the other hand, the phase shift of the scattered neutrons may be either positive or negative, depending on the position of the resonance to which the scattering is due; x-ray frequencies are practically always much greater than atomic electron resonance frequencies. However, as pointed out by Teller and Weisskopf (F21), potential scattering, for which the phase shift is negative, predominates in the scattering of thermal neutrons by most nuclei. For a more detailed comparison of x-ray, electron, and neutron diffraction, the reader is referred to review articles by Shull and Wollan (S28) and by Lonsdale (L21).

Although much of x-ray diffraction theory can be used without significant alteration to describe neutron diffraction, the differences are important enough to require re-examination, reinterpretation, and some modification of the theory. The basic principles of the theory of coherent neutron scattering were first enunciated by Wick (W24) and their development can be found in articles by Halpern and Johnson (H11), by Weinstock (W14), by Goldberger and Seitz (G10), by Akhiezer and Pomeranchuk (A5), by Finkelstein (F30), and by Cassels (C4). An excellent discussion appears in a compilation of notes on lectures by Fermi (O5). In the discussions in this section, the results of the theory will be stated where needed, without any serious attempt at derivation or proof.

In general, the scattering of neutrons of wavelength $\lambda = 2\pi/k$ can be described in terms of a set of "partial scattering amplitudes," c_l; the wave function at large distances from the scatterer has the form [1]

$$\psi \approx e^{ikz} + \sum_{l=0}^{\infty} \frac{c_l}{r} e^{ikr} P_l(\cos\theta) \tag{169}$$

In the special case (applicable to the scattering of slow neutrons by nuclei) of wavelength large compared to the dimensions of the scatterer, only the first term of the summation ($l = 0$, S-wave scattering) need be considered:

$$\psi \approx e^{ikz} - \frac{a}{r} e^{ikr} \tag{169a}$$

The first term represents the incident neutron beam; the second term, the scattered neutrons. The "scattering length" a is related to the scattering cross section [2]

$$\sigma_{sc} = 4\pi \left| a \right|^2 \tag{170}$$

As previously noted, the scattering length can have either sign. The minus sign in Eq. (169a) is chosen for convenience, in order to have a positive for a "normal" scatterer. However, in the vicinity of a resonance a can have either sign, and its magnitude is strongly dependent on the position of the resonance (see Section 2B, especially Fig. 5).

In the absence of appreciable absorption, a is real. The effect of absorption is to make a complex:

$$a = a_r + ia_i \tag{171}$$

The imaginary part of the scattering length is related to the absorption cross section:

$$\frac{a_i}{a_r} = \frac{2\pi}{\lambda} \frac{\sigma_a}{(4\pi\sigma_{sc})^{1/2}} \tag{171a}$$

[1] See, for example, L. I. Schiff, *Quantum Mechanics*, McGraw-Hill Book Co., New York, 1949.

[2] The scattering cross section, σ_{sc}, is usually given for free atoms. In many cases the neutron energy is much less than the energy of binding of the atom in, say, a crystal, and the atom behaves as though it had infinite mass. In this case

$$\sigma_{sc}(\text{bound}) = [(A+1)/A]^2 \sigma_{sc}(\text{free})$$

$$a(\text{bound}) = [(A+1)/A]a(\text{free}) \tag{170'}$$

(for the independent scattering by a single atom). Intermediate cases such as scattering by molecules will be considered when needed.

The preceding discussion applies to the scattering of a neutron beam by a single atom. In any practical case, however, it is necessary to consider the scattering by a sample containing a very large number of nuclei. Formally, this problem can be treated by appropriate modification of the solution of the wave equation (Eqs. 169 and 169a), wherein the second term in the neutron wave function, representing the scattered wave, becomes a summation over all the nuclei in the sample, each term with its appropriate scattering length a_j and distance $\mathbf{r}_j$ between the scatterer and the observer. Thus the resultant amplitude of scattering involves many terms, with a definite phase relationship between any two. Correspondingly, the resultant cross section, obtained by squaring the total amplitude (Eq. 170), is in general not simply equal to the sum of the individual atom cross sections since it includes, in addition, a second summation over the "cross terms." It is this second summation which gives rise to the interference or "coherence" effects which are the subject of this section.

Now, under the circumstances usually encountered in neutron scattering experiments, this second (interference) term in the scattering cross section can, to a very good approximation, be neglected. In this case, the nuclei are said to scatter "incoherently," and the total cross section of the sample is simply the sum of the individual atom cross sections. We illustrate this (normal) type of scattering with three examples: (1) Scattering by a monatomic gas or by a mixture of monatomic gases. Owing to the complete randomness in the distribution of atoms, the phase differences between waves scattered from the various atoms are randomly distributed. Since the number of atoms involved is always very large, the cross term ($\Sigma a_j a_k \sin \delta_{jk}$) in the summation will contain essentially equal positive and negative contributions and will therefore be very much smaller than the square term by a factor of $\sim N^{1/2}$, where N is the number of scatterers in the sample. (2) Scattering by a completely amorphous solid. This example differs from the previous one only in that the average distance between atoms is considerably smaller and in that the relative positions of the atoms are essentially fixed in time. Nevertheless, the random spatial disposition of the atoms is sufficient to insure that the interference term in the scattering is negligibly small. However, it is necessary to bear in mind, in this case, the difference between a truly amorphous solid and one which, although it appears amorphous, actually consists of very small crystals, randomly distributed; for the latter type of scatterer, coherence effects are observed, but we will postpone their discussion. (3) Scattering by an ordered array of atoms (crystal) of neutrons of wavelength very short compared to the interatomic distances. In this case, nature comes to our aid with the assurance that there is no such thing as an absolutely perfect crystal. If the nuclei were exactly fixed in space, the scattering from different atoms would always be coherent and the interference term in the cross section could never be neglected. However, for neutrons of very short wavelength, even a small random deviation of the atoms from their positions of perfect alignment is reflected in a randomness of phase and, consequently, in the vanishing of the cross-term summation in the scattering cross section. Such random deviations arise from crystal imperfections and from the thermal motion of the atoms about their equilibrium positions. Even in a perfect crystal at the absolute zero of temperature, the atoms are randomly distributed about their equilibrium positions owing to the zero-point oscillations of the atoms; as long as the neutron wavelength is small, as compared to the amplitude of these oscillations, the scattering will be incoherent.

At the opposite extreme, of neutron wavelength large compared to the interatomic spacings, the phase differences in the scattering by pairs of nuclei will be definite and (provided we consider always pairs with the same relative position in the crystal) fixed. In this case, the square of the total amplitude will, in general, be very different from the sum of the squares of the individual atom scattering amplitudes, and the scattering is said to be "completely coherent." Since the relative phases of the scattered waves depend on the direction of scattering (see Eq. 169a), the sum of the amplitudes, and hence the cross section, will depend on the direction of scattering, and the scattering cross section will exhibit strong variations with the angle of scattering. This coherent scattering from crystals will be taken up later.

In a large number of cases, the situation corresponds to neither of the extremes of completely coherent or incoherent scattering. For example, consider the scattering by a gas of polyatomic molecules of neutrons of wavelength large compared to the molecular dimensions. The scattering from the atoms in a given molecule is coherent, while the various molecules scatter incoherently. Another example is the scattering of long-wavelength neutrons by a liquid. Here, neighboring atoms may scatter coherently, but the coherence disappears as we consider the scattering of atoms farther apart. These are but two examples in which the material exhibits a "short-range order" together with a "long-range disorder." These and other examples will be discussed later in somewhat greater detail.

Thus far, our discussion of coherence differs from one which could be found in a textbook on physical optics only in that the word "neutron" is substituted for "x-ray." Indeed, one further effect, common to both fields, should be mentioned: scattering in the forward direction is *always* coherent. Indeed, as will be shown below, this coherence leads to a modification of wave propagation, in passing through a scattering medium, which can be described in terms of the "index of refraction."

There is, however, a type of "incoherence" which is not observable in x-ray scattering but which may be, and usually is, important in the neutron case. This is a phenomenon arising from the fact that different atoms of the same element may scatter with different amplitudes. Let us consider an element consisting of a number of isotopes, of relative abundances f_j and scattering lengths a_j. Now, if this element is contained in a sample from which the scattering is completely incoherent, the average scattering cross section per atom of the element is [1]

$$\sigma_{sc} = 4\pi \sum_j f_j \left| a_j \right|^2 = \sum_j f_j \sigma_{scj} \tag{170a}$$

It is this quantity which is generally obtained from transmission measurements with (say) resonance neutrons, and which is usually referred to as "the scattering cross section."

Suppose, on the other hand, that the element in question is in crystalline form (whether the crystal contains only the one or a number of elements is, for the present discussion, completely immaterial). We assume, for the moment, a perfect crystal from which we would, for the x-ray case, expect the scattering to be completely coherent. In the case of neutron scattering, we must take into account the fact that any one of the isotopes can occupy lattice position belonging to the element in question. Hence, as far as the coherent scattering is concerned, the element behaves as though its scattering amplitude is the isotopic average, and its effective cross section for coherent scattering is

$$\sigma_{coh} = 4\pi \left| \sum_j f_j a_j \right|^2 = 4\pi \left| a_{coh} \right|^2 \tag{170b}$$

However, because of the random distribution (weighted, of course, by the relative abundances f_j) of the isotopes among the lattice points belonging to the element in question, the crystal can no longer be considered perfect for neutron scattering. The effect of this "disorder" is to bring about an additional scattering which has all the attributes of incoherent scattering, e.g., independence of the scattering angle and

---

[1] The choice between using the "free" or "bound" amplitudes and cross sections depends on the state of the scatterer and on the neutron energy; thus, the first and third of the above examples require the "free" values, while the second usually demands the "bound" values.

of the neutron wavelength. The cross section, per atom of the element, for this incoherent (diffuse) scattering turns out to be

$$\sigma_{incoh} = \sigma_{sc} - \sigma_{coh} \tag{170c}$$

The above expressions are somewhat more transparent if we consider an element containing just two isotopes, with relative abundances f_1 and $f_2 = 1 - f_1$. Then

$$\sigma_{sc} = 4\pi(f_1 |a_1|^2 + f_2 |a_2|^2) \tag{170a'}$$

$$\sigma_{coh} = 4\pi |f_1 a_1 + f_2 a_2|^2 \tag{170b'}$$

$$\sigma_{incoh} = 4\pi f_1 f_2 |a_1 - a_2|^2 \tag{170c'}$$

From the above, we see that the degree of isotope incoherence is in direct proportion to the difference in the scattering properties of the two isotopes. For equal amplitudes, $a_1 = a_2 = a$, $\sigma_{coh} = \sigma_{sc} = 4\pi |a|^2$, and $\sigma_{incoh} = 0$.

Another special property of neutron scattering, which leads to similar incoherence effects, is the "spin dependence." In general, for a nucleus with spin I, the two possible spin states involved in the interaction with slow neutrons ($J_+ = I + \frac{1}{2}$ and $J_- = I - \frac{1}{2}$) have different scattering amplitudes, a_+ and a_-. For a random distribution of spin orientations or of neutron polarizations or both, the relative probabilities for scattering in the two states are $f_+ = (I + 1)/(2I + 1)$ and $f_- = I/(2I + 1)$. The element behaves, with respect to neutron scattering, exactly as though it were di-isotopic, with

$$\sigma_{sc} = 4\pi \left(\frac{I+1}{2I+1} |a_+|^2 + \frac{I}{2I+1} |a_-|^2 \right) \tag{170a''}$$

$$\sigma_{coh} = 4\pi \left| \frac{I+1}{2I+1} a_+ + \frac{I}{2I+1} a_- \right|^2 \tag{170b''}$$

$$\sigma_{incoh} = 4\pi \frac{I(I+1)}{(2I+1)^2} |a_+ - a_-|^2 \tag{170c''}$$

From the considerations outlined above, it is clear that the only certain case of completely coherent neutron scattering is for a perfect crystal containing monoisotopic elements of zero spin; to the usual sources of incoherence, described in the x-ray texts, we must always, for neutron scattering, add the possibilities of isotopic and spin incoherence.

There is an additional physical feature of spin incoherence which is experimentally observable. As shown by Wick (W24) and by Halpern and Johnson (H11), the existence of spin-dependent scattering is associated with a "spin-flip" process whereby polarized neutrons are depolarized on scattering. The probability of spin-flip, per scattering, is given by the expression

$$Q = \frac{2}{3}\left(\frac{\sigma_{incoh}}{\sigma_{sc}}\right) \tag{172}$$

This process has recently been investigated experimentally by Meyerhof and Nicodemus (M28).

Before we leave this general discussion, we take notice of two points:

(1) In the scattering by a di-isotopic element of spin zero or a mono-isotopic element with spin I, the cross sections are determined by two independent scattering amplitudes. However, their values cannot be uniquely determined by measurement of two of the three scattering cross sections, σ_{sc}, σ_{coh}, and σ_{incoh}. [*Note:* Owing to the relationship expressed by Eq. (170c), only two of these are independent quantities.] This circumstance arises from the fact that the cross sections involve the amplitudes in a quadratic relationship. Any given pair of measurements can, in general, be satisfied by two sets of amplitudes. The choice between these must be made on the basis of some other, independent, measurement; a number of such possibilities will be discussed.

(2) In addition to spin and isotopic incoherence, there are other sources of diffuse scattering, such as lattice imperfections and thermal motion (temperature-dependent diffuse scattering). These must be taken into account, either experimentally or theoretically, in the interpretation of neutron diffraction measurements.

As in the case of electromagnetic radiation, the transmission of neutrons through a material medium can be treated either from the microscopic point of view—as the superposition of the unscattered radiation and the radiation scattered by all the atoms in the medium—or by a macroscopic approach, in which the atomic scattering and absorption are summarized in two constants, the index of refraction n and the extinction (absorption) coefficient, κ. The net effect of the coherent superposition of the scattered amplitudes in the forward direction is to alter the propagation constant for the wave in the medium (as compared to vacuum), which is equivalent to ascribing to the medium an index of refraction.

The connection between the scattering length and the index of refraction can be obtained by a simple argument (O5), ascribed to H. A.

Lorentz. Consider the situation depicted in Fig. 64. A plane wave of amplitude $\psi_0 = e^{ikz}$ impinges normally on a thin, infinite slab of thickness T and density N atoms/cm^3. The wave amplitude at the point P, for $z \gg T$, is obtained by a coherent superposition of the incident wave

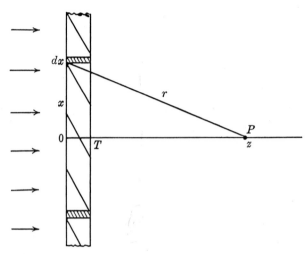

Fig. 64. Plane wave of slow neutrons impinging (from the left) on an infinite slab of scattering material. The symbols are those used in the calculation of the connection between the index of refraction and the scattering length.

(the attenuation by the thin slab is assumed to be negligible) and waves scattered by all of the atoms in the slab:

$$\psi_P \approx e^{ikz} - 2\pi NT \int_0^\infty \frac{a}{r} e^{ikr} x \, dx \qquad (169a')$$

Now, since $x^2 + z^2 = r^2$, whence $x \, dx = r \, dr$,

$$\psi_P \approx e^{ikz} - 2\pi NTa \int_z^\infty e^{ikr} \, dr \qquad (169a'')$$

Unfortunately, the integral in Eq. (169a'') is indeterminate at the upper limit. However, the contribution to the integral from large $x \gg z$ is expected to be weakened for a number of physical reasons (attenuation in passing obliquely through large thicknesses of the material, etc.). This can be taken into account by multiplying the integrand by a factor which decreases slowly from 1 to 0 as r goes from z to ∞. A common technique for evaluating the integral follows: Let

$$\int_z^\infty e^{ikr}\, dr = \lim_{(b^2 \to 0)} \int_z^\infty e^{ikr} e^{-b^2 r}\, dr = -\frac{e^{ikz}}{ik}$$

Then,

$$\psi_P \approx \left(1 - \frac{i2\pi NTa}{k}\right) e^{ikz} \tag{169b}$$

Now, if the net effect of the slab material is to alter the propagation vector (in the slab) from k to $nk (k \equiv 2\pi/\lambda)$, we may write

$$\psi_P = e^{ik(z-T)+inkT} = e^{ikz} e^{ik(n-1)T} \tag{169c}$$

and, for $(n - 1)kT \ll 1$,

$$\psi_P \approx [1 + ik(n - 1)T] e^{ikz} \tag{169c'}$$

Equating (169b) to (169c'),

$$n = 1 - \frac{2\pi Na}{k^2} = 1 - \frac{\lambda^2}{2\pi} Na \tag{173}$$

We note that for positive a, or "normal" scattering, the index of refraction is less than 1, just as for x-rays.

Equation (173) can be generalized to describe mixtures of nuclei and to include the possibility of neutron absorption (complex a):

$$n = 1 - \frac{\lambda^2 N}{2\pi} \sum_j f_j a_j \left[1 - \left(\frac{a_{ij}}{a_{rj}}\right)^2\right]^{1/2}$$

$$= 1 \mp \frac{\lambda^2 N}{2\pi} \sum_j f_j \left[\frac{\sigma_{scj}}{4\pi} - \left(\frac{\sigma_{aj}}{2\lambda}\right)^2\right]^{1/2} \tag{173'}$$

where $a_j = \pm(a_{rj}^2 + a_{ij}^2)^{1/2}$, the sign being determined by the sign of a_{rj}. The extinction coefficient of the medium (defined by $\psi = e^{ik(n+i\kappa)z}$ for the wave *amplitude* in the medium) is

$$n\kappa = \frac{N\lambda}{4\pi} \sum_j f_j \sigma_{aj} \tag{174}$$

It is to be noted that, under all but the most extreme conditions of absorption, $a_i/a_r \ll 1$. For example, assuming $\lambda \approx 10^{-8}$ cm and $\sigma_{sc} \approx 3 \cdot 10^{-24}$ cm^2, Eq. (171a) gives $a_i/a_r \approx 10^{20}\sigma_a$; a_i will be comparable to a_r only in case there happens to be an absorption resonance in the thermal energy range (e.g., cadmium). For most substances the factor a_i/a_r can be neglected in Eq. (173'). Assuming the above values for λ and σ_{sc}, and taking $N \approx 10^{23}$, substitution into Eq. (173) yields $(1 - n) \approx \pm 10^{-6}$; thus, effects of the index of refraction will be very small for thermal neutrons. Nevertheless, as will be seen subsequently, such effects are of considerable importance under certain circumstances.

Having outlined above the general considerations required for the interpretation of neutron diffraction phenomena, we now proceed to a summary of the experimental results. The investigations will be divided, rather arbitrarily, into three catagories: (1) studies of the structure of matter; (2) evidence concerning nuclear scattering properties, i.e., the scattering length; and (3) the production and use of beams of polarized neutrons.

B. Neutron Diffraction and the Structure of Matter

X-ray diffraction studies have yielded, and continue to yield, a vast amount of information concerning the ordered structure of matter. Most problems which are susceptible to study by x-ray diffraction can also be attacked by neutron diffraction techniques. However, mono-energetic neutron sources of sufficient intensity for such work (i.e., piles) are very few in number, and the intensity of these is still insufficient to enable the attainment of as good resolutions as with x-rays. The investigations with these sources have been concentrated on problems for which neutron diffraction provides information that cannot be obtained with x-rays. There are quite a number of such problems, and they are of great interest and importance. This section is intended as a summary of the results of work on a number of these.

1. Crystal Structure Studies. As illustrated by Fig. 63, Laue crystal diffraction patterns can be obtained with neutrons. Their interpretation (which is along the same lines as that for x-ray Laue photographs) has been discussed by Shull and Wollan (S28, W39). However, as in the x-ray case, most crystal structure studies involve the observation of Bragg reflections from single crystals or from crystalline powders (the Debye-Scherrer-Hull technique).

Bragg reflection of slow neutrons has been discussed previously on pages 434 to 439 in connection with the production of monoenergetic slow neutrons. Given a monoenergetic slow-neutron beam (wavelength λ), the reflection of this beam from a single crystal shows strong maxima at angles given by the Bragg condition,

$$m\lambda = 2d \sin \theta \tag{175}$$

where m is an integer, d the distance between crystal planes, and θ the angle, of incidence and reflection, between the neutron beam and the crystal planes.

Measurement of the angles of Bragg reflection yield the distances between crystal planes; information concerning the relative positions of different atoms in the crystal can be obtained from the relative intensities of Bragg scattering in different orders or for different sets of crystal planes. The intensity of Bragg scattering is determined by the "form factor," defined as the effective coherent scattering amplitude per unit cell of the crystal:

$$F = \left| \sum_j a_j e^{2\pi i m d_j / d} \right| \tag{176}$$

In Eq. (176) the subscript j refers to the various atoms in the unit cell; the a_j's are their scattering lengths. d_j is the perpendicular distance of the jth atom from a given member of the set of crystal planes under consideration.

The effect of the form factor on the relative intensities of Bragg maxima is illustrated in the following example: Consider the scattering from a face-centered cubic crystal containing two types of atoms in which the planes are equidistant and contain, alternately, only one element. The (1,1,1) planes of sodium chloride or lithium chloride are examples of such a configuration for which $d_2 = d_1 + d/2$. From Eq. (176), $F(m=1) = |a_1 - a_2|$ and $F(m=2) = |a_1 + a_2|$, since $e^{im\pi} = (-1)^m$. Thus, for such a crystal the successive orders of Bragg reflection from the (1,1,1) planes will alternate in intensity, either the even or odd orders being more intense, depending on whether the signs of a_1 and a_2 are like or opposite. Measurements of intensity will, in this case, lead to an assignment of the relative signs of the scattering amplitudes, but this is the subject of a later discussion. From the point of view of determining the crystal structure, it is clear that the measured intensities in different orders and in the scattering from different crystal planes will, in general, be consistent with very few (frequently only one) structure possibilities.

Large single crystals are relatively hard to come by, and those which are available are frequently imperfect. Crystal imperfections (e.g., a mosaic structure in which the subcrystals are not exactly aligned) are an additional source of incoherent scattering. For these reasons, and because of the greater ease in obtaining data, the Debye-Scherrer-Hull crystalline powder technique has been widely used in diffraction studies. The powder diffraction technique has the additional advantage that it is the most reliable means for obtaining absolute values of the scattered neutron intensity.

It is to be noted that the minimum size of crystal required to obtain well-resolved Bragg scattering patterns is quite small, of the order of 10^{-4} cm on a side. We can estimate the depth of penetration of neutrons into the crystal, for scattering at a Bragg angle, as follows: Let the crystal have surface area A and density of unit cells N_0. Assuming the depth of penetration δ, the number of coherently scattering cells is $N_0 A \delta$. For an incident beam of unit intensity, the amplitude of the beam scattered by each unit cell is F/r; thus, the total coherently scattered intensity is

$$\left(\frac{F}{r} N_0 A \delta\right)^2 \times (\text{Area of the scattered beam})$$

(r is the distance from the crystal to the detector.) Owing to the finite area subtended by the crystal, the scattered intensity is concentrated within the finite solid angle $\lambda^2/A \sin \theta$, or over the finite area $\lambda^2 r^2/A \sin \theta$. Equating the total scattered intensity to the incident intensity subtended, and assumed removed from the beam, by the crystal,

$$\left(\frac{F}{r} N_0 A \delta\right)^2 \frac{\lambda^2 r^2}{A \sin \theta} \approx A \sin \theta$$

or

$$\delta \approx \frac{\sin \theta}{N_0 \lambda F} = \frac{m}{2d N_0 F} \qquad (177)$$

Letting $m = 1$, $d \approx 10^{-8}$ cm, $N_0 \approx 1/d^3 \approx 10^{24}/\text{cm}^3$, $F \approx (\frac{1}{2}) \cdot 10^{-12}$ cm, we obtain $\delta \approx 10^{-4}$ cm, or $\sim 10^4$ atomic layers. Thus, microcrystals of volume $\gtrsim 10^{-12}$ cm^3 will effectively scatter all the neutrons which strike them at one of the Bragg angles.

The crystalline powder diffraction technique has been extensively applied to the study of crystal structure and associated problems, mainly by Wollan and Shull (W41) and co-workers. The arrangement of their spectrometer is shown in Fig. 65, together with a number of typical diffraction patterns obtained therewith.

The main advantage of neutrons over x-rays, however, is shown in the study of crystals containing light elements, *especially hydrogen.* X-ray diffraction studies usually fail to detect the presence of hydrogen because of the proportionality of the scattering amplitude to the atomic number Z. However, unfortunately for the neutron case, although the bound scattering cross section of the proton is abnormally large (80 barns), the scattering of neutrons by protons is very strongly spin dependent; the coherent bound neutron-proton scattering cross section turns out to be rather small (2 barns). Nevertheless, this cross section is of the same order of magnitude as that for heavier nuclei, so that the presence of hydrogen can be detected in crystal diffraction patterns, provided that the diffraction effects can be observed over the large incoherent scattering background.

It turns out that deuterium has a much more favorable ratio of coherent to incoherent scattering cross sections ($\sigma_{coh} = 5.2b$, $\sigma_{sc} = 7.4b$, both for bound deuterons) than the lighter isotope.   Hence, when

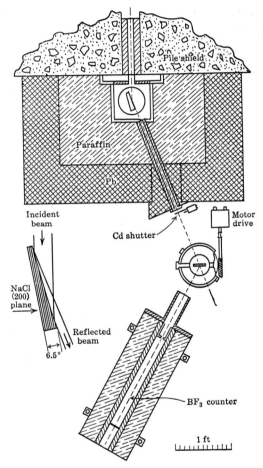

Fig. 65a.   Spectrometer of Wollan and Shull (W41) for the study of crystalline powder diffraction patterns.

deuterium-substituted crystals are available, the diffraction measurements are much easier to perform.   Thus, using a powdered sample of heavy water crystals, Wollan, Davidson, and Shull (W42) have studied the crystal structure of ice at $-90°C$; they have shown that the observed diffraction pattern fits only one of a number of proposed models.

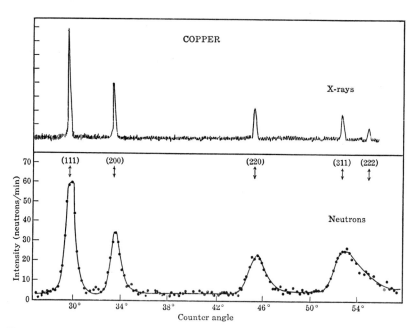

Fig. 65b. X-ray and neutron powder diffraction patterns of copper. This pattern is typical of a monatomic crystal. Note especially (1) the lower resolution of the neutron pattern, and (2) the rapid decrease with increasing angle of the intensity (F^2) in the x-ray peaks as compared to the neutron peaks.

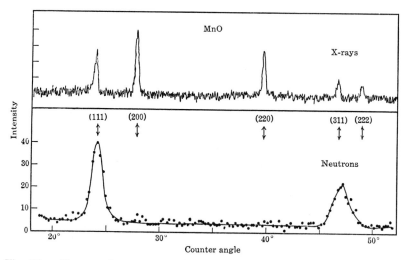

Fig. 65c. X-ray and neutron powder diffraction patterns of manganese oxide. Note the absence of some peaks in the neutron case; their absence is due to the opposite signs of the scattering amplitudes of manganese and oxygen. These patterns for copper, manganese oxide, and other crystals are given in a review article by Shull and Wollan (S28).

524

Application of the powder diffraction technique to the study of hydrogen- and deuterium-containing crystals is strikingly illustrated in Fig. 66, powder patterns from NaH and NaD due to Shull, Wollan, Morton, and Davidson (S29). From these patterns the authors conclude that the structure of NaH is similar to that of NaCl (face-centered cubic, type B1). In addition, a number of effects are strikingly evident: (1) the incoherent scattering of hydrogen is much greater than that of

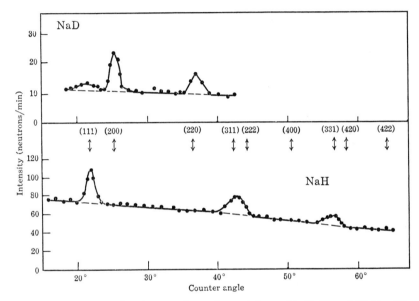

Fig. 66. Neutron diffraction powder patterns taken with NaH and NaD. The pronounced differences in the two patterns are caused by differences in neutron scattering by hydrogen and deuterium. It is to be noted that the diffuse scattering is much stronger for NaH than for NaD. Figure from (W39).

deuterium; (2) the coherent scattering lengths of hydrogen and deuterium have opposite signs; (3) the coherent scattering lengths of deuterium and sodium have the same sign.

Another approach to the problem of crystal structure analysis by slow-neutron diffraction has been applied by Fermi, Sturm, and Sachs (F20). They have measured the transmission of polycrystalline samples as a function of the neutron energy (as distinguished from the usual powder crystal technique, in which the angular distribution of scattered monoenergetic neutrons is observed). Their results for the cross section of polycrystalline beryllium oxide are shown in Fig. 67. Polycrystalline samples of other materials have been studied, with this technique, by Winsberg, Meneghetti, and Sidhu (W36).

The theory for this technique has been developed by Halpern, Hamermesh, and Johnson (H15) and by Weinstock (W14). The main features of such cross-section curves are: (1) the sharp breaks in the curve, and (2) the rapid decrease with increasing energy, like λ^2 or $1/E$, of the

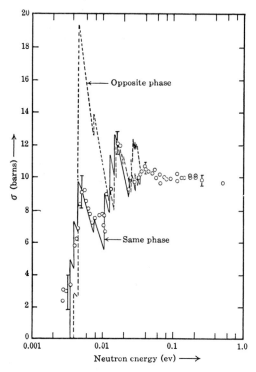

Fig. 67. Experimental and calculated total cross section as a function of neutron energy for beryllium oxide, showing the effects of the Bragg reflections from various planes in the crystal. The solid and dashed curves, calculated for the same and opposite phases of scattering for the two centers, show agreement with the data for the same phase. From Fermi, Sturm, and Sachs (F20).

cross section between breaks. The sharp breaks in the curve occur at neutron energies for which $m\lambda$ becomes equal to twice the distance between a set of crystal planes ($m\lambda = 2d_{hkl}$). For energies below this value ($m\lambda > 2d_{hkl}$), Eq. (175) shows that Bragg scattering from the planes in question is impossible, irrespective of the crystal orientation. Thus, as the neutron energy is decreased, values are successively reached below which a given set of crystal planes can no longer scatter coherently. Finally, at energies below the lowest break in the curve, corresponding to λ = twice the spacing of the widest set of crystal planes, the coherent scattering vanishes completely. Hence, given a beam of neutrons transmitted through a long column of polycrystalline material, most of the survivors will have energies below the last cut-off; this is the basis for the production of cold neutrons, discussed on page 438.

The shape of the cross-section curve between breaks is strongly dependent on the size of the microcrystals comprising the sample. In particular, in order to obtain the $1/E$ dependence observed in Fig. 67 (and the corresponding sharpness of the breaks) it is necessary that the microcrystals have very small dimensions, $l \ll \delta$, where δ is the depth of penetration in a large crystal, given by Eq. (177). The sharpness of the breaks would also be greatly diminished by the presence of appreciable incoherent scattering (F20).

Another phenomenon, associated with the transmission of neutrons through microcrystalline materials, is small-angle scattering, analogous to the optical phenomenon of diffraction by small bodies. This involves the coherent scattering of neutrons into angles $\theta \lesssim \lambda/l$, where l is the dimension of the scatterer; alternatively, the effect may be regarded as a kind of zero-order Bragg reflection. In addition, refraction may occur at the crystal boundaries. The theory of small-angle neutron diffraction has been developed by Halpern and Gerjuoy (H18) and by Weiss (W15). In particular, they have derived the dependence of the small-angle scattering on the nature and orientation of the scattering bodies. Experimental observation and study of these phenomena have been carried out by Hughes, Burgy, Heller, and Wallace (H71) and by Krueger, Meneghetti, Ringo, and Winsberg (K24). Weiss (W15) has demonstrated that the small-angle scattering can be used to determine coherent scattering cross sections and relative phases of slow-neutron scattering amplitudes.

2. Investigation of Order and Disorder in Solids, Liquids, and Gases. The x-ray diffraction technique is one of the most effective means for the study of the degree of order in the structure of matter. Clearly, neutron diffraction can be applied to such problems and, in some favorable instances, can yield new information. Although the application of neutron diffraction to the study of order and disorder has hardly advanced beyond the exploratory stage, sufficient work has been done to give some indications of types of problems for which neutrons are especially suited.

One example is the work of Shull and Siegel (S30) on order-disorder in alloys. They applied the powdered crystal technique to a number of substitutional solid solutions. When the mixing of components is completely disordered, the diffraction pattern is characteristic of the ordinary lattice, the effect of the mixture being only to introduce an additional source of incoherent scattering due to the different scattering amplitudes of the components. For an ordered array, on the other hand, additional Bragg lines appear which are characteristic of the "superlattice." The relative intensity of the superstructure lines to the normal lines, as well as the decrease in incoherent scattering, is a measure of the degree of order in the mixture. A unique advantage of neutrons over x-rays in such studies is the possibility of investigating mixtures of atoms having a relatively small difference in atomic number; for such atoms the x-ray scattering amplitudes differ by only a relatively small amount, while the neutron scattering amplitudes may be appreciably different. (Clearly, if the scattering amplitudes of the two atoms were identical, no difference could be discerned in the diffraction by ordered and disordered arrays.) Thus, Shull and Siegel were able to study the alloys FeCo and Ni_3Mn, and to observe superlattice effects which would be extremely difficult to detect with x-rays. On the other hand, they failed to detect the effects of ordering in Cu_3Au due to the fortuitously close values of the nuclear scattering amplitudes of the two components.

Another type of problem, in which x-ray diffraction has yielded important information, is the study of order in liquids (G5, S28, G24). Chamberlain (C11) has demonstrated the possibility of applying neutron diffraction techniques to these problems. His results for sulfur, lead, and bismuth agree with the x-ray work on these liquids.

A significant contribution of Chamberlain's work has been the development of a diffraction instrument capable of attaining much higher resolution than conventional neutron diffraction apparatus. This instrument takes advantage of the fact that the natural parameter, in diffraction studies, is $(\sin \theta)/\lambda$. Chamberlain's design provides for relatively large angular and energy spreads in the neutrons scattered by the sample and observed in the detector, while, at the same time, minimizing the spread in $(\sin \theta)/\lambda$.

Diffraction techniques can also be applied to the study of molecular structure in gases (S28). In such investigations, however, the intensity limitations are much more serious, owing to the low available gas densities. Nevertheless, Alcock and Hurst (A7) have been able to observe and study the diffraction of neutrons by a number of gases; their diffraction patterns are in excellent agreement with theory.

While the above-mentioned investigations have studied the diffraction patterns (angular distribution of the scattered intensity) for various neutron wavelengths, the alternative approach, measurement of the total cross section as a function of the neutron wavelength by means of a transmission experiment, is also applicable. There have, as yet, been few systematic studies of order based on this technique. Arnold and

Weber (A32) have applied this method to study deviations from randomness in the microcrystalline orientations in a number of samples of polycrystalline aluminum. Melkonian (M25) has investigated the transmission *vs.* neutron velocity of a number of gases and liquids; however, his investigations were intended mainly to ascertain the effect of the state of the sample on the measured hydrogen cross section, with the primary purpose of deriving the free proton cross section (M24, M27).

It has been suggested that neutron diffraction could be used to investigate phase transitions, especially in substances containing hydrogen. Kimura (K13) has studied the transmission of a conventional (unmonochromatized) thermal neutron beam through a sample of ammonium chloride (NH_4Cl), as a function of the temperature of the sample. He observed a small, discontinuous change in the transmission at $\sim -30°C$, possibly associated with the known phase transition at $-30.8°C$. However, it is difficult to conceive of the nuclear mechanism for changing the transmission of a beam of thermal neutrons; the coherent scattering cross section of hydrogen, even if it were not so small, would not change unless the proton spins were ordered—an effect which will not take place until *very* low temperatures are reached. This is not to say that changes in scattering will not result from phase transitions; indeed, such changes have been observed, but only in studies of the diffraction patterns for monochromatic neutrons and, even then, only for deuterium-substituted compounds (G18, L17). Even here, the evidence concerning the nature of the phase transition is not conclusive.[1]

For very low temperatures, in the neighborhood of absolute zero, ordering of the nuclear spin orientations can occur; the coherent scattering of slow neutrons would be very sensitive to the degree of spin order, provided that the neutron cross section was sufficiently spin-dependent, e.g., hydrogen (R18). Another type of ordering which requires very low temperatures is that observed in the transition from ordinary liquid helium to liquid helium II. The possibility of use of slow-neutron scattering for the study of such phenomena has been investigated by Goldstein, Sweeney, and Goldstein (G21, G22, G23).

In describing the scattering of slow neutrons, we have thus far considered only the scattering by atomic nuclei. (The spin-independent scattering by electrons has been discussed in Section 1, but these effects are normally too small to be observed.) There is, however, an additional

---

[1] The more recent work of Levy and Peterson [Phys. Rev., **86,** 766 (1952)] appears to have established the nature of the phase transition in question as being of the order-disorder type. This work involved, in addition to a study of the neutron diffraction by the deuterium-substituted compound, an investigation of the diffraction by a single crystal of NH_4Cl.

source of scattering by paramagnetic atoms or ions which is due to the interaction between the magnetic moment of the neutron and the magnetic moment of the unpaired electrons. This interaction, the Bloch effect, involves spin-dependent, coherent scattering by the atomic electrons, and is therefore observable only for neutrons of wavelength comparable to or greater than atomic dimensions.

The theory and observation of the magnetic scattering of neutrons will be discussed in detail in Section 5D. For our present purposes, we content ourselves with the observations that (1) the amplitude of magnetic scattering depends on the neutron wavelength and on the orientation of the atomic magnetic moment with respect to the neutron moment and the direction of the "scattering vector" and (2) the magnetic scattering amplitude can be of the same order of magnitude as the nuclear scattering amplitude (H11). It should therefore be possible to observe, in the diffraction of slow neutrons by crystals containing paramagnetic atoms or ions, effects due to the coherent superposition of the nuclear and magnetic scattering from the same and from neighboring atoms. Furthermore, such effects should be strongly dependent on the degree of order in the alignment of the atomic moments, and should therefore provide an effective tool for the investigation of problems involving magnetic ordering in paramagnetic and ferromagnetic substances.

Magnetic scattering by crystals containing paramagnetic ions has been observed by Ruderman, Havens, Taylor, and Rainwater (R23), and the properties of a number of such crystals have been studied by observations of transmission *vs.* wavelength on microcrystalline samples (R24).

The powder diffraction technique has been used by Shull, Strauser, and Wollan (S35) to study the magnetic structure of a number of crystals containing paramagnetic and ferromagnetic atoms; their findings are of great interest in the field of magnetism. In addition, Shull, Wollan, and co-workers (S32, S35) have studied the dependence of magnetic scattering on the direction of magnetization of the crystal, and obtained results of important theoretical and practical significance (see Section 5D).

Ferromagnetic substances are those in which the energy of the system has its minimum value when the atomic moments are aligned in a parallel array; such systems can be studied by a variety of techniques. However, it is also possible that the most stable structure of a crystal composed of paramagnetic atoms is one in which neighboring atoms or ions tend to assume anti-parallel orientations (due to a negative value of the electron exchange-integral). Such substances will show no net magnetization, either in or out of a magnetic field. Nevertheless, they are, in a manner of speaking, ferromagnetic, having, in essence, two lattices aligned in opposite directions. While such substances, called *anti-ferro-magnetic*, are difficult to detect by the conventional techniques for the investigation of magnetism, they are peculiarly susceptible to study by neutron diffraction.

One of the most significant results of neutron diffraction has been the demonstration, by Shull and Smart (S31), of the anti-ferromagnetic structure of crystalline manganese oxide. The powder crystal patterns for samples at room temperature and at 80°K are shown in Fig. 68. At

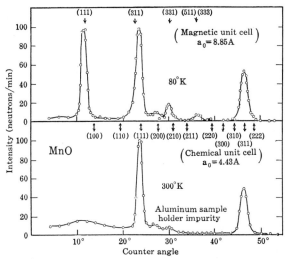

Fig. 68. Powder diffraction patterns for crystalline manganese oxide at 80°K and at room temperature, due to Shull and Smart (S31). The additional peaks, in the low-temperature pattern, are characteristic of a magnetic unit cell of twice the dimensions of the chemical unit cell, clearly indicating the anti-ferromagnetic structure of manganese oxide.

the higher temperature, the pattern is characteristic of an ordinary paramagnetic crystal (or a ferromagnetic crystal above the Curie temperature). At the lower temperature, however, additional peaks appear at positions not allowed on the basis of the known chemical unit cell, but corresponding to a magnetic unit cell of twice the dimensions of the chemical unit cell. Other anti-ferromagnetic crystals have been studied by Shull, Strauser, and Wollan (S35).

C. Neutron Diffraction and the Determination of Nuclear Scattering Amplitudes

In x-ray diffraction experiments, the observed patterns can be directly interpreted in terms of the structure of the scattering material, since the scattering amplitude of a given element is completely determined by its atomic number and is known in advance.   The situation with regard to neutron diffraction is considerably more complicated.   In the first place, the nuclear scattering amplitude cannot, in the present state of nuclear theory, be predicted; not even the sign of the amplitude is known *a priori*, although all but $\sim$10 percent of those known are positive (according to the convention adopted in Section 5A, Eq. 169a).   Furthermore, the scattering amplitudes may vary from isotope to isotope of the same element, or be dependent on the relative orientation of the neutron and nuclear spins, thus introducing an unpredictable incoherent scattering by materials in which the isotopes or spins or both are randomly distributed. Hence, it is necessary to determine the nuclear scattering amplitude before the observed diffraction can be interpreted in terms of the structure of the scatterer.   Although the determination of nuclear scattering amplitudes and the elucidation of the structure of the scatterer are sometimes included in the same set of measurements, it is clearly advantageous to possess the necessary nuclear data in advance of the attempted interpretation of a given diffraction pattern.

The available data on nuclear scattering amplitudes and cross sections have been summarized by Shull and Wollan (S33); their summary is reproduced in Table 37.   Column 1 lists the substances from whose diffraction or scattering the data were obtained.   Columns 2, 3, and 4 list the atomic number, the element, and the isotope involved.   Column 5 gives the spin, if known, when the element is monoisotopic, or when work has been performed on separated isotopes.   Columns 6 and 7 list the coherent scattering amplitudes and the corresponding coherent scattering cross sections (Eq. 170b) for bound nuclei.   Column 8 contains the bound nuclear scattering cross sections (Eq. 170a); these are usually obtained from transmission experiments with resonance neutrons, the measured free scattering cross sections being converted to the bound values by application of Eq. (170').   The differences between columns 8 and 7 are the bound incoherent scattering cross sections (Eq. 170c). For monoisotopic elements of zero spin, the coherent and atomic scattering cross sections should be equal.   For the others, the difference is due either to isotopic or spin incoherent scattering (Eqs. 170c', 170c'') or to both.   Finally, column 9 lists some potential scattering cross sections ($\sigma_{pot} = 4\pi R^2$) for elements with $Z \geq 13$.

While most of the coherent scattering amplitudes listed in Table 37 have been obtained by powder crystal diffraction techniques, there are a number of other effective diffraction methods for measuring coherent and incoherent scattering amplitudes and cross sections.   It will be assumed throughout that the free atom scattering cross section, σ_{sc}(free), is known or can be obtained by a transmission measurement with resonance neutrons.

TABLE 37

NEUTRON SCATTERING DATA AS DETERMINED BY NEUTRON DIFFRACTION AND TRANSMISSION STUDIES (S33)

Samples Examined	Z	Elements	Specific Nuclides	Nuclear Spin	a_{coh} † $(10^{-12}$ cm$)$	σ_{coh} (barns)	σ_{sc} ‡ (barns)	σ_{pot} (barns)
NaH	1	H	H^1	$\frac{1}{2}$	-0.40	2.0	80	
NaD, ThD$_2$, D$_2$O			H^2	1	0.64	5.2	7.4	
LiF, LiCl	3	Li			-0.18	0.4		
			Li^6	1	0.7 §	~6		
			Li^7	$\frac{3}{2}$	-0.25	0.8	~2	
BeO, Be	4	Be	Be^9	$\frac{3}{2}$	0.78	7.7	7.5	
Diamond, graphite	6	C	C^{12} ‖	0	0.64	5.2	5.2	
KN$_3$	7	N	N^{14} ‖	1	0.85	9.1	10	
Many oxides	8	O	O^{16} ‖	0	0.58	4.2	4.2	
NaF, CaF$_2$	9	F	F^{19}	$\frac{1}{2}$	0.55	3.8	~3.5	
Na, NaCl, NaF, NaBr	11	Na	Na^{23}	$\frac{3}{2}$	0.35	1.5	3.5	
Mg, MgO	12	Mg			0.44	2.4	4.2	
Al	13	Al	Al^{27}	$\frac{5}{2}$	0.35	1.5	1.5	2.5
PbS	16	S			0.31	1.2	~1.2	
NaCl, KCl, CuCl	17	Cl			0.99	12.2	15	
KCl	19	K			0.35	1.5	~2	
CaO, CaF$_2$	20	Ca			0.49	3.0	3.5	
			Ca^{40}	0	0.49	3.0	3.2	
			Ca^{44}	0	0.18	0.4		
Ti, TiC	22	Ti			-0.38	1.8	~6	
V, VC	23	V	V^{51}	$\frac{7}{2}$	<0.09 ¶	0.028 ††	5	3.7
Cr, FeCr	24	Cr			0.37	1.7	3.8	
MnO, Ni$_3$Mn	25	Mn	Mn^{55}	$\frac{5}{2}$	-0.33	1.35	2.2	3.8
Fe, FeO, Fe$_2$O$_3$	26	Fe			0.96	11.4	11.7	
			Fe^{54}	0	0.42	2.2	2.5	4.0
			Fe^{56}	0	1.00	12.6	13	
			Fe^{57}	(?)	0.23	0.64	2	
Co, CoO, FeCo	27	Co	Co^{59}	$\frac{7}{2}$	0.28	1.0	~5	4.2
Ni, NiO, Ni$_3$Mn	28	Ni			1.03	13.4	17.3	
			Ni^{58}	0	1.47	27.0	27.0	4.4
			Ni^{60}	0	0.28	0.97	1	
			Ni^{62}	0	-0.85	9.1	9	
Cu, Cu$_2$O, CuCl	29	Cu			0.76	7.3	7.8	
Zn, ZnO, CuZn	30	Zn			0.59	4.3	4.2	
Ge, GeO$_2$	32	Ge			0.84	8.8	8.5	
As, As$_2$O$_3$	33	As	As^{75}	$\frac{3}{2}$	0.63	5.0	~7	4.9
MnSe	34	Se			0.89	10.0	~10	
NaBr, KBr	35	Br			0.67	5.7	6.0	
RbCl	37	Rb			0.55	3.8	5.5	
SrO	38	Sr			0.57	4.1	9.5	
ZrC, ZrN	40	Zr			0.62	4.9	~7	
Nb	41	Nb	Nb^{93}	$\frac{9}{2}$	0.69 ‡‡	6.0	6.2	5.9

TABLE 37 (*Continued*)

NEUTRON SCATTERING DATA AS DETERMINED BY NEUTRON DIFFRACTION
AND TRANSMISSION STUDIES (S33)

Samples Examined	Z	Elements	Specific Nuclides	Nuclear Spin	a_{coh} † $(10^{-12}$ cm)	σ_{coh} (barns)	σ_{sc} ‡ (barns)	σ_{pot} (barns)
Mo	42	Mo			0.64 ‡‡	5.2	7.4	
Pd	46	Pd			0.63 ‡‡	5.0	4.8	
Ag, AgCl	47	Ag			0.61	4.6	7	
			Ag^{107}	$\frac{1}{2}$	0.83	8.7	10	6.4
			Ag^{109}	$\frac{1}{2}$	0.43	2.3	6	6.4
Sn, SnO, SnO$_2$	50	Sn			0.61	4.6	4.9	
Sb, Sb$_2$O$_3$	51	Sb			0.54	3.7	4.2	
NaI, KI	53	I	I^{127}	$\frac{5}{2}$	0.52	3.4	3.8	6.9
CsCl	55	Cs	Cs^{133}	$\frac{7}{2}$	0.49	3.0	~7	7.1
Ta, TaC	73	Ta	Ta^{181}	$\frac{7}{2}$	0.70	6.1	7.0	9.0
W, WO$_3$	74	W			0.51	3.3	5.7	
Pt	78	Pt			0.95	11.2	11.2	
Au, Cu$_3$Au	79	Au	Au^{197}	$\frac{3}{2}$	0.77	7.5	~9	9.3
Pb, PbS	82	Pb			0.96	11.5	11.6	
Bi	83	Bi	Bi^{209}	$\frac{9}{2}$	0.89	10.1	10	10.0
Th, ThO$_2$	90	Th	Th^{232}	0	1.01	12.8	12.8	

† All signs of scattering amplitudes are positive except where specifically noted otherwise.

‡ The bound scattering cross-section values are obtained from total cross-section measurements by transmission. Transmission results are either from Oak Ridge data or from a composite of Oak Ridge data and literature values.

§ By calculation from normal Li and Li^7 data.

‖ The scattering properties of C, N, and O are considered to be those of the major isotope since the element is so nearly monoisotopic.

¶ Phase of scattering unknown because of extremely small scattering cross section.

†† (M18).

‡‡ Phase of scattering determined by R. J. Weiss from small angle scattering measurements (W15).

1. Coherent Scattering Amplitudes by Total Reflection from Mirrors.

As pointed out in Section 5A, the transmission of a neutron beam through a scattering medium is describable in terms of an index of refraction:

$$n = 1 - \frac{N\lambda^2}{2\pi} \sum_j f_j a_j \qquad (173'')$$

where the symbols are as defined in Section 5A, and absorption effects are neglected. Consequently, neutron beams will be refracted at a boundary between two media, and will suffer total reflection when striking, at sufficiently small (glancing) angles, the surface of a medium of smaller index of refraction.

The critical angle for total reflection is defined as the largest angle between the direction of the beam and the surface of the scatterer for which total reflection is possible. Exactly as in the optical case, the critical angle is given by the condition

$$\sin \theta_c = \left[1 - \left(\frac{n_2}{n_1}\right)^2\right]^{\frac{1}{2}}$$ (178)

where n_2 and n_1 are, respectively, the indices of refraction of the scatterer and the medium from which the neutrons are incident. For the available neutron wavelengths, $\mu \equiv (1-n) \ll 1$, $\sin \theta_c \cong \theta_c$, whence

$$\theta_c \cong [2(\mu_2 - \mu_1)]^{\frac{1}{2}} = \left(\frac{\lambda}{\pi^{\frac{1}{2}}}\right) [N_2 \sum_j f_{2j}a_{2j} - N_1 \sum_j f_{1j}a_{1j}]^{\frac{1}{2}}$$ (178a)

In particular, for a neutron beam incident from air ($\mu_1 = 0$) on a plane scattering surface,

$$\theta_c \cong \left(\frac{\lambda}{\pi^{\frac{1}{2}}}\right)(N\Sigma f_j a_j)^{\frac{1}{2}}$$ (178a')

For a typical case, e.g., reflection of $\lambda \approx 2 \times 10^{-8}$ cm neutrons from a graphite mirror, $\theta_c \approx 10$ minutes of arc.

For angles less than the critical angle, the reflection coefficient (reflectivity, R) is 1. At glancing angles greater than θ_c, the reflectivity is

$$R = \left[\frac{1 - (1 - \theta_c^2/\theta^2)^{\frac{1}{2}}}{1 + (1 - \theta_c^2/\theta^2)^{\frac{1}{2}}}\right]^2$$ (179)

which falls off rapidly with increasing $\theta > \theta_c$. For example, for θ greater by 10 percent than θ_c, $R \approx 0.25$.

The depth of penetration of the neutron beam into the scattering material (for $\theta < \theta_c$) can be computed by a method similar to that applied to Bragg scattering (Section 5B1); it is

$$\delta \cong \frac{\lambda}{2\pi\theta_c}$$ (177')

For the typical case, $\delta \sim 10^{-6}$ cm or ~ 100 atomic layers. Thus, surface impurities of the scatterer will have an important influence on the total reflection.

From the considerations outlined above, it is possible to draw two important conclusions:

(1) Total reflection can occur only for substances with μ positive or, more generally, at an interface between two media of which the second has the smaller index of refraction. Since the sign of μ is the same as that of the coherent scattering amplitude, the sign of $a_{coh} = \Sigma f_j a_j$ is unambiguously determined by the occurrence (positive) or non-occur-

rence (negative) of total reflection at glancing angles. While the observation of strong thermal neutron reflection at glancing angles is usually good evidence for total reflection, it is, strictly speaking, necessary to establish the existence of a critical angle for monoenergetic neutrons beyond which the reflectivity falls off rapidly. It is most important to note that the observation of the occurrence or non-occurrence of *total reflection provides the only direct experimental means for the determination of the sign of the coherent scattering amplitude.*

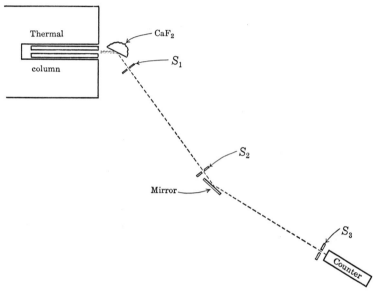

Fig. 69a. Experimental arrangement of Fermi and Marshall (F21) for the determination of the critical angle for reflection of monoenergetic neutrons from various mirrors.

(2) Determination of θ_c for a predetermined λ (or vice versa) yields the coherent scattering amplitude of the totally reflecting mirror. In this respect it is important to observe that there are no other factors entering into the determination; *the form factor* of the scattering substance *is identically unity.* Furthermore, the scattering amplitude involved in Eqs. (178), (178a), and (178a') is that corresponding to complete binding (effectively infinite mass for the scattering nuclei), irrespective of the physical state of the mirror; the only effect of the state of the mirror is through the nuclear density N (K17, M17, M20).

Observation of total reflection of slow neutrons was first achieved by Fermi and Zinn (F18), who used the intense thermal neutron sources

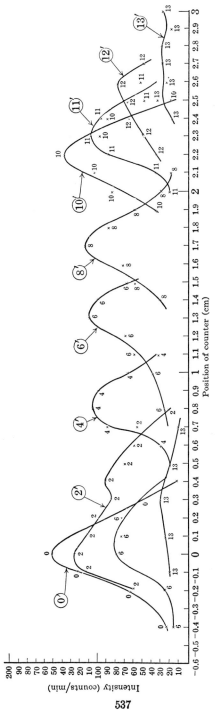

Fig. 69b. A typical set of measurements of the reflected intensity for monoenergetic neutrons on a beryllium mirror for various angles of incidence (F21).

537

available from the first piles. They reported total reflection from mirrors of beryllium, graphite, glass, aluminum, iron, nickel, copper, and zinc, with critical angles $\theta_c \lesssim 10$ min. Measurements of critical angles for a number of mirrors are described by Fermi and Marshall (F21), who observed total reflection of neutrons of $\lambda = 1.873$ A obtained by Bragg scattering from the (1,0,0) planes of a calcium fluoride crystal. Their experimental arrangement is shown in Fig. 69a. A typical set of measurements for a beryllium mirror is reproduced in Fig. 69b. The critical angles for the mirrors studied by Fermi and Marshall ranged from 12.0 min (Be) to 7.1 min (Zn).

There are many possible applications of total reflection to the measurement of (otherwise relatively unattainable) scattering amplitudes. Some of these, as suggested by Hamermesh (H25), are:

(1) Measurement of a_{coh} of substances for which $\sigma_{coh} \ll \sigma_{incoh}$. The special case of hydrogen has been studied, by total reflection, by Hughes, Burgy, and Ringo (H74), and will be discussed in a following section. Another application, by McReynolds and Weiss (M18), has been to vanadium.

(2) Measurement of a_{coh} of substances for which $\sigma_{sc} \ll \sigma_{abs}$. Hibdon, Muehlhause, Ringo, and Robillard (H60) have applied this technique to mercury, for which $\sigma_{th}(n,\gamma) \approx 370$ barns.

(3) Measurement of the spin-independent neutron-electron interaction, by comparison of a_{coh} from total reflection with a from σ_{sc}, for a heavy monoisotopic element of zero electronic spin. The effects of the neutron-electron interaction are emphasized in total reflection since the atomic form factor is 1. Such a measurement has recently been reported by Hughes (see Section 1C3).

2. Coherent Scattering Amplitudes from Crystal Scattering. The intensities of Bragg reflections from crystals with an ordered arrangement of two or more elements yield the relative signs of nuclear scattering amplitudes as described in Section 5B1. Such observations are interpreted through the crystal form factor, Eq. (176).

In Section 5B1 it was shown, for example, that the Bragg reflections from the (1,1,1) planes of a face-centered cubic crystal, such as NaCl or LiF, will alternate in intensity. If the even orders are more intense, as for NaCl, the scattering amplitudes of the two elements have the same sign. If the odd orders are more intense (LiF, NaH), the amplitudes have opposite sign. By such observations Fermi and Marshall (F21) (using Bragg reflection from single crystals), Shull and Wollan (S33) (employing powder diffraction techniques), and others have determined the relative signs of the coherent scattering amplitudes of a large number of pairs of elements.

From such observations the absolute sign of the scattering amplitudes can be established only if the sign of one member of the pair is known through some independent means, i.e., a total reflection observation. Thus, the determination of the signs of the coherent scattering amplitudes in Table 37 depends on linking the element under consideration to one of those for which total reflection has been observed; in some cases, this linkage is established through a chain containing many intermediate components.

It is important to note that the variation of intensity of Bragg reflection from different orders, given by Eq. (176), is superimposed on a monotonic decrease, with increasing θ, due to "temperature-diffuse" (incoherent) scattering. Strictly speaking, the form factor of Eq. (176) must be modified by multiplication with the Debye-Waller temperature factor (W14, W39):

$$F(T) = Fe^{-W(T)\sin^2\theta/\lambda^2} \tag{176'}$$

where F is the crystal form factor of Eq. (176); $W(T)$ is a monotonically increasing function of the ratio of the absolute temperature of the sample T to the Debye characteristic temperature of the crystal, Θ. Correspondingly, the cross section per unit cell for temperature-diffuse (incoherent) scattering is given by the expression

$$\sigma_{incoh}(T) = 4\pi[F^2 - F(T)^2] \tag{176'a}$$

The effect of temperature-diffuse scattering on the intensities under successive Bragg peaks and on the diffuse background scattering in the powder diffraction pattern of lead is shown in Fig. 70a and 70b, which are from Shull and Wollan (S33). The coherent scattering amplitude per unit cell, F, is determined by extrapolation of $F(T)$ to $\theta = 0$. The scale of the ordinate is determined by calibration with a sample of known coherent scattering cross section. Most of the coherent scattering amplitudes in Table 37 have been determined by this technique.

The analysis of crystal diffraction patterns becomes more complicated when the element in question exhibits isotopic or spin-dependent incoherent scattering or both. However, the temperature effects are normally not so large as those exhibited by lead, since Debye characteristic temperatures are usually considerably greater than that of lead. After correcting for the (normally small) temperature-diffuse (and multiple) scattering, the remaining incoherent scattering can be attributed to purely nuclear effects. When the element under investigation is monoisotopic, the measured incoherent scattering is due to spin dependence. An extreme example is the case of vanadium, for which the coherent scattering amplitude is very small ($<0.09 \times 10^{-12}$ cm) (M18). In this case, Shull and Wollan (S33) have been able to determine the value of $\sigma_{incoh} = \sigma_{sc}(\text{bound}) = 5.0$ barns from the incoherent scattering in the powder diffraction pattern of vanadium carbide.

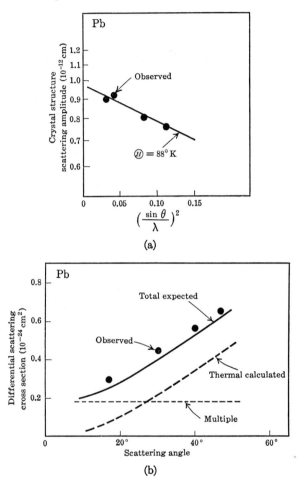

Fig. 70. Effect of temperature–diffuse scattering on the powder diffraction pattern of polycrystalline lead; due to Shull and Wollan (S33). (a) Coherent scattering amplitudes corresponding to successive Bragg peaks. The line shows the expected variation for a Debye characteristic temperature of 88°K. (b) Comparison between calculated and observed thermal diffuse scattering cross sections for powdered lead. The correction for multiple scattering was determined empirically.

The alternative method of crystal structure analysis—measurement of the transmission *vs.* neutron wavelength of microcrystalline samples —has been discussed in Section 5B1. The measurements of Fermi,

Sturm, and Sachs (F20), shown in Fig. 67, illustrate how this method was used to establish the relative signs (same) of the scattering amplitudes of beryllium and oxygen. This method can also be used to determine the incoherent scattering cross section by measuring the residual cross section of the sample for neutron wavelengths greater than the largest cut-off value (F21). This last method has been exploited by Bendt and Ruderman (B17), who interpreted the measured incoherent scattering cross sections of disordered solid solutions to show that copper and nickel scatter in phase, whereas manganese and nickel scatter with amplitudes of opposite signs. From their measurements of σ_{incoh} and σ_{sc}(free), they also determined the coherent scattering amplitudes of the elements involved.

3. Coherent Scattering by Gas Molecules. The molecules in a gas are randomly distributed, and therefore scatter neutrons incoherently. However, the atoms making up the molecule are more-or-less fixed relative to each other, and the scattering of neutrons by a single molecule should consequently exhibit coherence effects for neutron wavelengths greater than the interatomic spacings in the molecule.

In the extreme of very long wavelength neutrons and very low gas temperatures the molecular scattering amplitude is the sum of the amplitudes of the atomic constituents of the molecule.[1] If we assume mono-isotopic elements and no spin-dependent scattering, the molecular cross section is, under the conditions mentioned above,

$$\sigma_{coh}(\text{mol}) = 4\pi \left| \sum_j a_j(\text{mol}) \right|^2 \qquad (170\text{b}''')$$

where the summation is over the molecular constituents. From Eq. (170b''') it is clear that a comparison of σ_{coh}(mol) with the sum of the scattering cross sections of the constituents can yield information concerning the relative signs of the a_j's. In particular, for molecules containing only two elements, $\sigma_{coh}(\text{mol}) > \sum_j \sigma_{sc}$ means like signs, and vice

---

[1] In the molecular case, the scattering amplitudes are neither the "free" nor the "bound" ones, since the molecule as a whole can recoil. The appropriate scattering amplitude is intermediate between a(free) and a(bound) = $[(A + 1)/A]a$(free). In general, for an atom of atomic weight A in a molecule of molecular weight M, we have

$$a(\text{mol}) = \left(\frac{M}{M + 1}\right) a(\text{bound}) = \left(\frac{M}{M + 1}\right) \left(\frac{A + 1}{A}\right) a(\text{free}) \qquad (170'\text{a})$$

Equation (170'a) assumes rigid binding of the atom in the molecule. The factors $M/(M + 1)$ and $(A + 1)/A$ arise from the dependence, in the Born approximation, of the scattering cross section on the (square of the) reduced mass of the neutron (B24).

versa. This method of determining relative scattering phases was one of the techniques explored by Fermi and Marshall (F21). It has also been applied by Melkonian (M25). The alternative method—measurement of the angular distribution of the scattered neutrons—has been employed by Alcock and Hurst (A7); it has one advantage of avoiding the necessity of correcting the transmission for the effect of neutron absorption, which can be quite large at the long wavelengths required in such measurements.

While measurements of molecular scattering cross sections usually lead to unambiguous determinations of the relative signs of nuclear scattering amplitudes, it is far more difficult to extract the magnitudes of the a's. The difficulties arise from the effect on the observed scattering cross section of various incoherent scattering and other temperature-dependent phenomena. Some of these effects are molecular in origin, and their evaluation may require a detailed knowledge of the structure of the molecule involved (M27). Corrections must be applied for the Doppler effect, for the effect of molecular vibration and rotation on the molecular wave function (positions of the scattering nuclei), for the incoherent scattering involving transitions between rotational states of the molecule (inelastic scattering), and, in case the neutron wavelength is not very much larger than the molecular spacing, for the deviations from complete coherence in the scattering of the constituents. All these effects are, to a lesser or greater extent, dependent on the gas temperature, the first two being much more so than the last two.

The Doppler effect is very important for relatively light molecules, especially for H_2 or D_2. It tends to increase the observed cross section, since the molecular motion increases the number of collisions between neutrons and molecules over the number which would occur if the molecules were stationary. The Doppler effect correction increases with decreasing neutron velocity (increasing wavelength). Indeed, for sufficiently slow neutrons the molecules will be moving faster than the neutrons, in which case the scattering is essentially caused by the molecules running into the neutrons; thus, in the limit of zero velocity neutrons the observed cross section would approach infinity, even for a constant nuclear scattering cross section. (Of course, as $v \rightarrow 0$, $\sigma_a \propto 1/v$ also becomes infinite.) Thus, Fermi and Marshall (F21) observed, for neutrons of $\lambda = 5.1$ A, an increase in the cross section of H_2 from 81 barns at $T = 83°K$ to 170 barns at room temperature; most, but not all, of this increase was due to the Doppler effect.

Finally, an important source of "incoherent" scattering may arise from the spin dependence of the scattering amplitude. In fact, since the relative spin orientations of the atoms in a given molecule are fixed (although a given gas sample usually consists of a mixture of molecules in the different possible spin states), the existence of spin-dependent scattering may have a profound influence on the observed molecular scattering cross section. These effects are most important in the scattering by H_2 and (to a lesser extent) HD and D_2 molecules, which will now be discussed.

4. Spin-Dependent Scattering by H and D. In Section 1 we outlined the nature of the neutron-proton interaction. In particular, it was concluded that the interaction (potential) is strongly dependent on the relative neutron-proton spin orientation. The combination with total spin 1 (triplet) is, in the ground state, bound, i.e., the deuteron. The other possibility, with total spin 0 (singlet state), was stated to be only slightly unbound ($\epsilon_1 \approx -0.065$ Mev).

The suggestion that the neutron-proton interaction is strongly spin dependent was first made by Wigner in 1935. It was based on the observation that the cross section for scattering of slow neutrons by protons is very much greater than that predicted on the basis of the interaction leading to the bound deuteron state.[1] Thus, for a spin-dependent neutron-proton interaction the free neutron-proton scattering cross section is, from Eq. (170a'')[2],

$$\sigma_{sc}(H) = \pi(3a_+{}^2 + a_-{}^2) = \frac{\pi}{4}[(3a_+ + a_-)^2 + 3(a_+ - a_-)^2] \quad (180)$$

As a possible test of Wigner's hypothesis, Teller in 1936 (T6) suggested that a measurement of the coherent scattering cross sections of molecular hydrogen could determine the relative magnitudes as well as the relative signs of the two amplitudes. In particular, since there are two species of molecular hydrogen—orthohydrogen (total nuclear spin = 1) and parahydrogen (total spin 0)—a comparison of their cross sections would lead to unique assignments for the values of the scattering amplitudes. The theory of neutron scattering by ortho- and parahydrogen was developed by Schwinger and Teller (S7).

(a) *Neutron Scattering by Ortho- and Parahydrogen.* Molecular hydrogen, H_2, normally consists of two species. In one, the spins of the two protons are aligned, with a resultant nuclear spin of 1; this species is known as orthohydrogen. The second, parahydrogen, has the resultant

---

[1] The scattering length for slow neutrons can be obtained from the binding energy of the ground neutron-proton state, through Eq. (4), page 230. In particular, $a > 0$ for a bound state, while for an unbound ground state $a < 0$. (An unbound state corresponds to a resonance with $E_r > 0$.)

[2] In this section, all scattering amplitudes are for the "free" atom unless otherwise stated.

nuclear spin 0. From the quantum-mechanical requirement that the wave function of H_2 be anti-symmetrical with respect to exchange of the two protons, it follows that parahydrogen can only exist in states of even rotational spin (0,2,4, etc.), and orthohydrogen in states of odd rotational spin.[1]

At relatively high temperatures, e.g., room temperature, gaseous H_2 is a mixture containing three parts orthohydrogen to one part parahydrogen; the factor 3 is a result of the relative statistical weight, $2I + 1$, of the spin 1 as compared to the spin 0. When the equilibrium mixture is cooled to a low temperature, the ratio of ortho- to parahydrogen will remain 3:1, provided that there is no mechanism available for reversing the spin of one of the protons in the molecule without affecting the other. At sufficiently low temperatures (e.g., $\sim 20°K$), most of the orthohydrogen molecules will be in their lowest possible rotational state, of spin 1, while most of the parahydrogen molecules will have rotational spin 0.

The lowest energy state of the H_2 molecule has rotational spin 0. Hence, at very low temperatures the normal 3:1 mixture of ortho- and parahydrogen would prefer to transform into all parahydrogen. However, the conversion of ortho- into parahydrogen requires the presence of strong magnetic field gradients, capable of acting on one of the proton spins (and reversing it) without, at the same time, affecting the other. In pure liquid hydrogen the rate of conversion is very slow, so that the 3:1 mixture will remain, as a metastable configuration, for a long time. The conversion rate can be increased by the addition of a small impurity of paramagnetic atoms. It is thus possible to obtain samples of relatively pure parahydrogen in the 0 rotational state. By comparing the slow-neutron cross sections of pure parahydrogen and of the metastable 3:1 ortho-parahydrogen mixture, the separate cross sections can be deduced.

In the extreme of very long wavelength neutrons and very low gas temperatures, the elastic scattering cross sections are

$$\sigma_0(\text{para-}H_2) = \tfrac{16}{9}\pi(3a_+ + a_-)^2$$

$$\sigma_0(\text{ortho-}H_2) = \tfrac{16}{9}\pi[(3a_+ + a_-)^2 + 2(a_+ - a_-)^2] \qquad (181)$$

If the scattering amplitudes had the same sign (from the value of the free neutron-proton cross section and the binding energy of the deuteron, it can be deduced that the magnitudes of $3a_+$ and a_- are of the same

---

[1] The prefix ortho- is, by convention, assigned to the normally more abundant of the two species; hence the apparent contradiction that parahydrogen has anti-parallel proton spins, and vice versa for orthohydrogen. The nomenclature is even more confusing when applied to the species of D_2.

order), the cross sections would be large for both species of H_2, and would differ from each other by less than a factor of 2; both would be $\sim$4–6 times as large as $\sigma_{sc}(H)$. On the other hand, if the amplitudes have opposite sign, $\sigma(\text{para-}H_2) \ll \sigma(\text{ortho-}H_2) \sim 5\sigma_{sc}(H)$. Thus, even a crude comparison of the two cross sections results in a determination of the relative signs of a_+ and a_-.

The derivation of Eqs. (181) follows from relatively straightforward arguments. The amplitude for scattering by parahydrogen is simply a superposition, with the appropriate spin weighting factors, of the singlet and triplet amplitudes, since the combination of the neutron and one of the protons into the triplet state guarantees that the state of the neutron and other proton is the singlet,

$$a(\text{para-}H_2) = \frac{4}{3} \cdot \frac{2(3a_+ + a_-)}{4} \qquad (182)$$

The factor $\frac{4}{3}$ is necessary to convert from the "free" to "molecular" amplitudes according to Eq. (170'a); the factor 2 comes from the fact that there are two atoms in the molecule. Substitution into $\sigma_{coh} = 4\pi |a_{coh}|^2$ yields the first of Eqs. (181).

The cross section for scattering by orthohydrogen cannot be obtained by so simple an argument. Physically, the difficulty arises because the two protons, in a configuration of spin 1, are not exactly parallel, since the magnitude of the resultant spin vector is $[I(I + 1)]^{1/2} = (2)^{1/2}$ while the magnitudes of the component spin vectors are $[s(s + 1)]^{1/2} = (\frac{3}{4})^{1/2}$. Hence, when the neutron and one of the protons combine to give either the triplet or singlet configuration, the wave function describing the state of the neutron and second proton will contain both singlet and triplet components. This ambiguity in the relative states of the two neutron-proton systems results in an "incoherent" scattering, which is the origin of the second term in $\sigma_0(\text{ortho-}H_2)$ of Eqs. (181).

Following Schwinger and Teller (S7), the quantum-mechanical derivation of the cross sections proceeds as follows: We can describe the general spin-dependent, free amplitudes of a single nucleus by the expression

$$a_\pm = \frac{I + 1}{2I + 1} a_+ + \frac{I}{2I + 1} a_- + (a_+ - a_-) \frac{2\mathbf{s} \cdot \mathbf{I}}{2I + 1} \qquad (182a)$$

where $\mathbf{s}$ and $\mathbf{I}$ are the spin operators for the neutron and the scattering nucleus, respectively. For neutron-proton scattering

$$a_\pm(H) = \tfrac{3}{4}a_+ + \tfrac{1}{4}a_- + (a_+ - a_-)\mathbf{s} \cdot \mathbf{I}_p \qquad (182b)$$

with $s = I_p = \frac{1}{2}$. Now, $2\mathbf{s} \cdot \mathbf{I}_p = J(J + 1) - s(s + 1) - I_p(I_p + 1)$

$= J(J + 1) - \frac{3}{2}$. (J is the spin of the neutron-proton system; $J_+ = 1$, $J_- = 0$). Therefore,

$$a_\pm(H) = \tfrac{3}{4}a_+ + \tfrac{1}{4}a_- + \tfrac{1}{4}(a_+ - a_-)[2J(J + 1) - 3] \quad (182b')$$

which reduces to a_+ for $J_+ = 1$ and a_- for $J_- = 0$.

For two protons which scatter coherently (H_2),

$$a(H_2) = \tfrac{3}{2}a_+ + \tfrac{1}{2}a_- + (a_+ - a_-)\mathbf{s\cdot I} \quad (182c)$$

with $\mathbf{I} = \mathbf{I}_{p_1} + \mathbf{I}_{p_2}$; $I = 1$ (ortho) or 0 (para). For the cross section, we require

$$a^2(H_2) = \tfrac{1}{4}(3a_+ + a_-)^2 + \tfrac{1}{2}(3a_+ + a_-)(a_+ - a_-)\mathbf{s\cdot I}$$
$$+ (a_+ - a_-)^2(\mathbf{s\cdot I})^2 \quad (182c')$$

In particular, since the neutrons are unpolarized, we require an average for all possible orientations of $\mathbf{s}$. The second (cross) term vanishes on taking the average. In addition, $(\mathbf{s\cdot I})^2 = s_x^2 I_x^2 + s_y^2 I_y^2 + s_z^2 I_z^2$ and since, for unpolarized neutrons, $s_x^2 = s_y^2 = s_z^2 = \frac{1}{4}$, we obtain $(\mathbf{s\cdot I})^2 = \mathbf{I}^2/4 = I(I + 1)/4$, giving

$$a^2(H_2) = \tfrac{1}{4}[(3a_+ + a_-)^2 + (a_+ - a_-)^2 I(I + 1)] \quad (182c'')$$

Finally, for the molecular scattering cross section,

$$\sigma_0(H_2) = 4\pi \, \tfrac{16}{9} a^2(H_2)$$
$$= \tfrac{16}{9}\pi[(3a_+ + a_-)^2 + (a_+ - a_-)^2 I(I + 1)] \quad (181)$$

which reduces to the previous expressions for $I = 1$ (ortho) and $I = 0$ (para).

The theory outlined above is not sufficient for the interpretation of actual measurements. An accurate theory must take into account such phenomena as the Doppler effect, the internal motion of the protons in H_2, and the possibility of ortho-para conversion by inelastic scattering of the neutrons. The last effect, in particular, is energetically preferred (since it involves conversion from the rotational state $J = 1$ to $J = 0$, a state of lower energy). The conversion will therefore take place even at the lowest neutron energies. This contribution to $\sigma(\text{ortho-}H_2)$ will add to the "incoherent" term. Detailed consideration of such effects, by Hamermesh and Schwinger (H23), leads to the following cross sections for the scattering of neutrons of energy kT, $T = 20°K$, by H_2 molecules at a temperature of $20°K$:

$$\sigma(\text{para-}H_2) = 6.444(3a_+ + a_-)^2$$
$$\sigma(\text{ortho-}H_2) = 6.450(3a_+ + a_-)^2 + 14.653(a_+ - a_-)^2 \quad (181')$$

The first experiments on ortho- and para-H_2 scattering, by Halpern, Estermann, Simpson, and Stern (H10) in 1937, were sufficient to establish that the signs of a_+ and a_- are opposite, since the observed ortho-hydrogen cross section was several times greater than that for parahydrogen. However, owing to the wide spread and relatively high energy of the neutrons employed, their results could not be interpreted to give the values of the amplitudes. Improved measurements, by Brickwedde, Dunning, Hoge, and Manley (B64) and by Libby and Long (L18), further widened the gap between the observed ortho- and parahydrogen cross section. Alvarez and Pitzer (A14), using neutrons of low energy (kT, $T \approx 20°K$) and liquid hydrogen targets of $T \approx 20°K$, found $\sigma(\text{para-}H_2) = 5.2$ barns, $\sigma(\text{ortho-}H_2) = 100$ barns. However, attempted interpretation of their results by Schwinger (S9) yielded values of the scattering lengths which were inconsistent with known properties of the neutron-proton interaction.

More recent measurements by Sutton, Hall, Anderson, Bridge, De-Wire, Lavatelli, Long, Snyder, and Williams (S59) gave $\sigma(\text{para-}H_2) = 4.40$ barns and $\sigma(\text{ortho-}H_2) = 133$ barns, for neutrons of 0.001250 ev ($T = 15°K$). (They measured at a number of neutron energies between $T \approx 10°K$ and $30°K$, and corrected for the $1/v$ capture cross section and neutron inelastic scattering.) Assuming positive a_+, their results give

$$a_+ = 0.52 \times 10^{-12} \text{ cm}$$

$$a_- = -2.34 \times 10^{-12} \text{ cm}$$

Another very important conclusion from these experiments is that the *neutron spin is certainly* $\frac{1}{2}$. A spin of $\frac{3}{2}$, for instance, would be in strong contradiction to the observed ortho-, para-, and free hydrogen cross sections.

One difficulty in the above experiments comes from the fact that, in order to determine the orthohydrogen cross section, it is necessary to use the metastable 3:1 mixture and to be sure that the relative concentration of the two species remains unchanged, and accurately known, throughout the experiment. Sutton *et al.* found that, under the conditions of their experiment, the orthohydrogen was slowly converted to parahydrogen; over a period of about 6 hours, the ratio went from 3:1 to about 1:1.

A more serious difficulty arises from the circumstance that $\sigma(\text{ortho-}H_2) \gg \sigma(\text{para-}H_2)$, so that a very small admixture of orthohydrogen, in the supposedly pure parahydrogen sample, gives rise to a large error in the determination of $\sigma(\text{para-}H_2)$. The usual method of obtaining pure parahydrogen is to condense liquid hydrogen over activated charcoal.

It is necessary to wait a comparatively long time before equilibrium is reached. One sample of parahydrogen, used by Sutton *et al.*, obtained after about 2 days of condensation over activated charcoal, was 99.9 percent pure. However, with samples containing such a small fraction of orthohydrogen, it is exceedingly difficult to measure accurately the relative amounts of the two species. Schwinger has suggested the use of the nuclear resonance technique for the determination of the amount of orthohydrogen in a parahydrogen sample.

The large difference between $\sigma(\text{para-}H_2)$ and $\sigma(\text{ortho-}H_2)$ arises from the rather fortuitous circumstance that the coherent scattering amplitude, $(3a_+ + a_-)/4$ is small, owing to the difference in the signs of a_+ and a_-. It is not too likely that the same condition will apply for many other nuclei. However, the deuterium nucleus is of sufficient interest to have warranted investigation by similar techniques.

The deuteron spin being 1, molecular D_2 has three possible spin states, $I = 2, 1, 0$. Since the deuteron obeys Einstein-Bose statistics, the spin configurations 2 and 0 can only be in even rotational states (ortho-D_2), while $I = 1$ has only odd rotational spins (para-D_2). The equilibrium ortho- to para-D_2 ratio is 2:1. The free deuteron scattering cross section is

$$\sigma_{sc}(D) = \frac{4\pi}{3}(2a_+{}^2 + a_-{}^2) = \frac{4\pi}{9}[(2a_+ + a_-)^2 + 2(a_+ - a_-)^2] \quad (183)$$

Using techniques similar to those applied above to H_2, Hamermesh and Schwinger (H22) obtain, for the limiting cross sections,

$$\sigma_0(\text{ortho-}D_2) = \tfrac{64}{25}\pi[(2a_+ + a_-)^2 + \tfrac{5}{4}(a_+ - a_-)^2]$$
$$\sigma_0(\text{para-}D_2) = \tfrac{64}{25}\pi[(2a_+ + a_-)^2 + \tfrac{1}{2}(a_+ - a_-)^2] \quad (184)$$

Taking into account inelastic scattering and Doppler effect, the cross sections become, for D_2 at $T = 20°K$ and neutrons of energy kT, $T = 20°K$,

$$\sigma(\text{ortho-}D_2) = 8.33(2a_+ + a_-)^2 + 10.42(a_+ - a_-)^2$$
$$\sigma(\text{para-}D_2) = 8.33(2a_+ + a_-)^2 + 5.97(a_+ - a_-)^2 \quad (184')$$

Hamermesh and Schwinger point out that these cross sections are much less sensitive to the relative values of a_+ and a_- (owing to the relatively large "incoherent" term in both cross sections). If the two amplitudes have the same sign, $\sigma(\text{ortho-}D_2)/\sigma(\text{para-}D_2)$ never exceeds 1.11. For opposite signs, the ratio of the cross sections has a relatively sharp maximum of 1.75 when $a_+/a_- = -\tfrac{1}{2}$. Clearly, measurement of the cross sections of the two species is not a very sensitive method for obtaining a_+/a_-.

In practice, measurement of $\sigma(\text{ortho-}D_2)/\sigma(\text{para-}D_2)$ yields the constant

$$\rho \equiv \frac{(a_+ - a_-)^2}{(2a_+ + a_-)^2} \tag{185}$$

To a given value of ρ there correspond two values of a_+/a_-. The value of ρ can also be obtained from a comparison of $\sigma(D_2)$ and $\sigma_{sc}(D)$. In this case, there is no particular advantage in trying to separate the species of D_2. For the equilibrium mixture,

$$\sigma(D_2) = \tfrac{2}{3}\sigma(\text{ortho-}D_2) + \tfrac{1}{3}\sigma(\text{para-}D_2) \tag{184a}$$

The ratio $\sigma(D_2)/\sigma_{sc}(D)$ is most naturally interpreted in terms of the constant

$$\delta \equiv \frac{(a_+ - a_-)^2}{(2a_+^2 + a_-^2)} = \frac{3\rho}{(1 + 2\rho)} \tag{185a}$$

Fermi and Marshall (F24) have measured $\sigma_{sc}(D)$ for neutrons of a few ev, and $\sigma(D_2)$ for deuterium gas at $77.5°K$ and neutrons of $\lambda = 5.43$ A. They obtained $\sigma_{sc}(D) = 3.44$ barns and $\sigma(D_2) = 21.3$ barns, from which, after applying the appropriate corrections to $\sigma(D_2)$, they infer $\delta = 0.04 \pm 0.10$. Owing to the large uncertainty, it is difficult to draw any firm conclusions from this measurement. However, the small value of δ means that a_+ and a_- must certainly have the same sign. With regard to the interpretation of these measurements, it should be pointed out that similar cross section determinations on H_2, by the same authors (F21), gave results in rather poor agreement with the theory.

Another approach is to measure the angular distribution of slow-neutron scattering by D_2. Such measurements have been performed by Hurst and Alcock (H80), and interpreted according to the methods of Hamermesh and Schwinger (H22) and of Spiers (S48). The measurements lead to a value of $\rho = 0.173 \, {}^{+0.028}_{-0.022}$. (The corresponding value of δ is 0.385.) The angular distribution of the scattered neutrons is relatively less sensitive to the internal motion and velocity distribution of the molecules (S48) than is the total cross section, so that the above value of ρ appears to be quite reliable.

A possible means of removing the ambiguity in the (two) values of a_+/a_-, obtained from scattering experiments on D_2, has been suggested by Hamermesh and Schwinger (H22). They observe that a measurement of neutron scattering by molecular HD might have the desired effect. However, the limiting HD cross section,

$$\sigma_0(HD) = \tfrac{9}{16}\pi[(3a_+{}^H + a_-{}^H + 2a_+{}^D + a_-{}^D)^2 + 3(a_+{}^H - a_-{}^H)^2$$
$$+ 2(a_+{}^D - a_-{}^D)^2]$$
$$= \tfrac{9}{4}\sigma_{sc}(H) + \tfrac{81}{64}\sigma_{sc}(D) + \tfrac{9}{8}\pi(3a_+{}^H + a_-{}^H)(2a_+{}^D + a_-{}^D)$$

$$(186)$$

is unfortunately very insensitive to the interference term.

(b) *Diffraction by Crystals Containing H and D.* Shull, Wollan, Morton, and Davidson (S29) and Wollan, Shull, and Koehler (W43) have studied the powder diffraction patterns of NaH and NaD (see Section 5B1 and Fig. 66). Applying the techniques described in Section 5C2, they obtained for the coherent scattering amplitudes

$$a_{coh}(\text{bound H}) = (-0.396 \pm 0.02) \times 10^{-12} \text{ cm}$$
$$a_{coh}(\text{bound D}) = (0.64 \pm 0.02) \times 10^{-12} \text{ cm}$$

The above value of $a_{coh}(\text{bound H}) = (3a_+ + a_-)/2$, when combined with a value of $\sigma_{sc}(\text{free H}) = 20.36$ barns (M24), yields

$$a_+{}^H = 0.528 \times 10^{-12} \text{ cm}$$
$$a_-{}^H = -2.38 \times 10^{-12} \text{ cm}$$

in reasonably good agreement with the values from ortho- and parahydrogen scattering.

The coherent (bound) scattering cross section of D is, from the above, 5.2 ± 0.3 barns. The difference between this value and the corrected free scattering cross section of Fermi and Marshall (F24), $\sigma_{sc}(\text{bound D}) = (\tfrac{9}{4}) 3.44 = 7.74$ barns, is not sufficiently large to allow an accurate determination of the amplitudes for the two spin states. However, from their value of $\rho = 0.173$, the value $\sigma_{sc}(D) = 3.44 \pm 0.06$ barns, and the above observation that $a_{coh}(D) > 0$, Hurst and Alcock (H80) derive

$$\left. \begin{array}{l} a_+{}^D = (0.26 \pm 0.02) \times 10^{-12} \text{ cm} \\ a_-{}^D = (0.826 \pm 0.012) \times 10^{-12} \text{ cm} \end{array} \right\} \text{ or } \left\{ \begin{array}{l} (0.638 \pm 0.006) \times 10^{-12} \text{ cm} \\ (0.07 \pm 0.03) \times 10^{-12} \text{ cm} \end{array} \right.$$

The results of Wollan, Shull, and Koehler (W43) are in agreement with these, although the last-mentioned investigators prefer the first set of amplitude values on the basis of theoretical arguments.

It is interesting to note that among the 22 nuclei with spin $\neq 0$, for which coherent scattering measurements have been recorded by Shull and Wollan (Table 37), 8 show pronounced spin dependence (difference by more than a factor 2 between σ_{coh} and σ_{sc}), 8 show a slight spin dependence, and 5 show no appreciable spin incoherence (less than 10 per cent difference between the coherent and bound scattering cross sections).

(c) $a_{coh}(bound\ H)\ from\ Total\ Reflection.$ It was pointed out in Section 5C1 that measurement of the critical angle for total reflection of monoenergetic neutrons from a mirror yields, directly, the coherent (bound) scattering amplitude. This technique has been applied by Hughes, Burgy, and Ringo (H74), to measure the coherent scattering amplitude of H.

Since $a_{coh}(H) < 0$, a mirror of pure H would not exhibit total external reflection. However, if the H is mixed with another element with $a > 0$

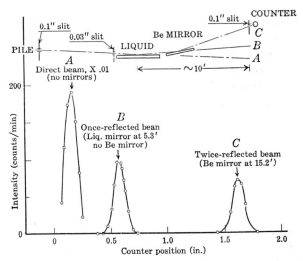

Fig. 71. Experimental arrangement of Hughes, Burgy, and Ringo (H74) for the measurement of a_{coh}(bound H) by total reflection from a liquid mirror. Also shown are typical curves of the variation of neutron intensity with the counter position.

and if, for the mixture, $a_{coh} = \sum_j f_j a_j > 0$, total external reflection will become possible. From a knowledge of the value of a of the diluent, and a measurement of θ_c, $a_{coh}(H)$ can be deduced from Eq. (178a').

The first experiment of Hughes, Burgy, and Ringo consisted in observing total reflection from a mirror of liquid triethylbenzene ($C_{12}H_{18}$). Since the (positive) amplitude of carbon is slightly larger than 1.5 times the (negative) amplitude of hydrogen, total reflection is possible. While the critical angle is small (6 min for $\lambda = 8$ A), the fact that θ_c measures a difference ($a_C - 1.5|a_H|$) has the result that a given error in θ_c implies a much smaller ($\sim 1/10$) error in the value of a_H.

The experimental arrangement and some typical measurements are shown in Fig. 71. The measurement actually consisted in setting the angle of the liquid mirror, θ_c, at a fixed value. The reflected beam, which contained neutrons (with a Maxwellian energy distribution) of all wavelengths longer than λ_c—corresponding to the given θ_c—was then analyzed by a beryllium mirror to determine λ_c. The value of a_{coh}(bound H) was obtained from the relationship

$$\theta_c = \lambda_c \left[\frac{N(a_C + 1.5a_H)}{\pi} \right]^{\frac{1}{2}} \tag{178'a}$$

where N is the density of carbon atoms in the liquid and $a_C = (0.663 \pm 0.003) \times 10^{-12}$ cm, corresponding to σ_{sc}(free C) $= 4.70 \pm 0.05$ barns. The result of a number of such measurements on a number of mirrors of different hydrogen to carbon ratio is a_{coh}(bound H) $= (-0.378 \pm 0.002) \times 10^{-12}$ cm.

This value is ~5 percent lower than that obtained by Shull, Wollan, Morton, and Davidson (S29). From it, and the value σ_{sc}(free H) $= 20.36 \pm 0.10$ barns (M24)

$$a_+{}^H = (0.5377 \pm 0.0023) \times 10^{-12} \text{ cm}$$

$$a_-{}^H = (-2.369 \pm 0.006) \times 10^{-12} \text{ cm}$$

The reason(s) for the disagreement is (are) not obvious.

D. Magnetic Scattering and Neutron Polarization

Because of its intrinsic magnetic moment (see Section 1B5), the neutron will interact with, and consequently be scattered by, magnetic fields. As first pointed out by Bloch in 1936 (B36), the interaction of a neutron with a paramagnetic atom or ion will depend on the relative orientation of their magnetic moments. Hence, the scattering of neutron beams by magnetized materials will be different for the two possible orientations of the neutron spin with respect to the direction of magnetization, giving rise to the possibility of obtaining polarized neutrons.[1]

The theory of the magnetic neutron-electron interaction and of the transmission of neutrons through magnetized iron was developed by Bloch (B36), by Schwinger (S6), and by Halpern and co-workers (H11, H14, H15, H21), who worked out the details of the dependence of the

---

[1] The magnetic neutron-electron interaction, which is the basis of the magnetic scattering discussed in this section, is, of course, a different phenomenon from the neutron-electron interaction of Section 1C3. The latter will be present even when the atom has no net magnetic moment but will, in the interaction with paramagnetic atoms, be completely masked by the *much larger* magnetic interaction.

interaction on the atomic and crystalline structure of the ferromagnetic material. Steinberger and Wick (S51) have recently re-examined some of these problems and, in particular, have recomputed the interaction of neutrons with iron atoms (i.e., the atomic form factor) in a (successful) attempt to reconcile apparent discrepancies between theory and experiment.

While one aspect of the magnetic neutron-electron interaction developed by the above-mentioned authors is the coherent scattering by crystalline materials, other effects have their origin in the dependence of the index of refraction of a medium on its magnetic properties (H15). In particular, the index of refraction (and, consequently, the critical angle for total reflection) of a magnetized scatterer will be different for the two neutron spin orientations, which provides another possible means for producing polarized neutrons. The theory for this effect has been developed by Akhiezer and Pomeranchuk (A5), by Halpern (H19), by Ekstein (E3), and by Lax (L9).

The most important consequences of the theories can be summarized as follows: The scattering of a slow neutron by a single paramagnetic atom is described in terms of the scattering length,

$$a = a_0 \pm a_{mag} \tag{187}$$

where a_0 is the nuclear scattering length and a_{mag} is that due to the atomic neutron-electron interaction. The $+$ and $-$ signs refer, respectively, to neutrons whose spin directions are parallel and antiparallel to the direction of the atomic magnetic moment. The scattering length for the magnetic interaction can be written

$$a_{mag} = \left(\frac{e^2}{mc^2}\right) \gamma_n S_a F_a f(\theta,\varphi) \tag{187a}$$

in which the symbols have the following meanings: $(e^2/mc^2) = 2.8 \times 10^{-13}$ cm is the so-called classical electron radius. $\gamma_n = |\mu_n|/(e\hbar/2Mc)$ is the magnitude of the neutron's magnetic moment in nuclear magneton units. S_a is the electron spin quantum number of the atom. (It is assumed that the atomic moment is $\mu_a = -2\mu_0 S_a$, where μ_0 is the Bohr magneton.) F_a is the atomic form factor, a measure of the coherence in the scattering of the neutrons from different regions of the atom; the form factor depends on the angle through which the neutron is scattered, as well as on the neutron wavelength λ. The factor $f(\theta,\varphi)$ is a function of the relative directions of the atomic magnetization, the neutron spin, and the scattering vector.

In the form of the theory developed by Schwinger (S6) and by Halpern and Johnson (H11),

$$f(\theta,\varphi) = \left| 2\mathbf{s}_n \cdot \mathbf{q} \right| \tag{187b}$$

$\mathbf{s}_n$ is the neutron spin vector and

$$\mathbf{q} = (\mathbf{e}\cdot\mathbf{m})\mathbf{e} - \mathbf{m} \tag{187b'}$$

where $\mathbf{m}$ is a unit vector in the direction of the magnetization and $\mathbf{e}$ is a unit vector in the direction of the change of neutron momentum, $\mathbf{e} = (\mathbf{k} - \mathbf{k}')/|\mathbf{k} - \mathbf{k}'|$. The vector $\mathbf{q}$ is perpendicular to $\mathbf{e}$ (i.e., $\mathbf{q}\cdot\mathbf{e} = 0$), and has the magnitude $q^2 = \sin^2 \alpha$, where α is the angle between $\mathbf{e}$ and $\mathbf{m}$ ($\mathbf{e}\cdot\mathbf{m} = \cos \alpha$). From these relationships and the properties of the neutron spin vector $\mathbf{s}_n$ ($s_n^2 = (\frac{1}{2})(\frac{3}{2}) = \frac{3}{4}$; $s_{nz} = \pm\frac{1}{2}$, $\overline{s_{nx}} = \overline{s_{ny}} = 0$; $\overline{s_{nx}^2} = \overline{s_{ny}^2} = \overline{s_{nz}^2} = s_n^2/3 = \frac{1}{4}$), the following properties of $f(\theta,\varphi)$ follow: For neutrons polarized with respect to the fixed direction $\mathbf{m}$, $f(\theta,\varphi) = \sin^2 \alpha$. Thus, for scattering in the plane perpendicular to $\mathbf{m}$, $f(\theta,\varphi) = 1$ and $a_{mag} = \pm(e^2/mc^2)\gamma_n S_a F_a$. For the scattering of unpolarized neutrons by atoms with a fixed direction of magnetization, $\overline{f(\theta,\varphi)} = 0$ and $\overline{f^2(\theta,\varphi)} = q^2 = \overline{\sin^2 \alpha}$. Finally, for a random distribution of magnetization vectors, $\overline{f(\theta,\varphi)} = 0$ and $\overline{f^2(\theta,\varphi)} = \frac{2}{3}$.

Since $d\sigma/d\Omega = (a_0 \pm a_{mag})^2$, the cross section will, in general, involve both an interference term, $\pm 2a_0 a_{mag}$, and a pure magnetic term, a_{mag}^2. The dependence of the interference term on the angle of scattering is through the product $F(\lambda,\theta)f(\theta,\varphi)$. For the special case of neutrons incident normally to the fixed direction of magnetization, $F(\lambda,\theta)f(\theta,\varphi) = F(\lambda,\theta)[1 - \frac{1}{2}\cos^2 \varphi \,(1 + \cos \theta)]$. Averaging over φ, this becomes $F(\lambda,\theta)\overline{f(\theta)} = F(\lambda,\theta)(3 - \cos \theta)/4 = F(\lambda,\theta)[1 + \sin^2(\theta/2)]/2$. The last expression is appropriate to the computation of the cross section for magnetic scattering by magnetized polycrystalline samples, discussed below.

The expression for $f(\theta,\varphi)$ is different in the theory as originally presented by Bloch (B36). The value of a_{mag} is still given by Eq. (187a), and $f(\theta,\varphi)$ by Eq. (187b), but with $\mathbf{q} = (\mathbf{e}\cdot\mathbf{m})\mathbf{e}$; this change results in the substitution of $\cos^2 \alpha$ wherever $\sin^2 \alpha$ appears above. Correspondingly, $a_{mag} = 0$ for scattering in the plane perpendicular to a fixed m. As pointed out by Bloch (B36), the difference arises from his original description of the neutron moment as a point dipole, in contrast to the approach of the other authors, in which the neutron moment is represented as arising from a current distribution and treated by the methods of Dirac. Ekstein (E3) has shown that the "Dirac" treatment implies an interaction energy of the form $-\mu_n \cdot \mathbf{B}$, while that of Bloch implies $-\mu_n \cdot \mathbf{H}$. Experiments, as we shall see, have decided in favor of the "Dirac" interaction.

Most magnetic substances, e.g., iron, are polycrystalline in nature. For such substances the scattering of slow neutrons involves the coherent superposition of the amplitudes from different atoms in the same crystal. Thus, the coherent scattering cross section will contain, in addition to the atomic form factor in a_{mag}, a crystal form factor. In general, the transmission of a beam of neutrons through a magnetized (to saturation) sample is described in terms of two cross sections,

$$\sigma_{\pm} = \sigma_0 \pm p \tag{188}$$

where the two signs refer, respectively, to neutron spins parallel and anti-parallel to the direction of magnetization. σ_0 is the cross section for a completely unmagnetized sample, and includes the effects of magnetic (the term with a_{mag}^2) as well as nuclear scattering. $p = 8\pi a_0 a_{mag} F_{crystal}$, arises from the interference between the nuclear and magnetic amplitudes. It follows that the coherent scattering will vanish for wavelengths larger than the last Bragg cut-off ($\lambda > 2d_{max}$) which, for iron, is 4.04 A. For wavelengths smaller than 4.04 A, the value of p will be strongly dependent on λ. (See Section 5B1 and Fig. 67 on the scattering of polycrystalline samples.) For $\lambda > 4.04$ A, the only scattering will be incoherent, owing to isotopic, spin-dependent, and inelastic lattice scattering. It is interesting to note that only the last is expected to depend on the orientation of the neutron spin (H16).

The index of refraction of a magnetized substance is, as a result of the two scattering amplitudes (Eq. 187), also a double-valued quantity. Since the index of refraction involves only forward scattering, the form factors (atomic and crystal) are unity, and the resulting expression is particularly simple:

$$n_{\pm} = 1 - \frac{\lambda^2 N a_0}{2\pi} \mp \frac{\mu_n B}{2E_n} \tag{189}$$

where μ_n is the magnitude of the neutron magnetic moment, B the magnetic flux density in the scatterer, and E_n the neutron energy. For $a_0 > 0$, there will always be at least one neutron spin direction for which total reflection is possible ($n_+ < 1$); if the nuclear term exceeds the magnetic, both orientations will exhibit total reflection, but with different critical angles: [1]

$$\theta_{c\pm} \cong (1 - n_{\pm}^2)^{1/2} \cong \left(\frac{\lambda^2 N a_0}{\pi} \pm \frac{\mu_n B}{E_n}\right)^{1/2} \tag{190}$$

The derivation of the magnetic scattering length proceeds along straightforward quantum-mechanical lines, and is described in detail in a number of the references quoted above. It involves the evaluation, by the Born approximation, of the scattering due to the interaction integral:

$$b_{mag} = \int V \, d\tau = \boldsymbol{\mu}_n \cdot \mathbf{M}_{atom} = \pm \mu_n M_{atom} \tag{191}$$

[M_{atom} is the atomic magnetization. μ_n is the absolute value of the neutron moment, which is actually negative; hence the signs in (191).] We shall not repeat this computation. However, a simple estimate can be made of the order of magnitude of a_{mag}. In this estimate we neglect the atomic form factor and the angular dependence.

Consider a magnetized substance with N atoms/cm^3, each having a moment $\mu_a = (e\hbar/mc)S_a$. Then

$$B \cong N M_{atom} = 4\pi N \mu_a \tag{191a}$$

$$M_{atom} \cong 4\pi \left(\frac{e\hbar}{mc}\right) S_a$$

and

$$b_{mag} \cong \pm 4\pi \gamma_n \left(\frac{e\hbar}{2Mc}\right)\left(\frac{e\hbar}{mc}\right) S_a \tag{191'}$$

The Born approximation gives

$$a_{mag} = \frac{M b_{mag}}{2\pi \hbar^2} \cong \pm \left(\frac{e^2}{mc^2}\right) \gamma_n S_a \tag{192}$$

which is Eq. (187a) without the form factor or the angular dependence. For a rough estimate, $\gamma_n \approx 2$ and $S = 5/2$, giving $a_{mag} \approx 1.4 \times 10^{-12} F f(\theta,\varphi)$; taking $\overline{F^2 f^2} \approx 0.1$, $\sigma_{mag} = 4\pi \overline{a_{mag}^2} \approx 2.5$ barns.

---

[1] Strictly speaking, Eq. (189) holds only for mirrors magnetized in the plane of the surface. Otherwise, B must be regarded as the component of the field in the plane of the surface. The normal component of B is continuous across the surface, and hence, according to Eq. (178a), its effects cancel. It should be noted that the original formulation of Bloch, in which the magnetic term would involve $\mu_n H$, predicts only a single value of θ_c for magnetization parallel to the surface, since H is then continuous across the surface; also since $H \ll B$ in a ferromagnet, its effect on the index of refraction would be small. Finally, it is really the magnetization part of B ($B' = B - H$) which belongs in (189), since H is the same on both sides of the scattering surface; for ferromagnets, the difference between B and B' is negligible.

This method of estimating a_{mag} should be exact for the index of refraction, where $F = f = 1$:

$$1 - n_{mag} = \frac{\lambda^2 N a_{mag}}{2\pi} = \pm \frac{\lambda^2 M \mu_n B}{h^2} = \pm \frac{\mu_n B}{2E_n} \qquad (192')$$

(the same as in Eq. 189). Taking $B \approx 10{,}000$ gauss and $E_n \approx 0.02$ ev ($\lambda \approx 2$ A), we get $1 - n_{mag} \approx \pm 2 \times 10^{-6}$.

1. Neutron Transmission through Magnetized Iron. (a) *The Single Transmission Effect*. The most direct method of determining σ_0 and p (Eq. 188) is by measuring the neutron transmission of unmagnetized and magnetized samples. Consider a slab of polycrystalline iron of thickness d and atomic density N. If the sample is in an unmagnetized state, the transmission is

$$\frac{I}{I_0} = e^{-N\sigma_0 d} \qquad (193a)$$

When the sample is magnetized to saturation, the two possible neutron spin orientations will have different cross sections and, hence, different transmissions. For an initially unpolarized beam ($I_{+0} = I_{-0} = \frac{1}{2}I_0$)

$$\frac{I_+}{I_0} = \frac{1}{2} e^{-N(\sigma_0 + p)d}$$

$$\frac{I_-}{I_0} = \frac{1}{2} e^{-N(\sigma_0 - p)d} \qquad (193b)$$

If we define the "single transmission effect," E_1, as the relative increase in transmission due to the magnetization of the sample,

$$E_1 \equiv \frac{\Delta I}{I} = \frac{(I_+ + I_- - I)}{I} \qquad (193)$$

$$E_{1s} = -1 + \cosh Npd \cong \frac{1}{2}(Npd)^2 \qquad \text{(for } Npd \ll 1) \qquad (193')$$

Correspondingly, the degree of polarization of the beam emerging from the magnetized sample is

$$P \equiv \frac{(I_- - I_+)}{(I_- + I_+)} = \tanh Npd \cong Npd \qquad (194)$$

Actually, Eq. (193') applies only to samples which are magnetized to complete saturation. For unsaturated samples different regions in the magnet are imperfectly aligned, and neutron depolarization results.

The effects of incomplete magnetization on the single transmission effect have been shown, by Halpern and Holstein (H14), to result in a modification of Eq. (193′):

$$E_1 \cong E_{1s} f\left(\frac{\varepsilon d}{\delta_c}\right) \qquad (193'')$$

with $E_{1s} \cong \frac{1}{2}(Npd)^2$. $\varepsilon = (M_s - M)/M_s$ is the relative deviation of the magnetization from saturation, and δ_c is a characteristic length, which depends on the neutron velocity and on the crystalline properties of the sample:

$$f(x) = \left(\frac{2}{x^2}\right)(e^{-x} + x - 1) \qquad (193''a)$$

approaches 1 as $x \to 0$, and approaches 0 for large x. Since the characteristic length, δ_c, is normally very small, $\sim 10^{-4}$–10^{-2} cm in typical samples, very small deviations of ε from 0, say of $\sim 10^{-3}$, will lead to an appreciable decrease in E_1 as compared to E_{1s}.

The crystal structure of iron, as it affects the magnetic scattering of neutrons, can be described in terms of the "domains," which are relatively large macrocrystals; these are oriented at random in an unmagnetized sample. Each domain is a mosaic pattern of a large number of microcrystals (whose dimensions are normally much smaller than the depth of neutron penetration in a Bragg scattering). The atoms in each microcrystal scatter coherently, but the scattering from different microcrystals in the same domain is incoherent, as is the scattering from the different domains.

The application of an external magnetic field results, first, in the alignment of the magnetizations of the microcrystals in each domain and, second, in the alignment of the magnetization vectors of all the domains with the applied field; when, finally, they all point in the same direction, saturation is achieved. However, for magnetization approaching saturation ($\varepsilon \ll 1$), but not quite there, the magnetizations of domains in relatively homogeneous regions of the sample (called "grains") are parallel before those of all the grains have become completely aligned. In this situation, the depolarization scattering takes place at the boundaries between grains; for relatively weak magnetization, on the other hand, the depolarization scattering occurs at the boundaries between domains (H70).

Halpern and Holstein (H14) give the following expressions for the dependence of the characteristic length, δ_c, on the average domain (or grain, as the case may be) size, δ:

$$\delta_c \cong l^2/\delta \quad \text{for } \delta \ll l$$
$$\cong \delta \quad \text{for } \delta \approx l \quad (193''b)$$
$$\cong \delta/2 \quad \text{for } \delta \gg l$$

l is the distance a neutron travels through the iron while its moment is precessing (around B) through one radian; $l = v\hbar/2\mu_n B \approx 10^{-3}$ cm for thermal neutrons. [Physically, neutron depolarization has its origin in the application of a periodically varying field (due to successive passage across boundaries between imperfectly aligned regions of magnetization) to the precessing neutrons. The rate of depolarization, and consequently δ_c, is determined by the strength of that Fourier component of the periodic impulse whose frequency is equal to the neutron's Larmor precession frequency.]

The earliest experiments on the polarization of neutrons by passage through magnetized iron were performed by Hoffman, Livingston, and Bethe (H63), by Beyer, Carroll, Dunning, and Powers (D21, P26, P27, P28), and by Frisch, von Halban, and Koch (F47). The results of these investigations, while demonstrating the existence of a magnetic scattering effect (and, thus, of the magnetic moment of the neutron), were not sufficiently accurate to permit more than a rough comparison with theory.

The first accurate experimental check of the single-transmission formula (Eq. 193″) was achieved by Bloch, Hamermesh, and Staub (B37). Using a thermal neutron beam and a strongly magnetized sample ($\varepsilon \approx 0.24$ percent), they attained a single transmission effect of E_1 $\cong 8$ percent. By fitting the values of E_1, for various values of ε, to Eqs. (193″) and (193″a), they deduced $\bar{p} = 2.0 \pm 0.1$ barns. Although this value of $\bar{p}$ was already approximately twice that predicted by theory (H15), subsequent measurements by the Stanford group yielded even larger values (F50, B38, F31). Thus, Fleeman, Nicodemus, and Staub (F31), who achieved values of $E_1 \approx 30$ percent for (paraffin-moderated) thermal neutrons, deduced $\bar{p} = 2.35 \pm 0.1$ barns. These investigators, as well as Fryer (F50), also studied the variation of p with neutron energy. The largest values of E_1 (up to ∼60 percent) were attained by Hughes, Wallace, and Holtzman (H70), who used the intense thermal neutron beam from the Argonne heavy water pile; according to their measurements, $\bar{p} = 3.15$ barns. These authors also observed single transmission effects for magnetized nickel and obtained $\bar{p}(\text{Ni}) \approx 1$ barn.

The values of $\bar{p}$ quoted above are all very much higher than the first theoretical predictions (H15, H21). Measurements of p for monoenergetic neutron beams (F50, H70, F31) also resulted in larger values than were anticipated, although the shape of the cross section $vs.$ λ curve was as expected. The discrepancies prompted Steinberger and Wick (S51) to

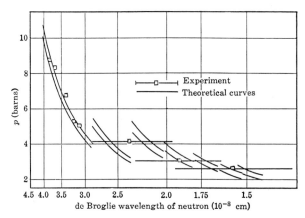

Fig. 72. Theoretical curve of p $vs.$ λ, due to Steinberger and Wick (S51). The two curves correspond to different assumptions concerning the wave function of the electrons responsible for the magnetic moment of iron. The points are from the experiments of Hughes, Wallace, and Holtzman (H70).

re-examine the theory. Their predicted curve of p $vs.$ λ is shown in Fig. 72, together with the results of the experiments of Hughes et $al.$ (H70). The agreement is now excellent.

In comparing experiments with the theory, it is necessary to take into account the change in the energy distribution ("hardening") of the neutron beam as it passes through the scatterer, since p is a strongly varying function of the neutron energy. In general, the value of $\bar{p}$ will be quite sensitive to the neutron energy distribution. The differences between the observations of the Stanford group and those of Hughes et $al.$ appear to be due to differences in the spectra of the neutrons employed (F31).

(b) The $Double$ $Transmission$ $Effect.$ An initially unpolarized neutron beam will, after transmission through a slab of magnetized iron, be partially polarized. While the magnitude of the single transmission effect, E_1, is itself a measure of the degree of polarization of the emerging beam (Eq. 194), a more direct observation of the polarization can be obtained by the use of an "analyzer." The natural form of analyzer is, in this case, a second slab of iron whose direction of magnetization is opposite to that of the first. The effectiveness of such a polarizer-analyzer combination, for producing and detecting neutron polarization, is measured by the "double-transmission effect."

Consider two slabs, of thicknesses d_1 (polarizer) and d_2 (analyzer), both containing N atoms/cm³. Let them both be magnetized to saturation, either in the same or in opposite directions. For an initial intensity I_0 of unpolarized neutrons, the transmissions for the two situations are (assuming that the polarization is unchanged in traversing the region between polarizer and analyzer)

$$I_{p\pm a} = I_0 e^{-N\sigma_0(d_1+d_2)} \cosh Np(d_1 \pm d_2) \qquad (195)$$

where the $+$ and $-$ signs refer, respectively, to parallel and antiparallel magnetizations of the polarizer and analyzer. The double transmission effect can be defined in a number of ways:

$$E_2 \equiv \frac{(I_{p+a} - I_{p-a})}{I}$$

$$E_{2s} = 2 \sinh Npd_1 \cdot \sinh Npd_2 \cong 2N^2p^2d_1d_2 \qquad (195a)$$

where $I = I_0 e^{-N\sigma_0(d_1+d_2)}$ is the transmission when both slabs are unpolarized; alternatively,[1]

$$E_2' \equiv \frac{2(I_{p+a} - I_{p-a})}{(I_{p+a} + I_{p-a})}$$

$$E_{2s}' = 2 \tanh Npd_1 \cdot \tanh Npd_2 \qquad (195b)$$

The influence of unsaturated magnetization on the double transmission effect has been considered by Halpern and Holstein (H14). For thin scatterers, they give

$$\frac{I_{p\pm a}}{I} \cong (1 + E_{1p})(1 + E_{1a}) \pm N^2p^2d_1d_2g(x_1)g(x_2) \qquad (195')$$

where E_{1p} and E_{1a} are the single transmission effects for the polarizer and analyzer, respectively (Eq. 193''), $x = \epsilon d/\delta_c$, and

$$g(x) = \frac{(1 - e^{-x})}{x} \qquad (195'a)$$

Thus
$$E_2 \cong E_{2s}g(x_1)g(x_2) \qquad (195a')$$

---

[1] This second form is somewhat more useful, from the experimental point of view, since it does not involve a measurement of I, the transmission through the unmagnetized system; such a measurement is subject to experimental uncertainties arising out of the small-angle scattering (refraction) of neutrons at boundaries between domains which are magnetized in different directions (H71, B76). This small-angle scattering disappears with magnetization. The effect of small-angle scattering is minimized in a "poor" geometry experiment.

The corresponding formula for E_2' is somewhat more complicated. Halpern and Holstein also give exact expressions for the transmission effects, which apply for arbitrary polarizer and analyzer thicknesses.

With the polarizer-analyzer set-up discussed above, it is possible to observe and measure changes in the state of polarization of the neutron beam which may occur in the region between the polarizer and analyzer. Let us consider two hypothetical situations:

(1) The directions of polarization of all of the neutrons are reversed, i.e., each neutron is "flopped" over just once, but no neutrons are removed from the beam. For crossed polarizer and analyzer (opposite magnetizations), the resulting intensity is the same as if both polarizer and analyzer were magnetized in the same direction and nothing happened in the intermediate region. The intensity will therefore increase, as a result of the spin reversals, by the full double transmission effect. Alternatively, if the magnetizations of polarizer and analyzer are in the same direction, the intensity after the "flopping" of the neutrons will be decreased by the full double transmission effect.

(2) The neutron beam is completely depolarized in the intermediate region without removing any neutrons from the beam. Since the double transmission effect arises from that portion of the neutron beam which is represented by the difference between the intensities of the two polarizations (clearly, the direction of magnetization has no effect on the transmission of an unpolarized neutron beam) and since the change in this difference, resulting from complete depolarization, is just half what it would be if the neutrons were all "flopped" once (case 1), the resulting change in the transmitted intensity will be just half of the full double transmission effect; the intensity will increase by $\frac{1}{2}E_2$ for crossed magnets, and decrease by $\frac{1}{2}E_2$ for parallel magnetizations.

It is evident that cases of partial flopping will produce changes of intensity intermediate between zero and E_2. Furthermore, the only difference between employing crossed or parallel magnets in depolarization studies is in the sign of the intensity change. Finally, the double transmission effect can be measured by introducing a known change of polarization (complete depolarization is the easiest to achieve) between the two magnets, without the necessity of reversing the direction of the analyzer.

The last fact, pointed out by Hughes and Burgy (H73), provides a simple means for overcoming the serious experimental difficulties involved in the measurement of E_2. These difficulties arise from the tendency of the neutron moment to preserve its direction with respect to the direction of a slowly varying magnetic field. Thus, if the field between a crossed polarizer and analyzer changes its direction uniformly and slowly, a neutron, on traversing the intermediate region, will undergo an adiabatic reversal of its direction of polarization. As a result, there will be no observable difference between the transmissions for parallel and anti-parallel magnetizations of polarizer and analyzer. This effect accounts for the small and inconsistent values of E_2 obtained in the early investigations (H63, P27, F47).

In their studies of the double transmission effect, Burgy, Hughes, Wallace, Heller, and Woolf (B76) succeeded in overcoming the above difficulty by means of careful magnetic shielding of the intermediate region and by the insertion into the neutron path of a short (compared to the Larmor precession distance) region in which the direction of the magnetic field is suddenly reversed; the neutrons, on traversing this region of sharp change, undergo non-adiabatic transitions and emerge with their direction unchanged (with respect to space—reversed with respect to the field). By this technique the above-mentioned investigators succeeded in observing the full expected double transmission effect.

In the same series of experiments, Burgy et al. studied the depolarization of neutrons on passing through (very) thin sheets of unmagnetized iron. As pointed out in the preceding, the rate of depolarization by unmagnetized iron is strongly dependent on the size of the polycrystalline domains (H14). The investigations of Burgy et al. on a variety of samples yielded half-thicknesses (for 50 percent depolarization) of $\sim 10^{-3}$–10^{-2} cm, corresponding to average domain sizes ranging from $\sim 3 \times 10^{-5}$ to 5×10^{-3} cm. From these results it is evident that the insertion of a relatively thin, say ~ 1 mm, sheet of unmagnetized iron into a beam of polarized neutrons will result in complete depolarization without appreciable loss of beam intensity.

2. Diffraction by Ferromagnetic Crystals. The application of neutron diffraction techniques to the study of magnetic ordering in crystals has been discussed in Section 5B2. The usefulness of these techniques is strikingly demonstrated in the observations, by Shull and co-workers (S31, S35), on the anti-ferromagnetic character of a number of substances.

In studies on the diffraction by a magnetic crystal, magnetite, Shull, Wollan, and Strauser (S32) observed that the structure is such as to permit a sensitive check on the theory of the angular dependence of magnetic scattering. This possibility arises from the circumstance that the (1,1,1) reflection intensity is almost entirely (to within ~ 2 percent) due to magnetic scattering. (The crystal form factor is such that nuclear scattering contributes very little to the coherent scattering amplitude.) Consequently, the scattering of unpolarized neutrons by the (1,1,1) planes should be proportional to a_{mag}^2. Shull *et al.* measured the variation of scattered intensity with the angle (α) between the magnetization direction and the direction of the scattering vector. They found, within an uncertainty of ~ 2 percent, $f^2(\theta, \varphi) = \sin^2 \alpha$, thereby verifying the appropriateness of the "Dirac" interaction.

Further investigation by Shull (S34) showed that the coherent amplitude for reflection from the (2,2,0) planes of magnetite (at $\alpha = 90°$) contains approximately equal contributions from the nuclear and the magnetic scattering. Since $a_{coh} \propto (a_0 \pm a_{mag})$, one of the two possible neutron polarizations will be almost completely absent in the Bragg scattering at $\alpha = 90°$ from the (2,2,0) planes of Fe_3O_4. Shull has verified the complete polarization (to within ~ 5 percent) of neutrons scattered under these circumstances. The intensity of the polarized (monoenergetic) neutron beams produced by this method was $\sim 10^5$ per second, for an incident flux of $\sim 10^{12}$ neutrons/cm^2/sec.

A possible application of this technique of neutron polarization, suggested by Shull and co-workers (S32, S34), is the production of pulsed beams of polarized neutrons. Since the applied field necessary to produce magnetization in a ferromagnetic crystal is relatively small, it should be possible to change the orientation of the magnetization (and polarization) very rapidly. Correspondingly, modulation of α, for the (1,1,1) reflection from magnetite, could result in a pulsed beam of unpolarized neutrons. The data on neutron scattering and polarization by ferromagnetic crystals are summarized by Shull, Wollan, and Koehler (S36).

In the interpretation of data on scattering from magnetic crystals, it is necessary to make corrections for inelastic scattering. The inelastic scattering cross section can be measured either by observations on the transmission of polycrystalline samples at neutron energies below the lowest cut-off or on the transmission of a single crystal at non-Bragg angles. Measurements on iron by Cassels and Latham (C3), using the first technique, indicated fair agreement with the theory of temperature-diffuse scattering (W14) at room temperature. Hughes, Burgy, and Woolf (H75) investigated the intensity and polarization of neutrons transmitted through a single crystal of iron at non-Bragg angles. Their results bear out the hypothesis that the incoherent scattering results from inelastic lattice scattering (H16), both in the magnitude and energy dependence of the cross section and in the observation of a single transmission (polarization) effect.

3. Total Reflection from Magnetized Mirrors. Given a mirror magnetized in the plane of its surface, and provided that a_0 is positive and greater than a_{mag}, an initially unpolarized neutron beam is expected to exhibit two critical angles for total reflection, with values of θ_c given by Eq. (190). This phenomenon has been demonstrated by Hughes and Burgy (H73). Figure 73 shows the reflected intensity, from a magnetized iron mirror, of neutrons originating from the thermal column of the Argonne heavy water reactor and filtered through polycrystalline

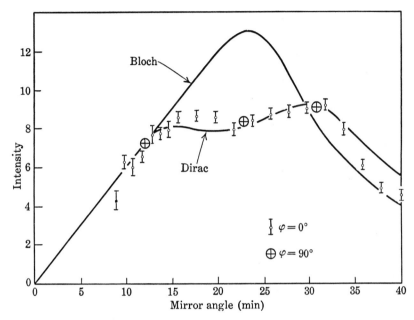

Fig. 73. Intensity of neutrons reflected from a mirror of iron magnetized in the plane of the surface, due to Hughes and Burgy (H73). The smooth curves are the predictions of the Bloch and "Dirac" forms of the theory of magnetic scattering. Measurements with the direction of magnetization in the plane of the beams ($\varphi = 0$) and perpendicular to this plane ($\varphi = 90°$) are in good agreement.

beryllium oxide, i.e., that part of the Maxwell energy distribution with $\lambda > 4.4$ A.

The curves in Fig. 73 were computed for $B = 22{,}500$ gauss and $4\pi a_0^2 = 10.3b$. The two curves correspond to assumed magnetic interactions of the original Bloch ($\mu_n \cdot H$) and "Dirac" ($\mu_n \cdot B$) forms (E3). The shape of the curves is determined by the geometry of the experiment, by the neutron energy distribution, and by the finite reflectivity for $\theta > \theta_c$. The agreement with the "Dirac" form of the interaction is excellent. Furthermore, as pointed out by Hamermesh and Eisner (H27), the observed (two-peaked) pattern of total reflection provides the most direct proof that the spin of the neutron is $\frac{1}{2}$.

The difference between the critical angles for the two directions of neutron polarization is sufficiently large ($\theta_c = 14.2$ min and 30.7 min for $\lambda = 4.4$ A, $B = 22{,}500$ gauss in Fig. 73) that it should be possible to produce essentially completely polarized neutron beams by total reflection of *monoenergetic* neutrons (H19). This could be achieved by choosing an angle of reflection between the values of $\theta_{c\pm}$; the resulting beam would be polarized in the direction of magnetization of the mirror. However, the intensity is severely limited by the low available intensities of monoenergetic neutrons.

Another possibility for the achievement of 100 percent polarization was suggested by Hamermesh (H24). Its basis lies in the observation that, if sufficiently large values of B were available, the magnetic term could exceed the nuclear term in the expressions for n and θ_c (Eqs. 189 and 190). For iron, the saturation value of B is too small ($a_0 = 0.96 \times 10^{-12}$ cm, a_{mag}(sat.) $\cong 0.60 \times 10^{-12}$ cm). However, Hamermesh pointed out that the situation is reversed for a cobalt mirror ($a_0 = 0.28 \times 10^{-12}$ cm, a_{mag}(sat.) $\cong 0.46 \times 10^{-12}$ cm). Thus, for sufficiently strongly magnetized cobalt mirrors ($B \gtrsim 0.65 B_{sat}$, according to the preceding numbers), only neutrons of polarization parallel to the field can be totally reflected; the reflection, at glancing angles, of the oppositely polarized neutrons will be negligibly small. Furthermore, the polarization will be complete for all energies capable of being totally reflected! Thus, for sufficiently small angles of reflection, a large portion of the thermal neutron beam could be simultaneously and completely polarized.

Hughes and Burgy (H73) have observed total reflection from magnetized cobalt mirrors and have determined that, under suitable experimental conditions, complete polarization can indeed be achieved. The cobalt mirrors consisted of thin (~ 10 mil) electroplated layers of cobalt on copper backing plates. The state of polarization, after the first reflection, was determined by reflection from a second cobalt mirror, oppositely magnetized (the reflection analogue of the double transmission effect)[1] or, alternatively and more easily, by keeping the directions of magnetization of the two mirrors the same and observing the change of intensity resulting from complete depolarization of the beam in the region between the mirrors; the depolarization was produced by passing the beam through a thin (~ 6 mil) sheet of unmagnetized iron.[2]

---

[1] In attempting the "double reflection" effect, it is necessary to observe the same precautions as have been described in the discussion of the double transmission effect. The space between magnets must be carefully shielded to make B vary slowly and smoothly except in the short region, of sudden reversal of the field, which induces the non-adiabatic transitions.

[2] Hughes and Burgy found it difficult to attain 100 percent polarization at relatively small angles of reflection; however, for the (relatively large) angle of 20′ (θ_c

By means of reflection from cobalt mirrors, it was possible to produce completely polarized neutron beams of intensity $\sim 10^5$ per minute. An advantage of this method of neutron polarization over those previously discussed is that it is inherently capable of polarizing neutrons of any and all wavelengths, including wavelengths larger than the Bragg limit (4.04 A for iron).

4. Other Methods of Neutron Polarization and Depolarization. While the above discussions of neutron polarization have all involved the use of magnetic scattering, the same principles could be applied to any spin-dependent scattering process, *provided that the directions of the scattering agents can be aligned.* Thus, the spin dependence of neutron scattering by many nuclei implies the possibility of producing polarized slow-neutron beams by transmission. However, the achievement of "nuclear ferromagnetism" requires the cooling of samples to very low temperatures (~ 0.1–$0.01°$K). Rose (R18) has discussed this problem and outlined a number of illuminating experiments which could be performed on such systems of polarized nuclei.

The problem of producing polarized fast-neutron beams has also received some attention. Schwinger has suggested two possible methods: The first (S10) involves the scattering of neutrons, by light nuclei of spin 0, in a resonance (of the compound nucleus) which involves a definite neutron orbital angular momentum $l > 0$ (P, D, etc.). Since a given resonance also requires a definite total angular momentum, $J = l + \frac{1}{2}$ or $l - \frac{1}{2}$, it follows that the two possible neutron orientations will have different angular distributions after scattering. Whereas the original suggestion of Schwinger, for application to the resonance scattering by helium, was based (in part) on faulty experimental data, the method is of general applicability. A theoretical discussion of this method has been given by Lepore (L15).

The second suggestion of Schwinger (S11) also involves the difference in the spin-orbit interactions of neutrons having different spin orientations. It depends on the interaction between the neutron's magnetic moment and the Coulomb field of a heavy nucleus, and requires the observation of neutrons scattered through small angles ($\sim 1°$). While the theory predicts strong polarization effects, the experimental difficulties involved in their observation are formidable.

The production and detection of polarized neutrons in neutron-proton scattering has been discussed by Wolfenstein (W37) and by Swanson

---

for $\lambda \approx 3.7$ A), the observed polarization was (100 $\pm$ 1) percent. The difficulty arose from the non-adiabatic transitions which were induced as the neutrons passed the edge of the mirror. This depolarization effect is in proportion to the smallness of the angle and the speed of the neutrons.

(S60). This possibility arises from the non-central character of the interaction (the tensor force). Wouters (W45) has reported the observation of polarization effects in the scattering of 150-Mev neutrons by protons.

Once a beam of polarized neutrons has been achieved, it can be usefully applied to various problems. Most of these are concerned with the study of incoherent scattering of one sort or another; e.g., the scattering at boundaries between imperfectly aligned magnetic domains, as discussed in the foregoing. Another source of incoherent scattering is spin dependence (see Section 5A, Eqs. 170c, etc.) The application of neutron depolarization measurements to the study of spin-incoherent scattering was suggested by Schwinger and Rabi (S8) as a means of obtaining the difference between the triplet and singlet proton scattering amplitudes. The method has been applied by Meyerhof and Nicodemus (M28) to hydrogen, carbon, and phosphorus.

However, when the spin dependence is small, many collisions are required before appreciable depolarization is achieved. Nevertheless, the effects of a small spin incoherence could be observed by measuring the depolarization of neutrons which have diffused through appreciable thicknesses of material (H22). The theory of neutron depolarization during diffusion has been developed by Borowitz and Hamermesh (B47) and by Halpern (H17).

5. Measurement of the Magnetic Moment of the Neutron. The most important application of neutron polarization has been to the precision measurement of the magnetic moment of free neutrons. Early studies by Frisch, von Halban, and Koch (F47) and Powers (P28) had established that the neutron does indeed have a magnetic dipole moment, of value $\mu_n \sim -2$ nuclear magnetons. (1 nuclear magneton $\equiv e\hbar/2Mc$.) These experiments involved the determination of the frequency and direction of precession of the neutron moment in its passage through magnetized iron;[1] because of the small effects observed and their complicated dependence on the structure of the magnetic materials, the early measurements could only establish the magnitude of μ_n to within a factor of ~ 2.

The principle of the method for the precision measurement, as outlined by Rabi (R1), is the same as that of the molecular beam magnetic resonance technique for measuring nuclear moments. A beam of slow neutrons passes, successively, through a polarizing magnet, an intermediate region of uniform magnetic field, and an analyzer; for experi-

---

[1] An incidental result of these measurements was the demonstration that the precession frequency in iron of a magnetic dipole is determined by the magnetic flux density B.

mental convenience, all three fields are parallel. A (weak) oscillating magnetic field, perpendicular to the uniform field, is applied in the intermediate region. When the frequency of the oscillating field is equal to the frequency of Larmor precession of the neutron moments in the homogeneous field, a resonance condition is established for reversal (flopping) of the neutron moments. Changes in the state of polarization in the intermediate region, induced by the oscillating field, are observed as changes in the intensity transmitted through the analyzer. Measurement of the frequency ν_0, corresponding to the maximum change of transmitted neutron intensity, and of the strength of the homogeneous field, B, lead directly to the magnetic moment through the expression $h\nu_0 = |\, 2\mu_n B\,|$.

The first application of this technique was by Alvarez and Bloch (A13); they obtained $|\, \mu_n\,| = 1.935 \pm 0.03$ nuclear magnetons. The precision of their measurement was limited by the uncertainties in the determination of B and by the smallness of the attainable double transmission effects.

With the development of the nuclear induction technique, it became possible to observe proton and neutron resonances in the same homogeneous field. Thus, the ratio of the neutron and proton moments can be determined without the necessity of a magnetic field measurement. The precision in the determination of $|\, \mu_n/\mu_p\,|$ is limited only by the homogeneity of the field and by the (almost unlimited) precision of the frequency measurements. This method was first applied by Arnold and Roberts (A34), who obtained $|\, \mu_n/\mu_p\,| = 0.68479 \pm 0.0004$. Subsequent improved measurements by Bloch, Nicodemus, and Staub (B39) gave $|\, \mu_n/\mu_p\,| = 0.685001 \pm 0.00003$.

The above-described methods can also yield the sign of the moment if the oscillating magnetic field is replaced by a rotating field. A resonance in the reorientation of the spin will occur only if the direction of rotation of the field is the same as that of the Larmor precession. Application of this modification, by Rogers and Staub (R16), showed that the moments of the neutron and proton are opposite in sign, and that the proton moment is positive and the neutron moment negative.

From the above data, and taking $\mu_p = (2.79255 \pm 0.00010)$ nuclear magnetons (M1), $\mu_n = (-1.91280 \pm 0.00009)$ nuclear magnetons.

REFERENCES

(A0)   Atomic Energy Commission, Neutron Cross Sections (AECU 2040).
(A1)   R. K. Adair, C. K. Bockelman, and R. E. Peterson, Phys. Rev., **76,** 308 (1949).
(A2)   R. K. Adair, Revs. Mod. Phys., **22,** 249 (1950).

(A3)   F. T. Adler, Phys. Rev., **60**, 279 (1941).
(A4)   F. Ajzenberg, Phys. Rev., **82**, 43 (1951).
(A5)   A. Akhiezer and I. Pomeranchuk, J. Exptl. Theoret. Phys. (U.S.S.R.), **18**, 475 (1948). Translation: Guide to Russian Scientific Periodical Literature, **1**, no. 6, 1 (1948), Brookhaven National Laboratory.
(A6)   A. Akhiezer and I. Pomeranchuk, J. Exptl. Theoret. Phys. (U.S.S.R.), **18**, 603 (1948). Translation: Guide to Russian Scientific Periodical Literature, **1**, no. 6, 6 (1948), Brookhaven National Laboratory.
(A7)   N. Z. Alcock and D. G. Hurst, Phys. Rev., **75**, 1609 (1949); **83**, 1100 (1951).
(A8)   A. J. Allen, J. F. Nechaj, K. H. Sun, and B. Jennings, Phys. Rev., **81**, 536 (1951).
(A9)   K. W. Allen, E. Almqvist, J. T. Dewan, T. P. Pepper, and J. H. Sanders, Phys. Rev., **82**, 262 (1951).
(A10) R. G. Allen, C. P. Stanford, T. E. Stephenson, and S. Bernstein, Phys. Rev., **85**, 767A (1952).
(A11) E. Almqvist, Can. J. Research, **A28**, 433 (1950).
(A12) L. W. Alvarez, Phys. Rev., **54**, 609 (1938).
(A13) L. W. Alvarez and F. Bloch, Phys. Rev., **57**, 111 (1940).
(A14) L. W. Alvarez and K. S. Pitzer, Phys. Rev., **58**, 1003 (1940).
(A15) L. W. Alvarez, Phys. Rev., **74**, 1217A (1948); **75**, 1127 (1949).
(A16) E. Amaldi, O. D'Agostino, and E. Segrè, Ric. sci., **5(2)**, 381 (1934).
(A17) E. Amaldi, O. D'Agostino, E. Fermi, B. Pontecorvo, F. Rasetti, and E. Segrè, Ric. sci., **6(1)**, 123 (1935).
(A18) E. Amaldi, O. D'Agostino, E. Fermi, B. Pontecorvo, and E. Segrè, Ric. sci., **6(1)**, 581 (1935).
(A19) E. Amaldi, O. D'Agostino, E. Fermi, B. Pontecorvo, F. Rasetti, and E. Segrè, Proc. Roy. Soc. (London), **A149**, 522 (1935).
(A20) E. Amaldi and E. Fermi, Phys. Rev., **50**, 899 (1936).
(A21) E. Amaldi, D. Bocciarelli, B. N. Cacciapuoti, and G. C. Trabacchi, Nuovo cimento, **3**, 15, 203 (1946); *Fundamental Particles and Low Temperatures*, Vol. I, The Physical Society, London, 1947.
(A22) P. Ammiraju, Phys. Rev., **76**, 1421 (1949).
(A23) H. L. Anderson, E. Fermi, and L. Szilard, Phys. Rev., **56**, 284 (1939).
(A24) H. L. Anderson, E. Fermi, and L. Marshall, Phys. Rev., **70**, 815 (1946).
(A25) H. L. Anderson, E. Fermi, A. Wattenberg, G. L. Weil, and W. H. Zinn, Phys. Rev., **72**, 16 (1947).
(A26) H. L. Anderson and B. T. Feld, Rev. Sci. Instr., **18**, 186 (1947).
(A27) H. L. Anderson, Preliminary Report No. 3, Nuclear Science Series, National Research Council, 1948.
(A28) H. L. Anderson, Phys. Rev., **80**, 499 (1950).
(A29) H. Aoki, Proc. Phys.-Math. Soc. Japan, **19**, 369 (1935).
(A30) H. V. Argo, H. T. Gittings, A. Hemmendinger, G. A. Jarvis, and R. F. Taschek, Phys. Rev., **78**, 691 (1950).
(A31) N. Arley, Kgl. Danske Videnskab. Selskab, Math.-fys. Medd., **XVI**, 1 (1938).
(A32) G. Arnold and A. H. Weber, Phys. Rev., **73**, 1385 (1948).
(A33) J. R. Arnold and N. Sugarman, J. Chem. Phys., **15**, 703 (1947).
(A34) W. R. Arnold and A. Roberts, Phys. Rev., **71**, 878 (1947).
(A35) H. Atterling, E. Bohr, and T. Sigurgeirsson, Arkiv Mat. Astron. Fysik, **32A**, no. 2 (1946).
(A36) P. Auger, Compt. rend., **194**, 877; **195**, 234 (1932).

(A37)   P. Auger, A. M. Munn, and B. Pontecorvo, Can. J. Research, **A25,** 143 (1947).
(B1)   R. F. Bacher, C. P. Baker, and B. D. McDaniel, Phys. Rev., **69,** 443 (1946).
(B2)   K. T. Bainbridge, Phys. Rev., **81,** 146 (1951).
(B3)   C. P. Baker and R. F. Bacher, Phys. Rev., **59,** 332 (1941).
(B4)   W. D. Baker, J. S. Howell, C. Goodman, and W. M. Preston, Phys. Rev., **81,** 48 (1951).
(B5)   E. Baldinger, P. Huber, and W. G. Proctor, Phys. Rev., **84,** 1058 (1951).
(B6)   G. C. Baldwin and H. W. Koch, Phys. Rev., **67,** 1 (1945).
(B7)   G. C. Baldwin and G. S. Klaiber, Phys. Rev., **73,** 1156 (1948).
(B8)   H. H. Barschall, M. E. Battat, W. C. Bright, E. R. Graves, T. Jorgensen, and J. H. Manley, Phys. Rev., **72,** 881 (1947).
(B9)   H. H. Barschall and H. A. Bethe, Rev. Sci. Instr., **18,** 147 (1947).
(B10)   H. H. Barschall and R. Taschek, Phys. Rev., **75,** 1819 (1949).
(B11)   G. Beck and L. H. Horsley, Phys. Rev., **47,** 510 (1935).
(B12)   W. W. Beeman, Phys. Rev., **72,** 986 (1947).
(B13)   L. E. Beghian, M. A. Grace, G. Preston, and H. Halban, Phys. Rev., **77,** 286 (1950).
(B14)   F. M. Beiduk, J. R. Pruett, and E. J. Konopinski, Phys. Rev., **77,** 622 (1950).
(B15)   P. R. Bell and H. A. Straus, Rev. Sci. Instr., **21,** 760 (1950).
(B16)   R. E. Bell and L. G. Elliott, Phys. Rev., **74,** 1552 (1948); **79,** 282 (1950).
(B17)   P. J. Bendt and I. W. Ruderman, Phys. Rev., **77,** 575 (1950).
(B18)   G. Bernardini, G. Cortini, and A. Manfredini, Phys. Rev., **76,** 1792 (1949).
(B19)   G. Bernardini, E. T. Booth, and S. J. Lindenbaum, Phys. Rev., **83,** 669 (1951); **85,** 826 (1952).
(B20)   H. A. Bethe and R. Peierls, Proc. Roy. Soc. (London), **A148,** 146 (1935).
(B21)   H. A. Bethe, Phys. Rev., **47,** 747 (1935).
(B22)   H. A. Bethe and R. F. Bacher, Revs. Mod. Phys., **8,** 82 (1936).
(B23)   H. A. Bethe, Phys. Rev., **50,** 332 (1936).
(B24)   H. A. Bethe, Revs. Mod. Phys., **9,** 69 (1937).
(B25)   H. A. Bethe and G. Placzek, Phys. Rev., **51,** 450 (1937).
(B26)   H. A. Bethe, S. A. Korff, and G. Placzek, Phys. Rev., **57,** 573 (1940).
(B27)   H. A. Bethe, L. Tonks, and H. Hurwitz, Jr., Phys. Rev., **80,** 11 (1950).
(B28)   H. G. Beyer and M. D. Whitaker, Phys. Rev., **57,** 976 (1940).
(B29)   H. Bichsel, W. Hälg, P. Huber, and A. Stebler, Phys. Rev., **81,** 456 (1951).
(B30)   G. R. Bishop, L. E. Beghian, and H. Halban, Phys. Rev., **83,** 1052 (1951).
(B31)   J. A. Bistline, Jr., Rev. Sci. Instr., **19,** 842 (1948).
(B32)   T. Bjerge and C. H. Westcott, Nature, **134,** 286 (1934).
(B33)   T. Bjerge and C. H. Westcott, Proc. Roy. Soc. (London), **A150,** 709 (1935).
(B34)   J. Blatt and V. F. Weisskopf, *Theoretical Nuclear Physics,* John Wiley & Sons, Inc., New York, 1952.
(B35)   M. Blau, I. W. Ruderman, and J. Czechowski, Rev. Sci. Instr., **21,** 232 (1950).
(B36)   F. Bloch, Phys. Rev., **50,** 259 (1936); **51,** 994 (1937).
(B37)   F. Bloch, H. Hamermesh, and H. Staub, Phys. Rev., **64,** 47 (1943).
(B38)   F. Bloch, R. I. Condit, and H. Staub, Phys. Rev., **70,** 972 (1946).
(B39)   F. Bloch, D. Nicodemus, and H. H. Staub, Phys. Rev., **74,** 1025 (1948).
(B40)   I. Bloch, M. H. Hull, Jr., A. A. Broyles, W. G. Bouricius, B. E. Freeman, and G. Breit, Revs. Mod. Phys., **23,** 147 (1951).

(B41) C. K. Bockelman, D. W. Miller, R. K. Adair, and H. H. Barschall, Phys. Rev., **84**, 69 (1951).

(B42) D. Bodansky, Phys. Rev., **80**, 481 (1950).

(B43) D. Bodansky and N. F. Ramsey, Phys. Rev., **82**, 831 (1951).

(B44) N. Bohr, Nature, **137**, 344 (1936).

(B45) N. Bohr and F. Kalckar, Kgl. Danske Videnskab. Selskab, Math.-fys. Medd., **XIV**, 10 (1937).

(B46) N. Bohr and J. A. Wheeler, Phys. Rev., **56**, 426, 1065 (1939).

(B47) S. Borowitz and M. Hamermesh, Phys. Rev., **74**, 1285 (1948).

(B48) S. Borowitz and W. Kohn, Phys. Rev., **76**, 818 (1949).

(B49) L. B. Borst, A. J. Ulrich, C. L. Osborne, and B. Hasbrouck, Phys. Rev., **70**, 557 (1946).

(B50) W. Bothe and H. Becker, Z. Physik, **66**, 289 (1930).

(B51) W. Bothe and H. Becker, Z. Physik, **76**, 421 (1932).

(B52) W. Bothe and W. Gentner, Naturwiss., **25**, 90, 284 (1937); Z. Physik, **106**, 236 (1937).

(B53) W. Bothe, Z. Physik, **120**, 437 (1943).

(B54) W. Bothe, Z. Naturforsch., **1**, 173, 179 (1946).

(B55) J. C. Bowe and P. Axel, Phys. Rev., **84**, 939 (1951).

(B56) A. Bracci, U. Facchini, E. Germagnoli, and E. Zimmer, Nuovo cimento, **7**, 512 (1950).

(B57) N. E. Bradbury, F. Bloch, H. Tatel, and P. A. Ross, Phys. Rev., **52**, 1023 (1937).

(B58) H. L. Bradt and D. J. Tendam, Phys. Rev., **72**, 1117 (1947).

(B59) A. Bratenahl, S. Fernbach, R. H. Hildebrand, C. E. Leith, and B. J. Moyer, Phys. Rev., **77**, 597 (1950).

(B60) G. Breit and E. P. Wigner, Phys. Rev., **49**, 519 (1936).

(B61) G. Breit, Phys. Rev., **58**, 506 (1940); **69**, 472 (1946).

(B62) E. Bretscher, G. B. Cook, G. R. Martin, and D. H. Wilkinson, Proc. Roy. Soc. (London), **A196**, 436 (1949).

(B63) E. Bretscher, Helv. Phys. Acta, **23**, supp. 3, 51 (1950).

(B64) F. G. Brickwedde, J. R. Dunning, H. J. Hoge, and J. H. Manley, Phys. Rev., **54**, 266 (1938).

(B65) T. Brill and H. V. Lichtenberger, Phys. Rev., **72**, 585 (1947).

(B66) British Government, His Majesty's Stationery Office, London, 1945.

(B67) E. Broda and W. Rieder, J. Chem. Soc., 356 (1949).

(B68) E. Broda, *Advances in Radiochemistry*, Cambridge University Press, 1950.

(B69) L. de Broglie, Compt. rend., **224**, 615 (1947).

(B70) M. de Broglie and L. Leprince-Ringuet, Compt. rend., **194**, 1616; **195**, 88 (1932).

(B71) J. E. Brolley, Jr., J. H. Coon, and J. L. Fowler, Phys. Rev., **82**, 190 (1951).

(B72) J. E. Brolley, Jr., J. L. Fowler, and E. J. Stovall, Jr., Phys. Rev., **82**, 502 (1951).

(B73) K. Brueckner, W. Hartsough, E. Haward, and W. M. Powell, Phys. Rev., **75**, 555 (1949).

(B74) K. Brueckner and W. M. Powell, Phys. Rev., **75**, 1274, 1970 (1949).

(B75) W. E. Burcham and M. Goldhaber, Proc. Cambridge Phil. Soc., **32**, 632 (1936).

(B76) M. Burgy, D. J. Hughes, J. R. Wallace, R. B. Heller, and W. E. Woolf, Phys. Rev., **80**, 953 (1950).

(B77) F. D. S. Butement, Phys. Rev., **75**, 1276 (1949).
(B78) S. T. Butler, Phys. Rev., **80**, 1095 (1950).
(B79) S. T. Butler and J. L. Symonds, Phys. Rev., **83**, 858 (1951).
(B80) P. R. Byerly, Jr., and W. E. Stephens, Phys. Rev., **81**, 473 (1951); **83**, 54 (1951).
(C1) Canadian Department of Reconstruction, Industrial Canada, Toronto, 1945.
(C2) K. M. Case, Phys. Rev., **76**, 1 (1949).
(C3) J. M. Cassels and R. Latham, Nature, **161**, 282 (1948); Phys. Rev., **74**, 103 (1948).
(C4) J. M. Cassels, *Progress in Nuclear Physics*, O. R. Frisch, Editor, Butterworth-Springer, London, 1950.
(C5) J. Chadwick, Nature, **129**, 312 (Feb. 27, 1932).
(C6) J. Chadwick, Proc. Roy. Soc. (London), **A136**, 692 (1932).
(C7) J. Chadwick, Proc. Roy. Soc. (London), **A142**, 1 (1933).
(C8) J. Chadwick and M. Goldhaber, Nature, **134**, 237 (1934); Proc. Roy. Soc. (London), **A151**, 479 (1935).
(C9) J. Chadwick and M. Goldhaber, Nature, **135**, 65 (1935); Proc. Cambridge Phil. Soc., **31**, 612 (1935).
(C10) J. Chadwick, N. Feather, and E. Bretscher, Proc. Roy. Soc. (London), **A163**, 366 (1937).
(C11) O. Chamberlain, Phys. Rev., **77**, 305 (1950).
(C12) S. Chandrasekhar, Revs. Mod. Phys., **15**, 1 (1943).
(C13) G. F. Chew and M. L. Goldberger, Phys. Rev., **77**, 470 (1950).
(C14) G. F. Chew, Phys. Rev., **79**, 219A (1950); **84**, 710, 1057 (1951).
(C15) R. S. Christian and E. W. Hart, Phys. Rev., **77**, 441 (1950).
(C16) J. D. Cockcroft, J. C. Duckworth, and A. W. Merrison, Nature, **163**, 869 (1949).
(C17) S. G. Cohen, Nature, **161**, 475 (1948).
(C18) V. W. Cohen, H. H. Goldsmith, J. Schwinger, and M. Hamermesh, Phys. Rev., **55**, 106 (1939); Phys. Rev., **57**, 352 (1940).
(C19) M. Y. Colby and R. N. Little, Jr., Phys. Rev., **70**, 437 (1946).
(C20) C. H. Collie and J. H. E. Griffiths, Proc. Roy. Soc. (London), **A155**, 434 (1936).
(C21) F. C. W. Colmer and D. J. Littler, Proc. Phys. Soc. (London), **63**, 1175 (1950).
(C22) A. H. Compton and S. K. Allison, *X-Rays in Theory and Experiment*, Van Nostrand, New York, 1935.
(C23) E. U. Condon and G. Breit, Phys. Rev., **49**, 229 (1936).
(C24) E. U. Condon, Phys. Rev., **49**, 459 (1936).
(C25) L. J. Cook, E. M. McMillan, J. M. Peterson, and D. C. Sewell, Phys. Rev., **72**, 1264 (1947); **75**, 7 (1949).
(C26) J. H. Coon and R. A. Nobles, Phys. Rev., **75**, 1358 (1949).
(C27) D. Coster, Hl. de Vries, and G. Diemer, Physica, **10**, 281, 299 (1943); with P. Noteboom, Physica, **8**, 825 (1941); with H. Groendijk, Physica, **10**, 312 (1943).
(C28) D. Coster, H. Groendijk, and Hl. de Vries, Physica, **14**, 1 (1948).
(C29) E. D. Courant, Phys. Rev., **82**, 703 (1951).
(C30) H. R. Crane, C. C. Lauritsen, and A. Soltan, Phys. Rev., **44**, 692 (1933); **45**, 226, 507 (1934); Compt. rend., **197**, 913 (1933).
(C31) H. R. Crane and C. C. Lauritsen, Phys. Rev., **44**, 783 (1933).

(C32) R. W. Crews, Phys. Rev., **82**, 100 (1951).

(C33) P. Cüer, J. phys. et radium, **8**, 83 (1947).

(C34) P. Cüer, M. Morand, and L. VanRossum, Compt. rend., **228**, 481 (1949).

(C35) B. B. Cunningham and A. Ghiorso, Phys. Rev., **82**, 558 (1951).

(C36) I. Curie, Compt. rend., **193**, 1412 (1931).

(C37) I. Curie and F. Joliot, Compt. rend., **194**, 273 (1932).

(C38) I. Curie and F. Joliot, Compt. rend., **194**, 708 (1932).

(C39) I. Curie and F. Joliot, Compt. rend., **194**, 876, 1229; with P. Savel, **194**, 2208 (1932).

(C40) I. Curie and F. Joliot, Compt. rend., **196**, 397 (1933).

(C41) I. Curie and F. Joliot, J. phys. et radium, **5**, 153 (1934); Compt. rend., **198**, 254, 559 (1934).

(C42) L. F. Curtiss and A. Carson, Phys. Rev., **76**, 1412 (1949).

(D1)   S. M. Dancoff, Phys. Rev., **72**, 1017 (1947).

(D2)   S. M. Dancoff and S. D. Drell, Phys. Rev., **76**, 205 (1949).

(D3)   M. Danysz, J. Rotblat, L. Wertenstein, and M. Zyw, Nature, **134**, 970 (1934).

(D4)   K. K. Darrow, Rev. Sci. Instr., **4**, 58 (1933).

(D5)   W. O. Davis, Phys. Rev., **80**, 150 (1950).

(D6)   P. I. Dee, Proc. Roy. Soc. (London), **A136**, 727 (1932).

(D7)   F. DeHoffmann and B. T. Feld, Phys. Rev., **72**, 567 (1947).

(D8)   F. DeHoffmann, Phys. Rev., **78**, 216 (1950).

(D9)   J. DeJuren and N. Knable, Phys. Rev., **77**, 606 (1950).

(D10) J. DeJuren, Phys. Rev., **80**, 27 (1950).

(D11) J. DeJuren, Phys. Rev., **81**, 458 (1951).

(D12) J. DeJuren and B. J. Moyer, Phys. Rev., **81**, 919 (1951).

(D13) E. Der Mateosian, M. Goldhaber, C. O. Muehlhause, and M. McKeown, Phys. Rev., **72**, 1271 (1947).

(D14) C. C. Dilworth, S. J. Goldsack, Y. Goldschmidt-Clermont, and F. Levy, Phil. Mag., **41**, 1032 (1950).

(D15) B. C. Diven and G. M. Almy, Phys. Rev., **80**, 407 (1950).

(D16) J. C. Duckworth, A. W. Merrison, and A. Whittaker, Nature, **165**, 69 (1950).

(D17) H. F. Dunlap and R. N. Little, Phys. Rev., **60**, 693 (1941).

(D18) J. R. Dunning, Phys. Rev., **45**, 586 (1934).

(D19) J. R. Dunning, G. B. Pegram, G. A. Fink, and D. P. Mitchell, Phys. Rev., **48**, 265 (1935).

(D20) J. R. Dunning, G. B. Pegram, G. A. Fink, D. P. Mitchell, and E. Segrè, Phys. Rev., **48**, 704 (1935).

(D21) J. R. Dunning, P. N. Powers, and H. G. Beyer, Phys. Rev., **51**, 51 (1937).

(D22) J. V. Dunworth, Nature, **159**, 436 (1947).

(E1)   A. A. Ebel, Ph.D. Thesis, M.I.T., 1950.

(E2)   W. Ehrenberg, Nature, **136**, 870 (1935).

(E3)   H. Ekstein, Phys. Rev., **76**, 1328 (1949); **78**, 731 (1950).

(E4)   W. Elsasser, J. phys. et radium, **4**, 549 (1933); **5**, 389, 625 (1934).

(E5)   W. M. Elsasser, Compt. rend., **202**, 1029 (1936).

(E6)   J. Erber, W. Rieder, and E. Broda, Nature, **165**, 810 (1950).

(F1)   C. E. Falk, E. Creutz, and F. Seitz, Phys. Rev., **76**, 322 (1949); **83**, 499 (1951).

(F2)   N. Feather, Proc. Roy. Soc. (London), **A136**, 709 (1932).

(F3)   N. Feather, Nature, **130**, 237 (1932).

(F4)   N. Feather, Nature, **162**, 213 (1948).
(F5)   E. Feenberg and J. K. Knipp, Phys. Rev., **48**, 906 (1935).
(F6)   E. Feenberg and K. C. Hammack, Phys. Rev., **75**, 1877, 1968 (1949).
(F7)   B. T. Feld, Phys. Rev., **70**, 429 (1946).
(F8)   B. T. Feld, R. Scalettar, and L. Szilard, Phys. Rev., **71**, 464A (1947).
(F9)   B. T. Feld, Phys. Rev., **75**, 1115 (1949).
(F10)   B. T. Feld, I. L. Lebow, and L. S. Osborne, Phys. Rev., **77**, 731 (1950).
(F11)   F. W. Fenning and F. R. Holt, Nature, **165**, 722 (1950).
(F12)   E. Fermi, E. Amaldi, O. D'Agostino, F. Rasetti, and E. Segrè, Proc. Roy. Soc. (London), **A146**, 483 (1934).
(F13)   E. Fermi, Ricerca sci., **5(1)**, 283 (1934); Nature, **133**, 757 (1934).
(F14)   E. Fermi, E. Amaldi, B. Pontecorvo, F. Rasetti, and E. Segrè, Ricerca sci., **5(2)**, 282 (1934).
(F15)   E. Fermi, Phys. Rev., **48**, 570 (1935).
(F16)   E. Fermi and E. Amaldi, Ricerca sci., **6(2)**, 344, 443 (1935).
(F17)   E. Fermi, Ricerca sci., **7(2)**, 13 (1936).
(F18)   E. Fermi and W. H. Zinn, Phys. Rev., **70**, 103A (1946).
(F19)   E. Fermi, Science, **105**, 27 (1947).
(F20)   E. Fermi, W. J. Sturm, and R. G. Sachs, Phys. Rev., **71**, 589 (1947).
(F21)   E. Fermi and L. Marshall, Phys. Rev., **71**, 666 (1947).
(F22)   E. Fermi, J. Marshall, and L. Marshall, Phys. Rev., **72**, 193 (1947).
(F23)   E. Fermi and L. Marshall, Phys. Rev., **72**, 1139 (1947).
(F24)   E. Fermi and L. Marshall, Phys. Rev., **75**, 578 (1949).
(F25)   S. Fernbach, R. Serber, and T. B. Taylor, Phys. Rev., **75**, 1352 (1949).
(F26)   G. E. F. Fertel, P. B. Moon, G. P. Thomson, and C. E. Wynn-Williams, Nature, **142**, 829 (1938); with D. F. Gibbs, Proc. Roy. Soc. (London), **A175**, 316 (1940).
(F27)   H. Feshbach, D. C. Peaslee, and V. F. Weisskopf, Phys. Rev., **71**, 145, 564 (1947).
(F28)   H. Feshbach and V. F. Weisskopf, Phys. Rev., **76**, 1550 (1949).
(F29)   G. A. Fink, Phys. Rev., **50**, 738 (1936).
(F30)   R. J. Finkelstein, Phys. Rev., **72**, 907 (1947).
(F31)   J. Fleeman, D. B. Nicodemus, and H. H. Staub, Phys. Rev., **76**, 1774 (1949).
(F32)   R. Fleischmann, Naturwiss., **38**, 465 (1951).
(F33)   S. Flügge, Naturwiss., **27**, 402 (1939).
(F34)   S. Flügge, Physik. Z., **44**, 445 (1943).
(F35)   S. Flügge, *Cosmic Radiation*, Dover Publications, New York, 1946, Chapter 14.
(F36)   S. Flügge, *An Introduction to Nuclear Physics* (with J. Mattauch, Nuclear Physics Tables), Interscience Publishers, New York, 1946, pp. 61–62.
(F37)   L. L. Foldy, Phys. Rev., **83**, 688 (1951); **87**, 693 (1952).
(F38)   K. W. Ford and D. Bohm, Phys. Rev., **79**, 745 (1950).
(F39)   I. L. Fowler and P. R. Tunnicliffe, Rev. Sci. Instr., **21**, 734 (1950).
(F40)   J. L. Fowler and J. M. Slye, Jr., Phys. Rev., **77**, 787 (1950).
(F41)   R. Fox, C. Leith, L. Wouters, and K. R. MacKenzie, Phys. Rev., **80**, 23 (1950).
(F42)   G. D. Freier, T. F. Stratton, and L. Rosen, Phys. Rev., **79**, 721 (1950).
(F43)   J. Frenkel, Physik. Z. Sowjetunion, **9**, 533 (1936).
(F44)   F. L. Friedman, *The Science and Engineering of Nuclear Power*, Addison-Wesley Press, Cambridge, Mass., 1947.

(F45)   O. R. Frisch and G. Placzek, Nature, **137**, 357 (1936).

(F46)   O. R. Frisch, Kgl. Danske Videnskab. Selskab, Math.-fys. Medd., **XIV**, 12 (1937).

(F47)   O. R. Frisch, H. von Halban, and J. Koch, Nature, **139**, 756, 1021; **140**, 360 (1937); Phys. Rev., **53**, 719 (1938).

(F48)   O. R. Frisch, H. von Halban, Jr., and J. Koch, Kgl. Danske Videnskab. Selskab, Math.-fys. Medd., **XV**, 10 (1938).

(F49)   O. R. Frisch, Nature, **143**, 276 (1939).

(F50)   E. M. Fryer, Phys. Rev., **70**, 235 (1946).

(F51)   E. Fünfer, Naturwiss., **25**, 235 (1937); Z. f. Physik, **111**, 351 (1938).

(G1)   S. Gallone and C. Salvetti, Nuovo cimento, **7**, 482, 626 (1950).

(G2)   G. R. Gamertsfelder and M. Goldhaber, Phys. Rev., **69**, 368 (1946).

(G3)   W. L. Gardner, N. Knable, and B. J. Moyer, Phys. Rev., **83**, 1054 (1951).

(G4)   W. M. Gibson and D. L. Livesey, Proc. Phys. Soc. (London), **60**, 523 (1948).

(G5)   N. S. Gingrich, Revs. Mod. Phys., **15**, 90 (1943).

(G6)   H. T. Gittings, H. H. Barschall, and G. G. Everhart, Phys. Rev., **75**, 1610 (1949).

(G6a)   S. Glasstone and M. C. Edlund, *Elements of Nuclear Reactor Theory*, Van Nostrand, New York, 1952.

(G7)   L. E. Glendenin, Phys. Rev., **75**, 337 (1949); with C. D. Coryell, **77**, 755 (1950); Technical Report No. 35, LNSE, M.I.T. (1949); with C. D. Coryell and R. R. Edwards, div. IV, National Nuclear Energy Series, McGraw-Hill Book Co., New York, 1950.

(G8)   E. Glückauf and F. A. Paneth, Proc. Roy. Soc. (London), **A165**, 229 (1938).

(G9)   R. L. Gluckstern and H. A. Bethe, Phys. Rev., **81**, 761 (1951).

(G10)   M. L. Goldberger and F. Seitz, Phys. Rev., **71**, 294 (1947).

(G11)   M. L. Goldberger, Phys. Rev., **74**, 1269 (1948).

(G12)   M. Goldhaber and G. H. Briggs, Proc. Roy. Soc. (London), **A162**, 127 (1937).

(G13)   M. Goldhaber, R. D. Hill, and L. Szilard, Phys. Rev., **55**, 47 (1939).

(G14)   M. Goldhaber and A. A. Yalow, Phys. Rev., **69**, 47 (1946).

(G15)   M. Goldhaber, C. O. Muehlhause, and S. H. Turkel, Phys. Rev., **71**, 372 (1947).

(G16)   M. Goldhaber and E. Teller, Phys. Rev., **74**, 1046 (1948).

(G17)   M. Goldhaber and C. O. Muehlhause, Phys. Rev., **74**, 1248A, 1877 (1948).

(G18)   G. H. Goldschmidt and D. G. Hurst, Phys. Rev., **83**, 88 (1951).

(G19)   H. H. Goldsmith and F. Rasetti, Phys. Rev., **49**, 891 (1936); **50**, 328 (1936).

(G20)   H. H. Goldsmith, H. W. Ibser, and B. T. Feld, Revs. Mod. Phys., **19**, 259 (1947).

(G21)   L. Goldstein, D. Sweeney, and M. Goldstein, Phys. Rev., **77**, 319 (1950).

(G22)   L. Goldstein and D. W. Sweeney, Phys. Rev., **80**, 141 (1950).

(G23)   L. Goldstein, Phys. Rev., **83**, 289 (1951).

(G24)   L. Goldstein, Phys. Rev., **84**, 466 (1951).

(G25)   W. E. Good and G. Scharff-Goldhaber, Phys. Rev., **58**, 89 (1940); **59**, 917 (1941).

(G26)   S. A. Goudsmit, Phys. Rev., **49**, 406 (1936).

(G27)   M. A. Grace, L. E. Beghian, G. Preston, and H. Halban, Phys. Rev., **82**, 969 (1951).

(G28)   G. A. R. Graham and H. Halban, Jr., Revs. Mod. Phys., **17**, 297 (1945).

(G29)   J. C. Grosskreutz, Phys. Rev., **76**, 482 (1949).

(G30)   J. C. Grosskreutz and K. B. Mather, Phys. Rev., **77**, 580 (1950).

(G31) P. C. Gugelot, Phys. Rev., **81**, 51 (1951).
(G32) E. Guth and C. J. Mullin, Phys. Rev., **74**, 833 (1948).
(H1)   J. Hadley, E. Kelly, C. Leith, E. Segrè, C. Wiegand, and H. York, Phys. Rev., **75**, 351 (1949).
(H2)   J. Hadley and H. York, Phys. Rev., **80**, 345 (1950).
(H3)   L. R. Hafstad, Scientific American, **184**, 43 (April, 1951); Bulletin of the Atomic Scientists, **7**, 109 (1951).
(H4)   O. Hahn and F. Strassmann, Naturwiss., **27**, 11 (1939).
(H5)   H. von Halban, Jr., F. Joliot, and L. Kowarski, Nature, **143**, 470 (1939).
(H6)   H. von Halban, Jr., L. Kowarski, and M. Magat, Compt. rend., **208**, 572 (1939).
(H7)   H. Halban, Jr., F. Joliot, and L. Kowarski, Compt. rend., **229**, 909 (1949).
(H8)   T. A. Hall, Phys. Rev., **77**, 411 (1950).
(H9)   I. Halpern, Phys. Rev., **76**, 248 (1949).
(H10) J. Halpern, I. Estermann, O. C. Simpson, and O. Stern, Phys. Rev., **52**, 142 (1937).
(H11) O. Halpern and M. H. Johnson, Phys. Rev., **51**, 992 (1937); **52**, 52 (1937); **55**, 898 (1939).
(H12) O. Halpern, R. Lueneburg, and O. Clark, Phys. Rev., **53**, 173 (1938).
(H13) O. Halpern and R. K. Luneberg, Phys. Rev., **76**, 1811 (1949).
(H14) O. Halpern and T. Holstein, Phys. Rev., **59**, 960 (1941).
(H15) O. Halpern, M. Hamermesh, and M. H. Johnson, Phys. Rev., **59**, 981 (1941).
(H16) O. Halpern, Phys. Rev., **72**, 260 (1947).
(H17) O. Halpern, Phys. Rev., **75**, 1633A (1949).
(H18) O. Halpern and E. Gerjuoy, Phys. Rev., **76**, 1117 (1949).
(H19) O. Halpern, Phys. Rev., **76**, 1130 (1949).
(H20) B. Hamermesh and V. Hummell, Phys. Rev., **78**, 73 (1950).
(H21) M. Hamermesh, Phys. Rev., **61**, 17 (1942).
(H22) M. Hamermesh and J. Schwinger, Phys. Rev., **69**, 145 (1946).
(H23) M. Hamermesh and J. Schwinger, Phys. Rev., **71**, 678 (1947).
(H24) M. Hamermesh, Phys. Rev., **75**, 1766 (1949).
(H25) M. Hamermesh, Phys. Rev., **77**, 140 (1950).
(H26) M. Hamermesh and C. O. Muehlhause, Phys. Rev., **78**, 175 (1950).
(H27) M. Hamermesh and E. Eisner, Phys. Rev., **79**, 888 (1950).
(H28) M. Hamermesh, G. R. Ringo, and A. Wattenberg, Phys. Rev., **85**, 483 (1952).
(H29) G. C. Hanna, B. G. Harvey, and N. Moss, Phys. Rev., **81**, 486 (1951).
(H30) G. C. Hanna, B. G. Harvey, N. Moss, and P. R. Tunnicliffe, Phys. Rev., **81**, 893 (1951).
(H31) J. L. Hansen and J. E. Willard, Phys. Rev., **76**, 577 (1949).
(H32) A. O. Hanson and J. L. McKibben, Phys. Rev., **72**, 673 (1947).
(H33) A. O. Hanson, Phys. Rev., **75**, 1794 (1949).
(H34) A. O. Hanson, R. F. Taschek, and J. H. Williams, Revs. Mod. Phys., **21**, 635 (1949).
(H35) A. O. Hanson, R. B. Duffield, J. D. Knight, B. C. Diven, and H. Palevsky, Phys. Rev., **76**, 578 (1949).
(H36) H. B. Hanstein, Phys. Rev., **59**, 489 (1941).
(H37) W. D. Harkins, D. M. Gans, and H. W. Newson, Phys. Rev., **43**, 208 (1933).
(H38) S. P. Harris, A. S. Langsdorf, Jr., and F. G. P. Seidl, Phys. Rev., **72**, 866 (1947).
(H39) S. P. Harris and C. O. Muehlhause, Phys. Rev., **76**, 189A (1949).

(H40)　S. P. Harris, C. O. Muehlhause, and G. E. Thomas, Phys. Rev., **79**, 11 (1950).

(H41)　S. P. Harris, Phys. Rev., **80**, 20 (1950).

(H42)　S. P. Harris, C. O. Muehlhause, S. Rasmussen, H. P. Schroeder, and G. E. Thomas, Phys. Rev., **80**, 342 (1950).

(H43)　S. P. Harris, C. T. Hibdon, and C. O. Muehlhause, Phys. Rev., **80**, 1014 (1950).

(H44)　W. Hauser and H. Feshbach, Phys. Rev., **87**, 366 (1952).

(H45)　W. W. Havens, Jr., and J. Rainwater, Phys. Rev., **70**, 154 (1946); **83**, 1123 (1951).

(H46)　W. W. Havens, Jr., I. I. Rabi, and L. J. Rainwater, Phys. Rev., **72**, 634 (1947); **75**, 1295 (1949).

(H47)　W. W. Havens, Jr., L. J. Rainwater, and I. I. Rabi, Phys. Rev., **82**, 345A (1951).

(H48)　L. J. Haworth, J. H. Manley, and E. A. Luebke, Rev. Sci. Instr., **12**, 591 (1941).

(H49)　O. Haxel, J. H. D. Jensen, and H. E. Suess, Phys. Rev., **75**, 1766 (1949).

(H50)　R. J. Hayden, J. H. Reynolds, and M. G. Inghram, Phys. Rev., **75**, 1500 (1949).

(H51)　J. Heidmann, Phil. Mag., **41**, 444 (1950); Phys. Rev., **80**, 171 (1950).

(H52)　J. Heidmann and H. A. Bethe, Phys. Rev., **84**, 274 (1951).

(H53)　A. C. Helmholz, E. M. McMillan, and D. C. Sewell, Phys. Rev., **72**, 1003 (1947).

(H54)　H. G. Hereward, G. C. Laurence, H. R. Paneth, and B. W. Sargent, Can. J. Research, **A25**, 15 (1947).

(H55)　D. C. Hess, Jr., and M. G. Inghram, Phys. Rev., **76**, 300 (1949).

(H56)　F. A. Heyn, Nature, **138**, 723 (1936); **139**, 842 (1937).

(H57)　C. T. Hibdon and C. O. Muehlhause, Phys. Rev., **76**, 100 (1949).

(H58)　C. T. Hibdon, C. O. Muehlhause, W. Selove, and W. Woolf, Phys. Rev., **77**, 730 (1950).

(H59)　C. T. Hibdon and C. O. Muehlhause, Phys. Rev., **79**, 44 (1950).

(H60)　C. T. Hibdon, C. O. Muehlhause, G. R. Ringo, and T. B. Robillard, Phys. Rev., **82**, 560 (1951).

(H61)　R. H. Hildebrand and C. E. Leith, Phys. Rev., **80**, 842 (1950).

(H62)　R. D. Hill, Phys. Rev., **76**, 333, 186A (1949).

(H63)　J. G. Hoffman, M. S. Livingston, and H. A. Bethe, Phys. Rev., **51**, 214 (1937).

(H64)　R. Hofstadter, J. A. McIntyre, H. Roderick, and H. I. West, Jr., Phys. Rev., **82**, 749 (1951).

(H65)　J. I. Hoover, W. H. Jordan, C. O. Moak, L. Pardue, H. Pomerance, J. D. Strong, and E. O. Wollan, Phys. Rev., **74**, 864 (1948).

(H66)　J. Hornbostel, H. H. Goldsmith, and J. H. Manley, Phys. Rev., **58**, 18 (1940).

(H67)　W. F. Hornyak, T. Lauritsen, P. Morrison, and W. A. Fowler, Revs. Mod. Phys., **22**, 291 (1950).

(H68)　D. J. Hughes, D. Hall, C. Eggler, and E. Goldfarb, Phys. Rev., **72**, 646 (1947).

(H69)　D. J. Hughes, J. Dabbs, A. Cahn, and D. Hall, Phys. Rev., **73**, 111 (1948).

(H70)　D. J. Hughes, J. R. Wallace, and R. H. Holtzman, Phys. Rev., **73**, 1277 (1948).

(H71)　D. J. Hughes, M. T. Burgy, R. B. Heller, and J. W. Wallace, Phys. Rev., **75**, 565 (1949).

(H72)　D. J. Hughes, W. D. B. Spatz, and N. Goldstein, Phys. Rev., **75**, 1781 (1949).

(H73)   D. J. Hughes and M. T. Burgy, Phys. Rev., **76**, 1413 (1949); **81**, 498 (1951).
(H74)   D. J. Hughes, M. T. Burgy, and G. R. Ringo, Phys. Rev., **77**, 291 (1950); **84**, 1160 (1951).
(H75)   D. J. Hughes, M. T. Burgy, and W. E. Woolf, Phys. Rev., **80**, 481 (1950).
(H76)   J. R. Huizenga, L. B. Magnusson, P. R. Fields, M. H. Studier, and R. B. Duffield, Phys. Rev., **82**, 561 (1951); **84**, 166 (1951).
(H77)   V. Hummel and B. Hamermesh, Phys. Rev., **82**, 67 (1951).
(H78)   G. T. Hunter and H. T. Richards, Phys. Rev., **76**, 1445 (1949).
(H79)   D. G. Hurst, A. J. Pressesky, and P. R. Tunnicliffe, Rev. Sci. Instr., **21**, 705 (1950).
(H80)   D. G. Hurst and N. Z. Alcock, Phys. Rev., **80**, 117 (1950); Can. J. Phys., **29**, 36 (1951).
(H81)   H. Hurwitz, Jr., and H. A. Bethe, Phys. Rev., **81**, 898 (1951).
(I1)   M. G. Inghram, D. C. Hess, Jr., and R. J. Hayden, Phys. Rev., **71**, 561 (1947).
(I2)   D. R. Inglis, Phys. Rev., **74**, 21 (1948).
(I3)   D. Iwanenko, Nature, **129**, 798 (1932).
(J1)   J. D. Jackson and J. M. Blatt, Revs. Mod. Phys., **22**, 77 (1950).
(J2)   G. A. Jarvis, A. Hemmendinger, H. V. Argo, and R. F. Taschek, Phys. Rev., **79**, 929 (1950).
(J3)   P. S. Jastram, A. H. Benade, M. R. Cleland, and A. L. Hughes, Phys. Rev., **81**, 327A (1951).
(J4)   H. E. Johns, L. Katz, R. A. Douglas, and R. N. H. Haslam, Phys. Rev., **80**, 1062 (1950).
(J5)   C. H. Johnson and H. H. Barschall, Phys. Rev., **80**, 818 (1950).
(J6)   C. H. Johnson, C. K. Bockelman, and H. H. Barschall, Phys. Rev., **82**, 117 (1951).
(J7)   C. H. Johnson, B. Petree, and R. K. Adair, Phys. Rev., **84**, 775 (1951).
(J8)   V. R. Johnson, M. J. Wilson Laubenstein, and H. T. Richards, Phys. Rev., **77**, 413 (1950).
(J9)   V. R. Johnson, F. Ajzenberg, and M. J. Wilson Laubenstein, Phys. Rev., **79**, 187 (1950).
(J10)   F. Joliot, Compt. rend., **193**, 1415 (1931).
(J11)   F. Joliot, Compt. rend., **208**, 341 (1939).
(J12)   W. B. Jones, Jr., Phys. Rev., **72**, 362 (1947).
(J13)   C. C. Jonker and J. Blok, Physica, **15**, 1032 (1949).
(K1)   H. Kahn, Nucleonics, **6**, 27 (May 1950); **6**, 60 (June 1950).
(K2)   P. L. Kapur and R. Peierls, Proc. Roy. Soc. (London), **A166**, 277 (1938).
(K3)   S. Katcoff, Phys. Rev., **72**, 1160 (1947); J. Chem. Phys., **17**, 421 (1949).
(K4)   L. Katz, H. E. Johns, R. G. Baker, R. N. H. Haslam, and R. A. Douglas, Phys. Rev., **82**, 271 (1951).
(K5)   G. R. Keepin, Jr., and J. H. Roberts, Phys. Rev., **76**, 154 (1949); Rev. Sci. Instr., **21**, 163 (1950).
(K6)   G. R. Keepin, Jr., Phys. Rev., **80**, 768 (1950).
(K7)   E. L. Kelly and C. Wiegand, Phys. Rev., **73**, 1135 (1948).
(K8)   E. L. Kelly and E. Segrè, Phys. Rev., **75**, 999 (1949).
(K9)   E. Kelly, C. Leith, E. Segrè, and C. Wiegand, Phys. Rev., **79**, 96 (1950).
(K10)   B. H. Ketelle, Phys. Rev., **76**, 1256 (1949).
(K11)   R. M. Kiehn, Technical Report No. 40, M.I.T. Laboratory for Nuclear Science and Engineering, 1950.
(K12)   S. Kikuchi, H. Aoki, and K. Husimi, Nature, **137**, 398 (1936); Proc. Phys.-Math. Soc. Japan, **18**, 115 (1936).

(K13) M. Kimura, Phys. Rev., **79**, 544 (1950).
(K14) L. D. P. King and L. Goldstein, Phys. Rev., **75**, 1366 (1949).
(K15) B. B. Kinsey, G. A. Bartholomew, and W. H. Walker, Phys. Rev., **78**, 481 (1950); **83**, 519 (1951).
(K16) B. B. Kinsey and G. A. Bartholomew, Phys. Rev., **80**, 918 (1950).
(K17) D. Kleinman and G. Snow, Phys. Rev., **82**, 952 (1951).
(K18) N. Knable, E. O. Lawrence, C. E. Leith, B. J. Moyer, and R. L. Thornton, Phys. Rev., **74**, 1217A (1948).
(K19) W. J. Knox, Phys. Rev., **75**, 537 (1949).
(K20) W. J. Knox, Phys. Rev., **81**, 687 (1951).
(K21) E. J. Konopinski and E. Teller, Phys. Rev., **73**, 822 (1948).
(K22) S. A. Korff, Am. J. Phys., **19**, 226 (1951).
(K23) L. Kowarski, Phys. Rev., **78**, 477 (1950).
(K24) H. H. A. Krueger, D. Meneghetti, G. R. Ringo, and L. Winsberg, Phys. Rev., **75**, 1098 (1949); **80**, 507 (1950).
(K25) D. N. Kundu and M. L. Pool, Phys. Rev., **73**, 22 (1948).
(K26) J. W. Kunstadter, Phys. Rev., **78**, 484 (1950).
(K27) F. H. D. Kurie, Phys. Rev., **43**, 771 (1933).
(L1) E. Lamba, Naturwiss., **24**, 251, 336 (1936).
(L2) L. Landau, Physik. Z. Sowjetunion, **11**, 556 (1937).
(L3) A. Langsdorf, Jr., Phys. Rev., **74**, 1216 (A) (1948).
(L4) R. E. Lapp, J. R. van Horn, and A. J. Dempster, Phys. Rev., **71**, 745 (1947).
(L5) C. M. G. Lattes and G. P. S. Occhialini, Nature, **159**, 331 (1947).
(L6) S. Lattimore, Phys. Rev., **81**, 643 (1951).
(L7) J. S. Laughlin and P. G. Kruger, Phys. Rev., **71**, 736 (1947).
(L8) E. O. Lawrence and M. S. Livingston, Phys. Rev., **45**, 220 (1934).
(L9) M. Lax, Phys. Rev., **80**, 299 (1950).
(L10) D. E. Lea, Nature, **133**, 24 (1934).
(L11) D. E. Lea, Proc. Roy. Soc. (London), **A150**, 637 (1935).
(L12) K. J. LeCouteur, Proc. Phys. Soc. (London), **A63**, 259 (1950).
(L13) A. I. Leipunsky, J. Phys. (U.S.S.R.), **3**, 231 (1940).
(L14) W. T. Leland and H. M. Agnew, Phys. Rev., **82**, 559 (1951).
(L15) J. V. Lepore, Phys. Rev., **79**, 137 (1950).
(L16) J. S. Levinger and H. A. Bethe, Phys. Rev., **78**, 115 (1950).
(L17) H. A. Levy and S. W. Peterson, Phys. Rev., **83**, 1270 (1951).
(L18) W. F. Libby and E. A. Long, Phys. Rev., **55**, 339 (1939).
(L19) M. Lindner, Phys. Rev., **84**, 240 (1951).
(L20) R. N. Little, R. W. Long, and C. E. Mandeville, Phys. Rev., **69**, 414 (1946).
(L21) K. Lonsdale, Nature, **164**, 205 (1949).
(L22) Los Alamos Scientific Laboratory, Phys. Rev., **79**, 238A (1950).
(L23) A. N. Lowan, P. M. Morse, H. Feshbach, and M. Lax, Scattering and Radiation from Circular Cylinders and Spheres, AMP Report No. 62.1R, 85–91, 1945.
(L24) R. D. Lowde, Rev. Sci. Instr., **21**, 835 (1950).
(L25) E. Lüscher, R. Ricamo, P. Scherrer, and W. Zünti, Helv. Phys. Acta, **23**, 561 (1950).
(M1) J. E. Mack, Revs. Mod. Phys., **22**, 64 (1950).
(M2) C. E. Mandeville and C. P. Swann, Phys. Rev., **84**, 214 (1951).
(M3) J. H. Manley, H. H. Goldsmith, and J. S. Schwinger, Phys. Rev., **55**, 39 (1939).

(M4)   J. H. Manley, L. J. Haworth, and E. A. Luebke, Phys. Rev., **61**, 152 (1942).

(M5)   R. E. Marshak, Revs. Mod. Phys., **19**, 185 (1947).

(M6)   H. S. W. Massey and C. B. O. Mohr., Proc. Roy. Soc. (London), **A148**, 206 (1935).

(M7)   M. G. Mayer, Phys. Rev., **74**, 235 (1948).

(M8)   M. G. Mayer, Phys. Rev., **75**, 1969 (1949).

(M9)   M. G. Mayer, Phys. Rev., **78**, 16, 22 (1950).

(M10)   J. J. G. McCue and W. M. Preston, Phys. Rev., **84**, 1150 (1951).

(M11)   B. D. McDaniel, Phys. Rev., **70**, 832 (1946).

(M12)   B. D. McDaniel, R. L. Walker, and M. B. Stearns, Phys. Rev., **80**, 807 (1950).

(M13)   J. McElhinney, A. O. Hanson, R. A. Becker, R. B. Duffield, and B. C. Diven, Phys. Rev., **75**, 542 (1949).

(M14)   H. A. C. McKay, *Progress in Nuclear Physics*, O. R. Frisch, Editor, Butterworth-Springer, London, 1950.

(M15)   J. L. McKibben, Phys. Rev., **70**, 101A (1946).

(M16)   K. G. McNeill and G. M. Keyser, Phys. Rev., **81**, 602 (1951).

(M17)   A. W. McReynolds and G. W. Johnson, Phys. Rev., **82**, 344A (1951).

(M18)   A. W. McReynolds and R. J. Weiss, Phys. Rev., **83**, 171 (1951).

(M19)   A. W. McReynolds, Phys. Rev., **83**, 172 (1951).

(M20)   A. W. McReynolds, Phys. Rev., **84**, 969 (1951).

(M21)   L. Meitner and L. Philipp, Naturwiss., **20**, 929 (1932).

(M22)   L. Meitner, Naturwiss., **22**, 759 (1934).

(M23)   L. Meitner and O. R. Frisch, Nature, **143**, 239 (1939).

(M24)   E. Melkonian, Phys. Rev., **76**, 1744 (1949).

(M25)   E. Melkonian, Phys. Rev., **76**, 1750 (1949).

(M26)   A. W. Merrison and E. R. Wiblin, Nature, **167**, 346 (1951).

(M27)   A. M. L. Messiah, Phys. Rev., **84**, 204 (1951).

(M28)   W. E. Meyerhof and D. B. Nicodemus, Phys. Rev., **82**, 5 (1951).

(M29)   J. W. Mihelich and R. D. Hill, Phys. Rev., **77**, 743 (A) (1950).

(M30)   J. M. W. Milatz and D. Th. J. ter Horst, Physica, **5**, 796 (1938).

(M31)   D. W. Miller, R. E. Fields, and C. K. Bockelman, Phys. Rev., **85**, 704 (A) (1952); H. H. Barschall, Phys. Rev., **86**, 431 (1952).

(M32)   R. D. Miller, D. C. Sewell, and R. W. Wright, Phys. Rev., **81**, 374 (1951).

(M33)   D. P. Mitchell and P. N. Powers, Phys. Rev., **50**, 486 (1936).

(M34)   R. C. Mobley and R. A. Laubenstein, Phys. Rev., **80**, 309 (1950).

(M35)   P. B. Moon and J. R. Tillman, Nature, **135**, 904 (1935); Proc. Roy. Soc. (London), **A153**, 476 (1936).

(M36)   P. B. Moon, Reports on Progress in Physics, **4**, 198 (1938).

(M37)   M. Morand, P. Cüer, J. Edmont, and H. Moucharafyeh, Compt. rend., **226**, 1008 (1948).

(M38)   W. G. Moulton and C. W. Sherwin, Rev. Sci. Instr., **20**, 766 (1949).

(M39)   B. J. Moyer, B. Peters, and F. H. Schmidt, Phys. Rev., **69**, 666; **70**, 446 (A) (1946).

(M40)   C. O. Muehlhause, Phys. Rev., **79**, 1002 (1950).

(M41)   A. M. Munn and B. Pontecorvo, Can. J. Research, **A25**, 157 (1947).

(M42)   V. Myers and A. Wattenberg, Phys. Rev., **75**, 992 (1949).

(M43)   L. Myssowsky and A. Jdanoff, Nature, **143**, 794 (1939).

(N1)   N. Nereson and F. Reines, Rev. Sci. Instr., **21**, 534 (1950).

(N2)   L. W. Nordheim, Phys. Rev., **75**, 1894, 1968 (1949).

(O1)   W. E. Ogle, L. J. Brown, and A. N. Corson, Phys. Rev., **78**, 63 (1950).

(O2) W. E. Ogle and R. E. England, Phys. Rev., **78**, 63 (1950).

(O3) M. L. E. Oliphant, P. Harteck, and Lord Rutherford, Proc. Roy. Soc. (London), **A144**, 692 (1934).

(O4) R. D. O'Neal and G. Scharff-Goldhaber, Phys. Rev., **69**, 368 (1946).

(O5) J. Orear, A. H. Rosenfeld, and R. A. Schluter, *Nuclear Physics, A Course by E. Fermi*, University of Chicago Press, 1950.

(O6) G. E. Owen, J. Neiler, and W. Ray, Phys. Rev., **83**, 675 (1951).

(P1) H. Palevsky and A. O. Hanson, Phys. Rev., **79**, 242 (1950).

(P2) F. A. Paneth and E. Glückauf, Nature, **139**, 712 (1937).

(P3) W. K. H. Panofsky, R. L. Aamodt, and J. Hadley, Phys. Rev., **81**, 565 (1951).

(P4) G. W. Parker, P. M. Lantz, M. G. Inghram, D. C. Hess, Jr., and R. J. Hayden, Phys. Rev., **72**, 85 (1947).

(P5) R. W. Parsons and C. H. Collie, Proc. Phys. Soc. (London), **A63**, 839 (1950).

(P6) R. W. Parsons, D. J. Lees, and C. H. Collie, Proc. Phys. Soc. (London), **A63**, 915 (1950).

(P7) W. Pauli, *Meson Theory of Nuclear Forces*, Interscience Publishers, New York, 1946.

(P8) D. C. Peaslee, Phys. Rev., **74**, 1001 (1948).

(P8a) C. Pecher, Phys. Rev., **58**, 843 (1940).

(P9) R. Peierls, Proc. Cambridge Phil. Soc., **35**, 610 (1939).

(P10) R. Peierls, Reports on Progress in Physics, **VII**, 87 (1940).

(P11) F. Perrin and W. M. Elsasser, Compt. rend., **200**, 450 (1935); J. phys. et radium, **6**, 195 (1935).

(P12) F. Perrin, Compt. rend., **208**, 1394, 1573 (1939).

(P13) R. E. Peterson, H. H. Barschall, and C. K. Bockelman, Phys. Rev., **79**, 593 (1950).

(P14) B. Petree, C. H. Johnson, and D. W. Miller, Phys. Rev., **83**, 1148 (1951).

(P15) D. D. Phillips and R. W. Davis, AEC Report La-740, 1949.

(P16) G. Placzek, Phys. Rev., **55**, 1130 (A) (1939); **69**, 423 (1946).

(P17) G. Placzek and H. A. Bethe, Phys. Rev., **57**, 1075A (1940).

(P18) G. Placzek and G. Volkoff, Can. J. Research, **A25**, 276 (1947).

(P19) G. Placzek, Phys. Rev., **75**, 1295 (A) (1949).

(P20) G. Placzek, *The Science and Engineering of Nuclear Power*, Vol. II, Addison-Wesley Press, Cambridge, Mass., 1949.

(P21) G. Placzek, B. R. A. Nijboer, and L. van Hove, Phys. Rev., **82**, 392 (1951).

(P22) H. Pomerance and J. I. Hoover, Phys. Rev., **73**, 1265 (A) (1948).

(P23) H. Pomerance, Phys. Rev., **83**, 641 (1951).

(P24) C. F. Powell and G. P. S. Occhialini, *Fundamental Particles*, The Physical Society, London, 1947, p. 150.

(P25) C. F. Powell and G. P. S. Occhialini, *Nuclear Physics in Photographs*, Clarendon Press, Oxford, England, 1947.

(P26) P. N. Powers, H. G. Beyer, and J. R. Dunning, Phys. Rev., **51**, 371 (1937).

(P27) P. N. Powers, H. Carroll, H. Beyer, and J. R. Dunning, Phys. Rev., **52**, 38 (1937).

(P28) P. N. Powers, Phys. Rev., **54**, 827 (1938).

(P29) P. Preiswerk and H. von Halban, Compt. rend., **203**, 73 (1936).

(P30) P. Preiswerk and H. v. Halban, Nature, **138**, 163 (1936).

(P31) G. A. Price and D. W. Kerst, Phys. Rev., **77**, 806 (1950).

(P32) E. M. Purcell and N. F. Ramsey, Phys. Rev., **78**, 807 (1950).

(R1) I. I. Rabi, Phys. Rev., **51**, 652 (1937).

(R2) V. Raievski and J. Yvon, Compt. rend., **231**, 345 (1950).

(R3)   J. Rainwater and W. W. Havens, Jr., Phys. Rev., **70**, 136 (1946).
(R4)   L. J. Rainwater, W. W. Havens, Jr., C. S. Wu, and J. R. Dunning, Phys. Rev., **71**, 65 (1947).
(R5)   L. J. Rainwater, W. W. Havens, Jr., J. R. Dunning, and C. S. Wu, Phys. Rev., **73**, 733 (1948).
(R6)   W. Rarita and J. Schwinger, Phys. Rev., **59**, 436 (1941).
(R7)   F. Rasetti, Naturwiss., **20**, 252 (1932); Z. Physik, **78**, 165 (1932).
(R8)   H. L. Reel and C. Grosjean, Compt. rend., **226**, 1598 (1948).
(R9)   R. Ricamo, Nuovo cimento, **8**, 383 (1951).
(R10)   H. T. Richards, R. V. Smith, and C. P. Browne, Phys. Rev., **80**, 524 (1950).
(R11)   L. N. Ridenour and W. J. Henderson, Phys. Rev., **52**, 889 (1937).
(R12)   J. H. Roberts, E. Nakaji, and W. Solano, Phys. Rev., **81**, 327 (A) (1951).
(R13)   R. B. Roberts, R. C. Meyer, and P. Wang, Phys. Rev., **55**, 510 (1939).
(R14)   R. B. Roberts and P. H. Abelson, Phys. Rev., **72**, 76 (1947).
(R15)   J. M. Robson, Phys. Rev., **78**, 311 (1950); **83**, 349 (1951).
(R16)   E. H. Rogers and H. H. Staub, Phys. Rev., **76**, 980 (1949).
(R17)   M. E. Rose and M. M. Shapiro, Phys. Rev., **74**, 1853 (1948).
(R18)   M. Rose, Phys. Rev., **75**, 213 (1949).
(R19)   L. Rosenfeld, *Nuclear Forces*, Interscience Publishers, New York, 1948, Vol. I.
(R20)   M. Ross and J. S. Story, Reports on Progress in Physics 1948–49, The Physical Society, London, **12**, 291 (1949).
(R21)   B. Rossi, Revs. Mod. Phys., **20**, 537 (1948).
(R22)   J. Rotblat, *Progress in Nuclear Physics*, O. R. Frisch, Editor, Butterworth-Springer, London, 1950.
(R23)   I. W. Ruderman, W. W. Havens, Jr., T. I. Taylor, and L. J. Rainwater, Phys. Rev., **75**, 895 (1949).
(R24)   I. W. Ruderman, Phys. Rev., **76**, 1572 (1949).
(R25)   L. H. Rumbaugh and G. L. Locher, Phys. Rev., **49**, 855 (1936).
(R26)   B. Russell, D. Sachs, A. Wattenberg, and R. Fields, Phys. Rev., **73**, 545 (1948).
(R27)   E. Rutherford, Proc. Roy. Soc. (London), **A97**, 374 (1920).
(S1)   C. Salvetti, Nuovo cimento, **6**, 303, 413 (1949).
(S2)   B. W. Sargent, D. V. Booker, P. E. Cavanagh, H. G. Hereward, and N. J. Niemi, Can. J. Research, **A25**, 134 (1947).
(S3)   R. B. Sawyer, E. O. Wollan, S. Bernstein, and K. C. Peterson, Phys. Rev., **72**, 109 (1947).
(S4)   L. Schecter, Phys. Rev., **83**, 695 (1951).
(S5)   T. Schmidt, Z. Physik, **106**, 358 (1937).
(S6)   J. Schwinger, Phys. Rev., **51**, 544 (1937).
(S7)   J. Schwinger and E. Teller, Phys. Rev., **51**, 775 (1937); **52**, 286 (1937).
(S8)   J. Schwinger and I. I. Rabi, Phys. Rev., **51**, 1003A (1937).
(S9)   J. Schwinger, Phys. Rev., **58**, 1004 (1940).
(S10)   J. Schwinger, Phys. Rev., **69**, 681 (A) (1946).
(S11)   J. Schwinger, Phys. Rev., **73**, 407 (1948).
(S12)   G. T. Seaborg, G. E. Gibson, and D. C. Graham, Phys. Rev., **52**, 408 (1937).
(S13)   L. Secrest, Phys. Rev., **77**, 141 (1950).
(S13a) E. Segrè, Atti accad. nazl. Lincei, **29**, 238 (1936).
(S14)   E. Segrè, Ricerca sci., **7(1)**, 389 (1936).
(S15)   E. Segrè and C. Wiegand, Rev. Sci. Instr., **18**, 86 (1947).
(S16)   F. G. P. Seidl and S. P. Harris, Rev. Sci. Instr., **18**, 897 (1947).
(S17)   F. G. P. Seidl, Phys. Rev., **75**, 1508 (1949).

(S18)   W. Selove, Phys. Rev., **76**, 187 (A) (1949).

(S19)   W. Selove, Phys. Rev., **77**, 557 (1950); **84**, 869 (1951).

(S20)   R. Serber, Phys. Rev., **72**, 1008 (1947).

(S21)   R. Serber, Phys. Rev., **72**, 1114 (1947).

(S22)   L. Seren, W. E. Moyer, and W. Sturm, Phys. Rev., **70**, 561 (1946).

(S23)   L. Seren, D. W. Engelkemeir, W. Sturm, H. N. Friedlander, and S. H. Turkel, Phys. Rev., **71**, 409 (1947).

(S24)   L. Seren, H. N. Friedlander, and S. H. Turkel, Phys. Rev., **72**, 888 (1947).

(S25)   M. M. Shapiro and J. R. Barnes, Phys. Rev., **73**, 1243 (A) (1948).

(S26)   R. Sher, J. Halpern, W. E. Stephens, and A. K. Mann, Phys. Rev., **81**, 154 (1951); **84**, 387 (1951).

(S27)   R. Sherr, Phys. Rev., **68**, 240 (1946).

(S28)   C. G. Shull and E. O. Wollan, Science, **108**, 69 (1948).

(S29)   C. G. Shull, E. O. Wollan, G. A. Morton, and W. L. Davidson, Phys. Rev., **73**, 842 (1948).

(S30)   C. G. Shull and S. Siegel, Phys. Rev., **75**, 1008 (1949).

(S31)   C. G. Shull and J. S. Smart, Phys. Rev., **76**, 1256 (1949).

(S32)   C. G. Shull, E. O. Wollan, and W. A. Strauser, Phys. Rev., **81**, 483 (1951).

(S33)   C. G. Shull and E. O. Wollan, Phys. Rev., **81**, 527 (1951).

(S34)   C. G. Shull, Phys. Rev., **81**, 626 (1951).

(S35)   C. G. Shull, W. A. Strauser, and E. O. Wollan, Phys. Rev., **83**, 333 (1951).

(S36)   C. G. Shull, E. O. Wollan, and W. C. Koehler, Phys. Rev., **84**, 912 (1951).

(S37)   A. J. F. Siegert, Phys. Rev., **56**, 750 (1939).

(S38)   J. A. Simpson, Phys. Rev., **83**, 1175 (1951).

(S39)   M. Slotnick and W. Heitler, Phys. Rev., **75**, 1645 (1949).

(S40)   J. H. Smith, Ph.D. thesis, Harvard University, 1951.

(S41)   L. W. Smith and P. G. Kruger, Phys. Rev., **83**, 1137 (1951).

(S42)   H. D. Smyth, *Atomic Energy for Military Purposes*, Princeton University Press, 1945.

(S43)   A. H. Snell and L. C. Miller, Phys. Rev., **74**, 1217A (1948).

(S44)   A. H. Snell, F. Pleasonton, and R. V. McCord, Phys. Rev., **78**, 310 (1950).

(S45)   T. M. Snyder and R. W. Williams, Phys. Rev., **81**, 171 (1951).

(S46)   H. Soodak, *The Science and Engineering of Nuclear Power*, Addison-Wesley Press, Cambridge, Mass., 1949, Vol. II.

(S47)   H. Soodak and E. C. Campbell, *Elementary Pile Theory*, John Wiley & Sons, Inc., New York, 1950.

(S48)   J. A. Spiers, Phys. Rev., **75**, 1765 (1949).

(S49)   J. W. T. Spinks and G. A. R. Graham, Can. J. Research, **A28**, 60 (1950).

(S50)   W. P. Staker, M. Pavalow, and S. A. Korff, Phys. Rev., **81**, 889 (1951).

(S51)   J. Steinberger and G. C. Wick, Phys. Rev., **76**, 994 (1949).

(S52)   P. H. Stelson, W. M. Preston, and C. Goodman, Phys. Rev., **80**, 287 (1950).

(S53)   P. H. Stelson and C. Goodman, Phys. Rev., **82**, 69 (1951).

(S54)   P. H. Stelson and W. M. Preston, Phys. Rev., **82**, 655 (1951).

(S55)   W. E. Stephens *et al.*, *Nuclear Fission and Atomic Energy*, The Science Press, Lancaster, Pa., 1948.

(S56)   W. J. Sturm, Phys. Rev., **71**, 757 (1947).

(S57)   N. Sugarman, Phys. Rev., **75**, 1287 (A), 1473 (1949).

(S58)   K. H. Sun, D. Harris, F. A. Pacjak, B. Jennings, A. J. Allen, and J. F. Nechaj, Phys. Rev., **82**, 266 (1951).

(S59)   R. B. Sutton, T. Hall, E. E. Anderson, H. S. Bridge, J. W. DeWire, L. S. Lavatelli, E. A. Long, T. Snyder, and R. W. Williams, Phys. Rev., **72**, 1147 (1947).

(S60) D. R. Swanson, Phys. Rev., **84**, 1068 (1951).
(S61) A. Szalay, Z. Physik, **112**, 29 (1939).
(S62) L. Szilard and T. A. Chalmers, Nature, **134**, 462 (1934).
(S63) L. Szilard and T. A. Chalmers, Nature, **134**, 494 (1934).
(S64) L. Szilard, Nature, **136**, 951 (1935).
(S65) L. Szilard, S. Bernstein, B. T. Feld, and J. Ashkin, Phys. Rev., **73**, 1307 (1948).
(T1)   R. F. Taschek and A. Hemmendinger, Phys. Rev., **74**, 373 (1948).
(T2)   R. F. Taschek, A. Hemmendinger, and G. A. Jarvis, Phys. Rev., **75**, 1464 (A) (1949).
(T3)   A. E. Taylor, T. G. Pickavance, J. M. Cassels, and T. C. Randle, Nature, **165**, 967 (1950); Phil. Mag., **42**, 20, 215, 328 (1951).
(T4)   H. J. Taylor and M. Goldhaber, Nature, **135**, 341 (1935); see also Proc. Roy. Soc. (London), **A150**, 382 (1935).
(T5)   T. Teichmann, Phys. Rev., **77**, 506 (1950).
(T6)   E. Teller, Phys. Rev., **49**, 420 (A) (1936).
(T7)   G. M. Temmer, Phys. Rev., **76**, 424 (1949).
(T8)   K. M. Terwilliger, L. W. Jones, and W. N. Jarmie, Phys. Rev., **82**, 820 (1951).
(T9)   J. R. Tillman and P. B. Moon, Nature, **136**, 66 (1935).
(T10) E. W. Titterton, Nature, **163**, 990 (1949).
(T11) C. W. Tittle, H. Faul, E. L. Secrest, and C. Goodman, Technical Report No. 21, Laboratory for Nuclear Science and Engineering, M.I.T., 1949.
(T12) C. W. Tittle, Phys. Rev., **80**, 756 (1950).
(T13) C. W. Tittle, Phys. Rev., **80**, 756 (1950).
(T14) C. W. Tittle and H. Faul, Phys. Rev., **80**, 908 (1950).
(T15) J. Tittman, C. Sheer, J. Rainwater, and W. W. Havens, Jr., Phys. Rev., **80**, 903 (1950); **83**, 746 (1951).
(T16) A. Tollestrup, W. A. Fowler, and C. C. Lauritsen, Phys. Rev., **78**, 372 (1950).
(T17) L. A. Turner, Revs. Mod. Phys., **12**, 1 (1940).
(U1)   United States Senate Report No. 1211, U. S. Government Printing Office, 1946.
(U2)   United States Atomic Energy Commission Release, Nucleonics, **8**, 78 (Jan. 1951); **10**, 64 (May 1952).
(V1)   J. H. Van Vleck, University of Pennsylvania Bicentennial Conference, 1941, p. 51.
(V2)   M. Verde and G. C. Wick, Phys. Rev., **71**, 852 (1947).
(W1)   H. Wäffler and O. Hirzel, Helv. Phys. Acta, **21**, 200 (1948).
(W2)   A. C. Wahl and N. A. Bonner, editors, *Radioactivity Applied to Chemistry*, John Wiley & Sons, Inc., New York, 1951, Chapter 8.
(W3)   R. L. Walker, Phys. Rev., **76**, 244 (1949).
(W4)   P. Wallace, Nucleonics, **4**, No. 2, 30 (1949); **4**, No. 3, 48 (1949).
(W5)   R. Wallace, Phys. Rev., **81**, 493 (1951).
(W6)   K. M. Watson and R. N. Stuart, Phys. Rev., **82**, 738 (1951).
(W7)   A. Wattenberg, Phys. Rev., **71**, 497 (1947).
(W8)   A. Wattenberg, Preliminary Report No. 6, Nuclear Science Series, National Research Council, 1949.
(W9)   K. Way, Phys. Rev., **75**, 1448 (1949).
(W10) K. Way, L. Fano, M. R. Scott, and K. Thew, National Bureau of Standards Circular 499, U. S. Government Printing Office, Washington, D. C., 1950.
(W11) D. F. Weeks, M. S. Livingston, and H. A. Bethe, Phys. Rev., **49**, 471 (1936).
(W12) A. M. Weinberg and H. C. Schweinler, Phys. Rev., **74**, 851 (1948).

(W13) A. M. Weinberg, *The Science and Engineering of Nuclear Power*, Addison-Wesley Press, Cambridge, Mass., 1949, Vol. II.
(W14) R. Weinstock, Phys. Rev., **65**, 1 (1944).
(W15) R. J. Weiss, Phys. Rev., **83**, 379 (1951).
(W16) V. F. Weisskopf, Phys. Rev., **52**, 295 (1937).
(W17) V. F. Weisskopf, Helv. Phys. Acta, **23**, 187 (1950).
(W18) C. H. Westcott and T. Bjerge, Proc. Cambridge Phil. Soc., **31**, 145 (1935).
(W19) W. J. Whitehouse and G. A. R. Graham, Can. J. Research, **A25**, 261 (1947).
(W20) B. G. Whitmore and W. B. Baker, Phys. Rev., **78**, 799 (1950).
(W21) B. G. Whitmore and G. E. Dennis, Phys. Rev., **84**, 296 (1951).
(W22) G. C. Wick, Z. Physik, **84**, 799 (1933).
(W23) G. C. Wick, Phys. Rev., **49**, 192 (1936).
(W24) G. C. Wick, Physik. Z., **38**, 403, 689 (1937).
(W25) G. C. Wick, Phys. Rev., **75**, 738 (1949).
(W26) C. Wiegand, Rev. Sci. Instr., **19**, 790 (1948).
(W27) E. P. Wigner, Z. Physik, **83**, 253 (1933).
(W28) E. P. Wigner, J. Appl. Phys., **17**, 857 (1946).
(W29) E. P. Wigner, Phys. Rev., **70**, 15, 606 (1946); **73**, 1002 (1948).
(W30) E. P. Wigner and L. Eisenbud, Phys. Rev., **72**, 29 (1947).
(W31) E. P. Wigner, Am. J. Phys., **17**, 99 (1949).
(W32) H. B. Willard, W. M. Preston, and C. Goodman, Phys. Rev., **81**, 329 (1951).
(W33) H. B. Willard and W. M. Preston, Phys. Rev., **81**, 480 (1951).
(W34) J. G. Wilson, *The Principles of Cloud-Chamber Operation*, Cambridge University Press, 1951.
(W35) R. Wilson, L. Beghian, C. H. Collie, H. Halban, and G. R. Bishop, Rev. Sci. Instr., **21**, 699 (1950).
(W36) L. Winsberg, D. Meneghetti, and S. S. Sidhu, Phys. Rev., **75**, 975 (1949).
(W37) L. Wolfenstein, Phys. Rev., **75**, 1664 (1949); **76**, 541 (1949).
(W38) L. Wolfenstein, Phys. Rev., **82**, 690 (1951).
(W39) E. O. Wollan and C. G. Shull, Nucleonics, **3**, 8 (July 1948); **3**, 17 (August 1948).
(W40) E. O. Wollan, C. G. Shull, and M. C. Marney, Phys. Rev., **73**, 527 (1948).
(W41) E. O. Wollan and C. G. Shull, Phys. Rev., **73**, 830 (1948).
(W42) E. O. Wollan, W. L. Davidson, and C. G. Shull, Phys. Rev., **75**, 1348 (1949).
(W43) E. O. Wollan, C. G. Shull, and W. C. Koehler, Phys. Rev., **83**, 700 (1951).
(W44) W. M. Woodward and I. Halpern, Phys. Rev., **76**, 107 (1949).
(W45) L. F. Wouters, Phys. Rev., **84**, 1069 (1951).
(Y1)   L. Yaffe, B. W. Sargent, M. Kirsch, S. Standil, and J. M. Grunlund, Phys. Rev., **76**, 617 (1949).
(Y2)   H. Yagoda, *Radioactive Measurements with Nuclear Emulsions*, John Wiley & Sons, Inc., New York, 1949.
(Y3)   H. F. York, Phys. Rev., **75**, 1467 (1949).
(Y4)   L. C. Yuan, Phys. Rev., **81**, 175 (1951).
(Z1)   W. H. Zachariasen, *Theory of X-Ray Diffraction in Crystals*, John Wiley & Sons, Inc., New York, 1945.
(Z2)   Y. B. Zeldovich and Y. B. Khariton, J. Exptl. Theoret. Phys. (U.S.S.R.), **9**, 1425 (1940); **10**, 29, 477 (1940); translations, AEC documents CP-2650, 2294.
(Z3)   W. H. Zinn, Phys. Rev., **71**, 752 (1947).

AUTHOR INDEX

Part VI begins on page 1, Part VII on page 208. In this index the entries pertaining to the two parts are separated by semicolons.

SUBJECT INDEX